PEARSON ALWAYS LEARNING

Statistical Reasoning
for STA1001
Pathway to Statistics

Taken from:
Statistical Reasoning: For Everyday Life, Fourth Edition
by Jeffrey Bennett, William L. Briggs, and Mario F. Triola

Using & Understanding Mathematics: A Quantitative Reasoning Approach,
Sixth Edition
by Jeffrey Bennett and William Briggs

Elementary Statistics, Twelfth Edition
by Mario F. Triola

Introductory Algebra: Through Applications, Third Edition
by Geoffrey Akst and Sadie Bragg

Cover Credit: Courtesy of Pearson Learning Solutions.

Taken from:

Statistical Reasoning: For Everyday Life, Fourth Edition
by Jeffrey Bennett, William L. Briggs, and Mario F. Triola
Copyright © 2014, 2009, 2003 by Pearson Education, Inc.
New York, NY 10013

Using & Understanding Mathematics: A Quantitative Reasoning Approach, Sixth Edition
by Jeffrey Bennett and William Briggs
Copyright © 2015, 2011, 2008 by Pearson Education, Inc.
New York, NY 10013

Elementary Statistics, Twelfth Edition
by Mario F. Triola
Copyright © 2014, 2010, 2007 by Pearson Education, Inc.
New York, NY 10013

Introductory Algebra: Through Applications, Third Edition
by Geoffrey Akst and Sadie Bragg
Copyright © 2013 by Pearson Education, Inc.
New York, NY 10013

Pearson Learning Solutions, 501 Boylston Street, Suite 900, Boston, MA 02116
A Pearson Education Company
www.pearsoned.com

Printed in the United States of America

11 16

000200010271986855

RD

ISBN 10: 1-323-18530-5
ISBN 13: 978-1-323-18530-8

BRIEF CONTENTS

CONTENTS

Speaking of Statistics

Is your drinking water safe? How many people approve of the President's budget plan? Are we getting good value for our health care dollars? Questions like these can be addressed only through statistical studies. In this first chapter, we will discuss basic principles of statistical research and lay a foundation for the more detailed study of statistics that follows in the rest of this book. Along the way, we will consider a variety of examples that show how well-designed statistical studies can provide guidance for social policy and personal decisions, as well as a few cases in which statistics can be misleading.

> Statistical thinking will one day be as necessary for efficient citizenship as the ability to read and write.
>
> —H. G. Wells

LEARNING GOALS

1.1 What Is/Are Statistics?

Understand the two meanings of the term *statistics* and the basic ideas behind any statistical study, including the relationships among the study's population, sample, sample statistics, and population parameters.

1.2 Sampling

Understand the importance of choosing a representative sample and become familiar with several common methods of sampling.

1.3 Types of Statistical Studies

Understand the differences between observational studies and experiments; recognize key issues in experiments, including the selection of treatment and control groups, the placebo effect, and blinding.

1.4 Should You Believe a Statistical Study?

Be able to evaluate statistical studies that you find in the media, so that you can decide whether the results are meaningful.

1.5 Data Types and Levels of Measurement

Identify data as qualitative or quantitative, discrete or continuous, and by level of measurement (nominal, ordinal, interval, or ratio).

FOCUS TOPICS

1.1   WHAT IS/ARE STATISTICS?

The subject of statistics is often stereotyped as dry or technical, but it touches on almost everything in modern society. Statistics can tell us whether a new drug is effective in treating cancer, it can help agricultural inspectors ensure that our food is safe, and it is essential for conducting and interpreting opinion polls. Businesses use statistics in market research and advertising. We even use statistics in sports, often as a way of ranking teams and athletes. Indeed, you'll be hard-pressed to think of any topic that is not linked with statistics in some important way.

The primary goal of this text is to help you learn the core ideas behind statistical methods. These basic ideas are not difficult to understand, although mastery of the details and theory behind them can require years of study. One of the great things about statistics is that even the small amount of theory covered in this text will give you the power to understand the statistics you encounter in the news, in your classes or workplace, and in your everyday life.

A good place to start is with the term *statistics* itself, which can be either singular or plural and has different meanings in the two cases. When it is singular, *statistics* is the *science* that helps us understand how to collect, organize, and interpret numbers or other information about some topic; we refer to the numbers or other pieces of information as *data*. When it is plural, *statistics* are the actual data that describe some characteristic. For example, if there are 30 students in your class and they range in age from 17 to 64, the numbers "30 students," "17 years," and "64 years" are all statistics that describe your class in some way.

BY THE WAY

Although you'll sometimes see the word *data* used as a singular synonym for *information*, technically it is plural: One piece of information is called a *datum*, and two or more pieces are called *data*.

> **Two Definitions of Statistics**
>
> - Statistics is the *science* of collecting, organizing, and interpreting data.
>
> - Statistics are the *data* (numbers or other pieces of information) that describe or summarize something.

How Statistics Works

According to news reports, 111.3 million Americans watched the New York Giants win Super Bowl XLVI, which explains why the networks can now ask advertisers to pay more than $3 million for a 30-second commercial. But you may wonder: Who counted all these million people?

The answer is *no one*. The claim that 111.3 million people watched the Super Bowl came from statistical studies conducted by a company called Nielsen Media Research. This company compiles its famous *Nielsen ratings* by monitoring the television viewing habits of people in only about 5,000 homes.

If you are new to the study of statistics, Nielsen's conclusion may seem like a stretch. How can anyone draw a conclusion about millions of people by studying just a few thousand? However, statistical science shows that this conclusion can be quite accurate, as long as the statistical study is conducted properly. Let's take the Nielsen ratings of the Super Bowl as an example and ask a few key questions that will illustrate how statistics works in general.

BY THE WAY

Statistics originated with the collection of census and tax data, which are affairs of state. That is why the word *state* is at the root of the word *statistics*.

What Is the Goal of the Research?

Nielsen's goal is to determine the total number of Americans who watched the Super Bowl. In the language of statistics, we say that Nielsen is interested in the **population** of all Americans. The number that Nielsen hopes to determine—the number of people who watched the Super Bowl—is a particular characteristic of the population. In statistics, characteristics of the population are called **population parameters.**

Although we usually think of a population as a group of people, a statistical population can be any kind of group—people, animals, or things. For example, in a study of automobile safety, the population might be *all cars on the road*. Similarly, the term *population parameter* can refer to any characteristic of a population. In the case of automobile safety, the population parameters might include the total number of cars on the road during a certain time period, the accident rate among cars on the road, or the range of weights of cars on the road.

EXAMPLE 1 Populations and Population Parameters

For each of the following situations, describe the population being studied and identify some of the population parameters that would be of interest.

a. You work for Farmers Insurance and you've been asked to determine the average amount paid to accident victims in cars without side-impact air bags.

b. You've been hired by McDonald's to determine the weights of the potatoes delivered each week for French fries.

c. You are a business reporter covering Genentech Corporation and you are investigating whether its new treatment is effective against childhood leukemia.

SOLUTION

a. The population consists of people who have received insurance payments for accidents in cars that lacked side-impact air bags. The relevant population parameter is the average amount paid to these people. (Later, the term "average" will be replaced by the more correct term "mean.")

b. The population consists of all the potatoes delivered each week for French fries. Relevant population parameters include the average weight of the potatoes and the variation of the weights (for example, are most of them close to or far from the average?).

c. The population consists of all children with leukemia. Important population parameters are the percentage of children who recover *without* the new treatment and the percentage of children who recover with the new treatment.   · · ●

What Actually Gets Studied?

If researchers at Nielsen were all-powerful, they might determine the number of people watching the Super Bowl by surveying every individual American. But no one can do that, so instead they try to estimate the number of Americans watching by studying a relatively small group of people. Nielsen attempts to learn about the population of all Americans by carefully monitoring the viewing habits of a much smaller **sample** of Americans. More specifically, Nielsen uses recording devices in about 5,000 homes, so the people who live in these homes are the sample of Americans that Nielsen studies.

The individual measurements that Nielsen collects from the people in the 5,000 homes constitute the **raw data.** Nielsen collects much raw data—for example, when and how long each TV in the household is on, what show it is tuned to, and who in the household is watching. Nielsen then consolidates these raw data into a set of numbers that characterize the sample, such as the percentage of viewers in the sample who watched each individual television show or the total number of people in the sample who watched the Super Bowl. These numbers are called **sample statistics.**

BY THE WAY

Arthur C. Nielsen founded his company and invented market research in 1923. He introduced the Nielsen Radio Index to rate radio programs in 1942 and extended his methods to television programming in the 1960s. The company now also tracks other media (Internet, smart phones, etc.) and must constantly adapt its methodology to new media technologies.

BY THE WAY

By the Labor Department definition, someone who is not working
is not necessarily unemployed.
For example, stay-at-home moms
and dads are not counted among
the unemployed unless they are
actively trying to find a job, and
people who tried to find work
but gave up in frustration are not
counted as unemployed.

EXAMPLE 2 Unemployment Survey

The U.S. Labor Department defines the *civilian labor force* as all those people who are either employed or actively seeking employment. Each month, the Labor Department reports the unemployment rate, which is the percentage of people actively seeking employment within the entire civilian labor force. To determine the unemployment rate, the Labor Department surveys 60,000 households. For the unemployment reports, describe each of the following.

a. population **b.** sample **c.** raw data **d.** sample statistics **e.** population parameters

SOLUTION

a. The *population* is the group that the Labor Department wants to learn about, which is all the people who make up the civilian labor force.

b. The *sample* consists of all the people among the 60,000 households surveyed.

c. The *raw data* consist of all the information collected in the survey.

d. The *sample statistics* summarize the raw data for the sample. In this case, the relevant sample statistic is the percentage of people in the sample who are actively seeking employment. (The Labor Department also calculates similar sample statistics for subgroups in the population, such as the percentages of teenagers, men, women, and veterans who are unemployed.)

e. The *population parameters* are the characteristics of the entire population that correspond to the sample statistics. In this case, the relevant population parameter is the actual unemployment rate. Note that the Labor Department does *not* actually measure this population parameter, because data are collected only for the sample and then are used to estimate the population parameter.   ⋅⋅●

How Do Sample Statistics Relate to Population Parameters?

Suppose Nielsen finds that 31% of the people in the 5,000 homes in its sample watched the Super Bowl. This "31%" is a sample statistic, because it characterizes the sample. But what Nielsen really wants to know is the corresponding population parameter, which is the percentage of all Americans who watched the Super Bowl.

There is no way for Nielsen researchers to know the exact value of the population parameter, because they've studied only a sample. However, Nielsen researchers hope that they've done their work correctly so that the sample statistic is a good estimate of the population parameter. In other words, they would like to conclude that because 31% of the sample watched the Super Bowl, approximately 31% of the population also watched the Super Bowl. One of the primary purposes of statistics is to help researchers assess the validity of this type of conclusion.

> **TIME ◯UT TO THINK**
>
> Suppose Nielsen concludes that 30% of Americans watched the Super Bowl. How many people does this represent? (The population of the United States is approximately 310 million.)

Statistical science provides methods that enable researchers to determine how well a sample statistic estimates a population parameter. For example, results from surveys or opinion polls are usually quoted along with a value called the **margin of error.** By adding and subtracting the margin of error from the sample statistic, we find a range of values, or **confidence interval,** that is *likely* to contain the population parameter. In most cases, the margin of error is defined so that we can have 95% confidence that this range contains the population parameter. We'll discuss the precise meaning of "likely" and "95% confidence," but for now you might find an explanation given by the *New York Times* useful (Figure 1.1). In the case of the Nielsen ratings, the margin of error is about 1 percentage point. Therefore, if 31% of the sample was watching the Super Bowl, then we can be 95% confident that the range from 30% to 32% contains the actual percentage of the population watching the Super Bowl.

How the Poll Was Conducted

The latest New York Times/CBS News Poll of New York State is based on telephone interviews conducted Oct. 23 to Oct. 28 with 1,315 adults throughout the state. Of those, 1,026 said they were registered to vote. Interviews were conducted in either English or Spanish.

In theory, in 19 cases out of 20 the results based on such samples will differ by no more than three percentage points in either direction from what would have been obtained by seeking out all adult residents of New York State. For smaller subgroups, the potential sampling error is larger.

Figure 1.1 The margin of error in a survey or opinion poll usually describes a range that is likely (with 95% confidence, meaning in 19 out of 20 cases) to contain the population parameter. This excerpt from the *New York Times* explains a margin of error of 3 percentage points.

One of the most remarkable findings of statistical science is that it is possible to get meaningful results from surprisingly small samples. Nevertheless, larger sample sizes are better (when they are feasible), because the margin of error is generally smaller for larger samples. For example, the margin of error for a 95% confidence interval in a well-conducted poll is typically about 5 percentage points for a sample size of 400, but drops to 3 percentage points for a sample size of 1,000 and to 1 percentage point for a sample of 10,000.

Definition

The **margin of error** in a statistical study is used to describe the range of values, or **confidence interval**, likely to contain the population parameter. We find this confidence interval by adding and subtracting the margin of error from the sample statistic obtained in the study. That is, the range of values likely to contain the population parameter is

from   (sample statistic − margin of error)

to   (sample statistic + margin of error)

The margin of error is usually defined to give a 95% confidence interval, meaning that 95% of samples of the size used in the study would contain the actual population parameter (and 5% would not).

EXAMPLE 3 Sex and Politics

The Pew Research Center for People and the Press interviewed 1,002 adult Americans and asked about the reason for a recent increase in sex scandals among elected officials. Fifty-seven percent of the respondents claimed that the increase is due to greater scrutiny by the media, while 19% felt that the increase is due to declining moral standards. The margin of error for the poll was 3 percentage points. Describe the population and the sample for this survey, and explain the meaning of the sample statistic of 57%. What can we conclude about the percentage of the population that believes the increase in political sex scandals is due to greater media scrutiny?

SOLUTION   The population is all adult Americans and the sample consists of the 1,002 people who were interviewed. The sample statistic of 57% is the *actual* percentage of people in the sample who answered that greater media scrutiny is responsible for the increase in political sex scandals. The 57% sample statistic and the margin of error of 3 percentage points tell us that the range of values

from $57\% - 3\% = 54\%$

to $57\% + 3\% = 60\%$

is likely (with 95% confidence) to contain the population parameter, which in this case is the true percentage of all adult Americans who believe that greater media scrutiny is responsible for the increase in political sex scandals.   · · ●

TIME OUT TO THINK

In the poll described in Example 3, the respondents were given the two possible explanations, greater media scrutiny and lower moral standards. Do you think the results might have been different if respondents were asked to provide their own explanations? Explain.

Putting It All Together: The Process of a Statistical Study

The process used by Nielsen Media Research is similar to that used in many statistical studies. Figure 1.2 and the box below summarize the basic steps in a statistical study. Keep in mind that these steps are somewhat idealized, and the actual steps may differ from one study to another. Moreover, the details hidden in the basic steps are critically important. For example, a poorly chosen sample in Step 2 can render the entire study meaningless, and great care must be taken in inferring conclusions about a population from results found for the much smaller sample of that population.

BY THE WAY

Statisticians often divide their subject into two major branches: **descriptive statistics,** which deals with *describing* raw data in the form of graphics and sample statistics, and **inferential statistics,** which deals with *inferring* (or estimating) population parameters from sample data. In this book, Chapters 3 through 5 primarily cover descriptive statistics.

Basic Steps in a Statistical Study

Step 1. State the goal of your study precisely; that is, determine the population you want to study and exactly what you'd like to learn about it.

Step 2. Choose a representative sample from the population.

Step 3. Collect raw data from the sample, and summarize these data by finding sample statistics of interest.

Step 4. Use the sample statistics to make inferences about the population.

Step 5. Draw conclusions; determine what you learned and whether you achieved your goal.

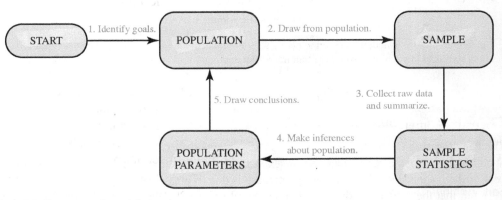

Figure 1.2   The process of a statistical study.

EXAMPLE 4 Identifying the Steps

Identify how researchers applied the five basic steps in the survey from Example 3.

SOLUTION   The steps apply as follows.

1. The researchers had a goal of learning what Americans think about the causes of recent political scandals. They chose adult Americans as the population, deliberately leaving out children.

2. They chose 1,002 adult Americans for their sample. Although we are not told how the sample was drawn, we will assume that it was drawn so that the 1,002 adult Americans are typical of the entire adult American population.

3. They collected the raw data by asking a simple question of the people in the sample. The raw data are the individual responses to the question. They summarized these data with sample statistics, such as the overall percentages of people in the sample who chose each answer.

4. Techniques of statistical science allowed the researchers to infer population characteristics. In this case, the inference consisted of estimating the relevant population parameter and calculating the margin of error.

5. By making sure that the study was conducted properly and interpreting the estimates of the population parameters, the researchers drew overall conclusions about Americans' attitudes concerning recent scandals.   ⋯●

Statistics: Decisions for an Uncertain World

Most of the examples we've discussed so far involve surveys or polls, but the subject of statistics encompasses much more, including experiments designed to test new medical treatments, analyses of the dangers of global warming, and even assessments of the value of a college education. Indeed, it is fair to say that the primary purpose of statistics is to help us make good decisions whenever we are confronted with a variety of possible options.

> **The Purpose of Statistics**
> Statistics has many uses, but perhaps its most important purpose is to help us make good decisions about issues that involve uncertainty.

This purpose will be clear in most of the case studies and examples we consider in this text, but occasionally we'll have to discuss a bit of theory that may seem somewhat abstract at first. If you keep the overall purpose of statistics in mind, you'll be rewarded in the end when you see how the theory helps us understand our world. The following case study will give you a taste of what lies ahead. It involves several important theoretical ideas that led to one of the 20th century's greatest accomplishments in public health.

ᑫASE STUDY   The Salk Polio Vaccine

If you had been a parent in the 1940s or 1950s, one of your greatest fears would have been the disease known as polio. Each year during this long polio epidemic, thousands of young children were paralyzed by the disease. In 1954, a large experiment was conducted to test the effectiveness of a new vaccine created by Dr. Jonas Salk (1914–1995). The experiment involved a sample of 400,000 children chosen from the population of all children in the United States. Half of these 400,000 children received an injection of the Salk vaccine. The other half received an injection that contained only salt water. (The salt water injection was a *placebo*; see Section 1.3.) Among the children receiving the Salk vaccine, only 33 contracted polio. In contrast, there were 115 cases of polio among the children who did not get the Salk vaccine. Using techniques of statistical science that we'll study later, the researchers concluded that the vaccine was effective at preventing polio. They therefore decided to launch a major effort to improve the Salk vaccine and distribute it to the population of *all* children. Thanks to this vaccine (and improved ones developed later), the horror of polio is now largely a memory of the past.

BY THE WAY

Polio quickly became rare in the United States after the development of the Salk vaccine, but it remained common in less-developed countries. A global effort to vaccinate children against polio began in 1998 and has achieved great success, though it has not yet reached its goal of completely eradicating the disease.

The greatest reward for doing is the opportunity to do more.

—Jonas Salk

Section 1.1 Exercises

Statistical Literacy and Critical Thinking

1. **Population and Sample.** What is a *population*, what is a *sample*, and what is the difference between them?

2. **Statistic and Statistics.** Suppose that, in a discussion, one person refers to baseball *statistics* and another refers to the use of *statistics* in showing that a particular drug is an effective treatment. Do both uses of the term *statistics* have the same meaning? If not, how do they differ?

3. **Statistics and Parameters.** What is a sample statistic, what is a population parameter, and what is the difference between them?

4. **Margin of Error.** What is the margin of error in a statistical study, and why is it important?

Does It Make Sense? For Exercises 5–10, decide whether the statement makes sense (or is clearly true) or does not make sense (or is clearly false). Explain clearly; not all of these have definitive answers, so your explanation is more important than your chosen answer.

5. **Statistics and Parameters.** My professor conducted a statistical study in which he was unable to measure any sample statistics, but he succeeded in determining the population parameters with a very small margin of error.

6. **Poor Poll.** A poll conducted two weeks before the election found that Smith would get 70% of the vote, with a margin of error of 3%, but he ended up losing the election anyway.

7. **Poll Certainty.** There is no doubt that Johnson won the election, because an exit poll showed that she received 54% of the vote and the margin of error is only 3 percentage points.

8. **Beating Nielsen.** A new startup company intends to compete with Nielsen Media Research by providing data with a larger margin of error for the same price.

9. **Depression Sample.** The goal of my study is to learn about depression among people who have suffered through a family tragedy, so I plan to choose a sample from the population of patients in support groups for loss of a spouse.

10. **New Product.** Our market research department surveyed 1,000 consumers on their attitude toward our new product. Because the people in this sample were so enthusiastic in their desire to purchase the product, we have decided to roll out a nationwide advertising campaign.

Concepts and Applications

Population, Sample, Statistic, and Parameter. Exercises 11–14 each describe a statistical study. In each case, identify the sample, the population, the sample statistic, and the population parameter.

11. **Smoking Poll.** In a Gallup poll of 1,018 adults in the United States, it was found that 22% smoked cigarettes in the past week.

12. **Birth Weights.** For 186 randomly selected babies, the average (mean) of their birth weights is 3,103 grams (based on data from "Cognitive Outcomes of Preschool Children with Prenatal Cocaine Exposure," by Singer et al., *Journal of the American Medical Association,* Vol. 291, No. 20).

13. **Garlic and Cholesterol.** In a test of the effectiveness of garlic for lowering cholesterol, 47 adult subjects were treated with Garlicin, which is garlic in a processed tablet form. Cholesterol levels were measured before and after the treatment. The changes in their levels of LDL cholesterol (in mg/dL) have an average (mean) of 3.2 (based on data from "Effect of Raw Garlic vs Commercial Garlic Supplements on Plasma Lipid Concentrations in Adults With Moderate Hypercholesterolemia," by Gardner et al, *Archives of Internal Medicine*, Vol. 167).

14. **Job Interview Mistakes.** In an Accountemps survey of 150 senior executives, 47% said that the most common job interview mistake is to have little or no knowledge of the company.

Identifying the Range of Values. In Exercises 15–18, use the given statistics and margin of error to identify the range of values (confidence interval) likely to contain the true value of the population parameter.

15. **Wake Up.** A Braun Research poll asked 1,000 office workers how they wake up in time for work; 60% of them said that they use an alarm clock. The margin of error of was 3 percentage points.

16. **Wash Up.** *USA Today* reported that among 6,028 adults observed in restrooms, 85% washed their hands. The margin of error was 1 percentage point.

17. **Claim to Wash Up.** In a Harris Interactive survey of 1,006 adults, 96% say that they wash their hands when in a public restroom. The margin of error was 3 percentage points.

18. **Body Temperatures.** One hundred and six adults are randomly selected and tested for their body temperatures. Based on that sample, researchers estimated that the average (mean) body temperature is 98.2° F with a margin of error of 0.1° F.

19. **Global Warming Poll.** A Pew Research Center poll asked 1,708 randomly selected adults whether "global warming is a problem that requires immediate government action." Results

showed that 55% of those surveyed said yes. The margin of error was 2 percentage points. Can a news reporter safely write that the majority (more than 50%) of people believe that immediate government action is required?

20. **Nielsen Survey.** In a survey of 25,047 Super Bowl viewers, 51% of them said that they enjoyed commercials more than the game. The margin of error is 0.6%. Can we conclude that the majority of Super Bowl viewers prefer commercials to the game? Why or why not?

21. **Do People Lie About Voting?** In a survey of 1,002 people, 701 (or 70%) said that they voted in the last presidential election (based on data from ICR Research Group). The margin of error was 3 percentage points. However, actual voting records show that only 61% of all eligible voters actually voted. Does this imply that people lied when they responded in the survey? Explain.

22. **Why the Discrepancy?** An Eagleton Institute poll asked men if they agreed with this statement: "Abortion is a private matter that should be left to women to decide without government intervention." Among the men who were interviewed by women, 77% agreed with the statement. Among the men who were interviewed by men, 70% agreed with the statement. Assuming that the discrepancy is significant, how might that discrepancy be explained?

Interpreting Real Studies. For each of Exercises 23–26, do the following:

a. Based on the given information, state what you think was the goal of the study. Identify a possible population and the population parameter of interest.

b. Briefly describe the sample, raw data, and sample statistic for the study.

c. Based on the sample statistic and the margin of error, identify the range of values (confidence interval) likely to contain the population parameter of interest.

23. **Death Penalty.** A Gallup poll asked 511 randomly selected adults if they favor the death penalty for a person convicted of murder, with 64% saying yes. The margin of error is 4 percentage points.

24. **Prescription Drugs.** A study of 3,005 adults ages 57 to 85 showed that 82% of them use at least one prescription drug. The margin of error is 2 percentage points (based on data from "Use of Prescription and Over-the-Counter Medications and Dietary Supplements Among Older Adults in the United States," by Qato, et al., *Journal of the American Medical Association*, Vol. 300, No. 24).

25. **Super Bowl.** In a recent Super Bowl, a Nielsen report found that 45% of the 9,000 surveyed U.S. households had TV sets tuned to the game. The margin of error is 1 percentage point.

26. **Piercings and Tattoos.** A Harris Interactive survey of 514 human resources professionals showed that 46% of them say that piercings or tattoos make job applicants less likely to be hired. The margin of error for the survey was 4 percentage points.

Five Steps in a Study. Describe how you would apply the five basic steps in a statistical study (as listed in the box on p. 6) to the issues in Exercises 27–30.

27. **Cell Phones and Driving.** You want to determine the percentage of drivers who use cell phones while they are driving.

28. **Credit Scores.** FICO (Fair Isaac Corporation) scores are routinely used to rate the quality of consumer credit. You want to determine the average (mean) FICO score of an adult in the United States.

29. **Passenger Weight.** Recognizing that overloading commercial aircraft would lead to unsafe flights, you want to determine the average (mean) weight of airline passengers.

30. **Pacemaker Batteries.** Because the batteries used in heart pacemakers are so critically important, you want to determine the average (mean) length of time that such batteries last before failure.

PROJECTS FOR THE INTERNET & BEYOND

31. **Current Nielsen Ratings.** Find the Nielsen ratings for the past week. What were the three most popular television shows? Explain the meaning of the "rating" and the "share" for each show.

32. **Nielsen Methods.** Nielsen Media Research supplies statistical data that is very important to advertisers and marketers. Visit the Nielsen Web site and read about one or more of their data products. Write a brief report on how they collect the data and how the data are used.

33. **Comparing Airlines.** The U.S. Department of Transportation routinely publishes on-time performance, lost baggage rates, and other statistics for different airline companies. Find a recent example of such statistics. Based on what you find, is it fair to say that any particular airline stands out as better or worse than others? Explain.

34. **Labor Statistics.** Use the Bureau of Labor Statistics Web site to find monthly unemployment rates over the past 12 months. If you assume that the monthly survey has a margin of error of about 0.2 percentage point, has there been a noticeable change in the unemployment rate over the past year? Explain.

35. **Statistics and Safety.** Identify a study that has been done (or should be done) to improve the safety of car drivers and passengers. Briefly describe the importance of statistics to the study.

36. **Pew Research Center.** The Pew Research Center for the People and the Press studies public attitudes toward the press, politics, and public policy issues. Go to its Web site and find the latest survey about attitudes. Select a particular recent survey, and write a summary of what was surveyed, how the survey was conducted, and what was found.

IN THE NEWS

37. Statistics in the News. Identify three stories from the past week that involve statistics in some way. In each case, write a brief statement describing the role of statistics in the story.

38. Statistics in Your Major. Write a brief description of some ways in which you think that the science of statistics can be used in your major field of study. (If you have not yet selected a major, answer the question for a major that you are considering.)

39. Statistics and Entertainment. The Nielsen ratings are well known for their role in gauging television viewing. Identify another way that statistics are used in the entertainment industry. Briefly describe the role of statistics in this application.

40. Statistics in Sports. Choose a sport and describe at least three different statistics commonly tracked by participants in or spectators of the sport. In each case, briefly describe the importance of the statistic to the sport.

41. Economic Statistics. The government regularly publishes many different economic statistics, such as the unemployment rate, the inflation rate, and the surplus or deficit in the federal budget. Study recent newspapers and identify five important economic statistics. Briefly explain the purpose of each of these five statistics.

1.2   SAMPLING

Not everything that can be counted counts, and not everything that counts can be counted.

—Albert Einstein

The only way to know the true value of a population parameter is to observe *every* member of the population. For example, to learn the exact mean height of all students at your school, you'd need to measure the height of every student. A collection of data from every member of a population is called a **census.** Unfortunately, conducting a census is often impractical. In some cases, the population is so large that it would be too expensive or time-consuming to collect data from every member. In other cases, a census may be ruled out because it would interfere with a study's overall goals. For example, a study designed to test the quality of candy bars before shipping could not involve a census because that would mean testing a piece of every candy bar, leaving none intact to sell.

> **Definition**
> A **census** is the collection of data from *every* member of a population.

Fortunately, most statistical studies can be done without going to the trouble of conducting a census. Instead of collecting data from every member of the population, we collect data from a sample and use the sample statistics to make inferences about the population. Of course, the inferences will be reasonable only if the members of the sample represent the population fairly, at least in terms of the characteristics under study. That is, we seek a **representative sample** of the population.

> **Definition**
> A **representative sample** is a sample in which the relevant characteristics of the sample members are generally the same as the characteristics of the population.

EXAMPLE ❶   A Representative Sample for Heights

Suppose you want to determine the mean height of all students at your school. Which is more likely to be a representative sample for this study: the men's basketball team or the students in your statistics class?

SOLUTION   The men's basketball team is not a representative sample for a study of height, both because it consists only of men and because basketball players tend to be taller than average. The mean height of the students in your statistics class is much more likely to be close to the mean height of all students, so the members of your class make a more representative sample than the members of the men's basketball team.   · · ●

Bias

Imagine that, for the 5,000 homes in its sample, Nielsen chose only homes in which the primary wage earners worked a late-night shift. Because late-night workers aren't home to watch late-night television, Nielsen would find late-night shows to be unpopular among the homes in this sample. Clearly, this sample would *not* be representative of all American homes, and it would be wrong to conclude that late-night shows were unpopular among all Americans. We say that such a sample is *biased* because the homes in the sample differed in a specific way from "typical" American homes. (In reality, Nielsen takes great care to avoid such obvious bias in the sample selection.) More generally, the term **bias** refers to any problem in the design or conduct of a statistical study that tends to favor certain results. We cannot trust the conclusions of a biased study.

> **Definition**
> A statistical study suffers from **bias** if its design or conduct tends to favor certain results.

Bias can arise in many ways. For example:

- A sample is biased if the members of the sample differ in some specific way from the members of the general population. In that case, the results of the study will reflect the unusual characteristics of the sample rather than the actual characteristics of the population.
- A researcher is biased if he or she has a personal stake in a particular outcome. In that case, the researcher might intentionally or unintentionally distort the true meaning of the data.
- The data set itself is biased if its values were collected intentionally or unintentionally in a way that makes the data unrepresentative of the population.
- Even if a study is done well, it may be reported in a biased fashion. For example, a graph representing the data may tell only part of the story or depict the data in a misleading way (see Section 3.5).

Preventing bias is one of the greatest challenges in statistical research. Looking for bias is therefore one of the most important steps in evaluating a statistical study or media reports about a statistical study.

BY THE WAY

Many medical studies are experiments designed to test whether a new drug is effective. In an article published in the *Journal of the American Medical Association*, the authors found that studies with positive results (the drug is effective) are more likely to be published than studies with negative results (the drug is not effective). This "publication bias" tends to make new drugs, as a group, seem more effective than they really are.

EXAMPLE 2   Why Use Nielsen?

Nielsen Media Research earns money by charging television stations and networks for its services. For example, NBC pays Nielsen to provide ratings for its television shows. Why doesn't NBC simply do its own ratings, instead of paying a company like Nielsen to do them?

SOLUTION   The cost of advertising on a television show depends on the show's ratings. The higher the ratings, the more the network can charge for advertising—which means NBC would have a clear bias if it conducted its own ratings. Advertisers therefore would not trust ratings that NBC produced on its own. By hiring an independent source, such as Nielsen, NBC can provide information that advertisers are more likely to believe.   · · ●

Sampling Methods

A good statistical study *must* have a representative sample. Otherwise the sample is biased and conclusions from the study are not trustworthy. Let's examine a few common sampling methods that, at least in principle, can provide a representative sample.

Simple Random Samples

In most cases, the best way to obtain a representative sample is by choosing *randomly* from the population. A **random sample** is one in which every member of the population has an equal chance of being selected to be part of the sample. For example, you could obtain a random sample by having everyone in a population roll a die and choosing those people who roll a 6. In contrast, the sample would not be random if you chose everyone taller than 6 feet, because not everyone would have an equal chance of being selected.

In statistics, we usually decide in advance the sample size that is needed. With **simple random sampling,** every possible sample of a particular size has an equal chance of being selected. For example, to choose a simple random sample of 100 students from all the students in your school, you could assign a number to each student in your school and choose the sample by drawing 100 of these numbers from a hat. As long as each student's number is in the hat only once, every sample of 100 students has an equal chance of being selected. As a faster alternative to using a hat, you might choose the student numbers with the aid of a computer or calculator that has a built-in *random number generator*.

Because simple random sampling gives every sample of a particular size the same chance of being chosen, it is likely to provide a representative sample, as long as the sample size is large enough.

EXAMPLE ❸ Local Resident Sampling

You want to conduct an opinion poll in which the population is all the residents in a town. Could you choose a simple random sample by randomly selecting names from local property tax records?

SOLUTION   A sample drawn from property tax records is not a simple random sample of the town population because these records would only list people who own property in the town. These records are therefore missing many town residents, and might also include people who live elsewhere but own property in the town.   ·· ●

Systematic Sampling

Simple random sampling is effective, but in many cases we can get equally good results with a simpler technique. Suppose you are testing the quality of microchips produced by Intel. As the chips roll off the assembly line, you might decide to test every 50th chip. This ought to give a representative sample because there's no reason to believe that every 50th chip has any special characteristics compared with other chips. This type of sampling, in which we use a system such as choosing every 50th member of a population, is called **systematic sampling.**

EXAMPLE 4 Museum Assessment

When the National Air and Space Museum wanted to test possible ideas for a new solar system exhibit, a staff member interviewed a sample of visitors selected by systematic sampling. She interviewed a visitor exactly every 15 minutes, choosing whoever happened to enter the current solar system exhibit at that time. Why do you think she chose systematic sampling rather than simple random sampling? Was systematic sampling likely to produce a representative sample in this case?

SOLUTION   Simple random sampling might occasionally have selected two visitors so soon after each other that the staff member would not have had time to interview each of them. The systematic process of choosing a visitor every 15 minutes prevented this problem from arising. Because there's no reason to think that the people entering at a particular moment are any different from those who enter a few minutes earlier or later, this process is likely to give a representative sample of the population of visitors during the time of the sampling.   · · ●

EXAMPLE 5 When Systematic Sampling Fails

You are conducting a survey of students in a co-ed dormitory in which males are assigned to odd-numbered rooms and females are assigned to even-numbered rooms. Can you obtain a representative sample when you choose every 10th room?

SOLUTION   No. If you start with an odd-numbered room, every 10th room will also be odd-numbered (such as room numbers 3, 13, 23, …). Similarly, if you start with an even-numbered room, every 10th room will also be even-numbered. You will therefore obtain a sample consisting of either all males or all females, neither of which is representative of the co-ed population.   · · ●

> **TIME OUT TO THINK**
> Suppose you chose every fifth room, rather than every 10th room, in Example 5. Would the sample then be representative?

Convenience Samples

Systematic sampling is easier than simple random sampling but might also be impractical in many cases. For example, suppose you want to know the proportion of left-handed students at your school. It would take great effort to select a simple random sample or a systematic sample, because both require drawing from all the students in the school. In contrast, it would be easy to use the students in your statistics class as your sample—you could just ask the left-handed students to raise their hands. This type of sample is called a **convenience sample** because it is chosen for convenience rather than by a more sophisticated procedure. For trying to find the proportion of left-handed people, the convenience sample of your statistics class is probably fine; there is no reason to think that there would be a different proportion of left-handed students in a statistics class than anywhere else. But if you were trying to determine the proportions of students with different majors, this sample would be biased because some majors require a statistics course and others do not. In general, convenience sampling tends to be more prone to bias than most other forms of sampling.

EXAMPLE 6 Salsa Taste Test

A supermarket wants to decide whether to carry a new brand of salsa, so it offers free tastes at a stand in the store and asks people what they think. What type of sampling is being used? Is the sample likely to be representative of the population of all shoppers?

SOLUTION   The sample of shoppers stopping for a taste of the salsa is a convenience sample because these people happen to be in the store and are willing to try the new product. (This type of convenience sample, in which people choose whether or not to be part of the sample, is also called a *self-selected sample*. We will study self-selected samples further in Section 1.4.) This sample is unlikely to be representative of the population of all shoppers, because different types of people may shop at different times (for example, stay-at-home parents are more likely to shop at midday than are working parents) and only people who like salsa are likely to participate. The data might be still be useful, however, because the opinions of people who like salsa are probably the most important ones in this case.   · · ●

Cluster Samples

Cluster sampling involves the selection of *all* members in randomly selected groups, or *clusters*. Imagine that you work for the Department of Agriculture and wish to determine the percentage of farmers who use organic farming techniques. It would be difficult and costly to collect a simple random sample or a systematic sample because either would require visiting many individual farms that are located far from one another. A convenience sample of farmers in a single county would be biased because farming practices vary from region to region. You might therefore decide to select a few dozen counties at random from across the United States and survey *every* farmer in each of those counties. We say that each county contains a *cluster* of farmers, and the sample consists of *every* farmer within the randomly selected clusters.

EXAMPLE 7 Gasoline Prices

You want to know the mean price of gasoline at gas stations located within a mile of rental car locations at airports. Explain how you might use cluster sampling in this case.

SOLUTION   You could randomly select a few airports around the country. For these airports, you would check the gasoline price at *every* gas station within a mile of the rental car location.   · · ●

BY THE WAY

As mandated by the U.S. Constitution, voting for the President is actually done by a small group of people called *electors*. Each state may select as many electors as it has members of Congress (counting both senators and representatives). When you cast a ballot for President, you actually cast a vote for your state's electors, each of whom has promised to vote for a particular presidential candidate. The electors cast their votes a few weeks after the general election.

Stratified Samples

Suppose you are conducting a poll to predict the outcome of the next U.S. presidential election. The population under study is all likely voters, so you might choose a simple random sample from this population. However, because presidential elections are decided by electoral votes cast on a state-by-state basis, you'll get a better prediction if you determine voter preferences within each state. Your overall sample should therefore consist of separate random samples from each of the 50 states. In statistical terminology, the populations of the 50 states represent subgroups, or **strata,** of the total population. Because your overall sample consists of randomly selected members from each stratum, you've used **stratified sampling.**

EXAMPLE 8 Unemployment Data

The U.S. Labor Department surveys 60,000 households each month to compile its unemployment report (see Example 2 in Section 1.1). To select these households, the department first groups cities and counties into about 2,000 geographic areas. It then randomly selects households to survey within these geographic areas. How is this an example of stratified sampling? What are the strata? Why is stratified sampling important in this case?

SOLUTION   The unemployment survey is an example of stratified sampling because it first breaks the population into subgroups. The subgroups, or strata, are the people in the 2,000 geographic regions. Stratified sampling is important in this case because unemployment rates are likely to differ in different geographic regions. For example, unemployment rates in rural Kansas may be very different from those in Silicon Valley. By using stratified sampling, the Labor Department ensures that its sample fairly represents all geographic regions.   · · ●

Summary of Sampling Methods

The following box and Figure 1.3 summarize the five sampling methods we have discussed. No single method is "best," as each one has its uses. (Some studies even combine two or more types of sampling.) But regardless of how a sample is chosen, keep in mind the following three key ideas:

- A study can be successful only if the sample is representative of the population.
- A biased sample is unlikely to be a representative sample.
- Even a well-chosen sample may still turn out to be unrepresentative just because of bad luck in the actual drawing of the sample.

Common Sampling Methods

- **Simple random sampling:** We choose a sample of items in such a way that every sample of the same size has an equal chance of being selected.

- **Systematic sampling:** We use a simple system to choose the sample, such as selecting every 10th or every 50th member of the population.

- **Convenience sampling:** We use a sample that happens to be convenient to select.

- **Cluster sampling:** We first divide the population into groups, or clusters, and select some of these clusters at random. We then obtain the sample by choosing *all* the members within each of the selected clusters.

- **Stratified sampling:** We use this method when we are concerned about differences among sub-groups, or *strata*, within a population. We first identify the strata and then draw a random sample within each stratum. The total sample consists of all the samples from the individual strata.

Simple Random Sampling:
Every sample of the same size has an equal chance of being selected. Computers are often used to generate random numbers.

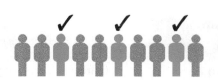

Systematic Sampling:
Select every *k*th member.

Convenience Sampling:
Use results that are readily available.

Election precincts in Carson County

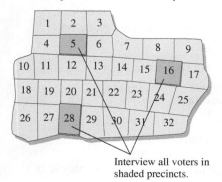

Interview all voters in shaded precincts.

Cluster Sampling:
Divide the population into clusters, randomly select some of those clusters, then choose all members of the selected clusters.

Stratified Sampling:
Partition the population into at least two strata, then draw a sample from each.

Figure 1.3 Common sampling methods.

EXAMPLE 9   Sampling Methods

Identify the type of sampling used in each of the following cases.

a. The apple harvest from an orchard is collected in 1,200 baskets. An agricultural inspector randomly selects 25 baskets and then checks every apple in each of these baskets for worms.

b. An educational researcher wants to know whether, at a particular college, men or women tend to ask more questions in class. Of the 10,000 students at the college, she interviews 50 randomly selected men and 50 randomly selected women.

c. In trying to learn about planetary systems, astronomers conduct a survey by looking for planets among 100 nearby stars.

d. To determine who will win autographed footballs, a computer program randomly selects the ticket numbers of 11 people in a stadium filled with people.

SOLUTION

a. The apple inspection is an example of cluster sampling because the inspector begins with a randomly selected set of clusters (baskets) and then checks every apple in the selected clusters.

b. The groups of men and women represent two different strata for this study, so this is an example of stratified sampling.

c. The astronomers presumably focus on nearby stars because they are easier to study in this case, so this is an example of convenience sampling.

d. Because the computer selects the 11 ticket numbers at random, every ticket number has an equal chance of being chosen. This is an example of simple random sampling. ·· ●

Section 1.2 Exercises

Statistical Literacy and Critical Thinking

1. **Census and Sample.** What is a *census,* what is a sample, and what is the difference between them?

2. **Biased Sample.** In a survey before a general election (as opposed to a primary), a sample is drawn randomly from a list of registered Democrats. Is there anything wrong with this sampling method?

3. **Cluster and Stratified Sampling.** Cluster sampling and stratified sampling both involve selecting subjects in subgroups of the population. What is the difference between those two types of sampling?

4. **Sample of Students.** A college statistics teacher conducted a study by recording whether each student in his class was right-handed. The objective was to form a conclusion about the proportion of college students that is right-handed. What type of sample was obtained? Is this sample likely to be biased? Why or why not?

Does It Make Sense? For Exercises 5–8, decide whether the statement makes sense (or is clearly true) or does not make sense (or is clearly false). Explain clearly; not all of these have definitive answers, so your explanation is more important than your chosen answer.

5. **Graduation Age.** For a statistics class project, I conducted a census to determine the mean age of students when they earn their bachelor's degrees.

6. **Convenience Sample.** For a statistics class project, I used a convenience sample, but the results may still be meaningful.

7. **Biased Sample.** The study must have been biased, because it concluded that 75% of Americans are more than 6 feet tall.

8. **Death Row.** There are currently 3,242 convicts on death row (based on 2010 data from the Bureau of Justice Statistics). We obtained a simple random sample of those convicts by compiling a numbered list, then using a computer to randomly generate 20 numbers between 1 and 3,242, then selecting the convicts that correspond to the generated numbers.

Concepts and Applications

Census. In Exercises 9–12, determine whether a census is practical in the situations described. Explain your reasoning.

9. **Laker Heights.** You want to determine the mean height of all basketball players on the LA Lakers team.

10. **High School Heights.** You want to determine the mean height of all high school basketball players in the United States.

11. **IQ Scores.** You want to determine the mean IQ score of all statistics instructors in the United States.

12. **Instructor Ages.** You want to determine the mean age of all statistics instructors at the University of Colorado.

Representative Samples? In Exercises 13–16, identify the sample, population, and sampling method. Then comment on whether you think it is likely that the sample is representative of the population.

13. **Senate Terms.** A political scientist randomly selects 4 of the 100 senators currently serving in Congress, then finds the lengths of time that they have served.

14. **Super Bowl.** During the Super Bowl game, Nielsen Media Research conducts a survey of 5,108 randomly selected households and finds that 44% of them have television sets tuned to the Super Bowl.

15. **Gun Ownership.** In a Gallup poll of 1,059 randomly selected adults, 39% answered "yes" when asked "Do you have a gun in your home?"

16. **Mail Survey.** A graduate student conducts a research project about how adult Americans send thank-you notes. She uses the U.S. Postal Service to mail a survey to 500 adults that she knows and asks them to mail back a response to this question: "Do you prefer to send thank you notes by e-mail or snail mail (the U.S. Postal Service)?" She gets back 65 responses, with 42 of them indicating a preference for snail mail.

Evaluate the Sample Choices. Exercises 17–18 each describe the goal of a study, then offer you four options for obtaining a sample. In each case, decide which sample is most likely to be a representative sample, and explain why. Then explain why each of the other choices is *not* likely to make a representative sample for the study.

17. **Credit Card Debt.** You want to determine the mean amount of credit card debt owed by adult consumers in Florida.

   - Sample 1: The Florida drivers who own and have registered Land Rover vehicles
   - Sample 2: The first 1,000 Florida residents listed in the Fort Lauderdale phone book
   - Sample 3: The first 1,000 Florida residents in a complete list of all Florida telephone numbers
   - Sample 4: The Florida residents who mail back a survey printed in the *Miami Herald*

18. **California Voters.** You want to conduct a survey to determine the proportion of eligible voters in California likely to vote for the Democratic presidential candidate in the next election.

   - Sample 1: All eligible voters in San Diego County
   - Sample 2: All eligible voters in the city of Sonoma
   - Sample 3: All eligible voters who respond to a CNN Internet survey
   - Sample 4: Every 1,000th person on a complete list of all eligible voters in California

Bias. Are there sources of bias in the situations described in Exercises 19–22? Explain.

19. **Movie Critic.** A film critic for ABC News gives her opinion of the latest movie from Disney, which also happens to own ABC.

20. **Car Reviews.** *Consumer Reports* magazine prints a review of new cars and does not accept free products or advertising from anyone.

21. **GMO Soybeans.** Monsanto hires independent university scientists to determine whether its new, genetically engineered soybean poses any threat to the environment.

22. **Drug Study Funding.** The *Journal of the American Medical Association* prints an article evaluating a drug, and some of the physicians who wrote the article received funding from the pharmaceutical company that produces the drug.

Sampling Methods. In Exercises 23–38, identify which of the following applies: simple random sample, systematic sample, convenience sample, stratified sample, or cluster sample. In each case, state whether you think the procedure is likely to yield a representative sample or a biased sample, and explain why.

23. **Clinical Trial.** In phase II testing of a new drug designed to increase the red blood cell count, a researcher obtains envelopes with the names and addresses of all treated subjects. She wants to increase the dosage in a sub-sample of 12 subjects, so she thoroughly mixes all of the envelopes in a bin, then pulls 12 of those envelopes to identify the subjects to be given the increased dosage.

24. **Sobriety Checkpoint.** Police set up a sobriety checkpoint at which every fifth driver is stopped and interviewed.

25. **Exit Polls.** On days of presidential elections, the news media organize an exit poll in which specific polling stations are randomly selected and all voters are surveyed as they leave the premises.

26. **Education and Sports.** A researcher for the Spaulding athletic equipment company is studying the relationship between level of education and participation sports. She conducts a survey of 40 randomly selected golfers, 40 randomly selected tennis players, and 40 randomly selected swimmers.

27. Ergonomics. An engineering student measures the strength of fingers used to push buttons by testing family members.

28. Tax Cheating. An Internal Revenue Service researcher investigates false reporting of tip income by waiters and waitresses by surveying all waiters and waitresses at 20 randomly selected restaurants.

29. MTV Survey. A marketing expert for MTV is planning a survey in which 500 people will be randomly selected from each age group of 10–19, 20–29, and so on.

30. Credit Card Data. A professor surveyed students in her class to obtain sample data consisting of the number of credit cards students possess.

31. Fundraising. Fundraisers for the College of Newport test a new telemarketing campaign by obtaining an alphabetical list of all alumni and selecting every 100th name on that list.

32. Telephone Poll. In a Gallup poll of 1,059 adults, the interview subjects were selected by using a computer to randomly generate telephone numbers that were then called.

33. Market Research. A market researcher has partitioned all California residents into categories of unemployed, employed full time, and employed part time. She is surveying 50 people from each category.

34. Student Drinking. Motivated by a student who died from binge drinking, the College of Newport conducts a study of student drinking by randomly selecting 10 different classes and interviewing all of the students in each of those classes.

35. Magazine Survey. *People* magazine chooses its "best-dressed celebrities" by compiling responses from readers who mail in a survey printed in the magazine.

36. Heart Transplants. A medical researcher at Johns Hopkins University obtains a numbered list of all patients waiting for a heart transplant, then uses a computer to select the patients corresponding to the 50 numbers randomly generated by computer.

37. Quality Control. A sample of manufactured CDs is obtained by using a computer to randomly generate a number between 1 and 1,000 for each CD, and the CD is selected if the generated number is 1,000.

38. Seat Belts. Every 500th seat belt is tested by stressing it until it fails.

Choose a Sampling Method. For each of Exercises 39–42, suggest a sampling method that is likely to produce a representative sample. Explain why you chose this method over other methods.

39. Student Election. You want to predict the winner of an upcoming election for student body president.

40. Blood Type. You want to determine the percentage of people in this country in each of the four major blood groups (A, B, AB, and O).

41. Heart Deaths. You want to determine the percentage of deaths due to heart disease each year.

42. Mercury in Tuna. You want to determine the average mercury content of the tuna fish consumed by U.S. residents.

PROJECTS FOR THE INTERNET & BEYOND

43. Public Opinion Poll. Use information available on the Web site of a polling organization, such as Gallup, Harris, Pew, or Yankelovich, to answer the following questions.

  a. How exactly is a sample of subjects selected?

  b. Based on what you have learned, do you think the poll results are reliable? If so, why? If not, why not?

44. Unemployment Sample. Use the Bureau of Labor Statistics Web page to find details on how the bureau chooses the sample of households in its monthly survey. Write a short summary of the procedure and why it is likely to yield a representative sample.

45. Selective Voting. The Academy Awards, the Heisman Trophy, and the *New York Times* "Bestseller List" are just three examples of selections that are determined by the votes of specially selected individuals. Pick one of these selection processes, and describe who votes and how those people are chosen. Discuss sources of bias in the process.

IN THE NEWS

46. Sampling in the News. Find a recent news report about a statistical study that you find interesting. Write a short summary of how the sample for the study was chosen, and briefly discuss whether you think the sample was representative of the population under study.

47. Opinion Poll Sample. Find a recent news report about an opinion poll carried out by a news organization (such as Gallup, Harris, *USA Today*, *New York Times*, or CNN). Briefly describe the sample and how it was chosen. Was the sample chosen in a way that was likely to introduce any bias? Explain.

48. Political Polls. Find results from a recent poll conducted by a political organization (such as the Republican or Democratic party or an organization that seeks to influence Congress on some particular issue). Briefly describe the sample and how it was chosen. Was the sample chosen in a way that was likely to introduce any bias? Should you be more concerned about bias in such a poll than you would be in a poll conducted by a news organization? Explain.

1.3 TYPES OF STATISTICAL STUDIES

Statistical studies are conducted in many different ways. In all cases, the people, animals (or other living things), or objects chosen for the sample are called the **subjects** of the study. If the subjects are people, it is common to refer to them as **participants** in the study.

> **Definition**
>
> The **subjects** of a study are the people, animals (or other living things), or objects chosen for the sample; if the subjects are people, they may be called the **participants** in the study.

There are two basic types of statistical study: observational studies and experiments. In an **observational study,** we observe or measure specific characteristics while trying to be careful to avoid influencing or modifying the characteristics we are observing. The Nielsen ratings are an example of an observational study, because Nielsen uses devices to *observe* what the subjects are watching on TV, but does not try to influence what they watch.

Note that an observational study may involve activities that go beyond the usual definition of *observing*. Measuring people's weights requires interacting with them, as in asking them to stand on a scale. But in statistics, we consider these measurements to be observations because the interactions do not change people's weights. Similarly, an opinion poll in which researchers conduct in-depth interviews is considered observational as long as the researchers attempt only to learn people's opinions, not to change them.

In contrast, consider a medical study designed to test whether large daily doses of vitamin C help prevent colds. To conduct this study, the researchers must ask some people in the sample to take large doses of vitamin C every day. This type of statistical study is called an **experiment.** The purpose of an experiment is to study the effects of some **treatment**—in this case, large daily doses of vitamin C.

You can observe a lot by just watching.

—Yogi Berra

> **Two Basic Types of Statistical Study**
>
> • In an **observational study,** researchers observe or measure characteristics of the subjects, but do not attempt to influence or modify these characteristics.
>
> • In an **experiment,** researchers apply some **treatment** and observe its effects on the subjects of the experiment.

EXAMPLE 1 Type of Study

Identify the study as an observational study or an experiment.

a. The Salk polio vaccine study (see the Case Study on page 7)

b. A poll in which college students are asked if they commute or live on campus

SOLUTION

a. The Salk vaccine study was an *experiment* because researchers tested a treatment—in this case, the vaccine—to see whether it reduced the incidence of polio.

b. The poll is an *observational study* because it attempts to determine how college students go to their classes, and it does not try to influence how they get there.   · · ●

Identifying the Variables

Statistical studies—whether observations or experiments—generally are attempts to measure what we call **variables of interest.** The term *variable* refers to an item or quantity that can vary or take on different values, and variables of interest are those we seek to learn about. For example, variables of interest in the Nielsen studies of television viewing habits include *show being watched* and *number of viewers*. The variable *show being watched* can take on different values such as "Super Bowl" or "*60 Minutes.*" The variable *number of viewers* depends on the popularity of a particular show. In essence, the raw data in any statistical study are the different values of the variables of interest.

In cases where we think cause and effect may be involved, we sometimes subdivide the variables of interest into two categories. For example, each person in the study of vitamin C and colds may take a different daily dose of vitamin C and may end up with a different number of colds over some period of time. Because we are trying to learn if vitamin C causes a lower number of colds, we say that *daily dose of vitamin C* is an **explanatory variable**—it may explain or cause a change in the number of colds. Similarly, we say that *number of colds* is a **response variable,** because we expect it to respond to changes in the explanatory variable (the dose of vitamin C).

> **Definitions**
>
> A variable is any item or quantity that can vary or take on different values.
>
> The **variables of interest** in a statistical study are the items or quantities that the study seeks to measure.
>
> When cause and effect may be involved, an **explanatory variable** is a variable that may explain or cause the effect, while a **response variable** is a variable that responds to changes in the explanatory variable.

EXAMPLE 2   Identify the Variables

Identify the variables of interest for each study.

a. The Salk polio vaccine study

b. A poll in which college students are asked if they commute or live on campus

SOLUTION

a. The two variables of interest in the Salk vaccine study are *vaccine* and *polio*. They are variables because they can take on two different values: A child either did or did not get the vaccine and either did or did not contract polio. In this case, because the study seeks to determine whether the vaccine prevents polio, we say that *vaccine* is the explanatory variable (it may explain a change in the incidence of polio) and *polio* the response variable (it is supposed to change in response to the vaccine).

b. The variables of interest are the responses to the question asking how students get to their classes, and the proportions of responses to the possible different choices (such as commute, live on campus, refuse to answer, don't know). (There is no cause and effect involved in this study, so we do not need to decide whether the variable is explanatory or response.) $\cdots \bullet$

Observational Studies

The observational studies we have discussed up to this point, such as Nielsen ratings, opinion polls, and determining the mean height of students, are studies in which the data are all generally collected around the same time. Sometimes, however, observational studies look at past data or are designed to look at future data over a long period of time.

A **retrospective study** (also called a *case-control* study) is an observational study that uses data from the past—such as official records or past interviews—to learn about some issue of concern. Retrospective studies are especially valuable in cases where it may be impractical or unethical to perform an experiment. For example, suppose we want to learn how alcohol consumed during pregnancy affects newborn babies. Because it is already known that consuming alcohol during pregnancy can be harmful, it would be highly unethical to ask pregnant mothers to test the "treatment" of consuming alcohol. However, because many mothers consumed alcohol in past pregnancies (either before the dangers were known or choosing to ignore the dangers), we can do a retrospective study in which we compare children born to those mothers to children born to mothers who did not consume alcohol.

Sometimes, the data we need to reach clear conclusions are not available in past records. In those cases, researchers may set up a **prospective study** (sometimes called a *longitudinal* study) designed to collect observations in the future from groups that share common factors. A classic example of a prospective study is the Harvard Nurses' Health Study, which was started in 1976 in order to collect data about how different lifestyles affect women's health (see the "Focus on Public Health" section at the end of this chapter). The study, still ongoing today, has followed thousands of nurses over more than three decades, collecting data about their lifestyles and health.

Variations on Observational Studies

The most familiar observational studies are those in which data are collected all at once (or as close to that as possible). Two variations on observational studies are also common:

- A **retrospective** (or **case-control**) **study** uses data from the past, such as official records or past interviews.

- A **prospective** (or **longitudinal**) **study** is set up to collect data in the future from groups that share common factors.

EXAMPLE ③ Observational Study

You want to know whether children born prematurely do as well in elementary school as children born at full term. What type of study should you do?

SOLUTION   An observational, retrospective study is the only real option in this case. You would collect data on past births and compare the elementary school performance of those born prematurely to that of those born at full term. $\cdots \bullet$

Experiments

Because experiments require active intervention, such as applying a treatment, we must take special care to ensure that they are designed in ways that will provide the information we seek. Let's examine a few of the issues that arise in the design of experiments.

The Need for Controls

Consider an experiment that gives some participants in a study vitamin C to determine its effect on colds. Suppose the people taking vitamin C daily get an average of 1.5 colds in a three-month period. How can the researchers know whether the subjects would have gotten more colds without the vitamin C? To answer this type of question, the researchers must conduct their experiment with two (or more) groups of subjects: One group takes large doses of vitamin C daily and another group does not. As we'll discuss shortly, in most cases it is important that participants be *randomly* assigned to the two groups.

The group of people who are randomly assigned to take vitamin C is called the **treatment group** because its members receive the treatment being tested (vitamin C). The group of people who do *not* take vitamin C is called the **control group.** The researchers can be confident that vitamin C is an effective treatment only if the people in the treatment group get significantly fewer colds than the people in the control group.

BY THE WAY

The control group gets its name from the fact that it helps control the way we interpret experimental results.

Treatment and Control Groups

The **treatment group** in an experiment is the group of subjects who receive the treatment being tested.

The **control group** in an experiment is the group of subjects who do *not* receive the treatment being tested.

EXAMPLE 4 Treatment and Control

Look again at the Salk polio vaccine Case Study (page 7). What was the treatment? Which group of children constituted the treatment group? Which constituted the control group?

SOLUTION   The treatment was the Salk vaccine. The treatment group consisted of the children who received the Salk vaccine. The control group consisted of the children who did not get the Salk vaccine and instead got an injection of salt water. $\cdots\bullet$

EXAMPLE 5 Mozart Treatment

A study divided college students into two groups. One group listened to Mozart or other classical music before being assigned a specific task and the other group simply was assigned the task without listening to the music. Researchers found that those listening to the classical music performed the task slightly better, but only if they did the task within a few minutes of listening to the music. (The two groups performed equally on tasks given later). Identify the treatment and the control and treatment groups.

SOLUTION   The treatment was the classical music. The treatment group consisted of the students who listened to the music. The control group consisted of the students who did not listen to the music. $\cdots\bullet$

Confounding Variables

Using control groups helps to ensure that we account for known variables that could affect a study's results. However, researchers may be unaware of or be unable to account for other important variables. Consider an experiment in which a statistics teacher seeks to determine whether students who study collaboratively (in study groups with other students) earn higher grades than students who study independently. The teacher chooses five students who will study collaboratively (the treatment group) and five others who will study independently (the control group). To ensure that the students all have similar abilities and will study diligently, the teacher chooses only students with high grade-point averages. At the end of the semester, the teacher finds that the students who studied collaboratively earned higher grades.

The variables of interest for this study are *collaborative study* (whether they do so or not) and *final grade*. But suppose that, unbeknownst to the teacher, the collaborative students all lived in a dormitory where a curfew ensured that they got plenty of sleep. This fact introduces a new variable—which we might call *amount of sleep*—that might partially explain the results. In other words, the experiment's conclusion may *seem* to support the benefits of collaborative study, but this conclusion is not justified because the teacher did not account for how much students slept.

In statistical terminology, this study suffers from **confounding.** The higher grades may be due either to the variable of interest (*collaborative study*) or to the differing amounts of sleep or to a combination of both. Because the teacher did not account for differences in the amount of sleep, we say that *amount of sleep* is a **confounding variable** for this study. You can probably think of other potentially confounding variables that could affect a study like this one.

BY THE WAY

The so-called Mozart effect holds that listening to Mozart can make babies smarter. The supposed effect spawned an entire industry of Mozart products for children. The state of Georgia even began passing out Mozart CDs to new mothers. However, more recent studies of the Mozart effect have been unable to substantiate the claimed effect.

> **Definition**
>
> A study suffers from **confounding** if the effects of different variables are mixed so we cannot determine the specific effects of the variables of interest. The variables that lead to the confusion are called **confounding variables.**

CASE STUDY **Confounding Drug Results**

An advisory panel of the Federal Drug Administration (FDA) recently recommended revoking the approval of the advanced breast cancer drug Avastin, which at the time was the world's best-selling cancer drug. Early trials had found that, when used in combination with a certain chemotherapy drug, Avastin delayed the growth of tumors by five months compared to using the chemotherapy drug alone. However, additional trials found less significant delays and no improvement in the length or quality of the lives of those taking Avastin. The differing results in different trials suggest that confounding variables have not all been accounted for. One possible confounding variable may be the choice of chemotherapy drug. Indeed, studies in Europe found Avastin to be effective, but were based on using it in combination with a different chemotherapy drug than the one approved in the United States. As a result, European regulators were approving Avastin for expanded use at the same time that regulators in the United States were recommending against it. The lesson should be clear: Even when thousands of lives and millions of dollars are on the line, confounding variables may be very difficult to eliminate, making decisions far more uncertain than doctors or patients (or government regulators) would like.

Assigning Treatment and Control Groups

As the collaborative study experiment illustrates, results are almost sure to suffer from confounding if the treatment and control groups differ in important ways (other than receiving or not receiving the treatment). Researchers generally employ two strategies to prevent such differences and thereby ensure that the treatment and control groups can be compared fairly. First, they assign participants to the treatment and control groups *at random*, meaning that they use a technique designed to ensure that each participant has an equal chance of being assigned to either group. When the participants are randomly assigned, it is less likely that the people in the treatment and control groups will differ in some way that will affect the study results.

Second, researchers try to ensure that the treatment and control groups are sufficiently large. For example, in the collaborative study experiment, including 50 students in each group rather than five would have made it much less likely that all the students in one group would live in a special dormitory.

> **Strategies for Selecting Treatment and Control Groups**
> - **Select groups at random.** Make sure that the subjects of the experiment are assigned to the treatment or control group at random, meaning that each subject has an equal chance of being assigned to either group.
> - **Use sufficiently large groups.** Make sure that the treatment and control groups are both sufficiently large that they are unlikely to differ in a significant way (aside from the fact that one group gets the treatment and the other does not).

EXAMPLE 6 Salk Study Groups

Briefly explain how the two strategies for selecting treatment and control groups were used in the Salk polio vaccine study.

SOLUTION A total of about 400,000 children participated in the study, with half receiving an injection of the Salk vaccine (the treatment group) and the other half receiving an injection of salt water (the control group). The first strategy was implemented by choosing children for the two groups randomly from among all the children. The second strategy was implemented by using a large number of participants (200,000 in each group) so that the two groups were unlikely to differ by chance.

There are men on whom the mere sight of medicine is operative.

—French philosopher Michel de Montaigne (1533–1592)

The Placebo Effect

When an experiment involves people, effects can occur simply because people know they are part of the experiment. For example, suppose you are testing the effectiveness of a new anti-depression drug. You find 500 people who suffer from depression and randomly divide them into a treatment group that receives the new drug and a control group that does not. A few weeks later, interviews with the patients show that people in the treatment group tend to be feeling much better than people in the control group. Can you conclude that the new drug works?

Unfortunately, it's quite possible that the mood of people receiving the drug improved simply because they were happy to be getting some kind of treatment, which means you cannot be sure that the drug really helped. This type of effect, in which people improve because they believe that they are receiving a useful treatment, is called the **placebo effect.** (The word *placebo* comes from the Latin "to please.")

To distinguish between results caused by a placebo effect and results that are truly due to the treatment, researchers try to make sure that the participants do not know whether they are part of the treatment or control group. To accomplish this, the researchers give the people in the control group a **placebo**: something that looks or feels just like the treatment being tested, but lacks its active ingredients. For example, in a test of a drug that comes in pill form, the placebo might be a pill of the same shape and size that contains sugar instead of the real drug. In a test of an injected vaccine, the placebo might be an injection that contains only a saline solution (salt water) instead of the real vaccine. In a recent test of the effectiveness of acupuncture, the placebo consisted of treatment with needles as in real acupuncture, except the needles were not put in the special places that acupuncturists claim to be important.

As long as the participants do not know whether they received the real treatment or a placebo, the placebo effect ought to affect the treatment and control groups equally. If the results for the two groups are significantly different, it is reasonable to believe that the differences can be attributed to the treatment. For example, in the study of the anti-depression drug, we would conclude that the drug was effective only if the control group received a placebo and members of the treatment group improved much more than members of the control group. For even better control, some experiments use three groups: a treatment group, a placebo group, and a control group. The placebo group is given a placebo while the control group is given nothing.

BY THE WAY

The placebo effect can be remarkably powerful. In some studies, up to 75% of the participants receiving the placebo actually improve. Nevertheless, different researchers disagree about the strength of the placebo effect, and some even question the reality of the effect.

> ### Definitions
>
> A **placebo** lacks the active ingredients of a treatment being tested in a study, but looks or feels like the treatment so that participants cannot distinguish whether they are receiving the placebo or the real treatment.
>
> The **placebo effect** refers to the situation in which patients improve simply because they believe they are receiving a useful treatment.
>
> Note: Although participants should not know whether they belong to the treatment or control group, for ethical reasons it is very important that participants be told that some of them will be given a placebo, rather than the real treatment.

BY THE WAY

A related effect, known as the *Hawthorne effect,* occurs when treated subjects somehow respond differently simply because they are part of an experiment—regardless of the particular way in which they are treated. The Hawthorne effect gets its name from the fact that it was first observed in a study of factory workers at Western Electric's Hawthorne plant.

EXAMPLE 7   Vaccine Placebo

What was the placebo in the Salk polio vaccine study? Why did researchers use a placebo in this experiment?

SOLUTION   The placebo was the salt water injection given to the children in the control group. To understand why the researchers used a placebo for the control group, suppose that a placebo had *not* been used. When improvements were observed in the treatment group, it would have been impossible to know whether the improvements were due to the vaccine or to the placebo effect. In order to remove this confounding, all participants had to believe that they were being treated in the same way. This ensured that any placebo effect would occur in both groups equally, so that researchers could attribute any remaining differences to the vaccine.   • • •

TIME UT TO THINK

Although participants should not know whether they belong to the treatment or control (placebo) group, for ethical reasons they should be told that some of them will receive a placebo rather than the real treatment. This was not always the case in decades past, when participants were sometimes told that they all received a treatment when in fact some received a placebo. Should researchers be allowed to use results of past studies that do not meet today's ethical criteria? Defend your opinion.

Experimenter Effects

Even if the study subjects don't know whether they received the real treatment or a placebo, the *experimenters* may still have an effect. In testing an anti-depression drug, for example, experimenters will probably interview patients to find out whether they are feeling better. But if the experimenters know who received the real drug and who received the placebo, they may inadvertently smile more at the people in the treatment group. Their smiles might improve those participants' moods, making it seem as if the treatment worked when in fact the improvement was caused by the experimenter. This type of confounding, in which the experimenter somehow influences the results, is called an **experimenter effect** (or a Rosenthal effect). The only way to avoid experimenter effects is to make sure that the experimenters don't know which subjects are in which group.

Definition

An **experimenter effect** occurs when a researcher or experimenter somehow influences subjects through such factors such as facial expression, tone of voice, or attitude.

EXAMPLE 8   Child Abuse?

In a famous case, two couples from Bakersfield, California, were convicted of molesting dozens of preschool-age children at their daycare center. The evidence for the abuse came primarily from interviews with the children. However, the conviction was overturned—after one man had served 14 years in prison—when a judge re-examined the interviews and concluded that the children had given answers that they thought the interviewers wanted to hear. If we think of the interviewers as experimenters, this is an example of an experimenter effect because the interviewers influenced the children's answers through the tone and style of their questioning.   · · ●

Blinding

In statistical terminology, the practice of keeping people in the dark about who is in the treatment group and who is in the control group is called **blinding.** A **single-blind** experiment is one in which the participants don't know which group they belong to, but the experimenters do know. If neither the participants nor the experimenters know who belongs to each group, the study is said to be **double-blind.** Of course, *someone* has to keep track of the two groups in order to evaluate the results at the end. In a double-blind experiment, the researchers conducting the study typically hire experimenters to make any necessary contact with the participants. The researchers thereby avoid any contact with the participants, ensuring that they cannot influence them in any way. The Salk polio vaccine study was double-blind because neither the participants (the children) nor the experimenters (the doctors and nurses giving the injections and diagnosing polio) knew who got the real vaccine and who got the placebo.

Blinding in Experiments

An experiment is **single-blind** if the participants do not know whether they are members of the treatment group or members of the control group, but the experimenters do know.

An experiment is **double-blind** if neither the participants nor any experimenters know who belongs to the treatment group and who belongs to the control group.

BY THE WAY

Many similar cases of supposedly widespread child abuse at daycare centers and preschools are being re-examined to see if experimenter effects (by those who interviewed the children) may have led to wrongful convictions. Similar claims of experimenter effects have been made in cases involving repressed memory, in which counseling supposedly helped people retrieve lost memories of traumatic events.

EXAMPLE ⑨ What's Wrong with This Experiment?

For each of the experiments described below, identify any problems and explain how the problems could have been avoided.

a. A new drug for attention deficit disorder (ADD) is supposed to make affected children more polite. Randomly selected children suffering from ADD are divided into treatment and control groups. The experiment is single-blind. Experimenters evaluate how polite the children are during one-on-one interviews.

b. Researchers wonder whether drinking coffee before an exam improves performance. Fifty coffee-drinkers are told not to drink coffee in the four hours before an exam, and 50 non-coffee-drinkers are asked to drink at least two cups of coffee in the four hours before an exam. Both groups had the same average performance on the exam.

c. Researchers wonder if the effects of a rare degenerative disease can be slowed by exercise. They identify six people suffering from the disease and randomly assign three to a treatment group that exercises every day and three to a control group that avoids exercise. After six months, they compare the amounts of degeneration in each group.

d. A chiropractor performs adjustments on 25 patients with back pain. Afterward, 18 of the patients say they feel better. He concludes that the adjustments are an effective treatment.

SOLUTION

a. The experimenters assess politeness in interviews, but because they know which children received the real drug, they may inadvertently speak differently to these children during the interviews. Or, they might interpret the children's behavior differently because they know which subjects received the real drug. These are experimenter effects that can confound the study results. The experiment should have been double-blind.

b. Both groups took the exam under conditions that were unnatural for them: Coffee-drinkers were deprived of coffee and non-coffee-drinkers were forced to drink it. This fact almost certainly introduced confounding variables that were not taken into account in interpreting the results. In fact, this is an experiment that is difficult to design flawlessly.

c. The results of this study will be difficult to interpret because the sample sizes are not sufficiently large. In addition, if those who exercise are asked not to (or vice versa), it may create other health problems that could confound the results.

d. The 25 patients who receive adjustments represent a treatment group, but this study lacks a control group. The patients may be feeling better because of a placebo effect rather than any real effect of the adjustments. The chiropractor might have improved his study by hiring an actor to do a fake adjustment (one that feels similar, but doesn't actually conform to chiropractic guidelines) on a control group. Then he could have compared the results in the two groups to see whether a placebo effect was involved.   ⋅ ⋅ ●

EXAMPLE ⑩ Identifying the Study Type

For each of the following questions, what type of statistical study is most likely to lead to an answer? Be as specific as possible.

a. What is the average (mean) income of stock brokers?

b. Do seat belts save lives?

c. Can lifting weights improve runners' times in a 10-kilometer (10K) race?

d. Does skin contact with a particular glue cause a rash?

e. Can a new herbal remedy reduce the severity of colds?

f. Do supplements of resveratrol (an extract from red grapes) increase life span?

With proper treatment, a cold can be cured in a week. Left to itself, it may linger for seven days.

—Medical Folk Saying

SOLUTION

a. An *observational study* can tell us the mean income of stock brokers. We need only survey the brokers, and the survey itself will not change their incomes.

b. It would be unethical to do an experiment in which some people were told to wear seat belts and others were told *not* to wear them. A study to determine whether seat belts save lives must therefore be *observational*. Because some people choose to wear seat belts and others choose not to, we can conduct a *retrospective study*. By comparing the death rates in accidents between those who do and do not wear seat belts, we can learn whether seat belts save lives. (They do.)

c. We need an *experiment* to determine whether lifting weights can improve runners' 10K times. We select randomly from a group of runners to create a treatment group of runners who are put on a weight-lifting program and a control group that is asked to stay away from weights. We must try to ensure that all other aspects of their training are similar. Then we can see whether the runners in the lifting group improve their times more than those in the control group. We cannot use blinding in this experiment because there is no way to prevent participants from knowing whether they are lifting weights.

d. An *experiment* can help us determine whether skin contact with the glue causes a rash. In this case, it's best to use a *single-blind experiment* in which we apply the real glue to participants in one group and apply a placebo that looks the same, but lacks the active ingredient, to members of the control group. There is no need for a double-blind experiment because it seems unlikely that the experimenters could influence whether a person gets a rash. (However, if the question of whether the subject *has* a rash is subject to interpretation, the experimenter's knowledge of who got the real treatment could affect this interpretation.)

e. We should use a *double-blind experiment* to determine whether a new herbal remedy can reduce the severity of colds. Some participants get the actual remedy, while others get a placebo. We need the double-blind conditions because the severity of a cold may be affected by mood or other factors that researchers might inadvertently influence. In the double-blind experiment, the researchers do not know which participants belong to which group and thus cannot treat the two groups differently.

f. Resveratrol has been identified and made available in supplement form only recently; we will need many years of data to determine whether it has an effect on life span. We therefore should use a prospective study designed to monitor participants over many years. The participants could keep written records regarding whether and how much of the supplement they take, and eventually researchers could analyze the data to see if resveratrol has an effect on life span.

··●

BY THE WAY

Experiments have found that mice live longer and have greater endurance when taking large doses of resveratrol, an extract from the skin of red grapes. However, it is not yet known whether high doses of resveratrol would have the same effects for humans, nor is it known whether such doses are safe for humans. Moreover, some scientists question whether the results from the mice studies have been properly interpreted.

Meta-Analysis

All individual statistical studies are either observational studies or experiments. In recent years, however, statisticians have found it useful to "mine" groups of past studies to see if we can learn something that we were unable to learn from the individual studies. For example, hundreds of studies have considered the possible effects of vitamin C on colds, so researchers might decide to review the data from many of these studies as a group. This type of study, in which researchers review many past studies as a group, is called a **meta-analysis.**

> **Definition**
>
> In a **meta-analysis,** researchers review many past studies. The meta-analysis considers these studies as a combined group, with the aim of finding trends that were not evident in the individual studies.

CASE STUDY Music and Autism: A Meta-Analysis

Numerous individual studies with different approaches have suggested that music is beneficial to children and adolescents with autism, but the results have varying levels of significance. Rather than conducting a separate new study, a researcher at Florida State University decided to conduct a meta-analysis that combined data from all the existing studies. This meta-analysis provided a stronger correlation between music therapy and behavioral improvement than the individual studies provided by themselves, and it helped lead to much greater use of music therapy for autistic children. Of course, a meta-analysis can only be as good as the data from the studies that go into it, and in this case some psychologists remain unconvinced of the benefits of music therapy. They argue that all the studies have ignored confounding variables, especially the possibility that the children are responding more to the attention and enthusiasm of the therapists than to the music itself. While meta-analysis can be a very useful technique, it is still subject to the "garbage in, garbage out" phenomenon, so we must be just as careful in interpreting the conclusions of a meta-analysis as we are with any other type of statistical study.

Section 1.3 Exercises

Statistical Literacy and Critical Thinking

1. **Placebo.** What is a placebo, and why is it important in an experiment to test the effectiveness of a drug?

2. **Blinding.** What is blinding, and why is it important in an experiment to test the effectiveness of a drug?

3. **Confounding.** In testing the effectiveness of a new vaccine, suppose that researchers used males for the treatment group and females for the placebo group. What is confounding, and how would it affect such an experiment?

4. **Ethics.** A clinical trial of a new drug designed to treat hypertension (high blood pressure) is designed to last for three years, but after the first year it becomes clear that the drug is highly successful. Is it ethical to continue the trial with the result that some hypertensive subjects continue to receive a placebo instead of the effective treatment?

5. **Clothing Color.** A researcher plans to investigate the belief that people are more comfortable in the summer sun when they wear clothing with light colors instead of clothing with dark colors. Does it make sense to use a double-blind experiment in this case? Is it easy to implement blinding in this case? Explain.

6. **Lawn Treatment.** A researcher plans to test the effectiveness of a new fertilizer on grass growth. Does it make sense to use a double-blind experiment in this case?

7. **Treating Depression.** A psychologist has developed a procedure for modifying behavior so that subjects suffering from depression can greatly improve that condition. In formal tests of the effectiveness of the treatment, what is an experimenter effect, and how might it be avoided?

8. **Improving IQ Scores.** A psychologist develops a procedure for improving IQ scores by training subjects to become better at taking tests. A standard IQ test is used for evaluating the effectiveness of the procedure. In this case, is it necessary to take precautions against an experimenter effect? Why or why not?

Concepts and Applications

Type of Study. For Exercises 9–20, state the type of study. Be as specific as possible.

9. **Quality Control.** Apple selects a simple random sample of iPhone batteries. The voltage of each battery is measured.

10. **Quality Control.** Apple selects a simple random sample of iPhone batteries. The voltage of each battery is measured after being heated to 43°C.

11. **Magnetic Bracelets.** Some cruise ship passengers are given magnetic bracelets, which they agree to wear in an attempt to eliminate or diminish the effects of motion sickness. Others are given similar bracelets that have no magnetism.

12. **Touch Therapy.** Nine-year-old Emily Rosa became an author of an article in the *Journal of the American Medical Association* after she tested professional touch therapists (see the "Focus on Education" section). Using

a cardboard partition, she held her hand above the therapist's hand, and the therapist was asked to identify the hand that Emily chose.

13. Twins. In a study of hundreds of Swedish twins, it was determined that the level of mental skills was more similar in identical twins (twins coming from a single egg) than in fraternal twins (twins coming from two separate eggs) (*Science*).

14. Texting and Driving. A study of 2,500 fatal car crashes identified those that involved drivers who were texting and those who were not.

15. Gender Selection. In a study of the YSORT gender selection method developed by the Genetics & IVF Institute, 152 couples using the method had 127 baby boys and 25 baby girls.

16. AOL Poll. An America OnLine (AOL) poll resulted in 1,651 responses to the question that asked which of four organizations has the most unethical people in charge. Among the respondents, 36% chose government.

17. GMO Corn. Researchers at New York University found that the genetically modified corn known as Bt corn releases an insecticide through its roots into the soil, while the insecticide was not released by corn that was not genetically modified (*Nature*).

18. Hygiene Survey. In a Harris Interactive survey of 1,006 randomly selected subjects, 96% of adults said that they wash their hands in public restrooms.

19. Magnet Treatment. In a study of the effects of magnets on back pain, some subjects were treated with magnets while others were given non-magnetic devices with a similar appearance. The magnets did not appear to be effective in treating back pain (*Journal of the American Medical Association*).

20. Power Lines and Cancer. Hundreds of separate and individual scientific and statistical studies have been done to determine whether high-voltage overhead power lines increase the incidence of cancer among those living nearby. A summary study based on many previous studies concluded that there is no significant link between power lines and cancer (*Journal of the American Medical Association*).

What's Wrong with This Experiment? For each of the (hypothetical) studies described in Exercises 21–28, identify any problems that are likely to cause confounding and explain how the problems could be avoided. Discuss any other problems that might affect the results.

21. Poplar Tree Growth. An experiment is designed to evaluate the effectiveness of irrigation and fertilizers on poplar tree growth. Fertilizer is used with one group of poplar trees in a moist region, and irrigation is used with poplar trees in a dry region.

22. Internet Shopping. Two hundred volunteers are recruited for a study of how Internet shopping affects purchases. Each person is allowed to choose whether to be in the Internet user group or the group that agrees not to use the Internet for shopping. After one month, the purchases of the two groups are compared.

23. Octane Rating. In a comparison of gasoline with different octane ratings, 24 vans are driven with 87 octane gasoline, while 28 sport utility vehicles are driven with 91 octane gasoline. After being driven for 250 miles, the amount of gasoline consumed is measured for each vehicle.

24. Aspirin Trial. In Phase I of a clinical trial designed to test the effectiveness of aspirin in preventing heart attacks, aspirin is given to three people and a placebo to seven other people.

25. Treating Back Pain. A physician conducts a clinical trial of the effectiveness of running as a treatment for back pain. One group undergoes the running treatment while a control group does not.

26. Athlete's Foot. In a clinical trial of the effectiveness of a lotion used to treat tinea pedis (athlete's foot), the physicians who evaluate the results know which subjects were given the treatment and which were given a placebo.

27. Weight Lifting. In a test of the effects of lifting heavy weights on blood pressure, one group undergoes a treatment consisting of a weight-lifting program while another group lifts tennis balls.

28. Paint Mixtures. In durability tests of Benjamin Moore paint and Sherwin Williams paint, the researchers who evaluate the results know which samples are from each of the two different brands.

Analyzing Experiments. Exercises 29–32 present questions that might be addressed in an experiment. If you were to design the experiment, how would you choose the treatment and control groups? Should the experiment be single-blind, double-blind, or neither? Explain your reasoning.

29. Beethoven and Intelligence. Does listening to Beethoven make infants more intelligent?

30. Lipitor and Cholesterol. Does the drug Lipitor result in lower cholesterol levels?

31. Ethanol and Mileage. Does an ethanol additive in gasoline cause reduced mileage?

32. Home Siding. Does aluminum siding on a home last longer than wood siding?

PROJECTS FOR ▶ THE INTERNET & BEYOND

33. Experimenter Effects in Repressed Memory Cases. Search the Internet for articles and information about the controversy regarding recovering repressed memories. Briefly summarize one or two of the most interesting cases and, based on what you read, express your own opinion as to whether the allegedly recovered memories are being influenced by experimenter effects.

34. Ethics in Experiments. In an infamous study conducted in Tuskegee, Alabama, from 1932 to 1972, African American males were told that they were receiving treatment for syphilis, but in fact they were not. The researchers' hidden goal was to study the long-term effects of the disease. Use the Internet to learn about the history of the Tuskegee syphilis study. Have a class discussion about the ethical issues involved in this case, or write a short essay summarizing the case and its ethical lessons.

35. **Debate: Should We Use Data from Unethical Experiments?** Past research often did not conform to today's ethical standards. In extreme cases, such as research conducted by doctors in Nazi Germany, the researchers sometimes killed the subjects of their experiments. While this past unethical research clearly violated the human rights of the experimental subjects, in some cases it led to insights that could help people today. Is it ethical to use the results of unethical research?

36. **Study Stopped Early.** It sometimes happens that study is stopped early before its completion. Use the Internet to find an example of such a study. Why was the study stopped? Should it have been stopped, or would it be better to complete the study?

IN THE NEWS

37. **Observational Studies.** Search through recent newspapers or journals and find an example of a statistical study that was observational. Briefly describe the study and summarize its conclusions.

38. **Experimental Studies.** Search through recent newspapers or journals and find an example of a statistical study that involved an experiment. Briefly describe the study and summarize its conclusions.

39. **Retrospective Studies.** Search through recent newspapers or journals and find an example of an observational, retrospective study. Briefly describe the study and summarize its conclusions.

40. **Meta-Analysis.** Search through recent newspapers or journals and find an example of a meta-analysis. Briefly describe the study and summarize its conclusions.

 1.4

SHOULD YOU BELIEVE A STATISTICAL STUDY?

Much of the rest of this book is devoted to helping you build a deeper understanding of the concepts and definitions we've studied up to this point. But already you know enough to achieve one of the major goals of this text: being able to answer the question "Should you believe a statistical study?"

Most researchers conduct their statistical studies with honesty and integrity, and most statistical research is carried out with diligence and care. Nevertheless, statistical research is sufficiently complex that bias can arise in many different ways, making it very important that we always examine reports of statistical research carefully. There is no definitive way to answer the question "Should I believe a statistical study?" However, in this section we'll look at eight guidelines that can be helpful. Along the way, we'll also introduce a few more definitions and concepts that will prepare you for discussions to come later.

If I have ever made any valuable discoveries, it has been owing more to patient attention, than to any other talent.

—Isaac Newton

Eight Guidelines for Critically Evaluating a Statistical Study

1. *Get a Big Picture View of the Study.* For example, you should understand the goal of the study, the population that was under study, and whether the study was observational or an experiment.

2. *Consider the Source.* In particular, look for any potential biases on the part of the researchers.

3. *Look for Bias in the Sample.* That is, decide whether the sampling method was likely to produce a representative sample.

4. *Look for Problems Defining or Measuring the Variables of Interest.* Ambiguity in the variables can make it difficult to interpret reported results.

5. *Beware of Confounding Variables.* If the study neglected potential confounding variables, its results may not be valid.

6. *Consider the Setting and Wording in Surveys.* In particular, look for anything that might tend to produce inaccurate or dishonest responses.

7. *Check That Results Are Presented Fairly.* For example, check whether the study really supports the conclusions that are presented in the media.

8. *Stand Back and Consider the Conclusions.* For example, evaluate whether study achieved its goals. If so, do the conclusions make sense and have practical significance?

News reports do not always provide enough information for you to apply all eight guidelines, but you can usually find additional information on the Web. Look for clues such as "reported by NASA" or "published in the *New England Journal of Medicine*" to help you track down original sources or other relevant information.

Guideline 1: Get a Big Picture View of the Study

The first thing you should do when you hear about a statistical study is figure out what it was all about; that is, get a big picture view of the study that will allow you to consider its results in an appropriate context. A good starting point for gaining a big picture view comes in trying to answer these basic questions:

- What was the goal of the study?
- What was the population under study? Was the population clearly and appropriately defined?
- Was the study an observational study, an experiment, or a meta-analysis? If it was an observational study, was it retrospective? If it was an experiment, was it single- or double-blind, and were the treatment and control groups properly randomized? Given the goal, was the type of study appropriate?

EXAMPLE 1   Appropriate Type of Study?

Imagine the following (hypothetical) newspaper report: "Researchers gave 100 participants their individual astrological horoscopes and asked whether the horoscopes were accurate. 85% of the participants said their horoscopes were accurate. The researchers concluded that horoscopes are valid most of the time." Analyze this study according to Guideline 1.

SOLUTION   The goal of the study was to determine the validity of horoscopes. Based on the news report, it appears that the study was *observational*: The researchers simply asked the participants about the accuracy of the horoscopes. However, because the accuracy of a horoscope is somewhat subjective, the study goal would have been better served by a controlled experiment in which some people were given their actual horoscope and others were given a fake horoscope (which would serve as a placebo). Then the researchers could have looked for differences between the two groups. Moreover, because researchers could easily influence the results by how they questioned the participants, the experiment should have been double-blind. In summary, the type of study was inappropriate to the goal and its results are meaningless.   · · ●

TIME ◷UT TO THINK
Try your own test of horoscopes. Find yesterday's horoscope for each of the 12 signs and put each one on a separate piece of paper, without anything identifying the sign. Shuffle the pieces of paper randomly, and ask a few people to guess which one was supposed to be their personal horoscope. How many people choose the right one? Discuss your results.

EXAMPLE 2   Does Aspirin Prevent Heart Attacks?

A study reported in the *New England Journal of Medicine* (Vol. 318, No. 4) sought to determine whether aspirin is effective in preventing heart attacks. It involved 22,000 male physicians considered to be at risk for heart attacks. The men were divided into a treatment group that took aspirin and a control group that did not. The results were so convincing in favor of the benefits of aspirin that the experiment was stopped for ethical reasons before it was completed, and the subjects were informed of the results. Many news reports led with the headline that taking aspirin can help prevent heart attacks. Analyze this headline according to Guideline 1.

SOLUTION   The study was an experiment, which is appropriate, and its results appear convincing. However, the fact that the sample consisted only of men means that the results should be considered to apply only to the population of men. Because results of medical tests on men do not necessarily apply to women, the headlines misstated the results when they did not qualify the population.   · · ●

BY THE WAY

Surveys show that nearly half of Americans believe their horoscopes. However, in controlled experiments, the predictions of horoscopes come true no more often than would be expected by chance.

BY THE WAY

Many recent studies show substantial differences in the ways men and women respond to the same medical treatments. For example, aspirin is more effective at thinning blood in men than in women (thinning is thought to help prevent heart attacks in some people). Morphine controls pain better in women, but ibuprofen is more effective for men. And women reject heart transplants more often than men. These differences may stem from interactions with hormones that differ in men and women or from differences in the rates at which men and women metabolize different drugs.

Guideline 2: Consider the Source

Statistical studies are supposed to be objective, but the people who carry them out and fund them may be biased. It is therefore important to consider the source of a study and evaluate the potential for biases that might invalidate the study's conclusions.

Bias may be obvious in cases where a statistical study is carried out for marketing, promotional, or other commercial purposes. For example, a toothpaste advertisement that claims "4 out of 5 dentists prefer our brand" appears to be statistically based, but we are given no details about how the survey was conducted. Because the advertisers obviously want to say good things about their brand, it's difficult to take the statistical claim seriously without much more information about how the result was obtained.

Other cases of bias may be more subtle. For example, suppose that a carefully conducted study concludes that a new drug helps cure cancer. On the surface, the study might seem quite believable. But what if the study was funded by a drug company that stands to gain billions of dollars in sales if the drug is proven effective? The researchers may well have carried out their work with great integrity despite the source of funding, but it might be worth a bit of extra investigation to be sure.

Major statistical studies are usually evaluated by experts who are supposed to be unbiased. The most common process by which scientists examine each other's research is called **peer review** (because the scientists who do the evaluation are *peers* of those who conducted the research). Reputable scientific journals require all research reports to be peer reviewed before the research is accepted for publication. Peer review does not guarantee that a study is valid, but it lends credibility because it implies that other experts agree that the study was carried out properly.

> **Definition**
>
> **Peer review** is a process in which several experts in a field evaluate a research report before the report is published.

BY THE WAY

After decades of arguing to the contrary, in 1999 the Philip Morris Company—the world's largest seller of tobacco products—publicly acknowledged that smoking causes lung cancer, heart disease, emphysema, and other serious diseases. Shortly thereafter, Philip Morris changed its name to Altria.

EXAMPLE 3 Is Smoking Healthy?

By 1963, research had so clearly shown the health dangers of smoking that the Surgeon General of the United States publicly announced that smoking is bad for health. Research done since that time built further support for this claim. However, while the vast majority of studies showed that smoking is unhealthy, a few studies found no dangers from smoking and perhaps even health *benefits*. These studies generally were carried out by the Tobacco Research Institute, funded by the tobacco companies. Analyze these studies according to Guideline 2.

SOLUTION   Even in a case like this, it can be difficult to decide whom to believe. However, the studies showing smoking to be unhealthy came primarily from peer-reviewed research. In contrast, the studies carried out at the Tobacco Research Institute had a clear potential for bias. The *potential* for bias does not mean the research was biased, but the fact that it contradicts virtually all other research on the subject should be cause for concern.   ⋯●

EXAMPLE 4 Press Conference Science

Suppose the nightly TV news shows scientists at a press conference announcing that they've discovered evidence that a newly developed chemical can stop the aging process. The work has not yet gone through the peer review process. Analyze this study according to Guideline 2.

SOLUTION   Scientists often announce the results of their research at a press conference so that the public may hear about their work as soon as possible. However, a great deal of expertise may be required to evaluate their study for possible biases or other errors—which is the goal of the peer review process. Until the work is peer reviewed and published in a reputable journal, any findings should be considered preliminary—especially about an astonishing claim such as being able to stop the aging process.   ⋯●

Guideline 3: Look for Bias in the Sample

A statistical study cannot be valid unless the sample is representative of the population under study. Poor sampling methods almost guarantee a biased sample that makes the study results useless.

Biased samples can arise in many ways, but two closely related problems are particularly common. The first problem, called **selection bias** (or a **selection effect**), occurs whenever researchers *select* their sample in a way that tends to make it unrepresentative of the population. For example, a pre-election poll that surveys only registered Republicans has selection bias because it is unlikely to reflect the opinions of non-Republican voters.

The second problem, called **participation bias,** can arise when people *choose* to be part of a study—that is, when the participants are volunteers. The most common form of participation bias occurs in **self-selected surveys** (or **voluntary response surveys**)—surveys or polls in which people decide for themselves whether to participate. In such cases, people who feel strongly about an issue are more likely to participate, and their opinions may not represent the opinions of the larger population that has less emotional attachment to the issue.

> **Definitions**
>
> **Selection bias** (or a selection effect) occurs whenever researchers *select* their sample in a biased way.
>
> **Participation bias** occurs any time participation in a study is voluntary.
>
> A **self-selected survey** (or **voluntary response survey**) is one in which people decide for themselves whether to be included in the survey.

CASE STUDY   The 1936 Literary Digest Poll

The *Literary Digest*, a popular magazine of the 1930s, successfully predicted the outcomes of several elections using large polls. In 1936, editors of the *Literary Digest* conducted a particularly large poll in advance of the presidential election. They randomly chose a sample of 10 million people from various lists, including names in telephone books and rosters of country clubs. They mailed a postcard "ballot" to each of these 10 million people. About 2.4 million people returned the postcard ballots. Based on the returned ballots, the editors of the *Literary Digest* predicted that Alf Landon would win the presidency by a margin of 57% to 43% over Franklin Roosevelt. Instead, Roosevelt won with 62% of the popular vote. How did such a large survey go so wrong?

The sample suffered from both selection bias and participation bias. The selection bias arose because the *Literary Digest* chose its 10 million names in ways that favored affluent people. For example, selecting names from telephone books meant choosing only from those who could afford telephones back in 1936. Similarly, country club members are usually quite wealthy. The selection bias favored the Republican Landon because affluent voters of the 1930s tended to vote for Republican candidates.

The participation bias arose because return of the postcard ballots was voluntary, so people who felt strongly about the election were more likely to be among those who returned their ballots. This bias also tended to favor Landon because he was the challenger—people who did not like President Roosevelt could express their desire for change by returning the postcards. Together, the two forms of bias made the sample results useless, despite the large number of people surveyed.

EXAMPLE 5 Self-Selected Poll

The television show *Nightline* conducted a poll in which viewers were asked whether the United Nations headquarters should be kept in the United States. Viewers could respond to the poll by paying 50 cents to call a special phone number with their opinions. The poll drew

186,000 responses, of which 67% favored moving the United Nations out of the United States. Around the same time, a poll using simple random sampling of 500 people found that 72% wanted the United Nations to *stay* in the United States. Which poll is more likely to be representative of the general opinions of Americans?

SOLUTION   The *Nightline* sample was severely biased. It had selection bias because its sample was drawn only from the show's viewers, rather than from all Americans. The poll itself was a self-selected survey in which viewers not only chose whether to respond, but also had to *pay* 50 cents to participate. This cost made it even more likely that respondents would be those who felt a need for change. Despite its large number of respondents, the *Nightline* survey was therefore unlikely to give meaningful results. In contrast, the simple random sample of 500 people is quite likely to be representative, so the finding of this small survey has a better chance of representing the true opinions of all Americans.   ··●

BY THE WAY

NASA's *Kepler* mission, launched in 2009, is an orbiting telescope that has made the first detections of planets as small as Earth around other stars. *Kepler* looks for slight dimming of a star's light each time an orbiting planet passes in front of it (a "transit"), which means it can detect planets only for the small fraction of stars that happen to have their planetary systems aligned with our line of sight.

EXAMPLE 6   Planets Around Other Stars

Until the mid-1990s, astronomers had never found conclusive evidence for planets outside our own solar system. But improving technology made it possible to begin finding such planets, and more than 2,000 had been discovered by mid-2012. The existing technology makes it easier to find large planets than small ones and easier to find planets that orbit close to their stars than planets that orbit far from their stars. According to the leading theory of solar system formation, large planets should form far from their stars, not close by. But large planets in close orbits are quite common among the planets discovered to date. Does this mean there is something wrong with the leading theory of solar system formation?

SOLUTION   Even if large planets in close orbits are relatively rare, the fact that current technology makes these rare cases the easiest ones to find introduces a *selection effect* that biases the sample (of discovered planets) toward that type. In fact, most astronomers think the existing solar system formation theory is still correct and that large planets in close-in orbits are not as common as they appear. Those that do exist can be explained by physical interactions that can cause large planets to migrate inward as a planetary system forms.   ··●

Guideline 4: Look for Problems Defining or Measuring the Variables of Interest

Results of a statistical study may be difficult to interpret if the variables under study are difficult to define or measure. For example, imagine trying to conduct a study of how exercise affects resting heart rates. The variables of interest would be *amount of exercise* and *resting heart rate*. Both variables are difficult to define and measure. In the case of *amount of exercise*, it's not clear what the definition covers—does it include walking to class? Even if we specify the definition, how can we measure *amount of exercise* given that some forms of exercise are more vigorous than others?

> TIME ◯UT TO THINK
> What are the challenges of defining and measuring resting heart rate?

EXAMPLE 7   Can Money Buy Love?

A Roper poll reported in *USA Today* involved a survey of the wealthiest 1% of Americans. The survey found that these people would pay an average of $487,000 for *true love*, $407,000 for *great intellect*, $285,000 for *talent*, and $259,000 for *eternal youth*. Analyze this result according to Guideline 4.

SOLUTION   The variables in this study are very difficult to define. How, for example, do you define *true love*? And does it mean true love for a day, a lifetime, or something else?

Similarly, does the ability to balance a spoon on your nose constitute *talent*? Because the variables are so poorly defined, it's likely that different people interpreted them differently, making the results very difficult to interpret.   •• •

EXAMPLE 8   Illegal Drug Supply

A commonly quoted statistic is that law enforcement authorities succeed in stopping only about 10% to 20% of the illegal drugs entering the United States. Should you believe this statistic?

SOLUTION   There are essentially two variables in a study of illegal drug interception: *quantity of illegal drugs intercepted* and *quantity of illegal drugs NOT intercepted*. It should be relatively easy to measure the quantity of illegal drugs that law enforcement officials intercept. However, because the drugs are illegal, it's unlikely that anyone is reporting the quantity of drugs that are *not* intercepted. How, then, can anyone know that the intercepted drugs are 10% to 20% of the total? In a *New York Times* analysis, a police officer was quoted as saying that his colleagues refer to this type of statistic as "PFA" for "pulled from the air."   •• •

Guideline 5: Beware of Confounding Variables

Variables that are *not intended* to be part of a study can make it difficult to interpret results properly. As discussed in Section 1.3, it's not always easy to discover these *confounding variables*. Sometimes they are discovered only years after a study is completed, and other times they are not discovered at all, in which case a study's conclusion may be accepted even though it's not correct. Fortunately, confounding variables are sometimes more obvious and can be discovered simply by thinking hard about factors that may have influenced a study's results.

EXAMPLE 9   Radon and Lung Cancer

Radon is a radioactive gas produced by natural processes (the decay of uranium) in the ground. The gas can leach into buildings through the foundation and can accumulate to relatively high concentrations if doors and windows are closed. Imagine a (hypothetical) study that seeks to determine whether radon gas causes lung cancer by comparing the lung cancer rate in Colorado, where radon gas is fairly common, with the lung cancer rate in Hong Kong, where radon gas is less common. Suppose the study finds that the lung cancer rates are nearly the same. Would it be reasonable to conclude that radon is *not* a significant cause of lung cancer?

SOLUTION   The variables of interest are *amount of radon* (an explanatory variable in this case) and *lung cancer rate* (a response variable) However, radon gas is not the only possible cause of lung cancer. For example, smoking can cause lung cancer, so *smoking rate* may be a confounding variable in this study—especially because the smoking rate in Hong Kong is much higher than the smoking rate in Colorado. As a result, we cannot draw any conclusions about radon and lung cancer without taking the smoking rate into account (and perhaps other variables as well). In fact, careful studies have shown that radon gas *can* cause lung cancer, and the U.S. Environmental Protection Agency (EPA) recommends taking steps to prevent radon from building up indoors.   •• •

BY THE WAY

Many hardware stores sell simple kits that you can use to test whether radon gas is accumulating in your home. If it is, the problem can be eliminated by installing an appropriate "radon mitigation" system, which usually consists of a fan that blows the radon out from under the house before it can get into the house.

Guideline 6: Consider the Setting and Wording in Surveys

Even when a survey is conducted with proper sampling and with clearly defined terms and questions, you should watch for problems in the setting or wording that might produce inaccurate or dishonest responses. Dishonest responses are particularly likely when the survey concerns sensitive subjects, such as personal habits or income. For example, the question "Do you cheat on your income taxes?" is unlikely to elicit honest answers from those who cheat, unless they are assured of complete confidentiality (and perhaps not even then).

In other cases, even honest answers may not really be accurate if the wording of questions invites bias. Sometimes just the order of words in a question can affect the outcome. A poll conducted in Germany asked the following two questions.

• Would you say that traffic contributes more or less to air pollution than industry?
• Would you say that industry contributes more or less to air pollution than traffic?

The only difference is the order of the words *traffic* and *industry*, but this difference dramatically changed the results: With the first question, 45% answered traffic and 32% answered industry. With the second question, only 24% answered traffic while 57% answered industry.

EXAMPLE 10 Do You Want a Tax Cut?

The Republican National Committee commissioned a poll to find out whether Americans supported their proposed tax cuts. Asked "Do you favor a tax cut?," a large majority of respondents answered *yes*. Should we conclude that Americans supported the proposal?

SOLUTION   A question like "Do you favor a tax cut?" is biased because it does not give other options or discuss any consequences. In fact, other polls conducted at the same time showed a similarly large majority expressing great concern about federal deficits. Indeed, support for the tax cuts was far lower when the question was asked by independent organizations in the form "Would you favor a tax cut even if it increased the federal deficit?
· · ●

EXAMPLE 11 Sensitive Survey

Two surveys asked Catholics in the Boston area whether contraceptives should be made available to unmarried women. The first survey involved in-person interviews, and 44% of the respondents answered *yes*. The second survey was conducted by mail and telephone, and 75% of the respondents answered *yes*. Which survey was more likely to be accurate?

SOLUTION   Contraceptives are a sensitive topic, particularly among Catholics (because the Catholic Church officially opposes contraceptives). The first survey, with in-person interviews, may have encouraged dishonest responses. The second survey made responses seem more private and therefore was more likely to reflect the respondents' true opinions.
· · ●

Guideline 7: Check That Results Are Presented Fairly

Even when a statistical study is done well, it may be misrepresented in graphics or concluding statements. Researchers occasionally misinterpret the results of their own studies or jump to conclusions that are not supported by the results, particularly when they have personal biases. News reporters may misinterpret a survey or jump to unwarranted conclusions that make a story seem more spectacular. Misleading graphics are especially common (we will devote much of Chapter 3 to this topic). You should always look for inconsistencies between the interpretation of a study (in pictures and in words) and any actual data given along with it.

EXAMPLE 12 Does the School Board Need a Statistics Lesson?

The school board in Boulder, Colorado, created a hubbub when it announced that 28% of Boulder school children were reading "below grade level" and hence concluded that methods of teaching reading needed to be changed. The announcement was based on reading tests on which 28% of Boulder school children scored below the national average for their grade. Do these data support the board's conclusion?

SOLUTION   The fact that 28% of Boulder children scored below the national average for their grade implies that 72% scored at or above the national average. Thus, the school board's ominous statement about students reading "below grade level" makes sense only if "grade level" means the national average score for a particular grade. This interpretation of "grade level" is curious because it would imply that half the students in the nation are always below grade level—no matter how high the scores. It may still be the case that teaching methods needed to be improved, but these data did not justify that conclusion.
· · ●

Guideline 8: Stand Back and Consider the Conclusions

Finally, even if a study seems reasonable according to all the previous guidelines, you should stand back and consider the conclusions. Ask yourself questions such at these:

- Did the study achieve its goals?
- Do the conclusions make sense?
- Can you rule out alternative explanations for the results?
- If the conclusions make sense, do they have any practical significance?

EXAMPLE 13 Extraordinary Claims

A recent study by a respected psychologist, Daryl J. Bem (Cornell University) claimed to find evidence for the existence of extrasensory perception, or ESP. Dr. Bem's results showed relatively small effects; for example, in one experiment in which subjects were asked to identify a picture hidden behind a screen, 53% gave the right answer versus the 50% expected by pure chance. Nevertheless, Dr. Bem claimed that the results were statistically significant, and his results were peer reviewed and published in a respected scholarly journal. Should you conclude that ESP really exists?

Extraordinary claims require extraordinary evidence.

—Carl Sagan

SOLUTION   Although the study may well have been done carefully, the claim of ESP should be considered what scientists often call an "extraordinary claim," because decades of study have never previously turned up any indisputable evidence for ESP and its existence would seem to violate some well-established laws of physics. Moreover, Dr. Bem's claim that the results were statistically significant has been disputed by other scientists and statisticians, who argue that he used the wrong type of analysis and that a proper analysis shows the results were consistent with pure chance. Clearly, for a claim as extraordinary as one of ESP, we would need far stronger evidence before concluding that it actually exists.   ··●

EXAMPLE 14 Practical Significance

An experiment is conducted in which the weight losses of people who try a new "Fast Diet Supplement" are compared to the weight losses of a control group of people who try to lose weight in other ways. After eight weeks, the results show that the treatment group lost an average of one-half pound more than the control group. Assuming that it has no dangerous side effects, does this study suggest that the Fast Diet Supplement is a good treatment for people wanting to lose weight?

SOLUTION   Compared to the average person's body weight, a weight loss of one-half pound hardly matters at all. So while loss results may be interesting, they don't seem to have much practical significance.   ··●

Section 1.4 Exercises

Statistical Literacy and Critical Thinking

1. **Peer Review,** What is peer review? How is it useful?

2. **Selection Bias and Participation Bias,** Describe and contrast selection bias and participation bias in sampling.

3. **Self-Selected Surveys.** Why are self-selected surveys almost always prone to participation bias?

4. **Confounding Variables.** What are confounding variables, and what problems can they cause?

Does It Make Sense? For Exercises 5–8, decide whether the statement makes sense (or is clearly true) or does not make sense (or is clearly false). Explain clearly; not all of these have definitive answers, so your explanation is more important than your chosen answer.

5. **Large Survey.** A survey involving a larger sample of subjects is always better than one involving a smaller sample.

6. **Survey Location.** The survey of the use of credit among adult Americans suffered from selection bias because the questionnaires were handed out only on college campuses.

7. **Vitamin C and Colds.** My experiment proved that vitamin C can reduce the

severity of colds, because I controlled the experiment carefully for every possible confounding variable.

8. **Diet Effectiveness.** The Simon diet is effective because it was used by a sample of 1,000 subjects and there was a mean weight loss of 1.7 pounds during a six-month study.

Concepts and Applications

Applying Guidelines. In Exercises 9–16, determine which of the eight guidelines appears to be most relevant. Explain your reasoning.

9. **Hygiene.** The Winslow Supply Company manufactures deodorants and sponsored a survey showing that good personal hygiene is critically important for success in a job interview.

10. **Smoking.** A clinical trial involved the use of a nicotine gum as an aid to help smokers stop smoking. The clinical trial involved 1,000 college students who were paid for their participation, and the results showed that the nicotine gum treatment was highly successful. The researchers concluded that the use of their nicotine gum would be a successful treatment for the population of all smokers.

11. **Goodness.** In a study of 1,200 college students, each was asked whether he or she was a good person.

12. **Agriculture.** Researchers conclude that an irrigation system used to grow tomatoes in California is more effective than a competing system used in Arizona.

13. **New York City Subway Survey.** The New York City Transit Authority routinely conducts a survey of satisfaction by distributing surveys on subways. The passengers take the surveys home and return them by mail.

14. **Election Poll.** Under the headline "Turner predicted to win in a landslide," it was reported that 54% of voters in a pre-election poll prefer Turner, compared with 46% for her opponent.

15. **Nuclear Energy Poll.** Randomly selected adults were asked: "Do you agree or disagree with increasing the production of nuclear energy that could potentially kill thousands of innocent people?"

16. **Counterfeit Goods.** A consortium of manufacturers plans a study designed to compare the value of counterfeit goods produced in the United States in the year 2000 to the current year.

Bias. In each of Exercises 17–20, identify and explain at least one source of bias in the study described. Then suggest how the bias might have been avoided.

17. **Chocolate.** An article in *Journal of Nutrition* (Vol. 130, No. 8) noted that chocolate is rich in flavonoids. The article reports that "regular consumption of foods rich in flavonoids may reduce the risk of coronary heart disease." The study received funding from Mars, Inc., the candy company, and the Chocolate Manufacturers Association.

18. **Famous Book.** When author Shere Hite wrote *Woman and Love: A Cultural Revolution in Progress*, she based conclusions about the general population of all women on 4,500 replies that she received after mailing 100,000 questionnaires to various women's groups.

19. **Political Polling.** You receive a call in which the caller claims to be conducting a national opinion research poll. You are asked if your opinion about congressional candidate John Sweeney would change if you knew that Sweeney once had a car crash while driving under the influence of alcohol.

20. **Survey Method.** You conduct a survey to find the percentage of people in your state who can name the lieutenant governor, who plans to run for the United States Senate. You obtain addresses from a list of property owners in the state and you mail a survey to 850 randomly selected people from the list.

21. **It's All in the Wording.** Princeton Survey Research Associates did a study for *Newsweek* magazine illustrating the effects of wording in a survey. Two questions were asked:

   • Do you personally believe that abortion is wrong?

   • Whatever your own personal view of abortion, do you favor or oppose a woman in this country having the choice to have an abortion with the advice of her doctor?

To the first question, 57% of the respondents replied yes, while 36% responded no. In response to the second question, 69% of the respondents favored the choice, while 24% opposed the choice. Discuss why the two questions produced seemingly contradictory results. How could the results of the questions be used selectively by various groups?

22. **Tax or Spend?** A Gallup poll asked the following two questions:

   • Do you favor a tax cut or "increased spending on other government programs"? *Result*: 75% for the tax cut.

   • Do you favor a tax cut or "spending to fund new retirement savings accounts, as well as increased spending on education, defense, Medicare and other programs"? *Result*: 60% for the spending.

Discuss why the two questions produced seemingly contradictory results. How could the results of the questions be used selectively by various groups?

What Do You Want to Know? Exercises 23–26 pose two related questions that might form the basis of a statistical study. Briefly discuss how the two questions differ and how these differences would affect the goal of a study and the design of the study.

23. **Internet Dating**

   First question: What percentage of Internet dates lead to marriage?

   Second question: What percentage of marriages begin with Internet dates?

24. **Full-Time Faculty**

   First question: What percentage of introductory classes on campus are taught by full-time faculty members?

   Second question: What percentage of full-time faculty members teach introductory classes?

25. Binge Drinking

First question: How often do college students do binge drinking?

Second question: How often is binge drinking done by college students?

26. Statistics Courses

First question: What is the proportion of college graduates who have taken a statistics course?

Second question: What is the proportion of statistics courses taken by college students?

Accurate Headlines? Exercises 27 and 28 give a headline and a brief description of the statistical news story that accompanied the headline. In each case, discuss whether the headline accurately represents the story.

27. Headline: "Drugs shown in 98 percent of movies"

Story summary: A "government study" claims that drug use, drinking, or smoking was depicted in 98% of the top movie rentals (Associated Press).

28. Headline: "Sex more important than jobs"

Story summary: A survey found that 82% of 500 people interviewed by phone ranked a satisfying sex life as important or very important, while 79% ranked job satisfaction as important or very important (Associated Press).

Stat-Bytes. Politicians commonly believe that they must make their political statements (often called sound-bytes) very short because the attention span of listeners is so short. A similar effect occurs in reporting statistical news. Major statistical studies are often reduced to one or two sentences. The summaries of statistical reports in Exercises 29–32 are taken from various news sources. Describe what crucial information is missing in the given statement and what more you would want to know before you acted on the report.

29. Confidence in Military. *USA Today* reports on a Harris poll claiming that the percentage of adults with a "great deal of confidence" in military leaders stands at 54%.

30. Top Restaurants. CNN reports on a Zagat Survey of America's Top Restaurants that found that "only nine restaurants achieved a rare 29 out of a possible 30 rating and none of those restaurants are in the Big Apple."

31. Forecasting Weather. A *USA Today* headline reported that "More companies try to bet on forecasting weather." The article gave examples of companies believing that long-range forecasts are reliable, and four companies were cited.

32. Births in China. A *USA Today* headline reported that "China thrown off balance as boys outnumber girls," and an accompanying graph showed that for every 100 girls born in China, 116.9 boys are born.

PROJECTS FOR THE INTERNET & BEYOND

33. Analyzing a Statistical Study. Find a detailed report on some recent statistical study of interest to you. Write a short report applying each of the eight guidelines given in this section. (Some of the guidelines may not apply to the particular study you are analyzing; in that case, explain why the guideline is not applicable.)

34. Twin Studies. Researchers doing statistical studies in biology, psychology, and sociology are grateful for the existence of twins. Twins can be used to study whether certain traits are inherited from parents (nature) or acquired from one's surroundings during upbringing (nurture). Identical twins are formed from the same egg in the mother and have the same genetic material. Fraternal twins are formed from two separate eggs and share roughly half of the same genetic material. Find a published report of a twin study. Discuss how identical and fraternal twins are used to form case and control groups. Apply Guidelines 1–8 to the study and comment on whether you find the conclusions of the report convincing.

35. Professional Journals. Consult an issue of a professional journal. Select one specific article and use the ideas of this section to summarize and evaluate the study.

IN THE NEWS

36. Applying the Guidelines. Find a recent newspaper article or television report about a statistical study on a topic that you find interesting. Write a short report applying each of the eight guidelines given in this section. (Some of the guidelines may not apply to the particular study you are analyzing; in that case, explain why the guideline is not applicable.)

37. Believable Results. Find a recent news report about a statistical study whose results you believe are meaningful and important. In one page or less, summarize the study and explain why you find it believable.

38. Unbelievable Results. Find a recent news report about a statistical study whose results you *don't* believe are meaningful and important. In one page or less, summarize the study and explain why you don't believe its claims.

1.5 DATA TYPES AND LEVELS OF MEASUREMENT

One of the challenges in statistics is deciding how best to summarize and display data. Different types of data call for different types of summaries. In this section, we'll discuss how data are categorized, an idea that will help us when we consider data summaries and displays in later chapters.

Data Types

Data come in two basic types: qualitative and quantitative. **Qualitative data** have values that can be placed into *nonnumerical categories*. (For this reason, qualitative data are sometimes called *categorical* data.) For example, eye color data are qualitative because they are categorized by colors such as blue, brown, and hazel. Other examples of qualitative data include flavors of ice cream, names of employers, genders of animals, and movie or restaurant ratings, such as bad, average, good, and excellent.

    Quantitative data have numerical values representing counts or measurements. The times of runners in a race, the incomes of college graduates, and the numbers of students in different classes are all examples of quantitative data.

> ### Data Types
>
> **Qualitative (or categorical) data** consist of values that can be placed into nonnumerical categories.
>
> **Quantitative data** consist of values representing counts or measurements.

EXAMPLE 1   Data Types

Classify each of the following sets of data as qualitative or quantitative.

a. Brand names of shoes in a consumer survey

b. Scores on a multiple-choice exam

c. Letter grades on an essay assignment

d. Numbers on uniforms that identify players on a basketball team

SOLUTION

a. Brand names are categories and therefore represent qualitative data.

b. Scores on a multiple-choice exam are quantitative because they are counts of the number of correct answers.

c. Letter grades on an essay assignment are qualitative because they represent different categories of performance (failing through excellent).

d. The players' uniform numbers are qualitative because they do not represent a count or measurement; they are used solely for identification. You can tell that these numbers are qualitative rather than quantitative because you could not use them for computations. For example, it would make no sense to add or subtract the uniform numbers of different players.   ··●

Discrete versus Continuous Data

Quantitative data can be further classified as continuous or discrete. Data are **continuous** if they can take on *any* value in a given interval. For example, a person's weight can be anything between 0 and a few hundred pounds, so data that consist of weights are continuous. Data are **discrete** if they can take on only particular values and not other values in between. For example, the number of students in your class is discrete because it must be a whole number, and shoe sizes are discrete because they take on only integer and half-integer values such as 7, $7\frac{1}{2}$, 8, and $8\frac{1}{2}$. (Actual foot lengths are continuous, but such shoe sizes are discrete.)

> **Discrete versus Continuous Data**
>
> **Continuous** data can take on *any* value in a given interval.
>
> **Discrete** data can take on only particular, distinct values and not other values in between.

EXAMPLE 2   Discrete or Continuous?

For each data set, indicate whether the data are discrete or continuous.

a. Measurements of the time it takes to walk a mile

b. The numbers of calendar years (such as 2013, 2014, 2015)

c. The numbers of dairy cows on different farms

d. The amounts of milk produced by dairy cows on a farm

SOLUTION

a. Time can take on any value, so measurements of time are continuous.

b. The numbers of calendar years are discrete because they cannot have fractional values. For example, on New Year's Eve of 2016, the year will change from 2016 to 2017; we'll never say the year is $2016\frac{1}{2}$.

c. Each farm has a whole number of cows that we can count, so these data are discrete. (You cannot have fractional cows, for example.)

d. The amount of milk that a cow produces can take on any value in some range, so the milk production data are continuous.   ··●

Levels of Measurement

Another way to classify data is by their *level of measurement*. The simplest level of measurement applies to variables such as eye color, ice cream flavors, or gender of animals. These variables can be described solely by names, labels, or categories. We say that such data are at a **nominal level of measurement**. (The word *nominal* refers to *names* for categories.) The nominal level of measurement does not involve any ranking or ordering of the data. For example, we could not say that blue eyes come before brown eyes or that vanilla ranks higher than chocolate.

When we describe data with a ranking or ordering scheme, such as star ratings of movies or restaurants, we are using an **ordinal level of measurement**. (The word *ordinal* refers to *order*.) Such data generally cannot be used in any meaningful way for computations. For example, it doesn't make sense to add star ratings—watching three one-star movies is not equivalent to watching one three-star movie.

> **TIME ◷UT TO THINK**
>
> Consider a survey that asks "What's your favorite flavor of ice cream?" We've said that ice cream flavors represent data at the nominal level of measurement. But suppose that, for convenience, the researchers enter the survey data into a computer by assigning numbers to the different flavors. For example, they assign 1 = vanilla, 2 = chocolate, 3 = cookies and cream, 4 = cherry garcia, and so on. Does this change the ice cream flavor data from nominal to ordinal? Why or why not?

The ordinal level of measurement provides a ranking system, but it does not allow us to determine precise differences between measurements. For example, there is no way to determine the exact difference between a three-star movie and a two-star movie. In contrast, a temperature of 81°F is hotter than 80°F by the same amount that 28°F is hotter than 27°F. Temperature data are at a higher level of measurement, because the *intervals* (differences) between units on a temperature scale always mean the same definite amount. However, while intervals (which involve subtraction) between Fahrenheit temperatures are meaningful, *ratios* (which involve division) are not. For example, it is *not true* that 20°F is twice as hot as 10°F or that −40°F is twice as cold as −20°F. The reason ratios are meaningless on the Fahrenheit scale is that its *zero point is arbitrary* and does not represent a state of "no heat." If intervals are meaningful but ratios are not, as is the case with Fahrenheit temperatures, we say that the data are at the **interval level of measurement**.

When both intervals and ratios are meaningful, we say that data are at the **ratio level of measurement**. For example, data consisting of distances are at the ratio level of measurement because a distance of 10 kilometers really is twice as far as a distance of 5 kilometers. In general, the ratio level of measurement applies to any scale with a *true zero*, which is a value that means *none* of whatever is being measured. In the case of distances, a distance of zero means "no distance." Other examples of data at the ratio level of measurement include weights, speeds, and incomes.

Note that data at the nominal or ordinal level of measurement are always qualitative, while data at the interval or ratio level are always quantitative (and can therefore be either continuous or discrete). Figure 1.4 summarizes the possible data types and levels of measurement.

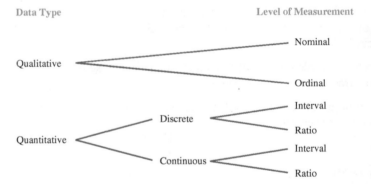

Figure 1.4 Data types and levels of measurement.

> **Levels of Measurement**
>
> The **nominal level of measurement** is characterized by data that consist of names, labels, or categories only. The data are qualitative and cannot be ranked or ordered.
>
> The **ordinal level of measurement** applies to qualitative data that can be arranged in some order (such as low to high). It generally does not make sense to do computations with data at the ordinal level of measurement.
>
> The **interval level of measurement** applies to quantitative data in which intervals are meaningful, but ratios are not. Data at this level have an arbitrary zero point.
>
> The **ratio level of measurement** applies to quantitative data in which both intervals and ratios are meaningful. Data at this level have a true zero point.

EXAMPLE 3 Levels of Measurement

Identify the level of measurement (nominal, ordinal, interval, ratio) for each of the following sets of data.

a. Numbers on uniforms that identify players on a basketball team

b. Student rankings of cafeteria food as excellent, good, fair, or poor

c. Calendar years of historic events, such as 1776, 1945, or 2001

d. Temperatures on the Celsius scale

e. Runners' times in the Boston Marathon

SOLUTION

a. As discussed in Example 1, numbers on uniforms don't count or measure anything. They are at the nominal level of measurement because they are labels and do not imply any kind of ordering.

b. A set of rankings represents data at the ordinal level of measurement because the categories (excellent, good, fair, or poor) have a definite order.

c. An interval of one calendar year always has the same meaning. But ratios of calendar years do not make sense because the choice of the year 0 is arbitrary and does not mean "the beginning of time." Calendar years are therefore at the interval level of measurement.

d. Like Fahrenheit temperatures, Celsius temperatures are at the interval level of measurement. An interval of $1°C$ always has the same meaning, but the zero point ($1°C =$ freezing point of water) is arbitrary and does not mean "no heat."

e. Marathon times have meaningful ratios—for example, a time of 6 hours really is twice as long as a time of 3 hours—because they have a true zero point at a time of 0 hours. ··●

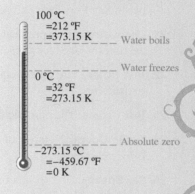

BY THE WAY

Scientists often measure temperatures on the Kelvin scale. Data on the Kelvin scale are at the ratio level of measurement, because the Kelvin scale has a true zero. A temperature of 0 Kelvin really is the coldest possible temperature. Called *absolute zero*, 0 K is equivalent to about −273.15°C or −459.67°F. (The degree symbol is not used for Kelvin temperatures.)

Section 1.5 Exercises

Statistical Literacy and Critical Thinking

1. Qualitative/Quantitative. What is the difference between qualitative data and quantitative data?

2. Quantitative/Qualitative. A football player is taking a statistics course and states that the names of the players on his team are qualitative, but they can be made quantitative by using the numbers on the jerseys of their uniforms. Is he correct? Why or why not?

3. Qualitative/Quantitative. Is a researcher correct when she argues that all data are either qualitative or quantitative? Explain.

4. ZIP Codes. A researcher argues that ZIP codes are quantitative data because they measure location, with low numbers in the east and high numbers in the west. Is she correct? Why or why not?

Concepts and Applications

Qualitative vs. Quantitative Data. In Exercises 5–16, determine whether the data described are qualitative or quantitative and explain why.

5. Blood Groups. The blood groups of A, B, AB, and O

6. White Blood Cells. The white blood cell counts of different people, consisting of the numbers of white blood cells per microliter of blood

7. Reaction Times. Braking reaction times (in seconds) are measured as part of a driver education program.

8. Physicians. The specialties of physicians (cardiac surgeon, pediatrician, etc.)

9. Multiple Choice Test Questions. The answers (a, b, c, d, e) to multiple choice test questions

10. Survey Responses. The responses (yes, no, refuse to answer) from survey subjects when asked a question

11. Nielsen Survey. The television shows being watched by households surveyed by Nielsen Media Research

12. Nielsen Ratings. The number of households with a television in use when surveyed by Nielsen Media Research

13. Head Circumferences. In studying different societies, an archeologist measures head circumferences of skulls

14. Shoe Sizes. The shoe sizes (such as 8 or $10\frac{1}{2}$) of test subjects

15. GPA. The grade point averages of randomly selected college students

16. Area Codes. The area codes (such as 617) of the telephones of survey subjects

Discrete or Continuous. In Exercises 17–28, state whether the data described are discrete or continuous and explain why.

17. Aircraft Baggage. The numbers of checked bags on flights between San Francisco and Atlanta

18. Aircraft Baggage. The weights of checked bags on flights between San Francisco and Atlanta

19. Flights. The total numbers of flights by different airlines between San Francisco and Atlanta in the past month

20. Flights. The lengths in minutes of each of the flights between San Francisco and Atlanta in the past month

21. Chemistry. An experiment in chemistry is repeated, and the times it takes for a reaction to occur are recorded.

22. Test Times. The times required by students to complete a statistics test

23. Test Scores. The numerical scores on a statistics test

24. Traffic Count. Number of cars crossing the Golden Gate Bridge each hour

25. Car Speeds. The speeds of cars as they pass the center of the Golden Gate Bridge

26. Movie Ratings. The movie ratings by a critic, with 0 stars, 1/2 star, 1 star, and so on

27. Stars. Number of stars in each galaxy in the universe

28. Cola. The exact amounts of cola in different cans

Levels of Measurement. For the data described in Exercises 29–40, identify the level of measurement (nominal, ordinal, interval, or ratio).

29. Weights of Textbooks. Weights of college textbooks

30. Movie Ratings. A critic's movie recommendations of "must see," "good," "fair," "poor," or "avoid"

31. Movie Types. Types of movies (drama, comedy, etc.)

32. Temperatures. Body temperatures in Fahrenheit of all students in a statistics class

33. Cars. Classifications of cars by size as subcompact, compact, intermediate, full-size

34. Clinical Trial. Results from a clinical trial consisting of "true positive," "false positive," "true negative," or "false negative"

35. Grades. Final course grades of A, B, C, D, F

36. Distances. Distances traveled by college students as they drive from their homes to their colleges

37. SSN. Social Security numbers

38. Weights. Weights of the cola in cans of Diet Coke

39. Word Counts. Numbers of words spoken in a day by a sample of males

40. Car Safety Ratings. *Consumer Reports* safety ratings of cars: 0 = unsafe up to 3 = safest

Meaningful Ratios? In Exercises 41–48, determine whether the given statement represents a meaningful ratio, so that the ratio level of measurement applies. Explain.

41. Movie Rating. A movie with a 4-star rating is twice as good as one with a 2-star rating.

42. Wind Speed. Wind with a speed of 40 mi/h moves four times as fast as wind with a speed of 10 mi/h.

43. IQ Score as a Measure of Intelligence. One subject has an IQ score of 140 while another subject has an IQ score of 70, so the first subject is twice as intelligent as the second subject.

44. Temperatures. On August 6, it was 80° F in New York City, so it was twice as hot as on December 7, when it was 40° F.

45. Art Dating. Using carbon dating, one sculpture is found to be 1,000 years old while a second sculpture is found to be 500 years old, so the first sculpture is twice as old as the second.

46. Carbon Dating. Using carbon dating, one sample of wood is found to be twice as old as another, because the first sample is found to be 200 years old while the other sample is 100 years old.

47. Salary. An employee with a salary of $150,000 earns twice as much as one with a $75,000 salary.

48. SAT Scores. A person with an SAT score of 2200 is twice as qualified for college as a person with a score of 1100.

Complete Classification. In Exercises 49–56, determine whether the data described are qualitative or quantitative and give their level of measurement. If the data are quantitative, state whether they are continuous or discrete. Give a brief explanation.

49. Marathon Times. Finish times of the New York City Marathon

50. Marathon Runners. Home nations (such as U. S., France, Kenya) of runners in a marathon

51. Employee ID Numbers. The employees of the Telektronics Corporation have six-digit identification numbers that are randomly generated.

52. Employee Service Times. Seniority of each employee at the Telektronics Corporation is based on the length of time that has passed since the employee was first hired.

53. Employee Hiring Years. The years in which employees were hired (such as 2000, 1995, 2012) are used to determine their pension plan.

54. Political Survey. In a survey of voter preferences, the political parties of respondents are recorded as coded numbers 1, 2, 3, 4, or 5 (where 1 = Democrat, 2 = Republican, 3 = Liberal, 4 = Conservative, 5 = other).

55. Product Ratings. *Consumer Reports* magazine lists ratings of "best buy," "recommended," or "not recommended" for each of several different computers.

56. Quality Control. Apple tests each of its manufactured iPhones and labels each as acceptable or defective.

1. **Tats.** A Harris poll surveyed 2,320 adults in the United States, among which 14% said that they have at least one tattoo. The margin of error is 2 percentage points.

   a. Interpret the margin of error by identifying the range of values likely to contain the percentage of adults with tattoos.

   b. Identify the population.

   c. Is this study an experiment or an observational study? Explain. Identify the variable of interest.

   d. Is the reported value of 14% a population parameter or a sample statistic? Why?

   e. If you learned that survey subjects responded to a magazine article asking readers to phone in their responses, would you consider the survey results to be valid? Why or why not?

   f. Describe a procedure for selecting the survey subjects using a simple random sample.

   g. Describe a procedure for selecting similar survey subjects using stratified sampling.

   h. Describe a procedure for selecting similar survey subjects using cluster sampling.

   i. Describe a procedure for selecting similar survey subjects using systematic sampling.

   j. Describe a procedure for selecting similar survey subjects using a convenience sample.

2. **Simple Random Sample.** An important element of this chapter is the concept of a simple random sample.

   a. What is a simple random sample?

   b. When the Bureau of Labor Statistics conducts a survey, it begins by partitioning the United States adult population into 2,007 groups called *primary sampling units*. Assume that these primary sampling units all contain the same number of adults. If you randomly select one adult from each primary sampling unit, is the result a simple random sample? Why or why not?

   c. Refer to the primary sampling units described in part b and describe a sampling plan that results in a simple random sample.

3. **Clinical Trial of Bystolic.** In clinical trials of the drug Bystolic used to treat hypertension (high blood pressure), 677 Bystolic users were observed for adverse reactions. It was found that among those treated with Bystolic, 7% experienced headaches.

   a. Based on the given information, can you conclude that in some cases, Bystolic causes headaches? Why or why not?

   b. While 677 subjects were treated with Bystolic, another 205 subjects were given a placebo, and 6% of the placebo group experienced headaches. What does this additional information suggest about headaches as an adverse reaction to the use of Bystolic?

   c. Is this clinical trial an observational study or an experiment? Explain.

   d. In this clinical trial, what is blinding and why is it important in testing the effects of Bystolic?

   e. What is an experimenter effect, and how might this effect be minimized?

4. **Wording of a Survey Question.** In *The Superpollsters*, David W. Moore describes an experiment in which different subjects were asked if they agree with the following statements:

   i. Too little money is being spent on welfare.

   ii. Too little money is being spent on assistance to the poor.

   Even though it is the poor who receive welfare, only 19% agreed when the word "welfare" was used, but 63% agreed with "assistance to the poor."

   a. Which of the two questions should be used in a survey? Why?

   b. If you are working on a campaign for a conservative candidate for Congress, and you want to emphasize opposition to the use of federal funds for assistance to the poor, which of the two questions would you use? Why?

   c. Is it ethical to deliberately word a survey question so that it influences responses? Why or why not?

Choose the best answer to each of the following questions. Explain your reasoning with one or more complete sentences.

1. You conduct a poll in which you randomly select 1,200 college students in California and ask if they have taken an online course. The *population* for this study is: (a) All students who have taken an online course; (b) the 1200 college students that you interview; (c) all college students in California.

2. For the poll described in Exercise 1, which sampling plan would likely yield results that are *most* biased: (a) Mail the survey to college students in California and use the returned responses; (b) randomly select 20 colleges in California, then randomly select 60 students at each college; (c) obtain a numbered list of all college students in California and select every 100th name until a sample size of 1,200 is obtained.

3. When we say that a sample is *representative* of the population, we mean that: (a) the results found for the sample are similar to those we would find for the entire population; (b) the sample is very large; (c) the sample was chosen in the best possible way.

4. Consider an experiment designed to see whether cash incentives can improve school attendance. The researcher chooses two groups of 100 high school students: She offers one group $10 for every week of perfect attendance. She tells the other group that they are part of an experiment but does not give them any incentive. The students who do not receive an incentive represent: (a) the treatment group; (b) the control group; (c) the observation group.

5. The experiment described in Exercise 4 is: (a) single-blind; (b) double-blind; (c) not blind.

6. The purpose of a *placebo* is: (a) to prevent participants from knowing whether they belong to the treatment group or the control group; (b) to distinguish between the cases and the controls in a case-control study; (c) to determine whether diseases can be cured without any treatment.

7. If we see a *placebo effect* in an experiment to test a new treatment designed to cure warts, it means: (a) the experiment was not properly double-blind; (b) the experimental groups were too small; (c) warts were cured among members of the control group.

8. An experiment is single-blind if: (a) it lacks a treatment group; (b) it lacks a control group; (c) the participants do not know whether they belong to the treatment or control group.

9. Poll X predicts that Powell will receive 49% of the vote, while Poll Y predicts that she will receive 53% of the vote. Both polls have a margin of error of 3 percentage points. What can you conclude? (a) one of the two polls must have been conducted poorly; (b) the two polls are consistent with one another; (c) Powell will receive 51% of the vote.

10. A survey reveals that 24% of adults believe that the most fun way to flirt is through instant messages. The margin of error is 3 percentage points. The confidence interval for this poll is: (a) from 18% to 30%; (b) from 24% to 27%; (c) from 21% to 27%.

11. A study conducted by the oil company Exxon Mobil shows that there was no lasting damage from a large oil spill in Alaska. This conclusion: (a) is definitely invalid, because the study was biased; (b) may be correct, but the potential for bias means you should look very closely at how the conclusion was reached; (c) could be correct if it falls within the confidence interval of the study.

12. The television show *American Idol* selects winners from votes cast by anyone who wants to vote. This means the winner: (a) is the person most Americans want to win; (b) may or may not be the person most American want to win, because the voting is subject to participation bias; (c) may or may not be the person most Americans want to win, because the voting should have been double-blind.

13. Consider an experiment in which you measure the weights of randomly selected cars. The variable of interest in this study is: (a) the size of the sample; (b) the weights of the cars; (c) the average (mean) weight of all cars.

14. Imagine a survey of randomly selected people in which it is found that people who use sunscreen were *more* likely to have been sunburned in the past year. Which explanation for this result seems most likely? (a) sunscreen is useless; (b) the people in this study all used sunscreen that had passed its expiration date; (c) people who use sunscreen are more likely to spend time in the sun.

15. If a statistical study is carefully conducted in every possible way, then: (a) its results must be correct; (b) we can have confidence in its results, but it is still possible that the results are not correct; (c) we say that the study is perfectly biased.

FOCUS ON
PSYCHOLOGY

Use this and other "Focus" sections found at the end of each chapter to focus in on particular topics of interest in statistics.

Are You Driving "Drunk" on Your Cell Phone?

One of the hottest topics in statistics deals with how cell phones and other types of distraction affect the abilities and reactions of drivers, and whether these distractions lead to more accidents and fatalities than would occur otherwise. These questions are studied by scientists in a variety of disciplines but are especially important to psychologists, because the answers depend on how the human brain reacts to different types of stimuli.

Many different types of statistical study have looked at the issue. Some researchers study accident reports to see what fraction of accidents involve talking on a cell phone, texting, or other distractions. Some have looked at cell phone records of people who have been in crashes, to see if the phone was in use at the time of the crash. These studies clearly indicate higher crash and fatality rates associated with distracted driving. Perhaps most notably, the University of Utah's Applied Cognition Lab has conduced a series of studies in which subjects use simulators to drive cars under a variety of distraction conditions, including use of a hand-held cell phone, use of a hands-free cell phone, and while texting. They compare these results with those in which the same subjects are not distracted and are either sober or intoxicated. Their astonishing conclusion: Even with hands-free devices, talking on a cell phone makes drivers as dangerous as drunk drivers, and texting and other distractions can make drivers even more likely to cause a crash.

Should we believe this claim that using your cell phone essentially makes you a drunk driver? As always, there are many ways to evaluate the claim, but for practice, let's use the eight guidelines given in Section 1.4 (p. 30).

Guideline 1: *Get a Big Picture View of the Study.* The goal of the Utah studies is to learn about the relative danger of different types of distraction, especially of cell phones, and the population under study is all drivers. The study is an experiment, because it has the same subjects drive simulators under different conditions of distraction, with the control being the results when they are undistracted and sober.

Guideline 2: *Consider the Source.* We can generally assume that a university lab operates independently, and we have no reason to suspect that any pressure is put on researchers to come up with a particular result. Indeed, if there were pressure, it would likely come from cell phone companies that would have a bias toward *not* finding danger in their products,

which is the opposite of what the researchers concluded. We similarly have no reason to suspect bias on the part of the researchers themselves. It's almost impossible to be sure that no bias is involved, but in this case the source seems likely to be trustworthy.

Guideline 3: *Look for Bias in the Sample.* For the results to be valid, the group of subjects must be a representative sample of all drivers. Media reports of the Utah studies rarely talk about the sample selection method, but in this case it does not seem like it should be difficult to get a representative sample, since it's unlikely that any particular group of people would be especially prone or immune to distractions. So unless we see evidence to the contrary, it seems safe to assume that the sample was well chosen.

Guideline 4: *Look for Problems Defining or Measuring the Variables of Interest.* The Utah researchers study variables such as the reaction times of drivers in surprising situations and how often they get into crashes in their simulated drives. These variables are straightforward to define and measure.

Guideline 5: *Beware of Confounding Variables.* It's almost impossible to eliminate all possible confounding variables, and we can easily think of some variables that might affect these studies. For example, the driver responses might depend on the order and time at which different tests are conducted, as a driver may be fatigued as tests progress or might not be feeling well on a particular day. However, the researchers can in principle avoid most of these problems by changing the order of the tests for different drivers on different days and by having a large enough test group so that things like minor illnesses should not affect the overall results.

Guideline 6: *Consider the Setting and Wording in Surveys.* The Utah studies are not survey based, so this guideline does not apply. However, studies such as those that look at real crash rates are essentially surveys based on crash reports compiled by police or insurance companies, so it's worth considering potential biases in them. For example, could it be that the role of cell phones in crashes might be either overreported or underreported? A little thought shows the former is unlikely, because no one would be expected to tell police they were on a cell phone if they weren't. But the opposite seems quite likely, because denying cell phone use might be a way of deflecting potential blame for a crash. We conclude that if the surveys are biased at all, it is most likely toward *under*estimating the danger of distracted driving.

Guideline 7: *Check That Results Are Presented Fairly.* The Utah studies have found clear evidence of the danger of cell phone use, with or without hand-free devices. The fact that these results are consistent with actual data from accidents gives further reason to believe that the results have been presented fairly.

Guideline 8: *Stand Back and Consider the Conclusions.* This last step is essentially our summary. We've found that the Utah studies have achieved their goals and lead to clear conclusions about the danger of using a cell phone while driving. In fact, the studies also show that similar or greater danger arises from texting while driving, programming your GPS while driving, finding music on your iPod while driving, and a variety of other distractions. Do these results have practical significance? They should, as they make it very clear that if you talk on your cell phone or are otherwise distracted while driving, you are putting your own life and the lives of others at risk.

1. Do *you* ever drive while talking on your cell phone, texting, or programming your GPS? If so, have you ever noticed evidence of your distraction, such as missing a turn or an especially close call for a collision? Have you seen such evidence of distraction when being driven by friends or family or taxi drivers?

2. Public safety advocates and many insurance companies are using the data about distracted driving to argue in favor of laws banning the use of cell phones while driving. Do you support or oppose such laws? Defend your opinion.

3. The fact that the studies found essentially no difference in danger between hand-held and hands-free devices comes as a surprise to most people. Research studies on brain activity that have provided an explanation for this surprising fact, often called "inattention blindness." Discuss how and why talking on a hands-free cell phone turns out to increase the risk of crashes, while talking to a passenger does not.

4. Find the latest statistics from the U.S. Department of Transportation concerning the number of crashes and fatalities estimated to be caused by distracted driving each year. Do you think the estimates are likely to be accurate? Why or why not?

• • • • • • • • • • • • • • •

F CUS ON
PUBLIC HEALTH

Is Your Lifestyle Healthy?

Consider the following findings from statistical studies:

- Smoking increases the risk of heart disease.
- Eating margarine can increase the risk of heart disease.
- One glass of wine per day can protect against heart disease but increases the risk of breast cancer.
- Potato chips and sugary sodas are the foods most strongly associated with weight gain.

You are probably familiar with some of these findings, and perhaps you've even altered your lifestyle as a result of them. But where do they come from? Remarkably, these and hundreds of other important findings on public health come from huge prospective studies that have provided data for hundreds of smaller statistical studies. The longest-running of these is the Harvard Nurses' Health Study, which began in 1976 when Dr. Frank E. Speizer decided to study the long-term effects of oral contraceptives. He mailed questionnaires to approximately 370,000 registered nurses and received more than 120,000 responses. He chose to survey nurses because he believed that their medical training would make their responses more reliable than those of the general public.

As Dr. Speizer and his colleagues sifted through the data in the returned questionnaires, they realized that the study could be expanded to include more than just the effects of contraceptives. Today, this research team continues to follow many of the original 120,000 respondents.

Annual questionnaires are still a vital part of the study, allowing researchers to gather data about what the nurses eat; what medicines and vitamins they take; whether and how much they exercise, drink, and smoke; and what illnesses they have contracted. Some of the nurses also provide blood samples, which are used to measure such things as cholesterol level, hormone levels, genetic variations, and residues from pesticides and environmental pollutants. Dr. Speizer's faith in nurses has proven justified, as they reliably complete surveys and almost always provide properly drawn and labeled blood samples upon request.

After more than three decades of correspondence, both the researchers and the nurses say they feel a sense of closeness. Many of the nurses look forward to hearing from the researchers and say that the study has helped them to pay more attention to how they live their lives. Today, as the original nurses become elderly, the study is beginning to turn out results that should shed light on factors that influence longevity and health in old age.

The success of the Harvard Nurses Study has spurred its expansion and many similar studies of large groups. When you see statistical reports based on these studies, remember the hundreds of thousands of people whose willingness to participate in these studies is making life better for everyone.

QUESTIONS FOR DISCUSSION

1. Consider some of the results that are likely to come from the Harvard Nurses' Health Study over the next 10 to 20 years. What types of results do you think will be most important? Do you think the findings will alter the way you live your life?

2. Explain why the Harvard Nurses' Health Study is an observational study. Critics sometimes say that the results would be more valid if obtained by experiments rather than observations. Discuss whether it would be possible to gather similar data by carrying out experiments in a practical and ethical way.

3. In principle, the Harvard Nurses' Health Study is subject to participation bias because only 120,000 of the original 370,000 questionnaires were returned. Should the researchers be concerned about this bias? Why or why not?

4. Another potential pitfall comes from the fact that the questionnaires often deal with sensitive issues of personal health, and researchers have no way to confirm that the nurses answer honestly. Do you think that dishonesty could be leading researchers to incorrect conclusions? Defend your opinion.

5. All of the participants in the Harvard Nurses' Health Study were women. Do you think that the results also are of use to men? Why or why not?

6. Do a Web search for news articles that discuss results from the Harvard Nurses' Health Study or other similar studies. Choose one recent result that interests you, and discuss what it means and how it may affect public health or your own health in the future.

Arithmetic for Statistics

2.1

FRACTIONS

A **fraction** can mean a part of a whole. For example, $\frac{2}{3}$ of a class means two of every three students. A fraction can also mean the quotient of two whole numbers.

A fraction has three components:

* the **denominator** (on the bottom), that stands for the number of parts into which the whole is divided,
* the **numerator** (on top) that tells us how many parts of the whole the fraction contains,
* the **fraction line** (or **fraction bar**) that separates the numerator from the denominator and stands for the phrase *out of* or *divided by*.

Note that the denominator of a fraction cannot be zero.

Two fractions are **equivalent** if they represent the same value. To generate fractions equivalent to a given fraction, say $\frac{1}{3}$, multiply both its numerator and denominator by the same nonzero whole number. For instance,

$$\frac{1}{3} = \frac{1 \cdot 2}{3 \cdot 2} = \frac{2}{6} \qquad\qquad \frac{1}{3} = \frac{1 \cdot 3}{3 \cdot 3} = \frac{3}{9}$$

A fraction is said to be in **simplest form** (or **reduced to lowest terms**) when the only common factor of its numerator and its denominator is 1. To simplify a fraction, we divide its numerator and denominator by the same number, or common factor. To find these common factors, it is often helpful to express both the numerator and denominator as the product of prime factors. We can then divide out (or cancel) all common factors.

PRACTICE 1

Reduce $\frac{24}{30}$ to lowest terms.

EXAMPLE 1

Write $\frac{42}{28}$ in lowest terms.

SOLUTION

$$\frac{42}{28} = \frac{2 \cdot 3 \cdot 7}{2 \cdot 2 \cdot 7}$$ Express the numerator and denominator as the product of primes.

$$= \frac{\overset{1}{\cancel{2}} \cdot 3 \cdot \overset{1}{\cancel{7}}}{\underset{1}{\cancel{2}} \cdot 2 \cdot \underset{1}{\cancel{7}}}$$ Divide out common factors.

$$= \frac{3}{2}$$ Multiply the remaining factors.

Fractions with the same denominator are said to be **like**; those with different denominators are called **unlike**.

To Add (or Subtract) Like Fractions

* Add (or subtract) the numerators.
* Use the given denominator.
* Write the answer in simplest form.

EXAMPLE 2

Find the sum of $\frac{7}{12}$ and $\frac{2}{12}$.

SOLUTION   Using the rule for adding like fractions, we get:

$$\frac{7}{12} + \frac{2}{12} = \overbrace{\frac{7 + 2}{12}}^{\text{Add numerators.}} = \frac{9}{12}, \quad \text{or} \quad \frac{3}{4}$$

Add numerators.

Keep the same denominator.

Simplest form

PRACTICE 2

Add: $\frac{7}{15} + \frac{3}{15}$

EXAMPLE 3

Find the difference between $\frac{11}{12}$ and $\frac{7}{12}$.

SOLUTION

$$\frac{11}{12} - \frac{7}{12} = \overbrace{\frac{11 - 7}{12}}^{\text{Subtract numerators.}} = \frac{4}{12}, \quad \text{or} \quad \frac{1}{3}$$

Subtract numerators.

Keep the same denominator.

Simplest form

PRACTICE 3

Subtract: $\frac{19}{20} - \frac{11}{20}$

Unlike fractions are more complicated to add (or subtract) than like fractions because we must first change the unlike fractions to equivalent like fractions. Typically, we use their **least common denominator (LCD)**, that is, the least common multiple of their denominators, to find equivalent fractions.

> **To Add (or Subtract) Like Fractions**
> - Rewrite the fractions as equivalent fractions with a common denominator, usually the LCD.
> - Add (or subtract) the numerators, keeping the same denominator.
> - Write the answer in simplest form.

EXAMPLE 4

Add: $\frac{5}{12} + \frac{5}{16}$

SOLUTION   First, find the LCD, which is 48.

$$\frac{5}{12} + \frac{5}{16} = \frac{20}{48} + \frac{15}{48} \qquad \text{Find equivalent fractions.}$$

$$= \frac{35}{48} \qquad \text{Add the numerators, keeping the same denominator.}$$

The fraction $\frac{35}{48}$ is already in lowest terms because 35 and 48 have no common factors other than 1.

PRACTICE 4

Add: $\frac{11}{12} + \frac{3}{4}$

PRACTICE 5

Calculate: $\dfrac{4}{5} - \dfrac{1}{2}$

EXAMPLE 5

Subtract $\dfrac{1}{12}$ from $\dfrac{1}{3}$.

SOLUTION   First, find the LCD, which is 12.

$$\dfrac{1}{3} - \dfrac{1}{12} = \dfrac{4}{12} - \dfrac{1}{12}$$ Write equivalent fractions with a common denominator.

$$= \dfrac{3}{12}$$ Subtract the numerators, keeping the same denominator.

$$= \dfrac{1}{4}$$ Reduce $\dfrac{3}{12}$ to lowest terms. $\cdots\bullet$

Now, let's look at how we multiply fractions.

> **To Multiply Fractions**
> - Multiply the numerators.
> - Multiply the denominators.
> - Write the answer in simplest form.

PRACTICE 6

Compute: $\dfrac{1}{2} \cdot \dfrac{3}{4}$.

EXAMPLE 6

Multiply: $\dfrac{2}{3} \cdot \dfrac{4}{5}$

SOLUTION $\dfrac{2}{3} \cdot \dfrac{4}{5} = \dfrac{2 \cdot 4}{3 \cdot 5} = \dfrac{8}{15}$

In multiplying some fractions, we can first simplify (or cancel) by dividing *any* numerator and *any* denominator by a common factor. Simplifying before multiplying allows us to work with smaller numbers and still gives us the same answer. $\cdots\bullet$

PRACTICE 7

Multiply $\dfrac{7}{10}$ by $\dfrac{5}{11}$.

EXAMPLE 7

Find the product of $\dfrac{4}{9}$ and $\dfrac{5}{8}$.

SOLUTION

Divide the numerator 4 and the denominator 8 by the same number 4. Then multiply.
$\downarrow$

$$\dfrac{4}{9} \cdot \dfrac{5}{8} = \dfrac{\overset{1}{\cancel{4}} \cdot 5}{9 \cdot \underset{2}{\cancel{8}}} = \dfrac{1 \cdot 5}{9 \cdot 2} = \dfrac{5}{18}$$ $\cdots\bullet$

Dividing fractions is equivalent to multiplying by the *reciprocal* of the divisor. The reciprocal is found by *inverting*—switching the position of the numerator and denominator of the divisor.

To Divide Fractions

- Change the divisor to its reciprocal.
- Multiply the resulting fractions.
- Write the answer in simplest form.

EXAMPLE 8

Divide: $\dfrac{4}{5} \div \dfrac{3}{10}$

PRACTICE 8

Divide: $\dfrac{3}{4} \div \dfrac{1}{8}$

SOLUTION

$$\frac{4}{5} \div \frac{3}{10} = \frac{4}{\cancel{5}} \times \frac{\overset{2}{\cancel{10}}}{3} = \frac{4 \times 2}{1 \times 3} = \frac{8}{3}, \text{ or } 2\frac{2}{3}$$

$\dfrac{3}{10}$ and $\dfrac{10}{3}$ are reciprocals.

EXAMPLE 9

The world's population is approximately 7,000,000,000. If China has $\dfrac{1}{5}$ of that population, what is the total population of the rest of the world? (*Source: The World Almanac and Book of Facts 2010*)

PRACTICE 9

About one-third of U.S. adults are considered obese. If there are approximately 240 million U.S. adults, about how many of them are not considered obese? (*Sources*: win.niddk.nih.gov and census.gov)

SOLUTION Let's break up the question into two parts:

1. First, find $\dfrac{1}{5}$ of 7,000,000,000.

$$\frac{1}{\cancel{5}} \times \overset{1,400,000,000}{\cancel{7,000,000,000}} = 1,400,000,000$$

2. Then, subtract that result from 7,000,000,000.

$$7,000,000,000 - 1,400,000,000 = 5,600,000,000$$

So the total population of the rest of the world is 5,600,000,000.

Section 2.1 Exercises

FOR EXTRA HELP MyMathLab Math XL PRACTICE   WATCH   READ   REVIEW

Write each mixed number as an improper fraction.

1. $3\dfrac{4}{5}$ **2.** $7\dfrac{3}{10}$

Write each fraction as a mixed number.

3. $\dfrac{23}{4}$ **4.** $\dfrac{31}{9}$

Simplify.

5. $\dfrac{14}{28}$ **6.** $\dfrac{30}{45}$

7. $5\dfrac{2}{4}$ **8.** $6\dfrac{12}{42}$

Calculate. Write answers in lowest terms.

9. $\dfrac{1}{9} + \dfrac{4}{9}$

10. $\dfrac{3}{10} + \dfrac{7}{10}$

11. $\dfrac{3}{8} - \dfrac{1}{8}$

12. $\dfrac{5}{3} - \dfrac{2}{3}$

13. $\dfrac{2}{5} + \dfrac{4}{7}$

14. $\dfrac{8}{9} + \dfrac{1}{2}$

15. $\dfrac{3}{10} - \dfrac{1}{20}$

16. $\dfrac{3}{5} - \dfrac{1}{4}$

17. $1\dfrac{1}{8} + 5\dfrac{3}{8}$

18. $3\dfrac{1}{5} + 4\dfrac{1}{5}$

19. $8\dfrac{7}{10} + 1\dfrac{9}{10}$

20. $5\dfrac{5}{6} + 2\dfrac{1}{6}$

21. $9\dfrac{11}{12} - 6\dfrac{7}{12}$

22. $2\dfrac{5}{9} - 2\dfrac{4}{9}$

23. $6\dfrac{1}{10} - 4\dfrac{3}{10}$

24. $5\dfrac{1}{4} - 2\dfrac{3}{4}$

25. $12 - 5\dfrac{1}{2}$

26. $3 - 1\dfrac{4}{5}$

27. $7\dfrac{1}{2} - 4\dfrac{5}{8}$

28. $5\dfrac{1}{12} - 4\dfrac{1}{2}$

29. $\dfrac{2}{3} \cdot \dfrac{1}{5}$

30. $\dfrac{3}{4} \cdot \dfrac{8}{9}$

31. $1\dfrac{2}{5} \cdot 10$

32. $20 \cdot 1\dfrac{5}{6}$

33. $3\dfrac{1}{4} \cdot 4\dfrac{2}{3}$

34. $2\dfrac{1}{2} \cdot 1\dfrac{1}{5}$

35. $2\dfrac{5}{6} \div \dfrac{1}{2}$

36. $1\dfrac{1}{3} \div \dfrac{4}{5}$

37. $\dfrac{2}{3} \div 6$

38. $\dfrac{1}{10} \div 4$

39. $8 \div 2\dfrac{1}{3}$

40. $4\dfrac{1}{2} \div 2\dfrac{1}{2}$

41. $\left(\dfrac{3}{4}\right)^2 - \dfrac{3}{8} \div 6$

42. $8\dfrac{2}{5} + 2 \div \left(\dfrac{1}{2} - \dfrac{1}{3}\right)$

2.2 DECIMALS

A number written as a *decimal* has

- a whole-number part, which precedes the decimal point, and
- a fractional part, which follows the decimal point.

Whole-number part   Fractional part

$$4 \, . \, \overline{5\,1}$$

Decimal point

A decimal without a decimal point shown is understood to have the decimal point at the end of the last digit and is the same as a whole number. For instance, 32 and 32. are the same number.

Each digit in a decimal has a place value. The place value system for decimals is an extension of the place value system for whole numbers.

The places to the right of the decimal point are called *decimal places*. For example, the number 64.149 is said to have three decimal places.

For a whole number, the place values are 1, 10, 100, and other powers of 10. By contrast, the place values for the fractional part of a decimal are $\dfrac{1}{10}, \dfrac{1}{100}, \dfrac{1}{1000}$, and the reciprocals of other powers of 10.

The first decimal place after the decimal point is the ten**ths** place. Working to the right, the next decimal places are the hundred**ths** place, the thousand**ths** place, the ten-thousand**ths** place, and so forth.

The following chart shows the place values in the numbers 0.54 and 513.285.

Hundreds	Tens	Ones	.	Tenths	Hundredths	Thousandths
100	10	1	and	$\frac{1}{10}$	$\frac{1}{100}$	$\frac{1}{1,000}$
		0	.	5	4	
5	1	3	.	2	8	5

Knowing the place value system is the key to changing a decimal to its equivalent fraction and to reading the decimal. For a given decimal, the place value of the rightmost digit is the denominator of the equivalent fraction.

$$0.9 = \frac{9}{10}$$

Read "nine tenths"

$$0.21 = \frac{21}{100}$$

Read "twenty-one hundredths"

Let's look at how to rewrite any decimal as a fraction or mixed number.

To Change a Decimal to the Equivalent Fraction or Mixed Number

- Copy the nonzero whole-number part of the decimal, and drop the decimal point.

- Place the fractional part of the decimal in the numerator of the equivalent fraction.

- Make the denominator of the equivalent fraction 1 followed by as many zeros as the decimal has decimal places.

- Simplify the resulting fraction, if possible.

EXAMPLE 1

Write each decimal as a fraction or mixed number.

a. 0.25   **b.** 1.398

SOLUTION

a. Write 0.25 as $\frac{25}{100}$, which simplifies to $\frac{1}{4}$. So $0.25 = \frac{1}{4}$.

b. The decimal 1.398 is equivalent to a mixed number whose whole-number part is 1. The fractional part of the decimal (398) is the numerator of the equivalent fraction. Since the decimal has three decimal places, the denominator of the fraction has three zeros (that is, it is 1000). So $1.398 = 1\frac{398}{1000} = 1\frac{199}{500}$.

PRACTICE 1

Express each decimal in fractional form.
a. 0.5
b. 2.073

PRACTICE 2

Write 4.003 in words.

EXAMPLE 2

Write 2.019 in words.

SOLUTION $2.019 = 2\dfrac{19}{1000}$

We read the original decimal as "two and nineteen thousandths," keeping the whole number unchanged. Note that we use the word *and* to separate the whole number and the fractional part.

⋅⋅●

In computations with decimals, we sometimes *round* the decimal to a certain number of decimal places.

> **To Round a Decimal to a Given Decimal Place**
> - Underline the place to which you are rounding.
> - Look at the digit to the right of the underlined digit—the *critical digit*. If this digit is 5 or more, add 1 to the underlined digit; if it is less than 5, leave the underlined digit unchanged.
> - Drop all digits to the right of the underlined digit.

PRACTICE 3

Round 748.0772 to the nearest hundredth.

EXAMPLE 3

Round 94.735 to the nearest tenth.

SOLUTION   First, we underline the digit 7 in the tenths place: 94.$\underline{7}$35. Since the critical digit 3 is less than 5, we do not add 1 to the underlined digit. Dropping all digits to the right of the 7, we get 94.7. So 94.735 ≈ 94.7 (the symbol ≈ is read "is approximately equal to"). Note that our answer has only one decimal place because we are rounding to the nearest tenth.

⋅⋅●

> **To Add Decimals**
> - Rewrite the numbers vertically, lining up the decimal points.
> - Add.
> - Insert a decimal point in the answer below the other decimal points.

PRACTICE 4

Add: 5.92 + 35.872 + 0.3

EXAMPLE 4

Add: 2.7 + 80.13 + 5.036

SOLUTION   Rewrite the numbers with decimal points lined up vertically so that digits with the same place value are in the same column. Then, add.

$$
\begin{array}{r}
2.7 \\
80.13 \\
+\ 5.036 \\
\hline
87.866
\end{array}
$$

└── Insert the decimal point in the answer.

⋅⋅●

To Subtract Decimals

- Rewrite the numbers vertically, lining up the decimal points.
- Subtract, inserting extra zeros if necessary for regrouping.
- Insert a decimal point in the answer below the other decimal points.

EXAMPLE 5

Subtract: $5 - 2.14$

SOLUTION

$$\begin{array}{r} 5.00 \\ -\,2.14 \\ \hline 2.86 \end{array}$$

Rewrite 5 as 5.00 and line up decimal points vertically.
Subtract.

└── Insert the decimal point in the answer.

PRACTICE 5

Find the difference: $3.8 - 2.621$

To Multiply Decimals

- Multiply the factors as if they were whole numbers.
- Find the total number of decimal places in the factors.
- Count that many places from the right end of the product and insert a decimal point.

EXAMPLE 6

Multiply: 6.1×3.7

SOLUTION   First, multiply: $61 \times 37 = 2257$

$$\begin{array}{r} 61 \\ \times\ 37 \\ \hline 427 \\ 183 \\ \hline 2257 \end{array}$$

Then, count the total number of decimal places.

$$\begin{array}{r} 6.1 \\ \times\ 3.7 \\ \hline 427 \\ 183 \\ \hline 22.57 \end{array}$$

← One decimal place (tenths)
← One decimal place (tenths)

← Two decimal places (hundredths) in the product

So the answer is 22.57.

A shortcut for multiplying a decimal by a power of 10 is to *move the decimal point to the right the same number of places as the power of 10 has zeros.*

PRACTICE 6

Find the product of 2.81 and 3.5.

EXAMPLE 7

Find the product: $(2.89)(1000)$

SOLUTION   We notice that 1000 is a power of 10 and has three zeros. To multiply 2.89 by 1000, we move the decimal point in 2.89 to the right three places.

PRACTICE 7

Multiply 32.7 by 10,000.

$$(2.890)(1000) = 2\,8\,9\,0. = 2890$$

Add a zero to move the decimal
point three places.

The product is 2890.   ··●

To Divide Decimals

- If the divisor is not a whole number, move the decimal point in the divisor to the right end of the number.

- Move the decimal point in the dividend the same number of places to the right as we did in the divisor.

- Insert a decimal point in the quotient directly above the decimal point in the dividend.

- Divide the new dividend by the new divisor, inserting zeros at the right end of the dividend as necessary.

PRACTICE 8

Divide: 2.706 ÷ 0.15

EXAMPLE **8**

Divide 0.035 by 0.25.

SOLUTION

Move the decimal point to the right end,
making the divisor a whole number.

$$0.25\overline{)0.035} \;\Rightarrow\; 0.25\,\overline{)0.035}$$

Move the decimal point in the
dividend the same number of places.

Finally, we divide 3.5 by 25, which gives us 0.14.

$$
\begin{array}{r}
0.1\,4 \\
25\overline{)3.5\,0} \\
\underline{2\,5} \\
1\,0\,0 \\
\underline{1\,0\,0} \\
0
\end{array}
$$

                                                                          ··●

A shortcut for dividing a decimal by a power of 10 is to *move the decimal point to the left the same number of places as the power of 10 has zeros.*

PRACTICE 9

Calculate: 0.86 ÷ 1000

EXAMPLE **9**

Compute: $\dfrac{7.2}{100}$

SOLUTION   Since we are dividing by the power of 10 with two zeros, we can find this quotient simply by moving the decimal point in 7.2 to the left two places.

$$\frac{7.2}{100} = .072, \quad \text{or} \quad 0.072$$

The quotient is 0.072.   ··●

EXAMPLE 10

The following graph shows the U.S. outlays for national defense in five consecutive years, expressed in hundreds of billions of current dollars.

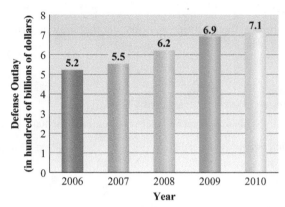

The defense outlay in 2010 was how many times as great as the corresponding outlay 4 years earlier? Round to the nearest tenth. (*Source:* census.gov)

SOLUTION   The defense outlay in 2010 was 7.1 and in 2006 it was 5.2 (both in hundreds of billions of dollars). To find how many times as great 7.1 is as compared to 5.2, we calculate their quotient.

$$5.2\overline{)7.1} = 52.\overline{)71.}$$

$$
\begin{array}{r}
1.36 \\
52\overline{)71.00} \\
\underline{52} \\
19\ 0 \\
\underline{15\ 6} \\
3\ 40 \\
\underline{3\ 12} \\
28
\end{array}
$$

Rounding the quotient to the nearest tenth, we conclude that the U.S. defense outlay in 2010 was 1.4 times greater than 4 years earlier.

⋅ ⋅ ●

PRACTICE 10

The table below gives the amount of selected foods consumed per capita in the United States in a recent year.

Food	Annual per Capita Consumption (in pounds)
Red meat	195.2
Poultry	66.5
Fish and shellfish	15.2

The amount of red meat consumed was how many times as great as the amount of poultry, rounded to the nearest tenth? (*Source:* USDA/ Economic Research Service)

Section 2.2 Exercises

FOR EXTRA HELP   MyMathLab   MathXL PRACTICE   WATCH   READ   REVIEW

Write each decimal as a fraction or mixed number.

1. 0.875   **2.** 2.006

Name the place that the underlined digit occupies.

3. 18.3<u>5</u>9   **4.** 8024.<u>5</u>

Write each decimal in words.

5. 0.72   **6.** 0.05

7. 3.009   **8.** 12.235

Round as indicated.

9. 7.31 to the nearest tenth

10. 9.52 to the nearest tenth

11. 4.3868 to two decimal places

12. 8.6874 to two decimal places

Calculate.

13. $8.2 + 3.91 + 6$ **14.** $8 + 3.25 + 12.88$

15. $3.8 - 1.927$ **16.** $2.5 - 1.6$

17. 7.28×0.4 **18.** 6.24×0.6

19. $2.71 \cdot 1000$ **20.** 100×5.3

21. $0.006 \div 4$ **22.** $31.9 \div 10$

23. $12 \div 2.4$ **24.** $42 \div 2.1$

25. $7.1 + 0.5^2$ **26.** $8.6 + 0.6^2$

27. $20.8 - 7(4 - 3.1)$ **28.** $18.6 + 3(9 - 4.2)$

2.3 PERCENTS

Percent means divided by 100. For instance, 18% means 18 divided by 100, or $\frac{18}{100}$, which simplifies to $\frac{9}{50}$. Therefore, the fraction $\frac{9}{50}$ is just another way of writing 18%, suggesting the following rule.

> **To Change a Percent to the Equivalent Fraction**
> * Drop the % sign from the given percent and place the number over 100.
> * Simplify the resulting fraction, if possible.

PRACTICE 1

Write 7% as a fraction.

EXAMPLE 1

Write 20% as a fraction.

SOLUTION   To change this percent to a fraction, drop the percent sign and write the 20 over 100. Then simplify.

$$20\% = \frac{20}{100} = \frac{1}{5}$$

A percent can also be written as a decimal, since $18\% = \frac{18}{100} = 0.18$. This suggests the following rule:

> **To Change a Percent to the Equivalent Decimal**
> * Move the decimal point two places *to the left* and drop the % sign.

PRACTICE 2

Write 5% as a decimal.

EXAMPLE 2

Find the decimal equivalent of 1%.

SOLUTION   The unwritten decimal point lies to the right of the 1. Moving the decimal point two places to the left and dropping the % sign, we get:

$$1\% = \underset{\smile}{0\,1}.\% = .01, \text{ or } 0.01$$

> **To Change a Decimal to the Equivalent Percent**
> * Move the decimal point two places *to the right* and insert a % sign.

PRACTICE 3

What percent is equivalent to the decimal 0.025?

EXAMPLE 3

Write 0.125 as a percent.

SOLUTION   First, move the decimal point two places to the right. Then, insert a % sign.

$$0.\underset{\overrightarrow{}}{1\,2\,5} = 0\,1\,2.5\% = 12.5\%$$

> **To Change a Fraction to the Equivalent Percent**
> - Change the fraction to a decimal.
> - Change the decimal to a percent.

EXAMPLE 4

Rewrite $\frac{1}{2}$ as a percent.

SOLUTION To change the given fraction to a percent, first, find the equivalent decimal. Then, express it as a percent.

$$\frac{1}{2} = 2\overline{\smash{)}1.0}\ \ {}^{0.5}_{1\,0} \quad \text{and} \quad 0.5\,0 = 50\%$$

> **PRACTICE 4**
>
> Rewrite $\frac{1}{4}$ as a percent.

EXAMPLE 5

A local sales tax rate is 0.0825 of selling prices. Express this tax rate as a percent.

SOLUTION $0.0825 = 0\,0\,8.2\,5\% = 8.25\%$

> **PRACTICE 5**
>
> Suppose that 40% of a student's income goes to paying college expenses. Rewrite this percent as a decimal.

Section 2.3 Exercises

Change each percent to a fraction or mixed number and simplify.

1. 75%   **2.** 4%

3. 106%   **4.** 250%

Change each percent to a decimal.

5. 6%   **6.** 8%

7. 150%   **8.** 180%

Change each decimal to a percent.

9. 0.31   **10.** 0.05

11. 0.0145   **12.** 0.0148

Change each fraction to a percent.

13. $\dfrac{1}{10}$ **14.** $\dfrac{3}{8}$

15. $\dfrac{4}{5}$ **16.** $\dfrac{7}{4}$

2.4 SCIENTIFIC NOTATION AND SIGNIFICANT DIGITS

Exponents

There are many mathematical situations in which we multiply a number by itself repeatedly. Writing such expressions using *exponents* (*or powers*) provides a shorthand method for representing this repeated multiplication of the same factor:

$$\underbrace{2\cdot2\cdot2\cdot2}_{\text{4 factors of 2}} = 2^{\overset{\longleftarrow\ \text{exponent}}{4}}$$

base

The expression 2^4 is read "2 to the fourth power" or simply "2 to the fourth."

To evaluate 2^4, we multiply 4 factors of 2:

$$2^4 = \underbrace{2\cdot2}\cdot2\cdot2$$
$$= \underbrace{4\cdot2}\cdot2$$
$$= \underbrace{8\cdot2}$$
$$= 16$$

So $2^4 = 16$.

Sometimes we prefer to shorten expressions by using exponents. For instance,

$$\underbrace{3\cdot3}_{\text{2 factors of 3}} \cdot \underbrace{4\cdot4\cdot4}_{\text{3 factors of 4}} = 3^2\cdot4^3$$

PRACTICE 1

Write $2\cdot2\cdot2\cdot2\cdot2$ as a power of 2.

EXAMPLE 1

Express $6\cdot6\cdot6$ using exponents.

SOLUTION $\underbrace{6\cdot6\cdot6}_{\text{3 factors of 6}} = 6^3$

· · ●

EXAMPLE 2

Calculate: $4^3\cdot5^3$

PRACTICE 2

Compute: $7^2\cdot2^4$

SOLUTION $4^3\cdot5^3 = (4\cdot4\cdot4)\cdot(5\cdot5\cdot5)$
$$= 64\cdot125$$
$$= 8000$$

It is especially easy to compute powers of 10:

$$10^2 = \underbrace{10\cdot10}_{\text{2 factors}} = \underbrace{100}_{\text{2 zeros}}$$

$$10^3 = \underbrace{10\cdot10\cdot10}_{\text{3 factors}} = \underbrace{1000}_{\text{3 zeros}}$$

and so on.

· · ●

EXAMPLE 3

The distance from the Sun to the star Alpha-one Crucis is about 1,000,000,000,000,000 mi. Express this distance as a power of 10. (*Source:* infoplease.com)

SOLUTION $1,\underbrace{000,000,000,000,000}_{\text{15 zeros}} = 10^{15}$

So the distance is 10^{15} mi.

$\cdots\bullet$

PRACTICE 3

In 1850, the world population was approximately 1,000,000,000. Represent this number as a power of 10. (*Source:* census.gov)

Scientific Notation

Scientific notation is an important application of exponents—whether they are positive, negative, or zero. Scientists use this notation to abbreviate very large or very small numbers. Note that scientific notation is based on powers of 10.

Example	Standard Notation	Scientific Notation
The speed of light	983,000,000 ft/sec	9.83×10^8 ft/sec
The length of a virus	0.000000000001 m	1×10^{-12} m

Scientific notation has several advantages over standard notation. For example, when a number contains a long string of 0's, writing it in scientific notation can take fewer digits. Also, numbers written in scientific notation can be relatively easy to multiply or divide.

Definition

A number is in **scientific notation** if it is written in the form

$$a \times 10^n$$

where n is an integer and a is greater than or equal to 1 but less than 10 ($1 \le a < 10$)

Note that any value of *a* that satisfies the inequality $1 \le a < 10$ must have *one non-zero digit* to the left of the decimal point. For instance, 7.3×10^5 is written in scientific notation. Do you see why the numbers 0.83×10^2, 5×3^7, and 13.8×10^{-4} are *not* written in scientific notation?

TIP   When written in scientific notation, large numbers have positive powers of 10, whereas small numbers have negative powers of 10. For instance, $3 * 10^{23}$ is large, whereas $3 * 10^{-23}$ is small.

Let's now consider how to change a number from scientific notation to standard notation.

EXAMPLE ④

Change the number 2.41×10^5 from scientific notation to standard notation.

SOLUTION   To express this number in standard notation, we need to multiply 2.41 by 10^5. Since $10^5 = 100,000$, multiplying 2.41 by 100,000 gives:

$$2.41 \times 10^5 = 2.41 \times 100,000 = 241,000.00 = 241,000$$

The number 241,000 is written in standard notation.

Note that the power of 10 here is *positive* and that the decimal point is moved five places *to the right*. So a shortcut for expressing 2.41×10^5 in standard notation is to move the decimal point in 2.41 five places to the right.

$$2.41 \times 10^5 = 2\,4\,1\,0\,0\,0. = 241,000$$

$\cdots\bullet$

PRACTICE 4

Express 2.539×10^2 in standard notation.

PRACTICE 5

Change 4.3×10^{-9} to standard notation.

EXAMPLE 5

Convert 3×10^{-5} to standard notation.

SOLUTION   Using the definition of a negative exponent, we get:

$$3 \times 10^{-5} = 3 \times \frac{1}{10^5}, \text{ or } \frac{3}{10^5}$$

Since $10^5 = 100{,}000$,   dividing 3 by 100,000 gives us:

$$\frac{3}{10^5} = \frac{3}{100{,}000} = 0.00003$$

Here we note that the power of 10 is *negative* and that the decimal point, which is understood to be at the right end of a whole number, is moved five places *to the left*. So a shortcut for expressing 3×10^{-5} in standard notation is to move the decimal point in 3. five places to the left.

$$3 \times 10^{-5} = 3. \times 10^{-5} = .00003 = .00003, \text{ or } 0.00003 \qquad \cdots \bullet$$

> **TIP**   When converting a number from scientific notation to standard notation, move the decimal point to the *right* if the power of 10 is *positive* and to the *left* if the power of 10 is *negative*.

Now, let's consider the reverse situation, namely changing a number in standard notation to scientific notation.

PRACTICE 6

Write 8,000,000,000,000 in scientific notation.

EXAMPLE 6

Express 37,000,000,000 in scientific notation.

SOLUTION   For a number to be written in scientific notation, it must be of the form

$$a \times 10^n$$

where n is an integer and $1 \le a < 10$.   We know that 37,000,000,000 and 37,000,000,000. are the same. We move the decimal point *to the left* so that there is one nonzero digit to the left of the decimal point. The power of 10 by which we multiply is the same as the number of places moved.

$$37{,}000{,}000{,}000 = 3.7000000000 \times 10^{10}$$

Move 10 places to the *left*.

$$= 3.7 \times 10^{10}$$

Since 3.7 and 3.7000000000 are equivalent, we can drop the trailing zeros. So 37,000,000,000 expressed in scientific notation is 3.7×10^{10}. $\qquad \cdots \bullet$

PRACTICE 7

Express 0.000000000071 in scientific notation.

EXAMPLE 7

Convert 0.00000000000000002 to scientific notation.

SOLUTION   We must write the number 0.00000000000000002 in the form

$$a \times 10^n$$

where n is an integer and $1 \le a < 10$.   We move the decimal point *to the right* so that there is one nonzero digit to the left of the decimal point. The power of 10 by which we multiply is the number of places moved, preceded by a *negative* sign.

$$0.00000000000000002 = 0\underbrace{0\,0\,0\,0\,0\,0\,0\,0\,0\,0\,0\,0\,0\,0\,0\,0\,2}.\, \times\, 10^{-17}$$

Move 17 places to the *right*.

$$= 2.\times 10^{-17} = 2 \times 10^{-17}$$

$\cdot\,\cdot\,\bullet$

Significant Digits

Suppose you measure your weight to be 132 pounds on a scale that can be read only to the nearest pound. Saying that you weigh 132.00 pounds would be misleading, because it would incorrectly imply that you know your weight to the nearest *hundredth* of a pound, rather than to the nearest pound. In other words, when dealing with measurements, 132 pounds and 132.00 pounds do *not* have the same meaning.

The digits in a number that represent actual measurements are called **significant digits.** For example, 132 pounds has 3 significant digits and implies a measurement to the nearest pound, while 132.00 pounds has 5 significant digits and implies a measurement to the nearest hundredth of a pound.

Note that zeros are significant when they represent actual measurements, but not when they serve only to locate the decimal point. We assume that the zeros in 132.00 pounds are significant because there was no reason to include them unless they represented an actual measurement. In contrast, we assume that the zeros in 600 centimeters are *not* significant, because they serve only to tell us that the decimal point comes to their right. Rewriting 600 centimeters as 6 meters makes it easier to see that only the 6 is a significant digit.

The only subtlety in counting significant digits arises when we cannot be sure whether zeros are truly significant. For example, suppose your professor states that there are 200 students in your class. Without further information, you have no way to know whether she means exactly 200 students or roughly 200. We can avoid this kind of ambiguity by writing numbers in scientific notation. In that case, zeros appear only when they are significant. For example, an enrollment of 2×10^2 implies a measurement to the nearest hundred students, while 2.00×10^2 implies exactly 200 students.

Summary When Are Digits Significant?

Type of Digit	Significance
Nonzero digits	Always significant
Zeros that follow a nonzero digit *and* lie to the right of the decimal point (as in 4.20 or 3.00)	Always significant
Zeros between nonzero digits (as in 4002 or 3.06) or other significant zeros (such as the first zero in 30.0)	Always significant
Zeros to the left of the first nonzero digit (as in 0.006 or 0.00052)	Never significant
Zeros to the right of the last nonzero digit but before the decimal point (as in 40,000 or 210)	Not significant unless stated otherwise

---

EXAMPLE 8 Counting Significant Digits

State the number of significant digits and the implied meaning of the following numbers.

a. a time of 11.90 seconds

b. a length of 0.000067 meter

c. a weight of 0.0030 gram

d. a population reported as 240,000

e. a population reported as 2.40×10^5

SOLUTION

a. The number 11.90 seconds has 4 significant digits and implies a measurement to the nearest 0.01 second.

b. The number 0.000067 meter has 2 significant digits and implies a measurement to the nearest 0.000001 meter. Note that we can rewrite this number as 67 micrometers, showing clearly that it has only 2 significant digits.

c. The number 0.0030 has 2 significant digits. The leading zeros are not significant because they serve only as placeholders, as we can see by rewriting the number as 3.0 milligrams. The final zero is significant because there is no reason to include it unless it was measured.

d. We assume that the zeros in 240,000 people are not significant. Therefore, the number has 2 significant digits and implies a measurement to the nearest 10,000 people.

e. The number 2.40×10^5 has 3 significant digits. Although this number means 240,000, the scientific notation shows that the first zero is significant, so it implies a measurement to the nearest 1000 people. $\cdots\bullet$

BRIEF REVIEW: ROUNDING

The basic process of rounding numbers takes just two steps.

Step 1. Decide which decimal place (e.g., tens, ones, tenths, or hundredths) is the smallest that should be kept.

Step 2. Look at the number in the next place to the *right* (for example, if rounding to tenths, look at hundredths). If the value in the next place is *less than 5*, round *down*; if it is *5 or greater*, round *up*.

For example, the number 382.2593 is given to the nearest ten-thousandth. It can be rounded in the following ways:

382.2593 rounded to the nearest thousandth is 382.259.

382.2593 rounded to the nearest hundredth is 382.26.

382.2593 rounded to the nearest tenth is 382.3.

382.2593 rounded to the nearest one is 382.

382.2593 rounded to the nearest ten is 380.

382.2593 rounded to the nearest hundred is 400.

(Some statisticians use a more complex rounding rule if the value in the next column is exactly 5: They round up if the last digit being kept is odd and down if it is even. We won't use that rule in this book.)

EXAMPLE **9** **Rounding with Significant Digits**

For each of the following operations, give your answer with the specified number of significant digits.

a. 7.7 mm $\times$ 9.92 mm; give your answer with 2 significant digits

b. 240,000 $\times$ 72,106; give your answer with 4 significant digits

SOLUTION

a. 7.7 mm $\times$ 9.92 mm = 76.384 mm^2. Because we are asked to give the answer with 2 significant digits, we round to 76 mm^2.

b. 240,000 $\times$ 72,106 = 1.730544×10^{10}. Because we are asked to give the answer with 4 significant digits, we round to 1.731×10^{10}. $\cdots\bullet$

Rewrite each product using exponents.

1. $6 \cdot 6 \cdot 6 \cdot 6 \cdot 6$

2. $7 \cdot 7 \cdot 7 \cdot 7 \cdot 7 \cdot 7 \cdot 7 \cdot 7$

3. $2 \cdot 2 \cdot 10 \cdot 10 \cdot 10$

4. $5 \cdot 5 \cdot 5 \cdot 5 \cdot 4 \cdot 4 \cdot 4$

Calculate.

5. $5^2 \cdot 10^3$

6. $2^4 \cdot 6^2$

Simplify.

7. $24 - 3 \cdot 7$

8. $20 - 4 \cdot 5$

9. $2 + 18 \div 3(9 - 7)$

10. $7 + 12 \div 2(7 - 2)$

11. $\dfrac{4^2 + 8}{9 - 3}$

12. $\dfrac{12 + 2^2}{15 - 9 + 2}$

2.5   USES OF PERCENTAGES IN STATISTICS

Statistical results are often stated with percentages. A percentage is simply a way of expressing a fraction; the words *per cent* literally mean "divided by 100." However, percentages are often used in subtle ways. Consider a statement that appeared in a front-page article in the *New York Times*:

> *The percentage of smokers among 8th graders is up 44 percent, to 10.4 percent.*

Although the statement uses percentages in a valid way, it can be difficult to understand what it means by "up 44%, to 10.4%." In this section, we will investigate some of the subtle uses and abuses of percentages. Before we begin, you should review the following basic rules regarding conversions between fractions and percentages.

Conversions Between Fractions and Percentages

To convert a percentage to a common fraction: Replace the % symbol with division by 100; simplify the fraction if necessary.

$$\text{Example:} \quad 25\% = \frac{25}{100} = \frac{1}{4}$$

To convert a percentage to a decimal: Drop the % symbol and move the decimal point two places to the left (that is, divide by 100).

$$\text{Example:} \quad 25\% = 0.25$$

To convert a decimal to a percentage: Move the decimal point two places to the right (that is, multiply by 100) and add the % symbol.

$$\text{Example:} \quad 0.43 = 43\%$$

To convert a common fraction to a percentage: First convert the common fraction to a decimal; then convert the decimal to a percentage.

$$\text{Example:} \quad \frac{1}{5} = 0.2 = 20\%$$

EXAMPLE 1 Newspaper Survey

A newspaper reports that 54% of 1,069 people surveyed said that the President is doing a good job. How many people said that the President is doing a good job?

SOLUTION   The 54% represents the fraction of respondents who said the President is doing a good job. Because "of" usually indicates multiplication, we multiply:

$$54\% \times 1{,}069 = 0.54 \times 1{,}069 = 577.26 \approx 577$$

About 577 out of the 1,069 people said the President is doing a good job. Note that we round the answer to 577 to obtain a whole number of people, because the number of people must be a discrete (integer) value. (The symbol $\approx$ means "approximately equal to.") $\cdot \cdot \bullet$

Using Percentages to Describe Change

Percentages are often used to describe how data change with time. For example, suppose the population of a town was 10,000 in 1970 and 15,000 in 2000. We can express this change in two basic ways:

- Because the population rose by 5,000 people (from 10,000 to 15,000), we say that the **absolute change** in the population was 5,000 people.
- Because the increase of 5,000 people was 50% of the starting population of 10,000, we say that the **relative change** in the population was 50%.

In general, calculating an absolute or relative change always involves two numbers: a starting number, or **reference value**, and a **new value**. Once we identify these two values, we can calculate the absolute and relative change with the following formulas. A change is positive if the new value is greater than the reference value and negative if the new value is less than the reference value.

Absolute and Relative Change

The **absolute change** is the actual increase or decrease from a reference value to a new value:

$$\text{absolute change} = \text{new value} - \text{reference value}$$

The **relative change** is the size of the absolute change in comparison to the reference value and can be expressed as a percentage:

$$\text{relative change} = \frac{\text{new value} - \text{reference value}}{\text{reference value}} \times 100\%$$

TIME ◷UT TO THINK

Compare the formulas for absolute and relative change to the formulas for absolute and relative error. Why are they so similar?

EXAMPLE 2 World Population Growth

Estimated world population in 1950 was 2.6 billion. By the end of 2010, it had reached 6.9 billion. Describe the absolute and relative change in world population from 1950 to 2010.

SOLUTION   The reference value is the 1950 population of 2.6 billion and the new value is the 2010 population of 6.9 billion.

$$\text{absolute change} = \text{new value} - \text{reference value}$$

$$= 6.9 \text{ billion} - 2.6 \text{ billion}$$

$$= 4.3 \text{ billion}$$

$$\text{relative change} = \frac{\text{new value} - \text{reference value}}{\text{reference value}} \times 100\%$$

$$= \frac{6.9 \text{ billion} - 2.6 \text{ billion}}{2.6 \text{ billion}} \times 100\%$$

$$= 165.4\%$$

World population increased by 4.3 billion people, or by about 165%, during the 60-year period from 1950 to 2010. $\cdots\bullet$

Using Percentages for Comparisons

Percentages are also commonly used to compare two numbers:

- The **reference value** is the number that we are using as the basis for a comparison.
- The **compared value** is the other number, which we compare to the reference value.

We can then express the absolute or relative difference between these two values with formulas very similar to those for absolute and relative change. The difference is positive if the compared value is greater than the reference value and negative if the compared value is less than the reference value.

> ### Absolute and Relative Difference
>
> The **absolute difference** is the difference between the compared value and the reference value:
>
> $$\text{absolute difference} = \text{compared value} - \text{reference value}$$
>
> The **relative difference** describes the size of the absolute difference in comparison to the reference value and can be expressed as a percentage:
>
> $$\text{relative difference} = \frac{\text{compared value} - \text{reference value}}{\text{reference value}} \times 100\%$$

EXAMPLE ③ Russian and American Life Expectancy

According to United Nations data, life expectancy for American men is about 76 years, while life expectancy for Russian men is about 63 years. Using the life expectancy of Russian men as the reference value, compare the life expectancy of American men with that of Russian men in absolute and relative terms.

SOLUTION   We want to compare the American male life expectancy with the Russian male life expectancy, so the Russian male life expectancy is the reference value and the American male life expectancy is the compared value:

$$\text{absolute difference} = \text{compared value} - \text{reference value}$$

$$= 76 \text{ years} - 63 \text{ years}$$

$$= 13 \text{ years}$$

$$\text{relative difference} = \frac{\text{compared value} - \text{reference value}}{\text{reference value}} \times 100\%$$

$$= \frac{76 \text{ years} - 63 \text{ years}}{63 \text{ years}} \times 100\%$$

$$\approx 21\%$$

The life expectancy of American men is 13 years greater in absolute terms and 21% greater in relative terms than the life expectancy of Russian men.   · · •

Of versus *More Than*

Consider a population that *triples* in size from 200 to 600. There are two equivalent ways to state this change with percentages:

- Using *more than*: The new population is 200% *more than* the original population. Here, we are looking at the relative change in the population:

$$\text{relative change} = \frac{\text{new value} - \text{reference value}}{\text{reference value}} \times 100\%$$

$$= \frac{600 - 200}{200} \times 100\%$$

$$= 200\%$$

- Using *of*: The new population is 300% *of* the original population, which means it is three times the original population. Here, we are looking at the *ratio* of the new population to the original population:

$$\frac{\text{new population}}{\text{original population}} = \frac{600}{200} = 3.00 = 300\%$$

Notice that the percentages in the "more than" and "of" statements are related by $300\% = 100\% + 200\%$. This leads to the following general relationship.

> **Of versus More Than (or Less Than)**
>
> - If the new or compared value is *P% more than* the **reference value**, then it is (100 + *P*)% *of* the reference value.
>
> - If the new or compared value is *P% less than* the reference value, then it is (100 − *P*)% *of* the reference value.

For example, 40% *more than* the reference value is 140% *of* the reference value, and 40% *less than* the reference value is 60% *of* the reference value. When you hear statistics quoted with percentages, it is very important to listen carefully for the key words *of* and *more than* (or *less than*)—and hope that the speaker knows the difference.

EXAMPLE **4** **World Population**

In Example 2, we found that world population in 2010 was about 165% more than world population in 1950. Express this change with an "of " statement.

SOLUTION   World population in 2010 was 165% more than world population in 1950. Because(100 + 165)% = 265%, the 2010 population was 265% *of* the 1950 population. This means that the 2010 population was 2.65 times the 1950 population.   · · •

EXAMPLE 5 Sale!

A store is having a "25% off " sale. How does a sale price compare to an original price?

SOLUTION The "25% off " means that a sale price is 25% *less than* the original price, which means it is $(100 - 25)\% = 75\%$ *of* the original price. For example, if an item's original price was $100, its sale price is $75.   · · ●

TIME (●)UT TO THINK

One store advertises "1/3 off everything!" Another store advertises "Sale prices just 1/3 of original prices!" Which store is having the bigger sale? Explain.

Percentages of Percentages

Percentage changes and percentage differences can be particularly confusing when the values *themselves* are percentages. Suppose your bank increases the interest rate on your savings account from 3% to 4%. It's tempting to say that the interest rate increases by 1%, but that statement is ambiguous at best. The interest rate increases by 1 *percentage point*, but the relative change in the interest rate is 33%:

$$\frac{4\% - 3\%}{3\%} \times 100\% = 0.33 \times 100\% = 33\%$$

You can therefore say that the bank raised your interest rate by 33%, even though the actual rate increased by only 1 percentage point (from 3% to 4%).

Percentage Points versus %

When you see a change or difference expressed in *percentage points*, you can assume it is an *absolute* change or difference. If it is expressed as a percentage, it probably is a *relative* change or difference.

EXAMPLE 6 Care in Wording

Assume that 40% of the registered voters in Carson City are Republicans. Read the following questions carefully and give the most appropriate answers.

a. The percentage of voters registered as Republicans is 25% higher in Freetown than in Carson City. What percentage of the registered voters in Freetown are Republicans?

b. The percentage of voters registered as Republicans is 25 percentage points higher in Freetown than in Carson City. What percentage of the registered voters in Freetown are Republicans?

SOLUTION

a. We interpret the "25%" as a relative difference, and 25% of 40% is 10% (because $0.25 \times 0.40 = 0.10$). Therefore, the percentage of registered Republicans in Freetown is $40\% + 10\% = 50\%$.

b. In this case, we interpret the "25 percentage points" as an absolute difference, so we simply add this value to the percentage of Republicans in Carson City. Therefore, the percentage of registered Republicans in Freetown is $40\% + 25\% = 65\%$.   · · ●

If you can't convince them, confuse them.

—Harry S. Truman

Section 2.5

Statistical Literacy and Critical Thinking

1. **Percentages.** Last year's budget for the legislative branch of the U.S. government was $4919 million, and this year it is $5333 million. Consider last year's budget of $4919 million to be the reference value.

   a. What is the absolute change in the budget from last year to this year?

   b. What is the relative change in the budget from last year to this year?

   c. Next year's budget is estimated to be $5185 million. What is the percentage decrease from this year's budget of $5333?

   d. If next year's budget is changed so that it is 5% less than this year's budget of $5333 million, what is the amount of next year's budget?

2. **Percentage** A *New York Times* editorial criticized a chart caption that described a dental rinse as one that "reduces plaque on teeth by over 300%." If the dental rinse removes all of the plaque, what percentage is removed? Is it possible to reduce plaque by over 300%?

3. **Percentage Points.** A Ridgid survey of 1,023 high school students showed that 25% of them plan to enter the field of information technology, and the margin of error is 3 percentage points. Why is it misleading to state that the margin of error is 3% instead of 3 percentage points?

4. ***Of* and *More Than*.** In an Opinion Research poll, 1,072 adults were asked what they would do with their old cell phones, and 44.0% of them said that they would donate them to charity. What is the actual number of respondents who plan to donate their old cell phones to charity? If another poll is to be conducted with a sample size that is 5% greater than the sample size of 1,072 adults, how many subjects will be included in this new poll?

Does It Make Sense? For Exercises 5–8, decide whether the statement makes sense (or is clearly true) or does not make sense (or is clearly false). Explain clearly; not all of these have definitive answers, so your explanation is more important than your chosen answer.

5. **Cell Phones.** The percentage of people with cell phones increased by 1.2 million people.

6. **Salary Percentages.** The CEO of the Brandon Marketing Group announces that all employees must take a 5% cut in pay this year, but they will all get a 5% raise next year, so the salaries will then be the same as they are now.

7. **Interest Rate.** The Jefferson Valley Bank increased its new-car loan rate by 100%.

8. **Interest Rate.** The Jefferson Valley Bank increased its new-car loan rate (annual) by 100 percentage points.

Concepts and Applications

9. **Fractions, Decimals, Percentages.** Express each of the following numbers in the three forms of a fraction, decimal, and percentage.

   a. 75%   **b.** 3/8   **c.** 0.4   **d.** 80%

10. **Fractions, Decimals, Percentages.** Express the following numbers in the three forms of fraction, decimal, and percentage.

    a. 350%   **b.** 2.5   **c.** −0.44   **d.** −200%

11. **Percentage Practice.** A study was conducted of pleas made by 1,348 criminals. Among those criminals, 956 pleaded guilty and 392 of them were sentenced to prison. Among 72 other criminals who pleaded not guilty, 58 were sent to prison (based on data from "Does It Pay to Plead Guilty?" by Brereton and Casper, *Law and Society Review*, Vol. 16, No. 1).

    a. What percentage of the criminals pleaded guilty?

    b. What percentage of the criminals were sent to prison?

    c. Among those who pleaded guilty, what is the percentage who were sent to prison?

    d. Among those who pleaded not guilty, what is the percentage who were sent to prison?

12. **Percentage Practice.** A study was conducted to determine whether flipping a penny or spinning a penny has an effect on the proportion of heads. Among 49,437 trials, 29,015 involved flipping pennies, and 14,709 of those pennies turned up heads. The other 20,422 trials involved spinning pennies, and 9,197 of those pennies turned up heads (based on data from Robin Lock as given in *Chance News*).

    a. What percentage of the trials involved flipping pennies?

    b. What percentage of the trials involved spinning pennies?

    c. Among the pennies that were flipped, what is the percentage that turned up heads?

    d. Among the pennies that were spun, what is the percentage that turned up heads?

Relative Change. Exercises 13–20 each provide two values. For each pair of values, use a percentage to express their relative change or difference. Use the second given value as the reference value, and express results to the nearest percentage point. Also, write a statement describing the result.

13. **Newspapers.** The number of daily newspapers in the United States is now 1,387, and it was 2,226 in 1900.

14. **Cars.** There are now 143,781,202 registered passenger cars, and in 1980 there were 121,601,000.

15. **Airline Flights.** This January there were 751,183 scheduled passenger flights in the United States, and in January of 1996 there were 634,343.

16. **Bankruptcies.** There were 1,531,997 bankruptcy cases filed last year, and in the year 2000 there were 1,276,900 bankruptcy cases filed.

17. **Newspapers.** The daily circulation of the *Wall Street Journal* is currently 2.09 million (the largest in the country). The daily circulation of *USA Today* is currently 1.83 million (the second largest in the country).

18. **Car Sales.** In the current month, 18,830 Toyota Camry cars were sold, and there were 18,341 Honda Civic cars sold.

19. **Airports.** Chicago's O'Hare Airport handled 67 million passengers last year. As the busiest airport in the world, Atlanta's Hartsfield Airport handled 89 million passengers last year.

20. **Tourists.** Last year, France ranked as the number one tourist destination with 78 million international arrivals. The United States ranked second with 58 million international arrivals.

Surveys. Some important analyses of survey results require that you know the actual number of subjects whose responses fall into a particular category. In Exercises 21–24, find the actual number of respondents corresponding to the given percentage.

21. **Personal Calls.** In an At-A-Glance survey of 1,385 office workers, 4.8% said that they do not make personal phone calls.

22. **Interview Mistakes.** In an Accountemps survey of 150 executives, 47% said that the most common interview mistake is to have little or no knowledge of the company.

23. **Televisions.** In a Frank N. Magid Associates survey of 1,005 adults, 83% reported having more than one television at home.

24. **Cell Phones.** In a Harris Interactive survey of 9,132 adults, 89% reported being cell phone users.

Of vs. *More Than.* Fill in the blanks in Exercises 25–28. Briefly explain your reasoning in each case.

25. **Weights.** If a truck weighs 40% more than a car, then the truck's weight is ____% of the car's weight.

26. **Areas.** If the area of Norway is 24% more than the area of Colorado, then Norway's area is ____% of Colorado's area.

27. **Population.** If the population of Montana is 20% less than the population of New Hampshire, then Montana's population is ____% of New Hampshire's population.

28. **Salary.** The Vice President's salary is currently 42% less than the President's salary, so the Vice President's salary is ____% of the President's salary.

29. **Margin of Error.** A Gallup poll of 1,012 adults showed that 89% of Americans say that human cloning should not be allowed. The margin of error was 3 percentage points. Would it matter if a newspaper reported the margin of error as "3%"? Explain.

30. **Margin of Error.** A Pew Research Center survey of 3,002 adults showed that the percentage who listen to National Public Radio is probably between 14% and 18%. How should a newspaper report the margin of error? Explain.

Percentages of Percentages. Exercises 31–34 describe changes in which the measurements themselves are percentages. Express each change in two ways: (1) as an absolute difference in terms of percentage points and (2) as a relative difference in terms of percent.

31. The percentage of high school seniors using alcohol decreased from 68.2% in 1975 to 52.7% now.

32. The percentage of the world's population living in developed countries decreased from 27.1% in 1970 to 19.5% now.

33. The five-year survival rate for Caucasians for all forms of cancer increased from 39% in the 1960s to 61% now.

34. The five-year survival rate for Blacks for all forms of cancer increased from 27% in the 1960s to 48% now.

PROJECTS FOR THE INTERNET & BEYOND

35. **World Population.** Find the current estimate of world population on the U.S. Census Bureau's world population clock. Describe the percentage change in population since the 6 billion mark was passed during 1999. Also find how the population clock estimates are made, and discuss the uncertainties in estimating world population.

36. **Drug Use Statistics.** Go to the Web site for the National Center on Addiction and Substance Abuse (CASA) and find a recent report giving statistics on substance abuse. Write a summary of the new research, giving at least some of the conclusions in terms of percentages.

IN THE NEWS

37. Percentages. Find three recent news reports in which percentages are used to describe statistical results. In each case, describe the meaning of the percentage.

38. Percentage Change. Find a recent news report in which percentages are used to express the change in a statistical result from one time to another (such as an increase in population or in the number of children who smoke). Describe the meaning of the change. Be sure to watch for key words such as *of* or *more than*.

39. Quote Interpretation. Consider this quote: "The rate [of smoking] among 10th graders jumped 45 percent, to 18.3 percent, and the rate for 8th graders is up 44 percent, to 10.4 percent." Briefly explain the meaning of each of the percentages in this statement.

USING TECHNOLOGY
INFLATION CALCULATOR

The U.S. Bureau of Labor Statistics (BLS) provides an online inflation calculator that allows you to adjust prices for any pair of years (based on the CPI). Search for "inflation calculator" on the BLS Web site.

CPI Inflation Calculator

$ 100.00

in 1965

Has the same buying power as:

$716.58

in 2011

Calculate

CHAPTER POSTTEST

FOR EXTRA HELP

CHAPTER Test Prep VIDEOS

The Chapter Test Prep Videos with test solutions are available on DVD, in MyMathLab, and on YouTube™ (search "AkstIntroductory Alg" and click on "Channels").

To see if you have mastered the topics in this chapter, take this test.

1. Calculate: $8^2 \cdot 2^3$

2. Find the value of $11 \cdot 2 + 5 \cdot 3$.

3. What are the factors of 20?

4. Write $3\frac{1}{4}$ as an improper fraction.

5. Reduce $\frac{10}{36}$ to lowest terms.

6. Find the sum: $\frac{5}{8} + \frac{7}{8}$

7. Add: $7\frac{7}{8} + 4\frac{1}{6}$

8. Calculate: $\frac{4}{9} - \frac{3}{10}$

9. Subtract: $12\frac{1}{4} - 8\frac{3}{10}$

10. Find the product of $\frac{3}{4}$ and $\frac{4}{5}$.

11. Find the quotient: $\frac{2}{3} \div \frac{1}{3}$

12. Calculate: $7 \div 3\frac{1}{5}$

13. Write 2.396 in words.

14. Find the sum: $5.2 + 3 + 8.002$

15. Find the difference: $10 - 3.01$

16. What is the product of 5.02 and 8.9?

17. Evaluate: 2.07×1000

18. Compute: $\frac{0.05}{100}$

19. Express $\dfrac{1}{8}$ as a decimal and as a percent.

20. Write 0.7 as a percent and as a fraction.

21. A trip to a nearby island takes 3 hours by boat and half an hour by airplane. How many times as fast as the boat is the plane?

22. According to a recent survey, the cost of medical care is approximately 1.94 times what it was a decade ago. Round this decimal to the nearest tenth. (*Source:* kff.org)

23. Find the area (in square meters) of the room pictured, rounded to one decimal place.

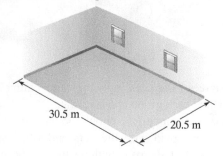

30.5 m   20.5 m

24. The following graph shows the distribution of investments for a retiree. Express as a decimal the percent of investments that are in equities.

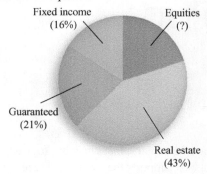

Fixed income (16%)   Equities (?)   Guaranteed (21%)   Real estate (43%)

25. Typically, the heaviest organ in the human body is the skin, weighing about 9 lb. By contrast, the heart weighs about 0.6 lb. How many times the weight of the heart is the weight of the skin? (*Sources:* faculty.washington.edu and infoplease.com)

FOCUS ON POLITICS

Who Benefited Most from Lower Tax Rates?

Politicians have a remarkable capacity to cast numbers in whatever light best supports their beliefs. There are many ways in which numbers can be made to support a particular position, but one of the most common occurs through selective use of relative (percentages) and absolute numbers.

Consider the two charts shown in Figure 2.1. Both purport to show effects of the tax rate cuts originally enacted under President Bush in 2001 and renewed under President Obama in 2010. (Under the 2001 law, the tax cuts would have expired at the end of 2010. The 2010 law extended them through 2012.) The chart in Figure 2.1a, created by supporters of the tax cuts, indicates that the rich ended up paying more under the tax cuts than they would have otherwise. Figure 2.1b, created by opponents of the tax cuts, shows that the rich received far more benefit from the tax cuts than lower-income taxpayers. The two charts therefore seem contradictory, because the first seems to indicate that the rich paid more while the second seems to indicate that they paid less.

Which story is right? In fact, both of the graphs are accurate and show data from reputable sources. (The Department of the Treasury, cited as the source of the data for Figure 2.1a, is an agency of the federal government; the Joint Committee on Taxation, cited in Figure 2.1b, is a nonpartisan committee of the U.S. Congress.) The seemingly opposing claims arise from the way in which each group chose its data.

The tax cut supporters show the *percentage of total taxes* that the rich paid with the cuts and what calculations suggest they would have paid without them. The title stating that the "rich pay more" therefore means that the tax cuts led them to pay a higher percentage of total taxes. However, if total tax revenue also was lower than it would have been without the cuts (as it was), a higher percentage of total taxes could still mean lower absolute dollars. It is these lower absolute dollars that are shown by the opponents of the tax cut.

Politicians and government officials usually abuse numbers and logic in the most elementary ways. They simply cook figures to suit their purpose, use obscure measures of economic performance, and indulge in horrendous examples of chart abuse, all in the name of disguising unpalatable truths.

—A. K. Dewdney, *200% of Nothing*

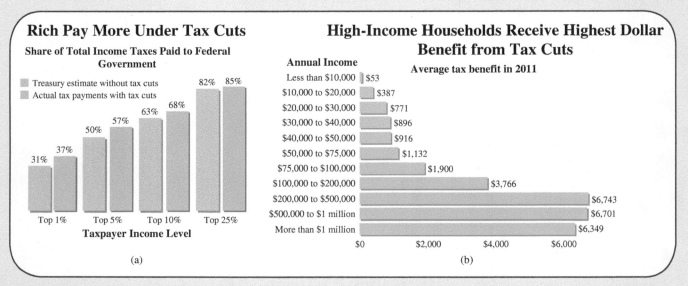

Figure 2.1 Both charts purport to show effects on higher-income households of tax cuts enacted in 2001 and renewed in 2010, but they are designed to support opposing conclusions. (a) Adapted from a graph published in *The American—The Journal of the American Enterprise Institute*. (b) Adapted from a graph published by the Center on Budget and Policy Priorities (cbpp.org).

Which side was being more fair? Neither, really. The supporters have deliberately focused on a percentage in order to mask the absolute change, which would be less favorable to their position. The opponents focused on the absolute change, but neglected to mention the fact that the wealthy pay most of the taxes. Unfortunately, this type of "selective truth" is very common when it comes to numbers, especially those tied up in politics.

QUESTIONS FOR DISCUSSION

1. Discuss the chart in Figure 2.1a. Why does it only show taxpayer income levels from the top 1% to the top 25%? What does it tell us about the relative tax burden on each group shown? Do you think its claim that the "rich pay more" is an honest depiction or a distortion of the facts? Defend your opinion.

2. Discuss the chart in Figure 2.1b. Why does it show actual incomes rather than incomes as a percentage of all taxpayers? What does it tell us about the effects of the tax cuts on each income level? Do you think it supports the claim in its title? Defend your opinion.

3. Do you think that either of the charts in Figure 2.1 accurately portrays the overall "fairness" of the tax cuts? If so, which one and why? If not, how do you think the data could have been portrayed more fairly?

5. Do a Web search on "benefit of tax cuts" and find an article arguing for or against a particular tax cut proposal or policy. Briefly summarize the article and discuss whether you think the article made its case well.

6. Have any tax law changes been proposed by the U.S. Congress or the President this year? Discuss the fairness of current proposals.

• • • • • • • • • • • • • • • • • •

FOCUS ON

ECONOMICS

Can a Redefined CPI Help Solve the Budget Crisis?

We're all aware that the U.S. government has a sky-high debt of more than $15 trillion, which amounts to approximately $50,000 for every man, woman, and child in the nation. The only way to pay off the debt is through some combination of increased government revenues or decreased government spending. Unfortunately, a quick look at the news will show that neither option is politically popular, because some people are adamantly opposed to tax increases while others are adamantly opposed to cuts in government benefits. But what if part of the problem exists only because of a misunderstanding and misapplication of the Consumer Price Index (CPI)?

Benefits are popular. Paying for benefits is extremely unpopular.

—John Danforth, former U.S. Senator
(Republican–Missouri)

This question arises because most economists believe that the CPI overstates the true effects of inflation. The thrust of the economic argument is that the standard calculation of the CPI contains at least two systematic errors that overstate how inflation affects the cost of living. First, from one month to the next, the CPI is based on changes in the prices of particular items at particular stores. In reality, however, if the price of an item rises at one store, consumers often buy it more cheaply at another store, and if the price rises at all stores, consumers may substitute a similar but lower-priced item (such as a different brand of the same product). This "price substitution" effect means that consumers don't find their actual costs rising as much as the CPI indicates. Second, the CPI tracks changes in the price of "typical" items purchased by consumers at any given time, but it does not account for the effects of changes or improvements in these items with time. For example, the data used in computing the CPI may show that a typical cell phone is 10% more expensive than a cell phone from a few years ago, but these data do not account for the fact that today's cell phones have many more capabilities. The data therefore overstate the effect of the cell phone price rise, because you are getting so much more for your money today.

The accuracy of the CPI as a measure of the increase in the cost of living may seem like an academic debate, but it has real consequences for the government budget. The reason is that many budget items are tied to inflation, including one that is particularly important to government revenue and another that is particularly important to government spending. On the revenue side, the government raises the income thresholds for different tax rates each year, with the goal of making sure that people's tax rates go up only if they actually increase their standard of living, as opposed to going up just because inflation has made living more costly. For decades, the increases in the thresholds have been tied to the CPI. But if the CPI overstates the effects of inflation on living standards, then instead of holding rates steady, the threshold changes have effectively lowered tax rates. On the spending side, the government annually increases the checks provided to recipients of Social Security and other benefits, again with the goal of making sure that the benefits reflect changes in the cost of living. (The annual increase is called a "cost of living adjustment," or COLA for short.) If the CPI is overstating the effects of inflation, then these cost of living adjustments have been larger than is really needed to maintain the same standard of living.

Clearly, the federal government's budget picture could be dramatically improved by linking changes in tax rates and cost of living adjustments to a value that more accurately reflects inflation than the current CPI. In fact, the government already computes something called a "chained CPI" that was designed specifically to address this problem. Figure 2.2 shows how both revenue and spending would be different if the government tied changes to the chained CPI rather than the standard CPI. If you add all the revenue increases and spending savings that are shown in the chart, you'll find that this simple change would reduce the government's deficit by more than $200 billion over the next decade. The savings would be even greater in the following decade, because each year's savings builds on the previous year's.

QUESTIONS FOR DISCUSSION

1. Find examples in your own spending or the spending of friends and family of substitution effects and the purchase of products that were unavailable or lower quality

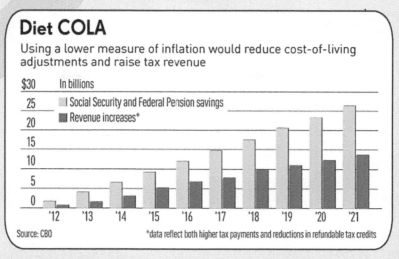

Diet COLA

Using a lower measure of inflation would reduce cost-of-living adjustments and raise tax revenue

In billions

- Social Security and Federal Pension savings
- Revenue increases*

Source: CBO   *data reflect both higher tax payments and reductions in refundable tax credits

Figure 2.2 Revenue increases and spending savings that would arise from trying to account for the ways in which the CPI tends to overstate inflation. Adapted from "Obama Mulls COLA Switch, Debt Talks Will Continue," by Jed Graham, from *Investor's Business Daily*, July 7, 2011. Copyright © 2011 by *Investor's Business Daily*. Reprinted with permission.

a few years ago. Overall, do you think these examples support the claim that the CPI overstates the effects of inflation? Defend your opinion.

2. Because adjusting the CPI would lead to a slower rise in the income thresholds for various tax rates, conservatives often claim that this change would mean "tax increases." Similarly, because the change would reduce the annual increases in cost of living adjustments, liberals often claim that it would mean a "benefit cut" to Social Security recipients. Do you think either claim is accurate? Defend your opinion.

3. As this text goes to press, the government is considering making a change to the chained CPI. Has it happened yet? Investigate the current status of the debate over whether the CPI should be adjusted for the purposes of setting tax rates and cost of living adjustments.

4. In Figure 2.2, notice that the revenue increases and spending savings get larger each year. Discuss why this occurs, focusing on how a change in the CPI compounds over time, much like compound interest in a bank account.

5. While most economists believe that the CPI overstates the effects of inflation, a few believe hat it actually understates the effects, especially on lower-income people. Research why some economists come to this conclusion, then draw your own conclusion: Does the CPI sometimes understate the effects of inflation?

Visual Displays of Data

Whether you look at a newspaper, a corporate annual report, or a government study, you are almost sure to see tables and graphs of statistical data. Some of these tables and graphs are very simple; others can be quite complex. Some make it easy to understand the data; others may be confusing or misleading. In this chapter, we'll study some of the many ways in which statistical data are commonly displayed in tables and graphs. Because the ability to convey concepts through graphs is so valuable in today's data-driven society, the skills developed in this chapter are crucial for success in nearly every profession.

The greatest value of a picture is when it forces us to notice what we never expected to see.

—John Tukey

LEARNING GOALS

3.1 Frequency Tables

Be able to create and interpret frequency tables.

3.2 Two-Way Tables

Interpret and carry out hypothesis tests for independence of variables with data organized in two-way tables.

3.3 Picturing Distributions of Data

Be able to create and interpret basic bar graphs, dotplots, pie charts, histograms, stemplots, line charts, and time-series graphs.

3.4 Graphics in the Media

Understand how to interpret the many types of more complex graphics that are commonly found in news media.

3.5 A Few Cautions About Graphics

Critically evaluate graphics and identify common ways in which graphics can be misleading.

FOCUS TOPICS

3.1 FREQUENCY TABLES

TABLE 3.1	Frequency Table for a Set of Essay Grades
Grade	Frequency
A	4
B	7
C	9
D	3
F	2
Total	25

A teacher records the following list of the grades she gave to her 25 students on a set of essays:

A C C B C D C C F D C C C
B B A B D B A A B F C B

This list contains all of the grades, but it isn't easy to read. A better way to display these data is with a **frequency table** (Table 3.1)—a table showing the number of times, or **frequency**, that each grade appears. The five possible grades (A, B, C, D, F) are called the **categories** (or classes) for the table.

> **Definitions**
>
> A basic **frequency table** has two columns:
>
> • The first column lists all the **categories** of data.
>
> • The second column lists the **frequency** of each category, which is the number of data values in the category.

EXAMPLE 1 Taste Test

The Rocky Mountain Beverage Company wants feedback on its new product, Coral Cola, and sets up a taste test with 20 people. Each individual is asked to rate the taste of the cola on a 5-point scale:

(bad taste) 1 2 3 4 5 (excellent taste)

The 20 ratings are as follows:

1 3 3 2 3 3 4 3 2 4
2 3 5 3 4 5 3 4 3 1

Construct a frequency table for these data.

TABLE 3.2	Taste Test Ratings
Taste scale	Frequency
1	2
2	3
3	9
4	4
5	2
Total	20

SOLUTION The variable of interest is *taste*, and this variable can take on five values: the taste categories 1 through 5. (Note that the data are qualitative and at the ordinal level of measurement.) We construct a table with these five categories in the left column and their frequencies in the right column, as shown in Table 3.2.

Relative and Cumulative Frequency

Look again at the essay grades listed in Table 3.1. In some cases, we might be more interested in the fraction (or percentage) of students, rather than the actual number of students, who received each grade. Such a fraction is called a **relative frequency**. For example, because 4 of the 25 students received A grades, the relative frequency of A grades is 4/25, or 0.16, or 16%.

In other cases, we might want to know the answer to questions like How many students got a grade of C or better? The answer to this question is the sum of the frequencies of A, B, and C grades, which we call the **cumulative frequency**. Table 3.3 repeats the data from Table 3.1, but this time with added columns showing the calculations for the relative and cumulative frequencies.

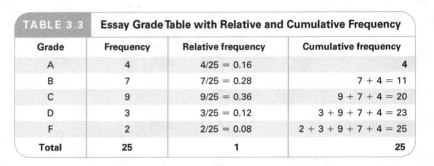

TABLE 3.3	Essay Grade Table with Relative and Cumulative Frequency		
Grade	Frequency	Relative frequency	Cumulative frequency
A	4	4/25 = 0.16	4
B	7	7/25 = 0.28	7 + 4 = 11
C	9	9/25 = 0.36	9 + 7 + 4 = 20
D	3	3/25 = 0.12	3 + 9 + 7 + 4 = 23
F	2	2/25 = 0.08	2 + 3 + 9 + 7 + 4 = 25
Total	25	1	25

Note that the sum of the relative frequencies must equal 1 (or 100%), because each individual relative frequency is a fraction of the total frequency. (Rounding sometimes causes the total to be slightly different from 1.) The cumulative frequency for the last category must always equal the total number of data values, because it represents the total number of data values in that category *and* all the preceding categories.

Definitions

The **relative frequency** of any category is the fraction (or percentage) of the data values that fall in that category:

$$\text{relative frequency} = \frac{\text{frequency in category}}{\text{total frequency}}$$

The **cumulative frequency** of any category is the number of data values in that category *and all preceding* categories.

Keep in mind that cumulative frequencies make sense only for data categories that have a clear order. That is, we can use cumulative frequencies for data at the ordinal, interval, and ratio levels of measurement, but not for data at the nominal level of measurement.

EXAMPLE 2   Taste Test: Relative and Cumulative Frequency

Using the taste test data from Example 1, create a frequency table with columns for the relative and cumulative frequencies. What percentage of the respondents gave the cola the highest rating? What percentage gave the cola one of the three lowest ratings?

SOLUTION   We find the relative frequencies by dividing the frequency in each category by the total frequency of 20. We find the cumulative frequencies by adding the frequency in each category to the sum of the frequencies in all preceding categories. Table 3.4 shows the results. The relative frequency column shows that 0.10, or 10%, of the respondents gave the cola the highest rating. The cumulative frequency column shows that 14 out of 20 people, or 70%, gave the cola a rating of 3 or lower.

> **TECHNICAL NOTE**
>
> A cumulative frequency divided by the total frequency, such as the 70% of respondents in the taste test giving a rating of 3 or higher, is called a *relative cumulative frequency*.

TABLE 3.4	Relative and Cumulative Frequencies		
Taste scale	**Frequency**	**Relative frequency**	**Cumulative frequency**
1	2	2/20 = 0.10	2
2	3	3/20 = 0.15	3 + 2 = 5
3	9	9/20 = 0.45	9 + 3 + 2 = 14
4	4	4/20 = 0.20	4 + 9 + 3 + 2 = 18
5	2	2/20 = 0.10	2 + 4 + 9 + 3 + 2 = 20
Total	20	1	20

Binning Data

When we deal with quantitative data categories, it's often useful to group, or **bin**, the data into categories that cover a range of possible values. For example, in a table of income levels, it might be useful to create bins of $0 to $20,000, $20,001 to $40,000, and so on. In this case, the frequency of each bin is simply the number of people with incomes in that bin.

USING TECHNOLOGY—FREQUENCY TABLES

Excel Excel is easy to use for statistical tables and calculations. The following steps work with the essay grade data from Table 3.1. The screenshot on the left shows the Excel table with the formulas, and the one on the right shows the results of the formulas.

1. Create columns for the grade and frequency data, which you must type in manually (columns B and C below). At the bottom of column C, use the SUM function to compute the total frequency, which is entered in cell C8.

2. Compute the relative frequency (Column D) by dividing each frequency in Column C by the total frequency from cell C8. You can enter the formula for the first row (= C3/$C$8) and then use the "fill down" editing option to put the correct formulas in the remaining rows. Note: When using the "fill down" option, you must include the dollar signs in front of C and 8 to make the reference to cell C8 an "absolute cell reference." Without these dollar signs, the "fill down" option would make the cell reference shift down (becoming C9, C10, etc.) in each row, which would be incorrect in this case.

3. Cumulative frequency (Column E) is the total of all the frequencies up to a given category. The first row shows "= C3" because cell C3 contains the frequency for A grades. The next row (= E3 + C4) starts with the value in the prior row (cell E3) and add the frequency for B grades (cell C4). The pattern continues for the remaining rows, which you can fill with the "fill down" option.

	A	B	C	D	E
1					
2		Grade	Frequency	Relative Frequency	Cumulative Frequency
3		A	4	=C3/$C$8	=C3
4		B	7	=C4/$C$8	=E3+C4
5		C	9	=C5/$C$8	=E4+C5
6		D	3	=C6/$C$8	=E5+C6
7		F	2	=C7/$C$8	=E6+C7
8		Total	=SUM(C3:C7)	=SUM(D3:D7)	=C8

	A	B	C	D	E
1					
2		Grade	Frequency	Relative Frequency	Cumulative Frequency
3		A	4	16%	4
4		B	7	28%	11
5		C	9	36%	20
6		D	3	12%	23
7		F	2	8%	25
8		Total	25	100%	25

EXAMPLE 3 Binned Exam Scores

Consider the following set of 20 scores from a 100-point exam:

76 80 78 76 94 75 98 77 84 88 81 72 91 72 74 86 79 88 72 75

Determine appropriate bins and make a frequency table. Include columns for relative and cumulative frequency, and interpret the cumulative frequency for this case.

SOLUTION   The scores range from 72 to 98. One way to group the data is with 5-point bins. The first bin represents scores from 95 to 99, the second bin represents scores from 90 to 94, and so on. Note that there is no overlap between bins. We then count the frequency (the number of scores) in each bin. For example, only 1 score is in bin 95 to 99 (the high score of 98) and 2 scores are in bin 90 to 94 (the scores of 91 and 94). Table 3.5 shows the complete frequency table. In this case, we interpret the cumulative frequency of any bin to be the total number of scores in *or above* that bin. For example, the cumulative frequency of 6 for the bin 85 to 89 means that there were 6 scores of 85 or higher.

"Data! Data! Data!" he cried impatiently. "I can't make bricks without clay."

— Sherlock Holmes in Sir Arthur Conan Doyle's *The Adventure of the Copper Beeches*

TABLE 3.5	Frequency Table for Binned Exam Scores		
Scores	**Frequency**	**Relative frequency**	**Cumulative frequency**
95 to 99	1	1/20 = 0.05	1
90 to 94	2	2/20 = 0.10	2 + 1 = 3
85 to 89	3	3/20 = 0.15	3 + 2 + 1 = 6
80 to 84	3	3/20 = 0.15	3 + 3 + 2 + 1 = 9
75 to 79	7	7/20 = 0.35	7 + 3 + 3 + 2 + 1 = 16
70 to 74	4	4/20 = 0.20	4 + 7 + 3 + 3 + 2 + 1 = 20
Total	**20**	**1**	**20**

Section 3.1 Exercises

Statistical Literacy and Critical Thinking

1. **Frequency Table.** What is a frequency table? Explain what we mean by the categories (or classes) and frequencies.

2. **Relative Frequency.** A frequency table of grades has five classes (A, B, C, D, F) with frequencies of 4, 12, 16, 6, and 2. What are the relative frequencies of the five classes?

3. **Cumulative Frequency.** A frequency table of grades has five classes with frequencies of 4, 12, 16, 6, and 2. What are the corresponding cumulative frequencies of the five classes?

4. **Frequency Table.** The first class in a frequency table of incomes shows a frequency of 24 corresponding to the range of values from $0 to $999. Using only this information about the frequency table, is it possible to identify the original 24 sample values that are summarized by this class? Explain.

Does It Make Sense? For Exercises 5–8, decide whether the statement makes sense (or is clearly true) or does not make sense (or is clearly false). Explain clearly. Not all of these statements have definitive answers, so your explanation is more important than your chosen answer.

5. **Frequency Table.** A friend tells you that her frequency table has two columns labeled *State* and *Median Income*.

6. **Relative Frequency.** The relative frequency of category A in a table is 0.27 or 27%.

7. **Cumulative Frequency.** The cumulative frequency of a category in a table is 25.5.

8. **Bins.** For a given data set of IQ scores, if you increase the width of the bins, the number of bins decreases.

Concepts and Applications

9. **Frequency Table Practice.** Professor Diaz records the following final grades in one of her courses:

    A A A B B B B B B B B B C C
    C C C C C C C C D D F F F F

    Construct a frequency table for these grades. Include columns for relative frequency and cumulative frequency.

10. **Frequency Table Practice.** A guidebook for San Francisco lists 2 one-star restaurants, 12 two-star restaurants, 18 three-star restaurants, 6 four-star restaurants, and 2 five-star restaurants. Make a frequency table for these ratings. Include columns for relative frequency and cumulative frequency.

11. **Weights of Coke.** Construct a frequency table for the weights (in pounds) given below of 36 cans of regular Coke. Start the first bin at 0.7900 pound and use a bin width of 0.0050 pound. Discuss your findings.

0.8192	0.8194	0.8211	0.8176
0.8062	0.8143	0.8110	0.8152
0.7901	0.8152	0.8079	0.8161
0.8161	0.8163	0.8194	0.8247
0.8165	0.8172	0.8150	0.8264
0.8207	0.8073	0.8295	0.8170
0.8150	0.8189	0.8181	0.8284
0.8128	0.8229	0.8251	0.8244
0.8244	0.8126	0.8044	0.8192

12. **Weights of Diet Coke.** Construct a frequency table for the weights (in pounds) given below of 36 cans of Diet Coke. Start the first bin at 0.7750 pound and use a bin width of 0.0050 pound. Discuss your findings.

0.7773	0.7874	0.7868	0.7802
0.7806	0.7907	0.7879	0.7833
0.7923	0.7910	0.7813	0.7859
0.7822	0.7896	0.7839	0.7861
0.7874	0.7852	0.7870	0.7826
0.7837	0.7872	0.7923	0.7760
0.7758	0.7822	0.7844	0.7892
0.7830	0.7771	0.7881	0.7822
0.7852	0.7879	0.7885	0.7811

13. **Oscar-Winning Actors.** The following data show the ages of all Academy Award–winning male actors at the time when they won their award, through 2012. Make a frequency table for the data, using bins of 20–29, 30–39, and so on. Discuss your findings.

    44 41 62 52 41 34 34 52 41 37 38 34 32 40 43
    56 41 39 49 57 41 38 42 52 51 35 30 39 41 44
    49 35 47 31 47 37 57 42 45 42 44 62 43 42 48
    49 56 38 60 30 40 42 36 76 39 53 45 36 62 43
    51 32 42 54 52 37 38 32 45 60 46 40 36 47 29
    43 37 38 45 50 48 60 50 39

14. **Body Temperatures.** The following data show the body temperatures (°F) of randomly selected subjects. Construct a frequency table with seven classes: 96.9–97.2, 97.3–97.6, 97.7–98.0, and so on.

98.6	98.6	98.0	98.0	99.0	98.4	98.4	98.4
98.4	98.6	98.6	98.8	98.6	97.0	97.0	98.8
97.6	97.7	98.8	98.0	98.0	98.3	98.5	97.3
98.7	97.4	98.9	98.6	99.5	97.5	97.3	97.6
98.2	99.6	98.7	99.4	98.2	98.0	98.6	98.6
97.2	98.4	98.6	98.2	98.0	97.8	98.0	98.4
98.6	98.6

15. Missing Information. The following table shows grades for a term paper in an English class. The table is incomplete. Use the information given to fill in the missing entries and complete the table.

Category	Frequency	Relative frequency
A	?	?
B	?	18%
C	?	24%
D	11	?
F	6	?
Total	50	?

16. Missing Information. The following table shows grades for performances in a drama class. The table is incomplete. Use the information given to fill in the missing entries and complete the table.

Category	Frequency	Cumulative frequency
A	?	1
B	6	?
C	7	?
D	?	23
F	?	25
Total	?	?

17. Loaded Die. One of the authors drilled a hole in a die, filled it with a lead weight, and then proceeded to roll it. The results are given in the following frequency table.

a. According to the data, how many times was the die rolled?

b. How many times was the outcome greater than 2?

c. What percentage of outcomes were 6?

d. List the relative frequencies that correspond to the given frequencies.

e. List the cumulative frequencies that correspond to the given frequencies.

Outcome	Frequency
1	27
2	31
3	42
4	40
5	28
6	32

18. Interpreting Family Data. Consider the following frequency table for the number of children in American families.

a. According to the data, how many families are there in America?

b. How many families have two or fewer children?

c. What percentage of American families have no children?

d. What percentage of American families have three or more children?

Number of children	Number of families (millions)
0	35.54
1	14.32
2	13.28
3	5.13
4 or more	1.97

19. Computer Keyboards. The traditional keyboard configuration is called a *Qwerty* keyboard because of the positioning of the letters QWERTY on the top row of letters. Developed in 1872, the Qwerty configuration supposedly forced people to type slower so that the early typewriters would not jam. Developed in 1936, the Dvorak keyboard supposedly provides a more efficient arrangement by positioning the most used keys on the middle row (or "home" row), where they are more accessible.

A *Discover* magazine article suggested that you can measure the ease of typing by using this point rating system: Count each letter on the home row as 0, count each letter on the top row as 1, and count each letter on the bottom row as 2. For example, the word *statistics* would result in a rating of 7 on the Qwerty keyboard and 1 on the Dvorak keyboard, as shown below.

	S	T	A	T	I	S	T	I	C	S	
Qwerty keyboard	0	1	0	1	1	0	1	1	2	0	(sum − 7)
Dvorak keyboard	0	0	0	0	0	0	0	0	1	0	(sum − 1)

Using this rating system with each of the 52 words in the Preamble to the Constitution, we get the rating values below.

Qwerty Keyboard Word Ratings:

2	2	5	1	2	6	3	3	4	2	4	0	5
7	7	5	6	6	8	10	7	2	2	10	5	8
2	5	4	2	6	2	6	1	7	2	7	2	3
8	1	5	2	5	2	14	2	2	6	3	1	7

Dvorak Keyboard Word Ratings:

2	0	3	1	0	0	0	0	2	0	4	0	3
4	0	3	3	1	3	5	4	2	0	5	1	4
0	3	5	0	2	0	4	1	5	0	4	0	1
3	0	1	0	3	0	1	2	0	0	0	1	4

a. Create a frequency table for the Qwerty word ratings data. Use bins of 0–2, 3–5, 6–8, 9–11, and 12–14 Include a column for relative frequency.

b. Create a frequency table for the Dvorak word ratings data, using the same bins as in part a. Include a column for relative frequency.

c. Based on your results from parts a and b, which keyboard arrangement is easier for typing? Explain.

20. Double Binning. The students in a statistics class conduct a transportation survey of students in their high school. Among other data, they record the age and mode of transportation between home and school for each student. The following table gives some of the data that were collected. For age: 1 = 14 years, 2 = 15 years, 3 = 16 years, 4 = 17 years, 5 = 18 years. For transportation: 1 = walk, 2 = school bus, 3 = public bus, 4 = drive, 5 = other.

Student	Age	Transportation	Student	Age	Transportation
1	1	1	11	3	5
2	5	1	12	5	5
3	2	2	13	1	2
4	3	5	14	5	5
5	4	3	15	5	5
6	1	1	16	4	4
7	5	2	17	2	2
8	2	1	18	3	1
9	3	4	19	3	3
10	1	3	20	1	4

a. Classify the two variables, *age* and *transportation*, as qualitative or quantitative, and give the level of measurement for each.

b. In order to be analyzed or displayed, the data must be binned with respect to both variables. Count the number of students in each of the 25 age/transportation categories and fill in the blank cells in the following table.

		Transportation				
		1	2	3	4	5
Age	1					
	2					
	3					
	4					
	5					

PROJECTS FOR 🌐 THE INTERNET & BEYOND

21. Energy Table. The U.S. Energy Information Administration (EIA) Web site offers dozens of tables relating to energy use, energy prices, and pollution. Explore the selection of tables. Find a table of raw data that is of interest to you and convert it to an appropriate frequency table. Briefly discuss what you can learn from the frequency table that is less obvious in the raw data table.

22. Endangered Species. The Web site for the World Conservation Monitoring Centre in Great Britain provides data on extinct, endangered, and threatened animal species. Explore these data and summarize some of your more interesting findings with frequency tables.

23. Navel Data. The *navel ratio* is defined to be a person's height divided by the height (from the floor) of his or her navel. An old theory says that, on average, the navel ratio of humans is the golden ratio: $(1+\sqrt{5})/2$. Measure the navel ratio of each person in your class. What percentage of students have a navel ratio within 5% of the golden ratio? What percentage of students have a navel ratio within 10% of the golden ratio? Does the old theory seem reliable?

24. Your Own Frequency Table (Unbinned). Collect your own frequency data for some set of categories that will *not* require binning. (For example, you might collect data by asking friends to do a taste test on some brand of cookie.) State how you collected your data, and make a list of all your raw data. Then summarize the data in a frequency table. Include a column for relative frequency, and also include a column for cumulative frequency if it is meaningful.

25. Your Own Frequency Table (Binned). Collect your own frequency data for some set of categories that *will* require binning (for example, weights of your friends or scores on a recent exam). State how you collected your data, and make a list of all your raw data. Then summarize the data in a frequency table. Include columns for relative frequency and cumulative frequency.

IN THE NEWS

26. Frequency Tables. Find a recent news article that includes some type of frequency table. Briefly describe the table and how it is useful to the news report. Do you think the table was constructed in the best possible way for the article? If so, why? If not, what would you have done differently?

27. Relative Frequencies. Find a recent news article that gives at least some data in the form of relative frequencies. Briefly describe the data, and discuss why relative frequencies were useful in this case.

28. Cumulative Frequencies. Find a recent news article that gives at least some data in the form of cumulative frequencies. Briefly describe the data, and discuss why cumulative frequencies were useful in this case.

29. Temperature Data. Look for a weather report that lists yesterday's high temperatures in many American cities. Choosing appropriate bins, make a frequency table for the high temperature data. Include columns for relative frequency and cumulative frequency. Briefly describe how and why you chose your bins.

3.2 TWO-WAY TABLES

Suppose that administrators at a college are concerned that there may be gender bias in the way degrees are awarded, so they collect data on the number of degrees awarded to men and women in different departments. These data concern two variables: *major* and *gender*. The variable *major* can take on many values, such as biology, business, mathematics, and music. The variable *gender* can take on only two values: male or female.

Displaying the Data in Two-Way Tables

Once the data have been collected, we need to find an efficient way to display them. Because we are dealing with two variables, we can display the data efficiently with a **two-way table** (also called a **contingency table**), so named because it displays two variables.

Table 3.6 shows what the two-way table might look like for data on the variables *major* and *gender*. Note that one variable (*major*) is displayed along the columns and the other (*gender*) along the rows. For this example, there are only two rows because *gender* can be only either male or female; there are many columns for the majors, with just the first few shown. Each cell shows a frequency (or count) for one combination of the two variables. For example, the cell in row *Women* and column *Biology* shows that 32 bachelor's degrees were awarded to women in biology. Similarly, the cell in row *Men* and column *Business* shows that 87 bachelor's degrees were awarded to men in business.

TABLE 3.6	Two-Way Table for the Variables *Major* and *Gender*				
variable 1 *major* →	**Biology**	**Business**	**Mathematics**	**Psychology**	...
Women	32	110	18	75	...
Men	21	87	15	70	...

variable 2 *gender*

> **Two-Way Tables**
>
> A **two-way table** shows the relationship between two variables by listing one variable in the rows and the other variable in the columns. The entries in the table's cells are called frequencies (or counts).

I cannot do it without counters.

—William Shakespeare,
The Winter's Tale

If we were looking for *any* relationship between major and gender, we would need a complete set of data for all majors, which means Table 3.6 would have dozens of columns. In addition, as we'll see shortly, carrying out the calculations for the hypothesis test requires that we find totals for all the rows and columns. Here, to simplify the calculations, let's focus on just two majors, biology and business. That is, instead of asking if there is a relationship between major and gender across all majors, we will look only at this simpler question: Does a person's gender influence whether he or she chooses to major in biology or business? Table 3.7 shows the biology and business data extracted from Table 3.6, along with row and column totals.

TABLE 3.7	Two-Way Table for Biology and Business Degrees		
	Biology	Business	Total
Women	32	110	142
Men	21	87	108
Total	53	197	250

TIME OUT TO THINK

Use Table 3.7 to answer the following questions: (a) How many business degrees were awarded to men? (b) How many business degrees were awarded in total? (c) Compare the total number of degrees awarded to men and women to the total number of degrees awarded in business and biology. Are these totals the same or different? Why?

EXAMPLE 1 A Two-Way Table for a Survey

Table 3.8 shows the results of a pre-election survey on gun control. Use the table to answer the following questions.

TABLE 3.8	Two-Way Table for Gun Control Survey (with totals)			
	Favor stricter laws	Oppose stricter laws	Undecided	Total
Democrat	456	123	43	622
Republican	332	446	21	799
Total	788	569	64	1,421

Source: Adapted from Malcolm W. Browne, "Following Benford's Law, or Looking Out for No. 1," *New York Times,* August 4, 1998.

a. Identify the two variables displayed in the table.

b. What percentage of Democrats favored stricter laws?

c. What percentage of all voters favored stricter laws?

d. What percentage of those who opposed stricter laws are Republicans?

SOLUTION   Note that the total of the row totals and the total of the column totals are equal.

a. The columns show the variable *survey response*, which can be either "favor stricter laws," "oppose stricter laws," or "undecided." The rows show the variable *party affiliation*, which in this table can be either Democrat or Republican.

b. Of the 622 Democrats polled, 456 favored stricter laws. The percentage of Democrats favoring stricter laws is $456/622 = 0.733$, or 73.3%.

c. Of the 1,421 people polled, 788 favored stricter laws. The percentage of all respondents favoring stricter laws is $788/1,421 = 0.555$, or 55.5%.

d. Of the 569 people polled who opposed stricter laws, 446 are Republicans. Since $446/569 = 0.783$, 78.3% of those opposed to stricter laws are Republicans.   ··•

Statistical Paradoxes

The government administers polygraph tests ("lie detectors") to new applicants for sensitive security jobs. The polygraph tests are reputed to be 90% accurate; that is, they catch 90% of the people who are lying and validate 90% of the people who are truthful. Most people therefore guess that only 10% of the people who fail a polygraph test have been falsely identified as lying. In fact, the actual percentage of false accusations can be *much* higher — more than 90% in some cases. How can this be?

We'll discuss the answer soon, but the moral of this story should already be clear: Even when we describe data carefully according to the principles discussed in the first three sections of this chapter, we may still be led to very surprising conclusions. Before we get to the polygraph issue, let's start with a couple of other statistical surprises.

Better in Each Case, but Worse Overall

Suppose a pharmaceutical company creates a new treatment for acne. To decide whether the new treatment is better than an older treatment, the company gives the old treatment to 90 patients and gives the new treatment to 110 patients. Some patients had mild acne and others had severe acne. Table 3.9 summarizes the results after four weeks of treatment, broken down by which treatment was given and whether the patient's acne was mild or severe. If you study the table carefully, you will notice these key facts:

- Among patients with *mild* acne:

  10 received the old treatment and 2 were cured, for a 20% cure rate.

  90 received the new treatment and 30 were cured, for a 33% cure rate.

- Among patients with *severe* acne:

  80 received the old treatment and 40 were cured, for a 50% cure rate.

  20 received the new treatment and 12 were cured, for a 60% cure rate.

TABLE 3.9	Results of Acne Treatments			
	Mild acne		Severe acne	
	Cured	Not cured	Cured	Not cured
Old treatment	2	8	40	40
New treatment	30	60	12	8

BY THE WAY

The general case in which a set of data gives different results for each of several group comparisons than it does when the groups are taken together is known as *Simpson's paradox*, so named because it was described by Edward Simpson in 1951. However, the same idea was actually described around 1900 by Scottish statistician George Yule.

Notice that the new treatment had a higher cure rate *both* for patients with mild acne (33% for the new treatment vs. 20% for the old) and for patients with severe acne (60% for the new treatment vs. 50% for the old). Is it therefore fair for the company to claim that their new treatment is better than the old treatment?

At first, this might seem to make sense. But instead of looking at the data for the mild and severe acne patients separately, let's look at the *overall* results:

- A total of 90 patients received the old treatment and 42 were cured (2 out of 10 with mild acne and 40 out of 80 with severe acne), for an overall cure rate of 42/90 = 46.7%.

- A total of 110 patients received the new treatment and 42 were cured (30 out of 90 with mild acne and 12 out of 20 with severe acne), for an overall cure rate of 42/110 = 38.2%.

Overall, the *old* treatment had the higher cure rate, despite the fact that the new treatment had a higher rate for both mild and severe acne cases.

This example illustrates that it is possible for something to appear better in each of two or more group comparisons but actually be worse overall. If you look carefully, you'll see that this occurs because of the way in which the overall results are divided into unequally sized groups (in this case, mild acne patients and severe acne patients).

EXAMPLE 2 Who Played Better?

Table 3.10 gives the shooting performance of two players in each half of a basketball game. Shaq had a higher shooting percentage in both the first half (40% to 25%) and the second half (75% to 70%). Can Shaq claim that he had the better game?

TABLE 3.10	Basketball Shots					
	First half			**Second half**		
Player	**Baskets**	**Attempts**	**Percent**	**Baskets**	**Attempts**	**Percent**
Shaq	4	10	40%	3	4	75%
Vince	1	4	25%	7	10	70%

SOLUTION No, and we can see why by looking at the overall game statistics. Shaq made a total of 7 baskets (4 in the first half and 3 in the second half) on 14 shots (10 in the first half and 4 in the second half), for an overall shooting percentage of 7/14 = 50%. Vince made a total of 8 baskets on 14 shots, for an overall shooting percentage of 8/14 = 57.1% Surprisingly, even though Shaq had a higher shooting percentage in both halves, Vince had a better overall shooting percentage for the game.
⋯•

Does a Positive Mammogram Mean Cancer?

We often associate tumors with cancers, but most tumors are not cancers. Medically, any kind of abnormal swelling or tissue growth is considered a tumor. A tumor caused by cancer is said to be *malignant* (or *cancerous*); all others are said to be *benign*.

Imagine you are a doctor or nurse treating a patient who has a breast tumor. The patient will be understandably nervous, but you can give her some comfort by telling her that only about 1 in 100 breast tumors turns out to be malignant. But, just to be safe, you order a mammogram to determine whether her tumor is one of the 1% that are malignant.

Now, suppose the mammogram comes back positive, suggesting that the tumor is malignant. Mammograms are not perfect, so the positive result does not necessarily mean that your patient has breast cancer. More specifically, let's assume that the mammogram screening is 85% accurate: It will correctly identify 85% of malignant tumors as malignant and 85% of benign tumors as benign. When you tell your patient that her mammogram was positive, what should you tell her about the chance that she actually has cancer?

Because the mammogram screening is 85% accurate, most people guess that the positive result means that the patient probably has cancer. Studies have shown that most doctors also believe this to be the case and would tell the patient to be prepared for cancer treatment. But a more careful analysis shows otherwise. In fact, the chance that the patient has cancer is still quite small—about 5%. We can see why by analyzing some numbers.

Consider a study in which mammograms are given to 10,000 women with breast tumors. Assuming that 1% of tumors are malignant, 1% × 10,000 = 100 of the women actually have cancer; the remaining 9,900 women have benign tumors. Table 3.11 summarizes the mammogram results. Notice the following:

- The mammogram screening correctly identifies 85% of the 100 malignant tumors as malignant. Thus, it gives positive (malignant) results for 85 of the malignant tumors; these cases are called **true positives**. In the other 15 malignant cases, the result is negative, even though the women actually have cancer; these cases are **false negatives**.

BY THE WAY

This mammogram example and the polygraph example that follows it illustrate cases in which conditional probabilities (discussed in Section 6.4) lead to confusion. The proper way of handling conditional probabilities was discovered by the Reverend Thomas Bayes (1702–1761) and is often called *Bayes rule*.

TABLE 3.11	Summary of Results for 10,000 Mammograms (when in fact 100 tumors are malignant and 9,900 are benign)		
	Tumor is malignant	**Tumor is benign**	**Total**
Positive mammogram	85 true positives	1,485 false positives	1,570
Negative mammogram	15 false negatives	8,415 true negatives	8,430
Total	100	9,900	10,000

- The mammogram screening correctly identifies 85% of the 9,900 benign tumors as benign. Thus, it gives negative (benign) results for 85% × 9,900 = 8,415 of the benign tumors; these cases are **true negatives**. The remaining 9,900 − 8,485 = 1,485 women get positive results in which the mammogram incorrectly identifies their tumors as malignant; these cases are **false positives**.

Overall, the mammogram screening gives positive results to 85 women who actually have cancer and to 1,485 women who do *not* have cancer. The total number of positive results is 85 + 1,485 = 1,570. Because only 85 of these are true positives (the rest are false positives), the chance that a positive result really means cancer is only 85/1,570 = 0.054, or 5.4%. Therefore, when your patient's mammogram comes back positive, you should reassure her that there's still only a small chance that she has cancer.

EXAMPLE 3   False Negatives

Suppose you are a doctor seeing a patient with a breast tumor. Her mammogram comes back negative. Based on the numbers in Table 3.11, what is the chance that she has cancer?

SOLUTION   For the 10,000 cases summarized in Table 3.11, the mammograms are negative for 15 women with cancer and for 8,415 women with benign tumors. The total number of negative results is 15 + 8,415 = 8,430. Thus, the fraction of women with cancer who have false negatives is 15/8,430 = 0.0018, or slightly less than 2 in 1,000. In other words, the chance that a woman with a negative mammogram has cancer is only about 2 in 1,000.   ··•

TIME ◔UT TO THINK

While the chance of cancer with a negative mammogram is small, it is not zero. Therefore, it might seem like a good idea to biopsy all tumors, just to be sure. However, biopsies involve surgery, which means they can be painful and expensive, among other things. Given these facts, do you think that biopsies should be routine for all tumors? Should they be routine for cases of positive mammograms? Defend your opinion.

Polygraphs and Drug Tests

We're now ready to return to the question asked at the beginning of this section, about how a 90% accurate polygraph test can lead to a surprising number of false accusations. The explanation is very similar to that used in the case of the mammograms.

Suppose the government gives the polygraph test to 1,000 applicants for sensitive security jobs. Further suppose that 990 of these 1,000 people tell the truth on their polygraph test, while only 10 people lie. For a test that is 90% accurate, we find the following results:

- Of the 10 people who lie, the polygraph correctly identifies 90%, meaning that 9 fail the test (they are identified as liars) and 1 passes.
- Of the 990 people who tell the truth, the polygraph correctly identifies 90%, meaning that 90% × 990 = 891 truthful people pass the test and the other 10% × 990 = 99 truthful people fail the test.

Figure 3.1 summarizes these results. The total number of people who fail the test is 9 + 99 = 108. Of these, only 9 were actually liars; the other 99 were falsely accused of lying. That is, 99 out of 108, or 99/108 = 91.7%, of the people who fail the test were actually telling the truth.

The percentage of people who are falsely accused in any real situation depends on both the accuracy of the test and the proportion of people who are lying. Nevertheless, for the numbers given here, we have an astounding result: Assuming the government rejects applicants who fail the polygraph test, then almost 92% of the rejected applicants were actually being truthful and may have been highly qualified for the jobs.

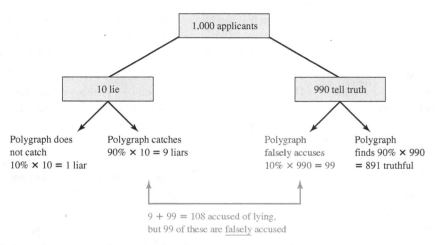

Figure 3.1 A tree diagram summarizes results of a 90% accurate polygraph test for 1,000 people, of whom only 10 are lying.

BY THE WAY

A polygraph, often called a "lie detector," measures a variety of bodily functions including heart rate, skin temperature, and blood pressure. Polygraph operators look for subtle changes in these functions that typically occur when people lie. However, polygraph results have never been allowed as evidence in criminal proceedings. First of all, 90% accuracy is far too low for justice. In addition, studies show that polygraphs are easily fooled by people who train to beat them.

TIME (O)UT TO THINK

Imagine that you are falsely accused of a crime. The police suggest that, if you are truly innocent, you should agree to take a polygraph test. Would you do it? Why or why not?

EXAMPLE 4 High School Drug Testing

All athletes participating in a regional high school track and field championship must provide a urine sample for a drug test. Those who fail are eliminated from the meet and suspended from competition for the following year. Studies show that, at the laboratory selected, the drug tests are 95% accurate. Assume that 4% of the athletes actually use drugs. What fraction of the athletes who fail the test are falsely accused and therefore suspended without cause?

SOLUTION   The easiest way to answer this question is by using some sample numbers. Suppose there are 1,000 athletes in the meet. Then 4%, or 40 athletes, actually use drugs; the remaining 960 athletes do not use drugs. In that case, the 95% accurate drug test should return the following results:

- 95% of the 40 athletes who use drugs, or $0.95 \times 40 = 38$ athletes, fail the test. The other 2 athletes who use drugs pass the test.
- 95% of the 960 athletes who do not use drugs pass the test, but 5% of these 960, or $0.05 \times 960 = 48$ athletes, fail.

The total number of athletes who fail the test is $38 + 48 = 86$. But 48 of these athletes who fail the test, or $48/86 = 56\%$, are actually nonusers. Despite the 95% accuracy of the drug test, more than half of the suspended students are innocent of drug use.   ·· ●

Section 3.2 Exercises

Statistical Literacy and Critical Thinking

1. **False Positive and False Negative.** A baseball player is given a test for banned substances. For this test, what is a false positive? What is a false negative? What is a true positive? What is a true negative?

2. **Positive Test Result.** Jennifer is given a pregnancy test. What does it mean when she is told that the result is positive?

3. **Test Result.** If you apply a test for the presence of alcohol, what is the result called if the test correctly indicates that the subject has not consumed alcohol?

4. **Better in Each Half, Worse Overall.** When the Giants and Patriots football teams play each other, can one of the quarterbacks have a

higher passing percentage in each half while having a lower passing percentage for the entire game?

Does It Make Sense? For Exercises 5–8, decide whether the statement makes sense (or is clearly true) or does not make sense (or is clearly false). Explain clearly; not all of these statements have definitive answers, so your explanation is more important than your chosen answer.

5. **Course Average.** Ann and Bret are taking the same statistics course, in which the final grade is determined by assignments and exams. Ann's mean score on the assignments is higher than Bret's, and Ann's mean score on the exams is higher than Bret's. It follows that Ann's overall mean score in the course is higher than Bret's.

6. **Batting Average.** Ann's batting average for the first half of the softball season is higher than Bret's, and Ann's batting average for the second half of the season is higher than Bret's. It follows that Ann's batting average for the entire season is higher than Bret's.

7. **Test Results.** After taking a test for the presence of a disease, a patient is happy because the physician announces that the test results are positive.

8. **Test Accuracy.** If a drug test is 90% accurate, it follows that 90% of those who test positive are actual drug users.

Concepts and Applications

9. **Batting Percentages.** The table below shows the batting records of two baseball players in the first half (first 81 games) and last half of a season.

Player	First half		
	Hits	At-bats	Batting average
Josh	50	150	0.333
Jude	10	50	0.200
	Second half		
Player	Hits	At-bats	Batting average
Josh	35	70	0.500
Jude	70	150	0.467

Who had the higher batting average in the first half of the season? Who had the higher batting average in the second half? Who had the higher overall batting average? Explain how these results illustrate Simpson's paradox.

10. **Passing Percentages.** The table below shows the passing records of two rival quarterbacks in the first half and second half of a football game.

Player	First half		
	Completions	Attempts	Percent
Allan	8	20	40%
Abner	2	6	33%
	Second half		
Player	Completions	Attempts	Percent
Allan	3	6	50%
Abner	12	25	48%

Who had the higher completion percentage in the first half? Who had the higher completion percentage in the second half? Who had the higher overall completion percentage? Explain how these results illustrate Simpson's paradox.

11. **Test Scores.** The table below shows eighth-grade mathematics test scores in Nebraska and New Jersey. The scores are separated according to the race of the student. Also shown are the state averages for all races.

	White	Nonwhite	Average for all races
Nebraska	281	250	277
New Jersey	283	252	272

Source: National Assessment of Educational Progress, from *Chance* magazine.

a. Which state had the higher scores in both racial categories? Which state had the higher overall average across both racial categories?

b. Explain how a state could score lower in both categories and still have a higher overall average.

c. Now consider the table below, which gives the percentages of whites and nonwhites in each state. Use these percentages to verify that the overall average test score in Nebraska is 277, as claimed in the first table.

	White	Nonwhite
Nebraska	87%	13%
New Jersey	66%	34%

d. Use the racial percentages to verify that the overall average test score in New Jersey is 272, as claimed in the first table.

e. Explain briefly, in your own words, how Simpson's paradox appeared in this case.

12. **Test Scores.** Consider the following table comparing the grade point averages (GPAs) and mathematics SAT scores of high school students in 1988 and 1998 (before the SAT test format was revised).

GPA	% students		SAT score		
	1988	1998	1988	1998	Change
A+	4	7	632	629	−3
A	11	15	586	582	−4
A−	13	16	556	554	−2
B	53	48	490	487	−3
C	19	14	431	428	−3
Overall average			504	514	+10

Source: Cited in *Chance*, Vol. 12, No. 2, 1999, from data in *New York Times*, September 2, 1999.

a. In general terms, how did the SAT scores of the students in the five grade categories change between 1988 and 1998?

b. How did the overall average SAT score change between 1988 and 1998?

c. How is this an example of Simpson's paradox?

13. Tuberculosis Deaths. The following table shows deaths due to tuberculosis (TB) in New York City and Richmond, Virginia, in 1910.

Race	New York	
	Population	**TB deaths**
White	4,675,000	8400
Nonwhite	92,000	500
Total	4,767,000	8900

Race	Richmond	
	Population	**TB deaths**
White	81,000	130
Nonwhite	47,000	160
Total	128,000	290

Source: Cohen and Nagel, *An Introduction to Logic and Scientific Method,* Harcourt, Brace and World, 1934.

a. Compute the death rates for whites, nonwhites, and all residents in New York City.

b. Compute the death rates for whites, nonwhites, and all residents in Richmond.

c. Explain why this is an example of Simpson's paradox and explain how the paradox arises.

14. Weight Training. Two cross-country running teams participated in a (hypothetical) study in which a fraction of each team used weight training to supplement a running workout. The remaining runners did not use weight training. At the end of the season, the mean improvement in race times (in seconds) was recorded in the table below.

	Mean improvement (seconds)		
	Weight training	**No weight training**	**Team average**
Gazelles	10	2	6.0
Cheetahs	9	1	6.2

Describe how Simpson's paradox arises in this table. Resolve the paradox by finding the percentage of each team that used weight training.

15. Basketball Records. Consider the following (hypothetical) basketball records for Spelman and Morehouse Colleges.

	Spelman College	**Morehouse College**
Home games	10 wins, 19 losses	9 wins, 19 losses
Away games	12 wins, 4 losses	56 wins, 20 losses

a. Give numerical evidence to support the claim that Spelman College has a better team than Morehouse College.

b. Give numerical evidence to support the claim that Morehouse College has a better team than Spelman College.

c. Which claim do you think makes more sense? Why?

16. Better Drug. Two drugs, A and B, were tested on a total of 2,000 patients, half of whom were women and half of whom were men. Drug A was given to 900 patients and Drug B to 1,100 patients. The results appear in the table below.

	Women	**Men**
Drug A	5 of 100 cured	400 of 800 cured
Drug B	101 of 900 cured	196 of 200 cured

a. Give numerical evidence to support the claim that Drug B is more effective than Drug A.

b. Give numerical evidence to support the claim that Drug A is more effective than Drug B.

c. Which claim do you think makes more sense? Why?

17. Polygraph Test. The results in the table below are from experiments conducted by researchers Charles R. Honts (Boise State University) and Gordon H. Barland (Department of Defense Polygraph Institute). In each case, it was known whether the subject lied, so the table indicates when the polygraph test was correct.

	Did the Subject Actually Lie?	
	No	**Yes**
Polygraph test indicated that the subject *lied*.	15	42
Polygraph test indicated that the subject did *not lie*.	32	9

a. Based on the test results, how many subjects appeared to be lying? Of these, how many were actually lying and how many were telling the truth? What percentage of those who appear to be lying were not actually lying?

b. Based on the test results, how many subjects appeared to be telling the truth? Of those, how many were actually telling the truth? What percentage of those who appeared to be telling the truth are actually truthful?

18. Disease Test. Suppose a test for a disease is 80% accurate for those who have the disease (true positives) and 80% accurate for those who do not have the disease (true negatives). Within a sample of 4,000 patients, the incidence rate of the disease matches the national average, which is 1.5%.

	Disease	**No disease**	**Total**
Test positive	48	788	836
Test negative	12	3,152	3,164
Total	60	3,940	4,000

a. Of those with the disease, what percentage test positive?

b. Of those who test positive, what percentage have the disease? Compare this result to the one in part a and explain why they are different.

c. Suppose a patient tests positive for the disease. As a doctor using this table, how would you describe the patient's chance of actually having the disease? Compare this figure to the overall incidence rate of the disease.

Further Applications

19. Hiring Statistics. (This problem is based on an example in "Ask Marilyn" column in *Parade Magazine*.) A company decided to expand, so it opened a factory, generating 455 jobs. For the 70 white-collar positions, 200 males and 200 females applied. Of the females who applied, 20% were hired, while only 15% of the males were hired. Of the 400 males applying for the blue-collar positions, 75% were hired, while 85% of the 100 females who applied were hired. How does looking at the white-collar and blue-collar positions separately suggest a hiring preference for women? Do the overall data support the idea that the company hires women preferentially? Explain why this is an example of Simpson's paradox and how the paradox can be resolved.

20. Drug Trials. (This problem is based on an example from the "Ask Marilyn" column in *Parade Magazine*.) A company runs two trials of two treatments for an illness. In the first trial, Treatment A cures 20% of the cases (40 out of 200) and Treatment B cures 15% of the cases (30 out of 200). In the second trial, Treatment A cures 85% of the cases (85 out of 100) and Treatment B cures 75% of the cases (300 out of 400). Which treatment had the better cure rate in the two trials individually? Which treatment had the better overall cure rate? Explain why this is an example of Simpson's paradox and how the paradox can be resolved.

21. HIV Risks. The New York State Department of Health estimates a 10% rate of HIV for the at-risk population and a 0.3% rate for the general population. Tests for HIV are 95% accurate in detecting both true negatives and true positives. Random selection and testing of 5,000 at-risk people and 20,000 people from the general population results in the following table.

	At-risk population	
	Test positive	**Test negative**
Infected	475	25
Not infected	225	4,275
	General population	
	Test positive	**Test negative**
Infected	57	3
Not infected	997	18,943

a. Verify that incidence rates for the general and at-risk populations are 0.3% and 10%, respectively. Also verify that detection rates for the general and at-risk populations are 95%.

b. Consider the at-risk population. Of those with HIV, what percentage test positive? Of those who test positive, what percentage have HIV? Explain why these two percentages are different.

c. Suppose a patient in the at-risk category tests positive for the disease. As a doctor using this table, how would you describe the patient's chance of actually having the disease? Compare this figure with the overall incidence rate of the disease.

d. Consider the general population. Of those with HIV, what percentage test positive? Of those who test positive, what percentage have HIV? Explain why these two percentages are different.

e. Suppose a patient in the general population tests positive for the disease. As a doctor using this table, how would you describe the patient's chance of actually having the disease? Compare this figure to the overall incidence rate of the disease.

PROJECTS FOR THE INTERNET & BEYOND

22. Polygraph Arguments. Visit Web sites devoted to either opposing or supporting the use of polygraph tests. Summarize the arguments on both sides, specifically noting the role that false negative rates play in the discussion.

23. Drug Testing. Explore the issue of drug testing either in the workplace or in athletic competitions. Discuss the legality of drug testing in these settings and the accuracy of the tests that are commonly conducted.

24. Cancer Screening. Investigate recommendations concerning routine screening for some type of cancer (for example, breast cancer, prostate cancer, or colon cancer). Explain how the accuracy of the screening test is measured. How is the test useful? How can its results be misleading?

IN THE NEWS

25. Polygraphs. Find a recent article in which someone or some group proposes a polygraph test to determine whether a person is being truthful. In light of what you know about polygraph tests, do you think the results will be meaningful? Why or why not?

26. Drug Testing and Athletes. Find a news report concerning drug testing of athletes. Summarize how the testing is being used, and discuss whether the testing is reliable.

3.3 PICTURING DISTRIBUTIONS OF DATA

A frequency table shows how a variable is distributed over chosen categories, so we say that it summarizes the **distribution** of data. We can often gain deeper insight into a distribution with a picture or graph. In this section, we'll study a few of the most common ways of visualizing data distributions.

> **Definition**
>
> The **distribution** of a variable refers to the way its values are spread over all possible values. We can summarize a distribution with a table or a graph.

Bar Graphs, Dotplots, and Pareto Charts

A **bar graph** uses a set of bars to represent the frequency (or relative frequency) of each category: the higher the frequency, the longer the bar. The bars can be either vertical or horizontal. Figure 3.2 shows a vertical bar graph based on the essay grade data in Table 3.1; there are five bars because there are five data categories (the grades A, B, C, D, F). Several key features help make the graph look good:

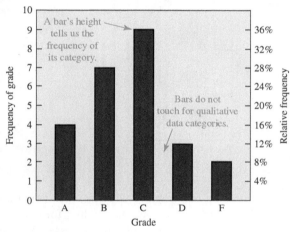

Figure 3.2 Bar graph for the essay grade data in Table 3.1.

- Because the highest frequency is 9 (for C grades), running the vertical scale from 0 to 10 allows all the bars to fit well.
- The height of each bar is proportional to its frequency. The graph is easy to read because we chose a total height of 5 centimeters, so that each centimeter of height corresponds to a frequency of 2.
- Because the data are qualitative, the bars do not need to touch. The widths of the bars have no special meaning. We therefore draw them with uniform widths.
- The graph is clearly labeled, in accord with the rules in the following summary.

> **Important Labels for Graphs**
>
> **Title/caption:** The graph should have a title or caption (or both) that explains what is being shown and, if applicable, lists the source of the data.
>
> **Vertical scale and label:** Numbers along the vertical axis should clearly indicate the scale and line up with the *tick marks*—marks along the axis that precisely locate the numerical values. Include an axis title that describes the variable that the numbers represent.
>
> **Horizontal scale and label:** The categories should be clearly indicated along the horizontal axis; tick marks are not necessary for qualitative data but should be used with quantitative data. Include an axis title that describes the variable that the categories represent.
>
> **Legend:** If multiple data sets are displayed on a single graph, include a legend or key to identify the individual data sets.

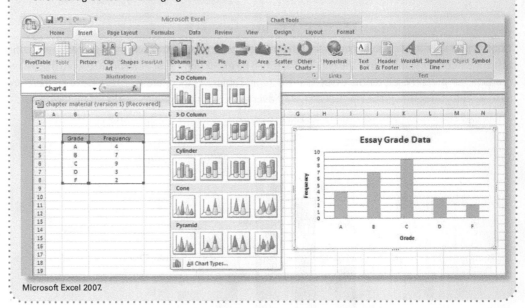

Microsoft Excel 2007.

A **dotplot** is a variation on a bar graph in which we use dots rather than bars to represent the frequencies. Each dot represents one data value; for example, a stack of 4 dots means a frequency of 4. Figure 3.3 shows a dotplot for the essay data set. Dotplots are convenient when making graphs of raw data by hand, because you can tally the data by making a dot for each data value. You may then convert the graph to a bar chart for a formal report.

Essay Grade Data

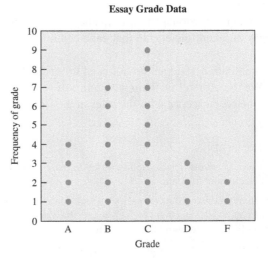

Figure 3.3   Dotplot for the essay grade data in Table 3.1.

A **Pareto chart** is a bar graph in which the bars are arranged in frequency order. This can be useful for data at the nominal level of measurement. For example, Figure 3.4 shows both a bar chart (with the cities in alphabetical order) and a Pareto chart for the populations of the five

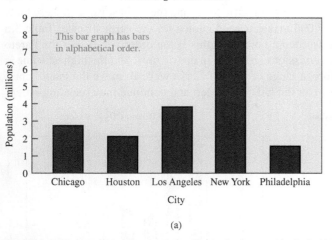
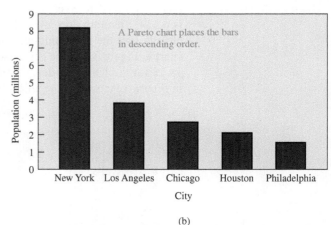

Figure 3.4 (a) Bar graph showing populations for the five largest cities in the United States (2010 census). (b) Pareto chart for the same data. *Source:* U.S. Census Bureau.

largest cities in the United States. Although the only difference is in the order of the bars, most people find the Pareto chart easier to study. Note that Pareto charts do not work for data at the ordinal level of measurement or higher; for example, it would not make sense to make a Pareto chart for the essay grade data, because the grades (A, B, C, D, F) already have a natural order.

Definitions

A **bar graph** consists of bars representing frequencies (or relative frequencies) for particular categories. The bar lengths are proportional to the frequencies.

A **dotplot** is similar to a bar graph, except each individual data value is represented with a dot.

A **Pareto chart** is a bar graph with the bars arranged in frequency order. Pareto charts make sense only for data at the nominal level of measurement.

BY THE WAY

Pareto charts were invented by Italian economist Vilfredo Pareto (1848–1923). Pareto is best known for developing methods of analyzing income distributions, but his most important contributions probably were in developing new ways of applying mathematics and statistics to economic analysis.

TIME OUT TO THINK

Would it be practical to make a dotplot for the population data in Figure 3.4? Would it make sense to make a Pareto chart for data concerning SAT scores? Explain.

EXAMPLE 1 Carbon Dioxide Emissions

Carbon dioxide (CO_2) is released into the atmosphere by the combustion of fossil fuels (oil, coal, natural gas). Table 3.12 lists the eight countries that emit the most carbon dioxide each year. Construct Pareto charts for the total emissions and for the average emissions per person. Why do the two charts appear to be so different?

TABLE 3.12	The World's Eight Leading Emitters of Carbon Dioxide	
Country/region	Total CO₂ emissions (millions of metric tons)	Per person CO₂ emissions (metric tons)
United States	5,833	19.18
China	6,534	4.91
Russia	1,729	12.29
Japan	1,495	1.31
India	1,214	9.54
Germany	829	10.06
Canada	574	17.27
United Kingdom	572	9.38

Source: U.S. Department of Energy, *Annual Energy Outlook 2011* (provides data for 2008 emissions).

SOLUTION The categories are the countries and the frequencies are the data values. The total emissions are given in units of "millions of metric tons" and the highest value in these units is 6,534; therefore, a range of 0 to 7,000 makes a good choice for the vertical scale. Table 3.6 already lists the total emissions in descending order, so this is the order we use for the Pareto chart in Figure 3.5a. The per person emissions are given in metric tons, and the highest value is 19.18 for the United States; therefore, a range of 0 to 20 works well. To make the Pareto chart in Figure 3.5b, we put the tallest bar (for the U.S.) at the left and continue in descending order.

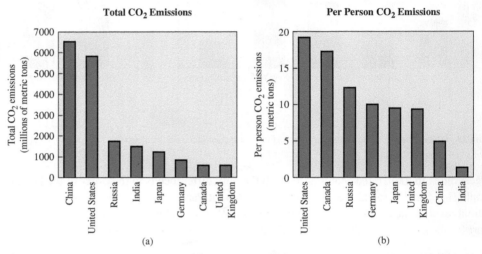

Figure 3.5 Pareto charts for (a) carbon dioxide emissions by country and (b) per person carbon dioxide emissions.

The fact that the two Pareto charts have the countries in different orders tells us that the biggest total emitters of carbon dioxide are not necessarily the biggest per person emitters. In particular, although China has the largest total emissions, the emissions per person are far higher in the United States and Canada. ··●

TIME ⏱ UT TO THINK

Most people around the world aspire to a standard of living like that in the United States. Suppose that to achieve this, the rest of the world's per person carbon dioxide emissions rose to the same level as that in the United States. What consequences might this have for the world? Defend your opinions.

Pie Charts

Pie charts are commonly used to show relative frequency distributions. The entire pie represents the total relative frequency of 100%, so the sizes of the individual slices, or wedges, represent the relative frequencies of the various categories. As a simple example, Figure 3.6 shows a pie chart for the essay grade data. Note that the size of each wedge reflects the relative frequencies that we found in Table 3.3. To make comparisons easier, the relative frequencies (as percentages) are written on the wedges.

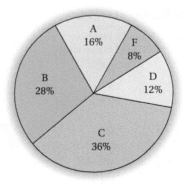

Figure 3.6 Pie chart for the essay grade data in Tables 3.1 and 3.3.

⏻ USING TECHNOLOGY—**PIE CHARTS**

Excel Making a pie chart in Excel is very similar to making a bar graph (p. 99), except:

• For a pie chart, you will probably want to select the relative frequencies rather than the frequencies (though both will work); it may be helpful to cut and paste these data so they are next to the grade letters.

• Choose a pie chart rather than a column chart from the Insert menu.

• The labeling process is different from that for bar graphs, as are the options for colors and other decorative features. The accompanying screen display shows one set of options used in Excel for Windows; you should experiment with other options to learn about the possibilities.

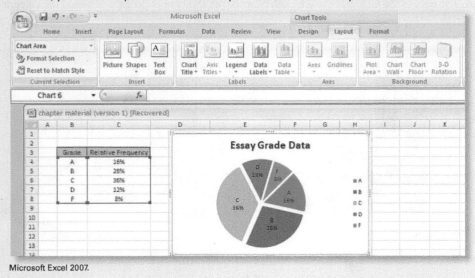

Microsoft Excel 2007.

Definition

A **pie chart** is a circle divided so that each wedge represents the *relative frequency* of a particular category. The wedge size is proportional to the relative frequency. The entire pie represents the total relative frequency of 100%.

EXAMPLE ❷ Simple Pie Chart

The registered voters of Rochester County are 25% Democrats, 25% Republicans, and 50% independents. Construct a pie chart to represent the party affiliations.

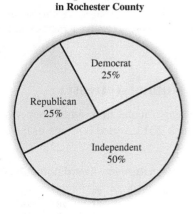

Figure 3.7 Pie chart for Example 2.

SOLUTION   Because Democrats and Republicans each represent 25% of the voters, the wedges for Republicans and Democrats each occupy 25%, or one-fourth, of the pie. Independents represent half of the voters, so their wedge occupies the remaining half of the pie. Figure 3.7 shows the result. As always, note the importance of clear labeling. ⋯●

Histograms and Line Charts

TECHNICAL NOTE

Different books define the terms *histogram* and *bar graph* differently, and there are no universally accepted definitions. In this text, a bar graph is any graph that uses bars, and histograms are the types of bar graphs used for quantitative data categories.

As we've seen, bar graphs and pie charts are used primarily for data in which the categories are qualitative, such as letter grades or countries. For quantitative data categories, the two most common types of graphics are *histograms* and *line charts*.

A **histogram** is essentially a bar graph in which the data categories are quantitative. The bars in a histogram must follow the natural order of the numerical categories. The widths of the bars must be equal, and they must have a specific meaning. For example, Figure 3.8a shows a histogram for the binned exam data of Table 3.5. Notice that the width of each bar represents 5 points on the exam. The bars in the histogram touch each other because there are no gaps between the categories.

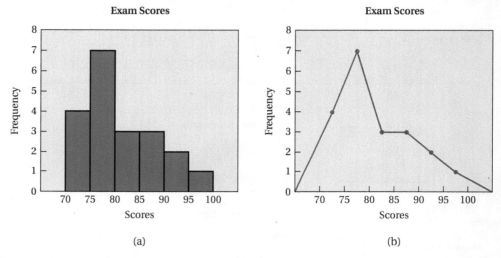

Figure 3.8   The numerical grade data from Table 3.5 shown as (a) a histogram and (b) a line chart.

TECHNICAL NOTE

A line chart created from a set of frequency data is often called a *frequency polygon* because it consists of many straight line segments that take the shape of a many-sided figure.

Figure 3.8b shows a **line chart** for the same data. To make the line chart, we use a dot (instead of a bar) to represent the frequency of each data category; that is, the dots go in the places where the tops of the bars go on the histogram. Because the data are binned into 5-point bins, we place the dot at the center of each bin. For example, the dot for the data category 70–75 goes at 72.5 along the horizontal axis. After the dots are placed, we connect them with straight lines. To make the graph look complete, we connect the points at the far left and far right back down to a frequency of zero.

> **Definitions**
>
> A **histogram** is a bar graph showing a distribution for quantitative data (at the interval or ratio level of measurement); the bars have a natural order and the bar widths have specific meaning.
>
> A **line chart** shows a distribution of quantitative data as a series of dots connected by lines. For each dot, the horizontal position is the *center* of the bin it represents and the vertical position is the frequency value for the bin.

EXAMPLE ❸   Oscar-Winning Actresses

The following data show the ages (at the time when they won the award) of all Academy Award–winning actresses through 2012, sorted into age order. Display the data using 10-year bins. Discuss the results.

Ages of Actresses at Time of Academy Award (through 2012)

21	22	24	24	25	25	25	25	26	26	26
26	26	27	27	27	27	28	28	28	28	29
29	29	29	29	29	29	29	30	30	30	31
31	31	32	32	32	32	33	33	33	33	33
33	34	34	34	35	35	35	35	35	36	36
37	37	38	38	38	38	39	39	40	41	41
41	41	41	42	42	45	45	48	49	49	54
60	61	61	61	62	63	74	80			

Source: Academy of Motion Picture Arts and Sciences.

SOLUTION   The first step is to bin the data. If you make a tally using 10-year bins of ages 20–29, 30–39, and so on, you'll find the frequencies shown in Table 3.13. Because the data are quantitative, either a histogram or line chart can be made to show the frequencies. Figure 3.9 shows both, with the line chart overlaying the histogram. Note that the vertical axis spans the range 0 to 40, which easily fits the largest frequency of 34 (for ages 30–39), and the dots for the line chart are placed at the center of each bin.

The data show that most actresses win the award at a fairly young age, which stands in contrast to the older ages of most male winners of Best Actor (see Exercise 13 in Section 3.1). Many actresses believe this difference arises because Hollywood producers rarely make movies that feature older women in strong character roles.

TABLE 3.13	Frequency table for Ages of Actresses at Time of Academy Award (through 2012)
Age	**Number of actresses**
20–29	29
30–39	34
40–49	13
50–59	1
60–69	6
70–79	1
80–89	1

Ages of Academy Award–Winning Actresses

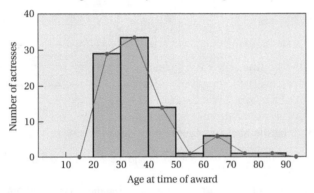

Figure 3.9   Histogram and line chart (overlaying the histogram) for the ages of Academy Award–winning actresses.

Variations on the Theme

There are many variations of histograms and line charts, but we'll discuss just two here. A histogram or line chart for which the data categories on the horizontal axis are time intervals is called a **time-series graph**. You've already seen some time-series diagrams in this book, such as the graph showing how gasoline prices have changed with time.

Another common variation, at least among statisticians if not the media, is called a **stemplot** (or stem-and-leaf plot). A stemplot looks somewhat like a histogram turned sideways, except in place of bars we see a listing of the raw data values. Stemplots can be made in several ways, but one common way is to separate the data values into two parts: the stem (such as the leftmost digit) and the leaf (such as the rightmost digit). The following example shows the process.

Definitions

A histogram or line chart in which the horizontal axis represents *time* is called a **time-series graph**.

A **stemplot** (or *stem-and-leaf plot*) is somewhat like a histogram turned sideways, except in place of bars we see a listing of data.

USING TECHNOLOGY—**LINE CHARTS AND HISTOGRAMS**

Excel Line charts are easy to create in Excel. The screen shot below shows the process for the binned data from Table 3.5 (p. 86). Follow these steps:

1. To get the dots in the centers of the bins for the scores, enter the center point of each bin in Column B. Then enter the frequencies in Column C.

2. Select the scores and frequencies, then choose the chart type "scatter" but with the option for connecting points with straight lines. You will get the graph as shown.

3. Use the chart options to improve design, labels, and more.

Note: You can also create a line chart with the "line" chart option in Excel. In that case, select *only* the frequencies when you begin the graphing process; then, in the "source data" dialog box, choose "series" and select the scores (Column B) as the "X values." The resulting graph should look the same as that created with the "scatter" option, except the data points will not have dots.

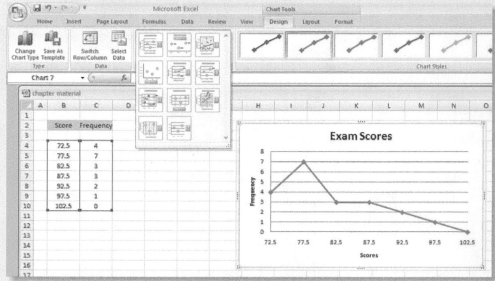

Microsoft Excel 2007.

Excel can also generate histograms with the use of add-ins, including the Data Analysis add-in that can be installed with some versions of Excel.

STATDISK To create a histogram in STATDISK, enter or open data in the STATDISK Data Window, click **Data,** click **Histogram,** and then click on the **Plot** button. To use your own settings, click on the "User defined" button before clicking on Plot. Click on the **Turn labels on** button to see the frequency for each class.

TI-83/84 PLUS To create a histogram using a TI-83/84 Plus calculator, enter or a list of data in L1 or use a list of values assigned to a name. Select the **STAT PLOT** function by pressing **2ND** **Y=** . Press **ENTER** and use the arrow keys to turn Plot1 to "On" and select the graph with bars. The screen display should be as shown here.

Image used with permission of Texas Instruments, Inc.

If you want to let the calculator determine the settings, press **ZOOM** **9** to get a histogram with default settings. (To use your own settings, press **WINDOW** and enter the maximum and minimum values. Press **GRAPH** to obtain the graph.)

EXAMPLE ④ Stemplot for Oscar-Winning Actresses

Make a stemplot for the data from Example 3. Discuss the pros and cons of the stemplot over a histogram.

SOLUTION The data are the ages of the actresses (at time of award), which range from 21 to 80. We therefore choose to use the tens column of the ages as the stems and the ones column as the leaves. Because the ages range from the 20s to the 80s, the stem values range from 2 to 8; we put these on the left side of the stemplot shown in Figure 3.10. On the right, we place all the ones values that go with each tens value. For example, the first row of data from Example 3 shows the following ages:

21   22   24   24   25   25   25   25   26   26   26

All of these ages are in the 20s, so they all have the same stem of "2" in Figure 3.10 We then place each of these ages as one of the leaves on the right, which is why the first set of the leaves begins 1, 2, 4, 4, 5, 5, 5, 5, 6, 6, 6. You can continue through the data from Example 3 to see how all the leaves were created. Notice, for example, that there is only one age in the 50s, and it is 54; that is why the stem 5 (which represents the 50s) has only a single leave with value 4.

The primary advantage of the stemplot over the histogram from Figure 3.9 is that the stemplot actually contains all of the original data. For example, the histogram shows only that there were 6 actresses with ages from 60–69; in contrast, by looking at the leaves that go with the stem "6" in the stemplot, you can see that the actual ages of these six actresses were 60, 61, 61, 61, 62, and 63. The primary drawback to the stemplot is that the extra information it contains makes it more visually complex than a histogram.

Stem (tens)	Leaves (ones)
2	1 2 4 4 5 5 5 5 6 6 6 6 6 7 7 7 7 8 8 8 8 9 9 9 9 9 9 9
3	0 0 0 1 1 1 2 2 2 2 3 3 3 3 3 4 4 4 5 5 5 5 5 6 6 7 7 8 8 8 8 9
4	0 1 1 1 1 1 2 2 5 5 8 9 9
5	4
6	0 1 1 1 2 3
7	7
8	0

Figure 3.10 Stemplot for the ages of Academy Award–winning actresses.

· · ●

EXAMPLE ⑤ Interpreting a Time-Series Graph

Figure 3.11 shows a time-series graph for the death rate (deaths per 1,000 people) in the United States since 1900. (For example, the 1905 death rate of 16 means that, for each 1,000 people living at the beginning of 1905, 16 people died during the year.) Discuss the general trend. Also consider the spike in 1918: If someone told you that this spike was due to battlefield deaths in World War I, would you believe it? Explain.

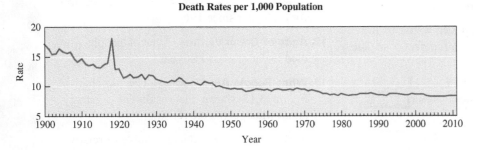

Figure 3.11 Historical U.S. death rates per 1,000 people.
Source: National Center for Health Statistics.

SOLUTION The general trend in death rates is clearly downward, presumably because of improvements in medical science. For example, bacterial diseases such as pneumonia were major killers in the early 1900s, but are largely curable with antibiotics today. Regarding the spike in 1918: Although it coincides with the end of World War I, if the war were the cause of this spike, then we might expect to see a similar spike during World War II, but we don't. This suggests that there must have been some other reason for the spike. In fact, the spike reflects the effects of the deadly flu pandemic of 1918, which killed 850,000 people in the United States and an estimated 20 million people worldwide.

TIME ⏱ OUT TO THINK

Do you get annual flu shots? Does knowing the tremendous impact of the 1918 flu epidemic affect your opinion as to the value of flu shots? Defend your opinion.

Section 3.3 Exercises

Statistical Literacy and Critical Thinking

1. **Distribution.** What do we mean by the distribution of data?

2. **Visualizing Data.** How is a histogram or line chart more helpful than a list of sample values for understanding a data distribution?

3. **Pareto Chart and Pie Chart.** What is an important advantage of a Pareto chart over a pie chart?

4. **Histogram and Stemplot.** Assume that a data set is used to construct a histogram and a stemplot. Using only the histogram, is it possible to re-create the original list of data values? Using only the stemplot, is it possible to re-create the original list of data values? What is an advantage of a stemplot over a histogram?

Does It Make Sense? For Exercises 5–8, decide whether the statement makes sense (or is clearly true) or does not make sense (or is clearly false). Explain clearly. Not all of these statements have definitive answers, so your explanation is more important than your chosen answer.

5. **Histogram.** I made a histogram to depict frequency counts of answers to the question "What political party do you belong to?"

6. **Pie Chart.** I used a pie chart to illustrate a data set showing how the cost of college has changed over time.

7. **Pareto Chart.** A quality control engineer wants to draw attention to the most serious causes of defects, so she uses a Pareto chart to illustrate the frequencies of the different causes of defects.

8. **Peak Values.** I made both a histogram and a line chart for a data set of the crime rate (number of crimes committed) each year from 1960 to 2010. The histogram showed that the crime rate peaked in 1982, while the line chart showed that it peaked in 1983.

Concepts and Applications

Most Appropriate Display. Exercises 9–12 describe data sets but do not give actual data. For each data set, state the type of graphic that you believe would be most appropriate for displaying the data, if they were available. Explain your choice.

9. **Incomes.** Incomes of college graduates who took a statistics course

10. **Political Party.** The political party affiliations of 1000 survey subjects

11. **Movie Theaters.** Number of movie theatres for each year since 1960

12. **Ages of Crash Victims.** Ages of people who died in car crashes last year

13. **What People Are Reading.** The pie chart in Figure 3.12 shows the results of a survey about what people are reading.

    a. Summarize these data in a table of relative frequencies.

    b. Construct a Pareto chart for these data.

    c. Which do you think is a better representation of the data: the pie chart or the Pareto chart? Why?

Figure 3.12 *Source:* Wall Street Journal Almanac, based on data from the Book Industry Study Group.

14. Histogram. The histogram in Figure 3.13 depicts cotinine levels (in milligrams per milliliter) of a sample of subjects who smoke cigarettes. Cotinine is a metabolite of nicotine, which means that cotinine is produced by the body when nicotine is absorbed. The data are from the Third National Health and Nutrition Examination Survey.

a. How many subjects are represented in the histogram?

b. How many subjects have cotinine levels below 400?

c. How many subjects have cotinine levels above 150?

d. What is the highest possible cotinine level of a subject represented in this histogram?

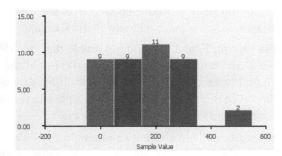

Figure 3.13

15. Weights of Coke. Exercise 11 in Section 3.1 required the construction of a frequency table from the weights (in pounds) of 36 cans of regular Coke. Use that frequency table to construct the corresponding histogram.

16. Weights of Diet Coke. Exercise 12 in Section 3.1 required the construction of a frequency table for the weights (in pounds) of 36 cans of Diet Coke. Use that frequency table to construct the corresponding histogram.

17. Oscar-Winning Actors. Exercise 13 in Section 3.1 required the construction of a frequency table for the ages of recent Academy Award–winning male actors at the time when they won their award. Use that frequency table to construct the corresponding histogram.

18. Body Temperatures. Exercise 14 in Section 3.1 required the construction of a frequency table for a list of body temperatures (°F) of randomly selected subjects. Use that frequency table to construct the corresponding histogram.

19. Job Hunting. A survey was conducted to determine how employees found their jobs. The table below lists the successful methods identified by 400 randomly selected employees. The data are based on results from the National Center for Career Strategies. Construct a Pareto chart that corresponds to the given data. Based on these results, what appears to be the best strategy for someone seeking employment?

Job sources of survey respondents	Frequency
Help-wanted ads	56
Executive search firms	44
Networking	280
Mass mailing	20

20. Job Sources. Refer to the data given in Exercise 19, and construct a pie chart. Compare the pie chart to the Pareto chart. Can you determine which graph is more effective in showing the relative importance of job sources?

21. Job Application Mistakes Chief financial officers of U.S. companies were surveyed about areas in which job applicants make mistakes. Here are the areas and the frequency of responses: interview (452); resume (297); cover letter (141); reference checks (143); interview follow-up (113); screening call (85). These results are based on data from Robert Half Finance and Accounting. Construct a pie chart representing the given data.

22. Job Application Mistakes Construct a Pareto chart of the data given in Exercise 21. Compare the Pareto chart to the pie chart. Which graph is more effective in showing the relative importance of the mistakes made by job applicants?

23. Dotplot. Refer to the QWERTY data in Exercise 19 in Section 3.1 and construct a dotplot.

24. Dotplot. Refer to the Dvorak data in Exercise 19 in Section 3.1 and construct a dotplot. Compare the result to the dotplot in Exercise 23. Based on the results, does either keyboard configuration appear to be better? Explain.

25. Time-Series Graph for Cell Phone Subscriptions. The following table shows the numbers of cell phone subscriptions (in thousands) in the United States for various years. Construct a time-series graph of the data. "Linear" growth would result in a graph that is approximately a straight line. Does the time-series graph appear to show linear growth?

Year	Number	Year	Number
1986	682	2000	109478
1988	2069	2002	140767
1990	5283	2004	182140
1992	11033	2006	233000
1994	24134	2008	262700
1996	44043	2010	302900
1998	69209		

26. Time Series for Motor Vehicle Deaths. The following values are numbers of motor vehicle deaths in the United States for years beginning with 1980. The data are arranged in order by row. Construct a time-series graph and then determine whether there appears to be a trend. If so, provide a possible explanation.

51,091	49,301	43,945	42,589	44,257	43,825
46,087	46,390	47,087	45,582	44,599	41,508
39,250	40,150	40,716	41,817	42,065	42,013
41,501	41,717	41,945	42,196	43,005	42,884
42,836	43,443	42,642	41,059	37,261	33,808
32,708					

27. Stemplot. Construct a stemplot of these test scores: 67, 72, 85, 75, 89, 89, 88, 90, 99, 100. How does the stemplot show the distribution of these data?

28. Stemplot. Listed below are the lengths (in minutes) of animated children's movies. Construct a stemplot. Does the stemplot show the distribution of the data? If so, how?

83	88	120	64	69	71	76	74	75	76	75
75	79	80	78	78	83	77	71	83	80	73
72	82	74	84	90	89	81	81	90	79	92
82	89	82	74	86	76	81	75	75	77	70
75	64	73	74	71	94					

PROJECTS FOR THE INTERNET & BEYOND

29. CO₂ Emissions. Look for updated data on international carbon dioxide emissions. Create a graph of the latest data and discuss any important features or trends that you notice.

30. Energy Table. Explore the energy tables at the U.S. Energy Information Administration (EIA) Web site. Choose a table that you find interesting and make a graph of its data. You may choose any of the graph types discussed in this section. Explain how you made your graph, and briefly discuss what can be learned from it.

31. Statistical Abstract. Go to the Web site for the *Statistical Abstract of the United States*. Explore the selection of "frequently requested tables." Choose one table of interest to you and make a graph from its data. You may choose any of the graph types discussed in this section. Explain how you made your graph and briefly discuss what can be learned from it.

32. Navel Data. Create an appropriate display of the navel data collected in Exercise 23 of Section 3.1. Discuss any special properties of this distribution.

IN THE NEWS

33. Bar Graphs. Find a recent news article that includes a bar graph with qualitative data categories.

   a. Briefly explain what the bar graph shows, and discuss whether it helps make the point of the news article. Are the labels clear?

   b. Briefly discuss whether the bar graph could be recast as a dotplot.

   c. Is the bar graph already a Pareto chart? If so, explain why you think it was drawn this way. If not, do you think it would be clearer if the bars were rearranged to make a Pareto chart? Explain.

34. Pie Charts. Find a recent news article that includes a pie chart. Briefly discuss the effectiveness of the pie chart. For example, would it be better if the data were displayed in a bar graph rather than a pie chart? Could the pie chart be improved in other ways?

35. Histograms. Find a recent news article that includes a histogram. Briefly explain what the histogram shows, and discuss whether it helps make the point of the news article. Are the labels clear? Is the histogram a time-series diagram? Explain.

36. Line Charts. Find a recent news article that includes a line chart. Briefly explain what the line chart shows, and discuss whether it helps make the point of the news article. Are the labels clear? Is the line chart a time-series diagram? Explain.

3.4 GRAPHICS IN THE MEDIA

The basic graphs we have studied so far are only the beginning of the many ways to depict data visually. In this section, we will explore some of the more complex types of graphics that are common in the media.

Multiple Bar Graphs and Line Charts

A **multiple bar graph** is a simple extension of a regular bar graph: It has two or more sets of bars that allow comparison between two or more data sets. All the data sets must have the same categories so that they can be displayed on the same graph. Figure 3.14 is a multiple bar graph with two sets of bars, one for men and one for women. (The median is a type of average; see Section 4.2.)

Notice that the data categories (the different levels of educational attainment by gender) in Figure 3.14 are qualitative, which makes a bar chart the best choice for display. In cases for which data categories are quantitative, a **multiple line chart** is often a better choice. Figure 3.15 shows time-series data using four different lines for four different data sets. The multiple line chart works because all four data sets represent the same pair of variables: time and unemployment rate. They differ only in the groups for which the data are plotted, with each line representing data for a different level of educational attainment.

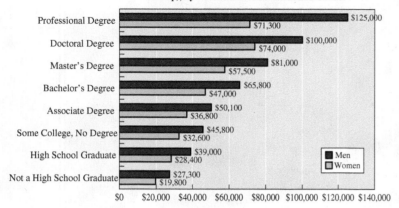

Figure 3.14 A multiple bar graph.

Source: The College Board, *Trends in Higher Education 2010*, based on 2008 data from the U.S. Census Bureau.

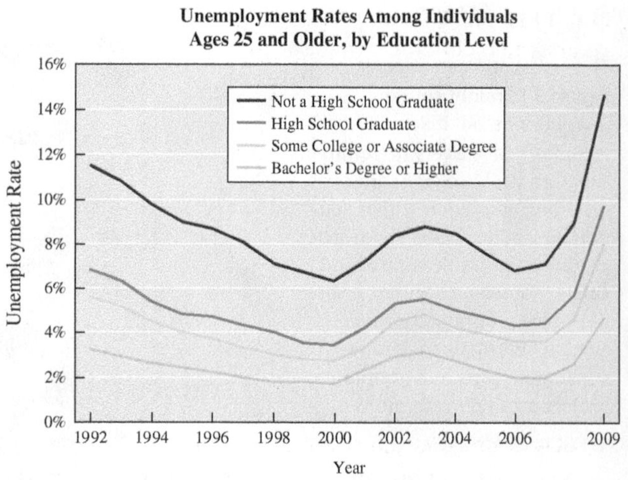

Figure 3.15 A multiple line chart.

Source: The College Board, *Trends in Higher Education 2010*, based on data through 2009 from the U.S. Bureau of Labor Statistics.

EXAMPLE 1 Education Pays

Study Figures 3.14 and 3.15. What general messages do they reveal? Comment on how the use of the multiple bar and line graphics helps convey these messages.

SOLUTION   Figure 3.14 conveys two clear messages. First, by looking at the bars across all the categories, we see clearly that people with greater education have significantly higher median incomes. For example, the median earnings for men with a bachelor's degree are more than $25,000 higher than for men without a college education. This means that over a typical 40-year career (age 25 to 65), a college education is worth an extra *$1 million* in income, at least on average. The second message conveyed by the graph is that for equivalent levels of educational attainment, women still earn much less than men.

Figure 3.15 shows another added value of education: no matter what the unemployment rate (at least over the time period shown), unemployment has always been significantly lower for more highly educated people.

The graphic choices work well because of the easy comparisons they allow. For example, if the bar graphs for men and women were shown separately, it would be much more difficult to see the fact that women earn less than men with the same education. Similarly, if the unemployment line charts were shown separately, our eyes would be drawn more to the trends with time than to the more important differences in the unemployment rates for people with different levels of education.   · · ●

BY THE WAY

More detailed data show that median earnings are higher for college graduates than non-graduates in nearly every field of work. However, the variations are quite significant. For example, students majoring in technical fields such as science or engineering generally earn more than students with other majors, and for any particular major, students who study more and get better grades tend to earn more than students who study less.

TIME ◐UT TO THINK

Together, Figures 3.14 and 3.15 make clear that education can be very valuable financially because it can easily raise your lifetime earnings by $1 million while dramatically reducing your risk of unemployment. Discuss whether these facts should alter the way you approach your own education or public policies regarding higher education.

Stack Plots

Another way to show two or more related data sets simultaneously is with a **stack plot**, which shows different data sets in a vertical stack. Data can be stacked in both bar charts and line charts.

Figure 3.16 shows a stack plot of federal government spending categories as a percentage of the total, with data projected through 2016. Note that government spending is broken into five broad categories, with each category represented by a wedge in the figure. The

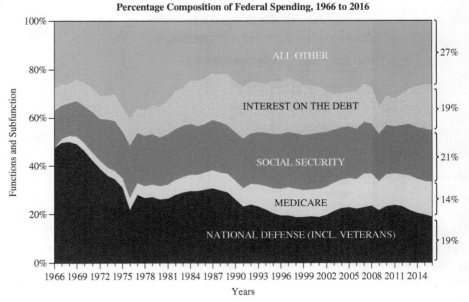

Figure 3.16   A stack plot for U.S. federal government spending by category as a percentage of total spending. Based on actual data through 2010, and projections made in 2010 for the years 2011 through 2016.

Source: U.S. Office of Management and Budget, Historical Tables published in 2011.

thickness of a wedge at a particular time tells you its value at that time. For example, the fact that the wedge for National Defense (which, in this chart, includes spending on Veterans) falls from about 48% in 1966 to about 19% in 2016 tells us that the percentage of the federal budget that goes to defense has declined dramatically in recent decades. The graph also makes clear that the trend over time is for Social Security, Medicare, and interest on the debt to make up a rapidly growing percentage of overall spending.

EXAMPLE **2** **Interpreting the Stack Plot**

As you are undoubtedly aware, the government currently spends much more money than it takes in; in fact, in recent years the revenue has been about one-third less than the spending. Therefore, balancing the budget requires either a dramatic reduction in spending, a substantial increase in tax revenue, or some combination of both. Suppose that you wanted to balance the budget with spending cuts only. How could you do it?

SOLUTION   Achieving a balanced budget through spending cuts alone would require cutting total spending by about one-third, which essentially means finding a way to take 33% out of the 2016 values shown at the right. In principle, there are many ways we could do this, but in practice there are difficult constraints. Interest on the debt is an obligation that cannot be reduced without a government default, and a default could potentially cripple the economy. In addition, many conservatives feel strongly that defense should not be cut any further, while many liberals tend to believe that there should be no cuts in Social Security and Medicare. Those constraints put heavy pressure on finding a way to cut spending without touching interest on the debt, Social Security, Medicare, or defense. However, because the remaining "all other" adds up to only about 27% of the budget in 2016, it's not possible to cut the budget by a third from this spending alone. The conclusion is that balancing the budget through spending cuts alone would require deep cuts not only to "all other" government programs but also to national defense, Social Security, and Medicare.   · · ●

TIME **⊙UT TO THINK**

If *you* were a member of Congress, how would you propose to balance the budget? Do you think your proposal could pass Congress? Do you think you'd be able to be re-elected if it did? Defend your opinions.

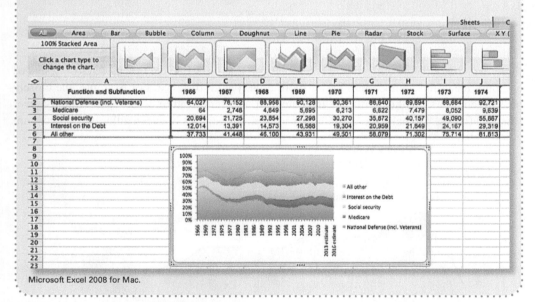

⏻ USING TECHNOLOGY—**GRAPHS WITH MULTIPLE DATA SETS**

Excel Excel provides a variety of options for making multiple bar graphs, multiple line graphs, stack plots, and more. The screen shot below shows some of the data that went into making Figure 3.16, along with a first attempt at a graph. Excel provides several ways of creating the desired graph, but here's a simple process: Notice that the years run along row 1, the different categories of spending are in column 1, and the data cells show the actual spending amounts in millions of dollars.

1. Enter all the data. Notice that the years run along row 1, the different categories of spending are in column 1, and the data cells show the actual spending amounts in millions of dollars.

2. Select all six rows, which means including both the data cells and the labels in row 1 and column 1. Then use the "Insert" menu to choose "Insert Chart..." That will bring up the chart selections that you see above row 1 in the screen shot below.

3. Choose your chart option. For this particular screen shot, we chose the third chart from the left; to the left of the chart options, you'll see that this chart type is identified as "100% stacked area," which means it makes the stack plot as percentages of each year's total rather than from the actual dollar values.

4. From this point, getting to a final graphic like that in Figure 3.16 is just a matter of choosing labeling options and other decorative features. Most of these features can be added within Excel, though sometimes it is easier to add them by importing the Excel graph into an art or photo editing program.

You should try your own similar data set and experiment with the various chart types. If you don't get the result that you expect, use Excel's "help" function to get more detailed instructions about making various types of graphs.

Microsoft Excel 2008 for Mac.

Geographical Data

There are many cases in which we are interested in geographical patterns in data. Figure 3.17 shows one common way of depicting **geographical data**. In this case, the map shows trends in energy use per capita (per person) in different states. The actual data values are shown in small print with each state, while the color coding shows the binned categories listed in the legend.

The display in Figure 3.17 works well for the energy data set because each state is associated with a unique energy usage per person. For data that vary continuously across geographical areas, a **contour map** is more convenient. Figure 3.18 shows a contour map of temperature over the United States at a particular time. Each of the *contours* (curvy lines) connects locations with the same temperature. For example, the temperature is 50°F everywhere along the contour labeled 50° and 60°F everywhere along the contour labeled 60°. Between

Per Person Energy Use by State (gallons of oil equivalent)

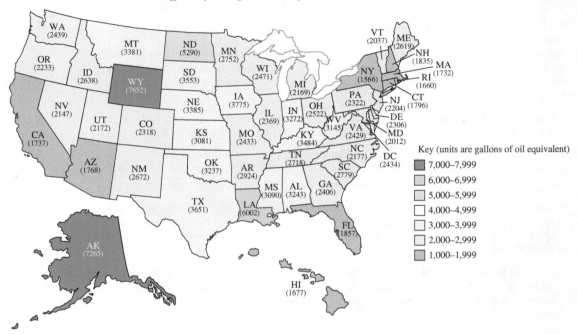

Figure 3.17 Geographical data can be displayed with a color-coded map. These data show per person energy usage by state, in units of "gallons of oil equivalent"; that is, the data represent the amount of oil that each person would use if all of the energy were generated by burning oil. In reality, about 40% of U.S. energy comes from oil, with most of the rest from coal, natural gas, nuclear, and hydroelectric power.

Source: U.S. Energy Information Administration, State Energy Data System (2009 data released 2011).

these two contours, the temperature is between 50°F and 60°F. Note that more closely spaced contours mean that temperature varies more greatly with distance. For example, the closely packed contours in the northeast indicate that the temperature varies substantially over small distances. To make the graph easier to read, the regions between adjacent contours are color-coded.

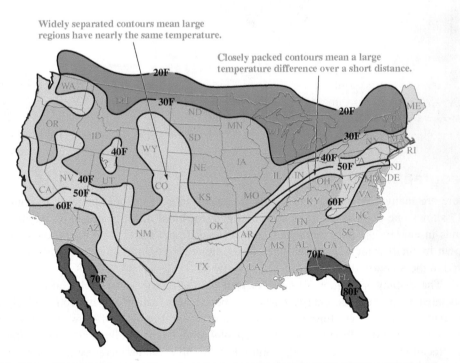

Figure 3.18 Geographical data that vary continuously, such as temperatures, can be displayed with a contour map.

EXAMPLE 3 Interpreting Geographical Data

Study Figures 3.17 and 3.18 and use them to answer the following questions.

a. Do you see any geographical trends that might explain the states with the lowest energy usage per person?

b. Were there any temperatures above 80°F in the United States on the date shown in Figure 3.18?

SOLUTION

a. The color coding shows that the states in the lowest category of energy use per person are all either warm-weather states (CA, AZ, FL, and HI) or states in the more densely populated regions of the northeast (NY, NH, CT, MA, and RI).

b. The 80°F contour passes through southern Florida, so the parts of Florida that lie south of this contour had temperatures above 80°F.   ･･●

Three-Dimensional Graphics

Today, computer software makes it easy to give almost any graph a three-dimensional appearance. For example, Figure 3.19 shows the same bar graph as Figure 3.2, but "dressed up" with a three-dimensional look. It may look nice, but the three-dimensional effects are purely cosmetic; they do not provide any information that wasn't already shown in Figure 3.2.

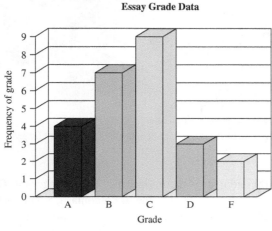

Essay Grade Data

Figure 3.19   This graph has a three-dimensional appearance, but it shows only two-dimensional data.

In contrast, each of the three axes in Figure 3.19 carries distinct information, making the graph a true three-dimensional graph. Researchers studying migration patterns of a bird species (the *Bobolink*) counted the number of birds flying over seven New York cities throughout the night. As shown on the inset map, the cities were aligned east-west so that the researchers would learn what parts of the state the birds flew over, and at what times of night, as they headed south for the winter. Notice that the three axes measure *number of birds, time of night,* and *east-west location.*

EXAMPLE 5 Bird Migration

Based on Figure 3.20, at about what time was the largest number of birds flying over the east-west line marked by the seven cities? Over what part of New York did most of the birds fly? Approximately how many birds passed over Oneonta around 12:00 midnight?

SOLUTION   The number of birds detected in all the cities peaked between 3 and 5 hours after 8:30 p.m., or between about 11:30 p.m and 1:30 a.m. More birds flew over the two easternmost cities of Oneonta and Jefferson than over cities farther west, which means that most of the birds were flying over the eastern part of the state. To answer the specific question about

SONIC MAPPING TRACES BIRD MIGRATION

Sensors across New York State counted each occurrence of the nocturnal flight call of the bobolink to trace the fall migration on the night of Aug. 28–29, 1993. Computerized, the data showed the heaviest swath passing over the eastern part of the state.

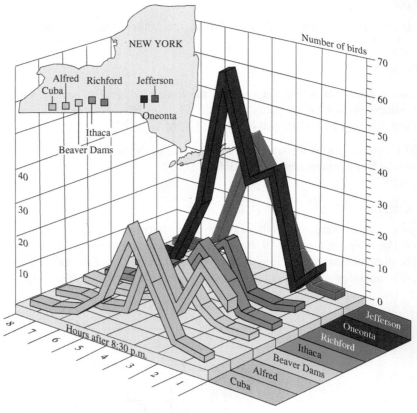

Figure 3.20   This graph shows true three-dimensional data.

Source: "Graph of Ornithology Data," by Bill Evans, from *New York Times.* © *New York Times.*

Oneonta, note that 12:00 midnight is the midpoint of time category 4. On the graph, this time aligns with the dip between peaks on the line at Oneonta. Looking across to the *number of birds* axis, we see that about 30 birds were flying over Oneonta at that time.   • • ●

Combination Graphics

All of the graphic types we have studied so far are common and fairly easy to create. But the media today are often filled with many varieties of even more complex graphics. For example, Figure 3.21 shows a graphic concerning the participation of women in the summer Olympics. This single graphic combines a line chart, many pie charts, and numerical data. It is certainly a case of a picture being worth far more than a thousand words.

EXAMPLE 6 Olympic Women

Describe three trends shown in Figure 3.21.

SOLUTION   The line chart shows that the total number of women competing in the summer Olympics has risen fairly steadily, especially since the 1960s, reaching nearly 5,000 in the 2012 games. The pie charts show that the percentage of women among all competitors has also increased, surpassing 44% in the 2012 games. The bold red numbers at the bottom show that the number of events in which women compete has also increased dramatically, reaching 140 in the 2012 games.

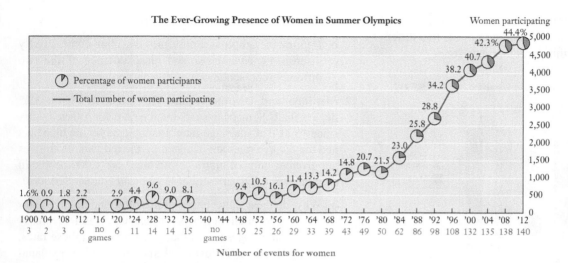

Figure 3.21 Women in the Olympics.

Source: Adapted from the *New York Times*, based on data from the International Olympic Committee.

TIME OUT TO THINK

Which of the trends shown in Figure 3.21 are likely to continue over the next few Olympic games? Which are not? Explain.

Section 3.4 Exercises

Statistical Literacy and Critical Thinking

1. **Three-Dimensional Histograms.** Can every histogram be converted to a three-dimensional graphic? Does the three-dimensional version of a histogram have more visual appeal? Does the three-dimensional version of a histogram provide any information not provided by the original histogram?

2. **Multiple Bar Graph.** What is a multiple bar graph, and how is it helpful?

3. **Geographical Data.** What are geographical data? Identify at least two ways to display geographical data.

4. **Contour Map.** What is a contour on a contour map? What does it mean when contours are close together? What does it mean when they are far apart?

Does It Make Sense? For Exercises 5–8, decide whether the statement makes sense (or is clearly true) or does not make sense (or is clearly false). Explain clearly. Not all of these statements have definitive answers, so your explanation is more important than your chosen answer.

5. **Three-Dimensional Graph.** A quality control engineer claims that because cars are three-dimensional objects, she needs a three-dimensional graph to display the production cost of a Corvette for each of the past 10 years.

6. **Contour Map.** A contour map could be used to display the ages of all full-time students at your college.

7. **Geographic Data.** A graphic artist for a magazine is depicting the populations of the 10 largest U.S. cities by using bars of different heights, with the bars positioned on the locations of the cities on a map of the United States.

8. **Stack Plot.** A multiple bar graph could be used to show the numbers of males, females, and total students at your college for each of the past 10 years.

Concepts and Applications

9. **Genders of Students.** The stack plot in Figure 3.22 shows the numbers of male and female higher education students for different years. Projections are from the U.S. National Center for Education Statistics.

   a. In words, discuss the trends revealed on this graphic.

b. Redraw the graph as a multiple line chart. Briefly discuss the advantages and disadvantages of the two different representations of this particular data set.

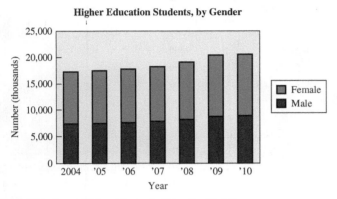

Figure 3.22 *Source:* National Center for Education Statistics.

10. Home Prices by Region. The graph in Figure 3.23 shows home prices in different regions of the United States. Note that the data have *not* been adjusted for the effects of inflation.

a. In words, describe the general trends that apply to the home price data for all regions.

b. In words, describe any differences that you notice among the different regions.

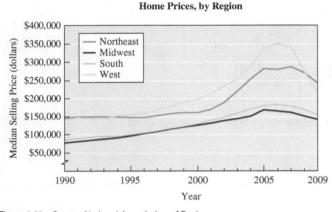

Figure 3.23 *Source:* National Association of Realtors.

11. Gender and Salary. Consider the display in Figure 3.24 of median salaries of males and females in recent years.

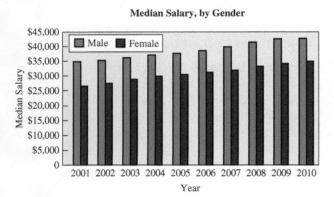

Figure 3.24 *Source:* U.S. Census Bureau.

a. What story does the graph convey?

b. Redraw the graph as a multiple (two) line chart. Briefly discuss the advantages and disadvantages of the two different representations of this particular data set.

12. Marriage and Divorce Rates. The graph in Figure 3.25 depicts the U.S. marriage and divorce rates for selected years since 1900. The marriage rates are depicted by the blue bars and the divorce rates are depicted by the red bars. Both rates are given in units of marriages/divorces per 1,000 people in the population (Department of Health and Human Services).

a. Why do these data consist of marriage and divorce *rates* rather than total numbers of marriages and divorces? Comment on any trends that you observe in these rates, and give plausible historical and sociological explanations for these trends.

b. Construct a stack plot of the marriage and divorce rate data. For each bar, place the divorce rate above the marriage rate. Which graph makes the comparisons easier: the multiple bar graph shown here or the stack plot? Explain.

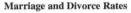
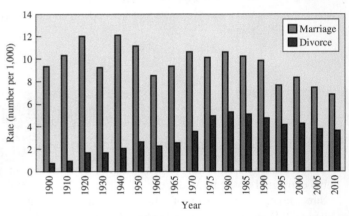

Figure 3.25 *Source:* National Center for Health Statistics.

13. Entitlement Spending. The stack plot in Figure 3.26 shows Congressional Budget Office data for actual (through 2011) and projected spending on entitlement programs through 2085 as percentages of the gross domestic product (GDP). Interpret the graph and summarize its message.

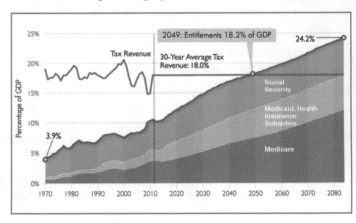

Figure 3.26 *Source:* "Tax Revenues Devoured By Medicare, Medicaid, and Social Security in 2045," from heritage.org, based on data from the Congressional Budget Office. Reprinted with permission.

14. College Degrees. The stacked line chart in Figure 3.27 shows the numbers of bachelor's degrees awarded to men and women since 1970.

Bachelor's Degrees Awarded

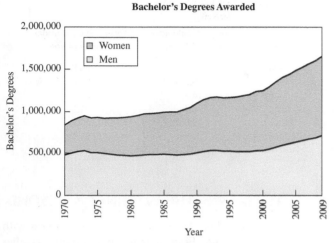

Figure 3.27   *Source:* National Center for Education Statistics.

a. Estimate the numbers of bachelor's degrees awarded to men and to women (separately) in 1970 and in 2010.

b. About when were the number of bachelor's degrees equal for males and females?

c. Comment on the overall trend.

d. Do you think the stacked line chart is an effective way to display these data? Briefly discuss other ways that might have been used instead.

15. Melanoma Mortality. Figure 3.28 shows how the mortality rate from *melanoma* (a form of skin cancer) varies on a county-by-county basis across the United States. The legend shows that the darker the shading in a county, the higher the mortality rate. Discuss a few of the trends revealed in the figure. If you were researching skin cancer, which regions might warrant special study? Why?

16. School Segregation. One way of measuring segregation is the likelihood that a black student will have classmates who are white. Figure 3.29 shows the probability that a black

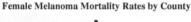

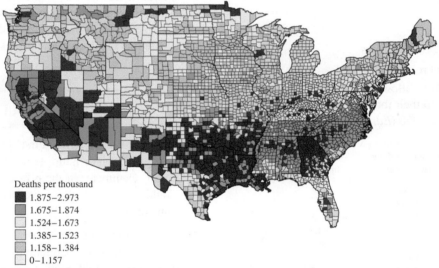

Figure 3.28   *Source:* "Female Melanoma Mortality Rates by County," by Professor Karen Kafadar, Mathematics Department, University of Colorado at Denver. Reprinted with permission.

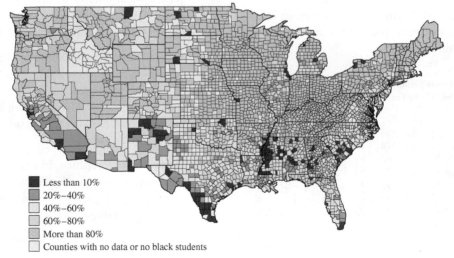

Figure 3.29   *Source: New York Times.*

student would have white classmates, by county, during a recent academic year. Do there appear to be any significant regional differences? Can you pick out any differences between urban and rural areas? Discuss possible explanations for a few of the trends that you see in the figure.

Creating Graphics. Exercises 17–20 give tables of real data. For each table, make a graphical display of the data. You may choose any graphic type that you feel is appropriate to the data set. In addition to making the display, write a few sentences explaining why you chose this type of display and a few sentences describing interesting patterns in the data.

17. **Drinking and Driving.** The following table lists the numbers of persons killed in fatal car crashes for three different categories of blood alcohol content (BAC) of drivers. The data are from the U.S. Census Bureau.

Year	BAC of 0.0 (No alcohol)	BAC of 0.01 to 0.07	BAC of 0.08 and higher
1990	24,083	2,810	17,572
1995	25,968	2,300	13,423
2000	26,300	2,349	13,171
2005	27,542	2,350	13,532
2010 (est)	21,787	1,988	11,242

18. **Daily Newspapers.** The following table gives the number of daily newspapers and their total circulation (in millions) for selected years since 1920 (*Editor & Publisher*).

Year	Number of daily newspapers	Circulation (millions)
1920	2,042	27.8
1930	1,942	39.6
1940	1,878	41.1
1950	1,772	53.9
1960	1,763	58.8
1970	1,748	62.1
1980	1,747	62.2
1990	1,611	62.3
2000	1,485	56.1
2010 (est)	1,402	50.0

19. **Firearm Fatalities.** The following table summarizes deaths due to firearms in different nations in a recent year (Coalition to Stop Gun Violence).

Country	Total firearms deaths	Homicides by firearms	Suicides by firearms	Fatal accidents by firearms
United States	35,563	15,835	18,503	1,225
Germany	1,197	168	1,004	25
Canada	1,189	176	975	38
Australia	536	96	420	20
Spain	396	76	219	101
United Kingdom	277	72	193	12
Sweden	200	27	169	4
Vietnam	131	85	16	30
Japan	93	34	49	10

20. **Working Mothers.** The following table lists labor force participation rates (as percentages) of mothers categorized according to the age of their youngest child (based on data from the Bureau of Labor Statistics).

Year	Youngest child aged 6 to 17 years	Youngest child under 6 years of age
1980	64.3	46.8
1985	69.9	53.5
1990	74.7	58.2
1995	76.4	62.3
2000	79.0	65.3
2005	76.9	62.6
2010 (est)	77.5	63.6

PROJECTS FOR THE INTERNET & BEYOND

21. **Weather Maps.** Many Web sites offer contour maps with current weather data. Find at least two contour weather maps and discuss what they show.

22. **The Federal Budget.** Go to the Web site for the U.S. Office of Management and Budget (OMB) and look for some of its charts related to the federal budget. Pick two charts of particular interest to you and discuss the data they show.

IN THE NEWS

23. **Multiple Bar Graphs.** Find an example of a multiple bar graph or multiple line chart in a recent news report. Comment on the effectiveness of the display. Could another display have been used to depict the same data?

24. **Stack Plots.** Find an example of a stack plot in a recent news report. Comment on the effectiveness of the display. Could another display have been used to depict the same data?

25. **Geographical Data.** Find an example of a graph of geographical data in a recent news report. Comment on the effectiveness of the display. Could another display have been used to depict the same data?

26. **Three-Dimensional Displays.** Find an example of a three-dimensional display in a recent news report. Are three dimensions needed, or are they included for cosmetic reasons? Comment on the effectiveness of the display. Could another display have been used to depict the same data?

27. **Fancy News Graphics.** Find an example in the news of a graphic that combines two or more of the basic graphic types. Briefly explain what the graphic is showing, and discuss the effectiveness of the graphic.

3.5 A FEW CAUTIONS ABOUT GRAPHICS

As we have seen, graphics can offer clear and meaningful summaries of statistical data. However, even well-made graphics can be misleading if we are not careful in interpreting them, and poorly made graphics are almost always misleading. Moreover, some people use graphics in deliberately misleading ways. In this section, we discuss a few of the more common ways in which graphics can lead us astray.

Perceptual Distortions

Many graphics are drawn in a way that distorts our perception of them. Figure 3.30 shows one of the most common types of distortion. Dollar-shaped bars are used to show the declining value of the dollar over time. The problem is that the values are represented by the *lengths* of the dollar bills; for example, a 2010 dollar was worth $0.39 in 1980 dollars and therefore is drawn so that it is 39% as long as the 1980 dollar. However, our eyes tend to focus on the *areas* of the dollar bills, and the area of the 2010 dollar is only about 15% of the area of the 1980 dollar (because both the length and width of the 2010 dollar are reduced to 39% of the 1980 sizes, and $0.39^2 \approx 0.15$). This gives the perception that the value of the dollar shrank even more than it really did.

1980 = $1.00

1990 = $0.63

2010 = $0.39

Figure 3.30 The lengths of the dollars are proportional to their spending power, but our eyes are drawn to the areas, which decline more than the lengths.

> **TIME** ⏱ **UT TO THINK**
> Suppose the three dollars shown in Figure 3.30 were each represented by a three-dimensional stack of pennies, with the height of the stack proportional to the value of the dollar. Would that make the visual distortion of the data greater, less, or the same as the distortion in Figure 3.30? Explain.

Watch the Scales

Figure 3.31a shows the percentage of college students since 1910 who were women. At first glance, it appears that this percentage grew by a huge margin after about 1950. But the vertical axis scale does not begin at zero and does not end at 100%. The increase is still substantial but looks far less dramatic if we redraw the graph with the vertical axis covering the full range of 0 to 100% (Figure 3.31b). From a mathematical point of view, leaving out the zero point on a scale is perfectly honest and can make it easier to see small-scale trends in data. Nevertheless, as this example shows, it can be visually deceptive if you don't study the scale carefully.

BY THE WAY

German researchers in the latter part of the 19th century studied many types of graphics. The type of distortion shown in Figure 3.30 was so common that they gave it its own name, which translates roughly as "the old goosing up the effect by squaring the eyeball trick."

Women as a Percentage of All College Students

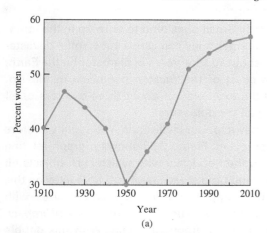

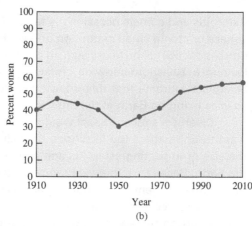

Figure 3.31 Both graphs show the same data, but they look very different because their vertical scales have different ranges.
Source: National Center for Education Statistics.

The easiest person to deceive is one's own self.

—Edward Bulwer-Lytton

Another issue can arise when graphs use nonlinear scales, meaning scales in which each increment does not always represent the same change in value. Consider Figure 3.32a, which shows how the speeds of the fastest computers have increased with time. At first glance, it appears that speeds have been increasing linearly. For example, it might look as if the speed increased by the same amount from 1990 to 2000 as it did from 1950 to 1960. However, if you look more closely, you'll see that each tick mark on the vertical scale represents a *tenfold* increase in speed. Now we see that computer speed grew from about 1 to 100 calculations per second from 1950 to 1960 and from about 100 million to 10 billion calculations per second between 1990 and 2000. This type of scale is called an **exponential scale** (or *logarithmic scale*) because it grows by powers of 10 and powers of 10 are *exponents*. (For example, 3 is the exponent in $10^3 = 1,000$.) It is always possible to convert an exponential scale back to an ordinary linear scale as shown in Figure 3.32b. However, comparing the two graphs should make clear why the exponential scale is so useful in this case: The exponential scale clearly shows the rapid gains in computer speeds, while the ordinary scale makes it impossible to see any detail in the early years shown on the graph. More generally, exponential scales are useful whenever data vary over a huge range of values.

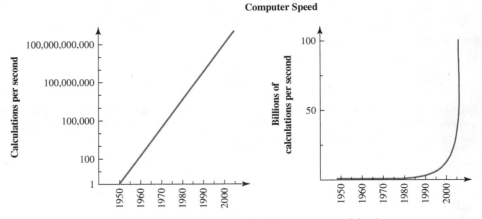

Figure 3.32   Both graphs show the same data, but the graph on the left uses an exponential scale.

TIME OUT TO THINK

Based on Figure 3.32a, can you predict the speed of the fastest computers in 2020? Could you make the same prediction with Figure 3.32b? Explain.

CASE STUDY   Asteroid Threat

Asteroids and comets occasionally hit the Earth. Small ones tend to burn up in the atmosphere or create small craters on impact, but larger ones can cause substantial devastation. About 65 million years ago, an asteroid about 10 kilometers in diameter hit the Earth, leaving a 200-kilometer-wide crater on the coast of the Yucatan peninsula in Mexico. Scientists estimate that this impact caused the extinction of about three-quarters of all species living on Earth at the time, including all the dinosaurs.

Clearly, a similar impact would be bad news for our civilization. We might therefore want to understand the likelihood of such an event. Figure 3.33 shows a graph relating the size of impacting asteroids and comets to the frequency with which such objects hit the Earth. Because of the wide range of sizes and time scales involved, *both* axes on this graph are exponential. The horizontal axis shows impactor (asteroid or comet) sizes, with each tick representing a power of 10. The vertical axis shows the frequency of impact; moving up on the vertical axis corresponds to more frequent events. With this double exponential graph, we can see trends clearly. For example, small objects of about 1 meter

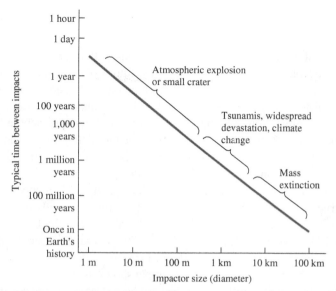

Figure 3.33   This graph shows how the frequency of impacts—and the magnitude of their effects—depends on the size of the impactor. Note that smaller impacts are much more frequent than larger ones.

in size strike the Earth every day, but cause little damage. At the other extreme, objects large enough to cause a mass extinction hit only about once every hundred million years.

The intermediate cases are probably the most worrisome. The graph indicates that objects that could cause "widespread devastation"—such as wiping out the population of a large city—can be expected as often as once every thousand years. This is often enough to warrant at least some preventive action. Currently, astronomers are trying to make more precise predictions about when an object might hit the Earth. If they discover an object that will hit the Earth, scientists will need to find a way to deflect it to prevent the impact.

Percentage Change Graphs

Is college getting more or less expensive? If you didn't look too carefully, Figure 3.34a might lead you to conclude that after peaking in the early 2000s, the cost of public colleges fell during the rest of that decade. But look more closely and you'll see that the vertical axis on this graph represents the *percentage change* in costs. The drop-off therefore means only that costs rose by smaller amounts, not that they fell. Actual college costs are shown in Figure 3.34b, which makes it clear that they rose every year. Graphs that show percentage change are very common; you'll find them in the financial news almost every day. But as you can see, they can be very misleading if you don't realize that they are showing change rather than actual values.

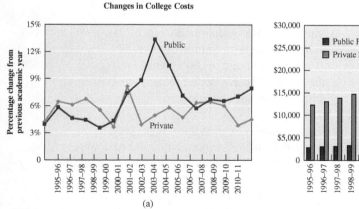

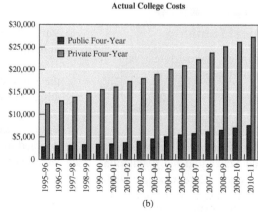

Figure 3.34   Trends in college costs: (a) annual percent change; (b) actual costs.
Source: The College Board.

Get your facts first, and then you can distort them as much as you please.

—Mark Twain

Pictographs

Pictographs are graphs embellished with additional artwork. The artwork may make the graph more appealing, but it can also distract or mislead. Figure 3.35 is a pictograph showing the rise in world population from 1804 to 2040 (numbers for future years are based on United Nations intermediate-case projections). The lengths of the bars correctly correspond to world population for the years listed. However, the artistic embellishments of this graph are deceptive in several ways. For example, your eye may be drawn to the figures of people lining the globe. Because this line of people rises from the left side of the pictograph to the center and then falls, it might give the impression that future world population will decline. In fact, the line of people is purely decorative and carries no information.

The more serious problem with this pictograph is that it makes it appear that world population has been rising linearly. However, notice that the time intervals on the horizontal axis are not the same in each case. For example, the interval between the bars for 1 billion and 2 billion people is 123 years (from 1804 to 1927), but the interval between the bars for 5 billion and 6 billion people is only 12 years (from 1987 to 1999).

Pictographs are very common. As this example shows, however, you have to study them carefully to extract the essential information and not be distracted by the cosmetic effects.

BY THE WAY

Demographers often characterize population growth by a doubling time—the time it takes the population to double. During the late 20th century, the doubling time for the human population was about 40 years. If the population continued to double at this rate, world population would reach more than 30 billion by 2100 and 190 billion by 2200. By about 2650, the human population would be so large that it would not fit on the Earth, even if everyone stood elbow to elbow everywhere.

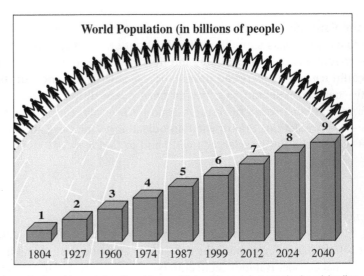

Figure 3.35   A pictograph of world population. The pictures add visual impact, but can also be misleading. Also notice that the horizontal scale (time) is not linear.

Source: United Nations Population Division, future projections based on intermediate case assumptions.

Section 3.5 Exercises

Statistical Literacy and Critical Thinking

1. **Exaggerating a Difference.** Under standard test conditions, the braking distance for a Honda Civic is 136 feet and the braking distance for a VW Jetta is 137 feet. Is that difference meaningful? How could a graph be constructed so that the difference is greatly exaggerated?

2. **Graph of Populations.** When constructing a graph showing the population of the United States and the population of Mexico, an illustrator draws two different people with heights proportional to the populations. Identify a way in which the graph might be misleading? What is the general name for such graphs that use drawings of people or objects?

3. **Vertical Scale.** A line chart has a vertical scale with values of 0, 1, 10, 100, 1000 and 10,000. What is the name of such a scale? What is an advantage of such a scale?

4. **Sugar Cubes.** To show how sugar production doubled from 1990 to now, an illustrator draws two sugar cubes. The first cube is drawn with a length of 1 cm on each side and the second cube is drawn with a length of 2 cm on each side. What are the volumes of the two sugar cubes? Is the illustration misleading? If so, how?

Concepts and Applications

5. Car Mileage. Figure 3.36 shows the highway fuel consumption (mi/gal) for the Chevrolet Aveo and the Honda Civic. How is the graph misleading? How could it be drawn so that it is not misleading?

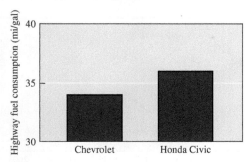

Figure 3.36 Car Mileage.

6. Comparing State Populations. Figure 3.37 depicts 2010 populations for California, Texas, and New York (based on data from the 2010 Census). How is this graph misleading? How could it be drawn so that it is not misleading?

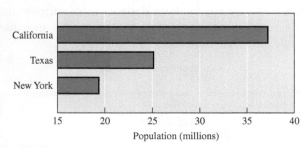

Figure 3.37 State Populations.

7. Pictograph. Figure 3.38 depicts the amounts of daily oil consumption in the United States and Japan. Does the illustration accurately depict the data? Why or why not?

**Daily Oil Consumption
(millions of barrels)**

Figure 3.38

8. Pictograph. Refer to Figure 3.38 used in Exercise 7 and construct a bar chart to depict the same data in a way that is fair and objective.

9. Three-Dimensional Pies. The pie charts in Figure 3.39 give the percentage of Americans in three age categories in 1990 and 2050 (projected).

a. Consider the 1990 age distribution. The actual percentages for the three categories for 1990 were 87.5% (others), 11.3% (60–84), and 1.2% (85+). Does the pie chart show these values accurately? Explain.

b. Consider the 2050 age distribution. The actual percentages for the three categories for 2050 were 80.0% (others), 15.4% (60–84), and 4.6% (85+). Does the pie chart show these values accurately? Explain.

c. Using the actual percentages given in parts a and b, draw flat (two-dimensional) pie charts to display these data. Explain why these pie charts give a more accurate picture than the three-dimensional pies.

d. Comment on the general trends shown in the two pie charts.

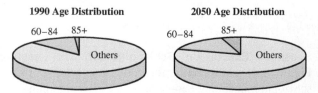

Figure 3.39 *Source:* U.S. Census Bureau.

10. Moore's Law. In 1965, Intel cofounder Gordon Moore initiated what has since become known as *Moore's law:* the number of transistors per square inch on integrated circuits will double approximately every 18 months. In the table below, the first row lists different years and the second row lists the number of transistors (in thousands) for different years.

Year	Transistors	Year	Transistors
1971	23	1997	7500
1974	5	2000	42,000
1978	29	2002	220,000
1982	120	2003	410,000
1985	275	2007	789,000
1989	1180	2011	2,600,000
1993	3100		

a. Construct a time-series graph of these data, using a uniform scale on both axes.

b. Make an exponential graph of these data in which the subdivisions on the vertical axis are 0, 1, 10, 100, 1,000, 10,000, 100,000, 1,000,000, and 100,000,000.

c. Compare the graphs in parts a and b.

11. **Percentage Change in the CPI.** The graph in Figure 3.40 shows the percentage change in the CPI over recent years. In what year (of the years displayed) was the change in the CPI the greatest? What happened in 2009? How do actual prices in 2010 compare to those in 1990? Based on this graph, what can you conclude about changes in prices during the period shown?

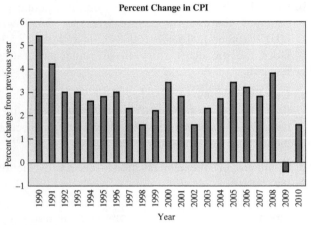

Figure 3.40   *Source:* U.S. Bureau of Labor Statistics.

12. **Seasonal Effects on Schizophrenia?** The graph in Figure 3.41 shows data regarding the relative risk of schizophrenia among people born in different months.

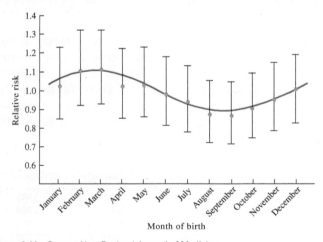

Figure 3.41   *Source: New England Journal of Medicine.*

   a. Note that the scale of the vertical axis does not include zero. Sketch the same risk curve using an axis that includes zero. Comment on the effect of this change.

   b. Each value of the relative risk is shown with a dot at its most likely value and with an "error bar" indicating the range in which the data value probably lies. The study concludes that "the risk was also significantly associated with the season of birth." Given the size of the error bars, does this claim appear justified? (Is it possible to draw a flat line that passes through all of the error bars?)

13. **Constant Dollars.** The graph in Figure 3.42 shows the minimum wage in the United States, together with its purchasing power, which is adjusted for inflation with 1996 used as the reference year. The graph represents the years from 1955 to 2011. Summarize what the graph shows.

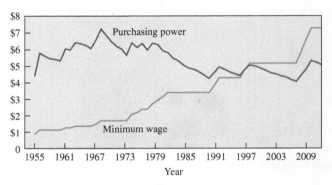

Figure 3.42   *Source:* U.S. Department of Labor.

14. **Double Horizontal Scale.** The graph in Figure 3.43 shows *simultaneously* the number of births in this country during two time periods: 1946–1964 and 1977–1994. When did the first baby boom peak? When did the second baby boom peak? Why do you think the designer of this display chose to superimpose the two time intervals, rather than use a single time scale from 1946 through 1994?

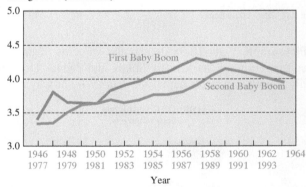

Figure 3.43   *Source:* Based on data from the National Center for Health Statistics.

PROJECTS FOR THE INTERNET & BEYOND

15. **USA Snapshot.** *USA Today* offers a daily pictograph for its "Snapshot." Find a snapshot from a recent issue of *USA Today*. Briefly discuss its purpose and effectiveness.

16. **Image Search.** Choose some topic that interests you for which you think that good statistical graphs should be available. Do an image search for the topic in Google, Bing, or other search engine. Does the search give you what you were looking for? Briefly discuss the value of the search results in terms of what you hoped to find.

IN THE NEWS

17. Distortions in the News. Find an example in a recent news report of a graph that involves some type of perceptual distortion. Explain the effects of the distortion, and describe how the graph could have been drawn more honestly.

18. Scale Problems in the News. Find an example in a recent news report of a graph in which the vertical scale does not start at zero. Suggest why the graph was drawn that way and also discuss any ways in which the graph might be misleading as a result.

19. Economic Graph in the News. Find an example in a recent news report of a graph that shows economic data over time. Are the data adjusted for inflation? Discuss the meaning of the graph and any ways in which it might be deceptive.

20. Pictograph in the News. Find an example of a pictograph in a recent news report. Discuss what the pictograph attempts to show, and discuss whether the artistic embellishments help or hinder this purpose.

21. Outstanding News Graph. Find a graph from a recent news report that, in your opinion, is truly outstanding in displaying data visually. Discuss what the graph shows, and explain why you think it is so outstanding.

22. Not-So-Outstanding News Graph. Find a graph from a recent news report that, in your opinion, fails in its attempt to display data visually in a meaningful way. Discuss what the graph was trying to show, explain why it failed, and explain how it could have been done better.

CHAPTER REVIEW EXERCISES

Listed below are measured weights (in pounds) of the contents in samples of cans of regular Pepsi and Diet Pepsi. Use these data for Exercises 1–3.

Regular Pepsi:

0.8258	0.8156	0.8211	0.8170	0.8216	0.8302
0.8192	0.8192	0.8271	0.8251	0.8227	0.8256
0.8139	0.8260	0.8227	0.8388	0.8260	0.8317
0.8247	0.8200	0.8172	0.8227	0.8244	0.8244
0.8319	0.8247	0.8214	0.8291	0.8227	0.8211
0.8401	0.8233	0.8291	0.8172	0.8233	0.8211

Diet Pepsi:

0.7925	0.7868	0.7846	0.7938	0.7861	0.7844
0.7795	0.7883	0.7879	0.7850	0.7899	0.7877
0.7852	0.7756	0.7837	0.7879	0.7839	0.7817
0.7822	0.7742	0.7833	0.7835	0.7855	0.7859
0.7775	0.7833	0.7835	0.7826	0.7815	0.7791
0.7866	0.7855	0.7848	0.7806	0.7773	0.7775

1. a. Construct a frequency table for the weights of regular Pepsi. Use bins of

0.8130–0.8179

0.8180–0.8229

0.8230–0.8279

0.8280–0.8329

0.8330–0.8379

0.8380–0.8429

b. Construct a frequency table for the weights of diet Pepsi. Use bins of

0.7740–0.7779

0.7780–0.7819

0.7820–0.7859

0.7860–0.7899

0.7900–0.7939

c. Compare the frequency tables from parts a and b. What notable differences are there? How can those notable differences be explained?

2. a. Construct a relative frequency table for the weights of regular Pepsi. Use bins of

0.8130–0.8179

0.8180–0.8229

0.8230–0.8279

0.8280–0.8329

0.8330–0.8379

0.8380–0.8429

b. Construct a cumulative frequency table for the weights of regular Pepsi.

3. a. Use the result from Exercise 1a to construct a histogram for the weights of regular Pepsi.

b. Use the result from Exercise 1b to construct a histogram for the weights of Diet Pepsi.

c. Compare the histograms from parts a and b. How are they similar and how are they different?

4. Pie Chart of Awful Sounds. In a survey, 1,004 adults were asked to identify the most frustrating sound that they hear in a day. Two hundred seventy-nine chose jackhammers, 388 chose car alarms, 128 chose barking dogs, and 209 chose crying babies (based on data from Kelton Research). Construct a pie chart depicting these data.

5. Pareto Chart. Construct a Pareto chart from the data given in Exercise 4. Compare the Pareto chart to the pie chart. Which graph is more effective in showing the numbers of frustrating sounds? Explain.

6. Bar Chart. Figure 3.44 shows the numbers of U.S. adoptions from China in the years 2005 and 2010. What is wrong with this graph? Draw a graph that depicts the data in a fair and objective way.

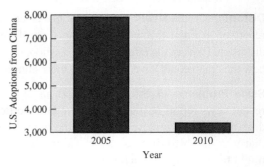

Figure 3.44

CHAPTER QUIZ

1. The IQ scores of 500 college football players are randomly selected. Which graph would be most appropriate for these data: histogram, bar chart, pie chart, multiple bar graph, or stack plot?

2. As a quality control manager at Sony, you find that defective CDs have various causes, including worn machinery, human error, bad supplies, and packaging mistreatment. Which of the following graphs would be best for describing the causes of defects: histogram, bar chart, Pareto chart, dotplot, or pie chart?

3. A stemplot is created from the intervals (min) between eruptions of the Old Faithful geyser in Yellowstone National Park, and one row of that stemplot is 6|1222279. Identify the values represented by that row.

4. The first class in a frequency table is 20–29 and the corresponding frequency is 15. What does the value of 15 indicate?

5. The first class in a relative frequency table is 20–29 and the corresponding relative frequency is 0.25. What does the value of 0.25 indicate?

6. The third class in a frequency table is 40–49 and the corresponding cumulative frequency is 80. What does the value of 80 indicate?

7. The bar chart in Figure 3.45 depicts the number of twin births in the United States in the years 2000 and 2008. In what way is this graph misleading?

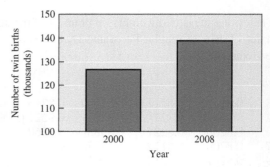

Figure 3.45

8. Construct a dotplot representing these six IQ scores: 90, 95, 95, 100, 105, 110.

9. Identify the values represented by the following stemplot:

```
0 | 0  1  1
1 | 0  1  2
3 |
4 | 9  9
```

10. In one county, the cost of snow removal tripled from 1980 to the current year. Why is it misleading to represent the amounts with images of two rectangular snowplows if the second is three times as wide and three times as tall as the first snowplow?

Can War Be Described with a Graph?

Can a war be described with a graph? Figure 3.46, created by Charles Joseph Minard in 1869, does so remarkably well. This graph tells the story of Napoleon's ill-fated Russian campaign of 1812, sometimes called Napoleon's death march.

The underlying map on Minard's graph shows a roughly 500-mile strip of land extending from the Niemen River on the Polish-Russian border to Moscow. The blue strip depicts the forward march of Napoleon's army. On Minard's original drawing, each millimeter of width represented 6,000 men; this reproduction is shown at a smaller size than the original. The march begins at the far left, where the strip is widest. Here, an army of 422,000 men triumphantly began a march toward Moscow on June 24, 1812. At the time, it was the largest army ever mobilized.

The narrowing of the strip as it approaches Moscow represents the unfolding decimation of the army. (The offshoots represent battalions that were sent off in other directions along the way.) Napoleon had brought only minimal food supplies, and hot summer weather accompanied by heavy rains brought rampant disease. Starvation, disease, and combat losses killed thousands of men each day. By the time the army entered Moscow on September 14, it had shrunk to 100,000 men. The worst was yet to come.

To Napoleon's dismay, the Russians evacuated Moscow prior to the French army's arrival. Deprived of the opportunity to engage the Russian troops and feeling that his army's condition was too poor to continue on to the Russian capital of St. Petersburg, Napoleon took his troops southward out of Moscow. The lower part of the strip on the graph (shown in maroon) represents the retreat, and the dark blue line near the bottom of the figure shows the nighttime temperatures as winter approached. We see that freezing temperatures had already set in by October 18.

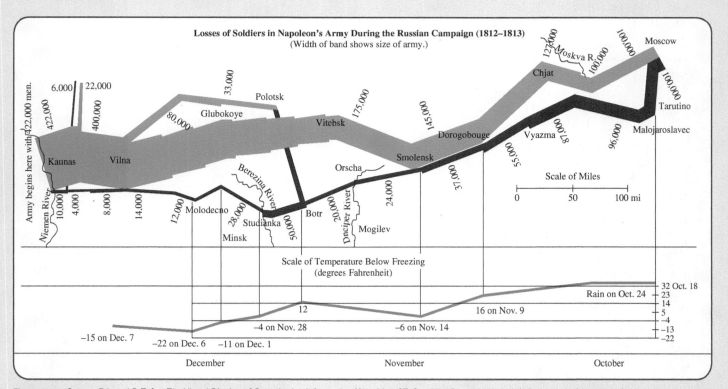

Figure 3.46 *Source:* Edward R. Tufte, *The Visual Display of Quantitative Information* (Cheshire, CT: Graphics Press, 1983, 2001). Reprinted with permission.

Temperatures plunged below 0°F in late November. The sudden narrowing of the lower strip around November 28 shows where 22,000 men perished on the banks of the Berezina River. Three-fourths of the survivors froze to death over the next few days, many on the bitter cold night of December 6. By the time the army reached Poland on December 14, only 10,000 of the original 422,000 remained.

In a famous analysis of graphical techniques, author Edward Tufte described Minard's graph as possibly "the best statistical graphic ever drawn." But a more dramatic statement came from a contemporary of Minard, E. J. Marey, who wrote that this graphic "brought tears to the eyes of all France."

QUESTIONS FOR DISCUSSION

1. Discuss how this graph helps to overcome the impersonal nature of the many deaths in a war. What kind of impact does it have on you personally?

2. Note that this graph plots six variables: two variables of direction (north-south and east-west), the size of the army, the location of the army, the direction of the army's movement, and temperatures during the retreat. Do you think Minard could have gotten the point across with fewer variables? Why or why not?

3. Discuss how you might make a similar graph for some other historical or political event.

• • • • • • • • • • • • • • • • •

FOCUS ON
ENVIRONMENT

Are We Changing Earth's Atmosphere?

Sometimes a well-drawn figure can teach important lessons even before you understand everything about it. Figure 3.47 is a case in point.

As the label shows, the graph shows how the concentration of carbon dioxide in Earth's atmosphere varies with time. The units used for the concentration are *parts per million*, which means the number of carbon dioxide molecules among each one million molecules of air. For example, a concentration of 300 parts per million means that there are 300 molecules of carbon dioxide among each one million molecules of air, which is equivalent to a concentration of 3 in 10,000 or 0.03%.

Notice that the main graph shows how the carbon dioxide concentration has varied over the past 800,000 years. Scientists obtain these data by measuring the concentration of carbon dioxide trapped in bubbles in ancient ice, which they collect by drilling ice cores out of the ice sheets in Greenland

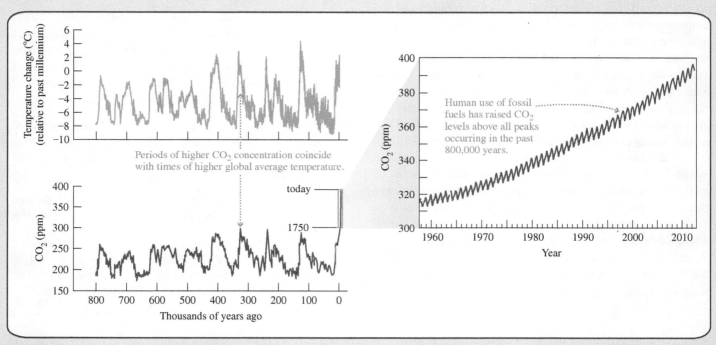

Figure 3.47 (Left) The atmospheric concentration of carbon dioxide and global average temperature reconstructed from ice core data for the past 800,000 years. *Source:* European Project for Ice Coring in Antarctica. (Right) The concentration has been directly measured in the atmosphere since the late 1950s. Note: The wiggles in the right graph represent seasonal fluctuations; the line running through the wiggles represents the general trend. *Source:* National Oceanic and Atmospheric Administration.

or Antarctica. The deepest ice cores drilled to date reach down to ice that was deposited more than 800,000 years ago, which is why the graph can show data going back that far. The zoom-in on the right shows the carbon dioxide concentration directly measured in Earth's atmosphere since the late 1950s.

Even without knowing anything about the role of carbon dioxide, the graph should certainly grab your attention. For one thing, the many ups and downs visible in the graph for the past 800,000 years show that the carbon dioxide concentration varies substantially through natural processes. But notice that in all of those ups and downs, the concentration never rose above about 300 parts per million until just a couple of centuries ago. Now, the zoom-out shows the concentration rising by some 2 to 3 parts per million per year, a rate at which it will pass 400 parts per million by 2015 and 500 parts per million by about 2060. Clearly, something dramatic is happening to the carbon dioxide concentration.

The dramatic change should lead you to ask other questions. First, you might wonder whether the carbon dioxide concentration is important, and the answer is revealed by the notes on the main graph. The same ice core data that allow reconstruction of the past carbon dioxide concentration also allow reconstruction of past temperatures on Earth, and comparison reveals that the carbon dioxide concentration and the temperature tend to rise and fall in tandem. That is, past ice ages were marked by low carbon dioxide concentrations, while past warm periods were marked by higher concentrations. This leads to the question of whether the change in carbon dioxide concentration *causes* the changes in temperature. Although this graph alone does not answer that question, other statistical studies, which we'll discuss in Chapter 8 (see Focus, p. 378), provide strong evidence that there is indeed a cause and effect.

If the cause and effect are real, then the current dramatic rise in the carbon dioxide concentration should be cause for great concern. During many of the past warm periods, Earth's average temperature was several degrees warmer than it is today, so the fact that the carbon dioxide concentration is now skyrocketing suggests that the same might happen to our planet's temperature. Moreover, notice that the past data show that the changes in concentration (and temperature) often happen quite rapidly, suggesting that the process can feed back on itself. In that case, there's a strong risk that we have already started a process that may cause Earth's temperature to rise rapidly and dramatically over the coming decades.

The remaining question is whether the current rise in the carbon dioxide concentration is a natural phenomenon like the past rises or something being caused by humans. On this point, there is no doubt. By carefully studying the isotopic makeup of the carbon dioxide in the atmosphere and comparing it to that of various carbon dioxide sources, scientists have found that added carbon dioxide is coming primarily from the burning of fossil fuels.

Perhaps you've heard debate about whether global warming is a real or imagined threat. With a bit of extra information, such as knowing that the added carbon dioxide comes from human activity, Figure 3.47 makes clear that there's nothing imaginary about it.

QUESTIONS FOR DISCUSSION

1. Study Figure 3.47 carefully. How does the carbon dioxide concentration today compare to that of 1750? How does that of 1750 compare to that during the past 800,000 years? What conclusions can you draw from your answers to these questions?

2. In the past, a carbon dioxide concentration of 300 parts per million accompanied global average temperatures as much as about 9°F (5°C) higher than the global average temperature today. What do you think would happen if Earth's temperature rose that much over the next century? Is that a worst-case scenario? Explain.

3. Discuss some of the factors that will affect the future concentration of carbon dioxide in the atmosphere. What do *you* think should be done to slow or stop the growth in the carbon dioxide concentration?

4. Find the latest data for the atmospheric carbon dioxide concentration. Is the level still rising? How fast is it rising?

5. The graphs in Figure 3.47 summarize a great deal of scientific data. How important are clear graphics to our understanding of these data? Defend your opinion.

• • • • • • • • • • • • • • • •

Describing Data

In Chapter 3, we discussed methods for displaying data distributions with tables and graphs. Now we are ready to study common methods for describing the center, shape, and variation of a collection of data. These methods are central to data analysis and, as you'll see, have applications to nearly every statistical study you encounter in the news. We'll conclude the chapter by studying a few surprises that occasionally turn up even when we look at data carefully.

It's no use trying to sum
people up. One must follow
hints, not exactly what is said,
nor yet entirely what is done.

—Virginia Woolf

LEARNING GOALS

4.1 Using Formulas

4.2 What Is Average?
Understand the difference between a mean, median, and mode; how each is affected by outliers; and when it is appropriate to use a weighted mean.

4.3 Shapes of Distributions
Describe the general shape of a distribution in terms of its number of modes, skewness, and variation.

4.4 Measures of Variation
Understand and interpret these common measures of variation: range, the five-number summary, and standard deviation.

FOCUS TOPICS

p. 170 Focus on the Stock Market:
What's Average About the Dow?

p. 172 Focus on Economics: Are the
Rich Getting Richer?

4.1 USING FORMULAS

A *formula* is an equation that indicates how variables are related to one another. Some formulas express geometric relationships; others express physical laws. Just as with algebraic expressions, the letters and mathematical symbols in a formula represent numbers and words.

The method of evaluating formulas is similar to that of evaluating algebraic expressions. We substitute all the given numbers for the variables and then carry out the computations using the order of operations rule.

PRACTICE 1

To convert a temperature C expressed in Celsius degrees to the temperature F expressed in Fahrenheit degrees, we multiply the Celsius temperature by $\frac{9}{5}$ and then add 32. Write a formula that expresses this relationship.

EXAMPLE ①

To predict the temperature T at a particular altitude a, meteorologists subtract $\frac{1}{200}$ of the altitude from the temperature g on the ground. Here, T and g are in degrees Fahrenheit and a is in feet. Translate this rule to a formula.

SOLUTION   Stating the rule briefly in words, the temperature at a particular altitude equals the difference between the temperature on the ground and $\frac{1}{200}$ times the altitude. Now, we translate this rule to mathematical symbols.

$$T = g - \frac{1}{200}a,$$

which is the desired formula. $\cdots\bullet$

The method of evaluating formulas is similar to that of evaluating algebraic expressions. We substitute all the given numbers for the variables and then carry out the computations using the order of operations rule.

EXAMPLE ②

PRACTICE 2

Given the distance formula $d = rt$, find the value of d if the rate r is 50 mph and the time t is 1.6 hr.

The formula for finding simple interest is $I = Prt$, where I is the interest in dollars, P is the principal (the amount invested) in dollars, r is the annual rate of interest, and t is the time in years that the principal has been on deposit. Find the amount of interest on a principal of \$3000 that has been on deposit for 2 years at a 6% annual rate of interest.

SOLUTION   We know that $P = 3000$, $r = 6\%$, and $t = 2$. Converting 6% to its decimal form, we get 0.06. Substituting into the formula gives us:

$$I = Prt$$
$$= 3000\,(0.06)\,(2)$$
$$= 360$$

So the interest earned is \$360. $\cdots\bullet$

EXAMPLE ③

PRACTICE 3

Kelvin and Celsius temperature scales are commonly used in science. To convert a temperature expressed in Celsius degrees C to degrees Kelvin, K, add 273 to the Celsius temperature.

a. Write this relationship as a formula.

b. Suppose that in a chemistry experiment, C equals −6. What is the value of K?

The markup M on an item is its selling price S minus its cost C.

a. Express this relationship as a formula.

b. If a digital camera cost a retailer \$399.95 and was then sold for \$559, how much was the markup on the camera?

SOLUTION

a. We write the formula $M = S - C$.

b. To find the markup, we substitute for S and C.

$$M = S - C$$
$$= 559 - 399.95$$
$$= 159.05$$

So the markup was \$159.05. $\cdots\bullet$

4.2   WHAT IS AVERAGE? ···

The term *average* comes up frequently in the news and other reports, but it does not always have the same meaning. As you will see in this section, the most appropriate definition of *average* depends on the situation.

Mean, Median, and Mode

Table 4.1 shows the number of movies (original and sequels or prequels) in each of five popular science fiction series. What is the average number of films in these series? One way to answer this question is to compute the **mean**. (The formal term of *arithmetic mean* is commonly referred to simply as the *mean*.) We find the mean by dividing the total number of movies by five (because there are five series listed in the data set):

$$\text{mean} = \frac{4 + 7 + 11 + 6 + 4}{5} = \frac{32}{5} = 6.4$$

In other words, these five series have a mean of 6.4 movies. More generally, we find the mean of any data set by dividing the sum of all the data values by the number of data values. The mean is what most people think of as the average. In essence, it represents the balance point for a quantitative data distribution, as shown in Figure 4.1.

We could also describe the average number of films by computing the **median**, or middle value, of the data set. To find a median, we arrange the data values in ascending (or descending) order, repeating data values that appear more than once. If the number of values is odd, there is exactly one value in the middle of the list, and this value is the median. If the number of values is even, there are two values in the middle of the list, and the median is the number that lies halfway between them. Putting the data in Table 4.1 in ascending order gives the list 4, 4, 6, 7, 11. The median number of movies is 6 because 6 is the middle number in the list.

The **mode** is the most common value or group of values in a data set. In the case of the movies, the mode is 4 because this value occurs twice in the data set, while the other values occur only once. A data set may have one mode, more than one mode, or no mode. Sometimes the mode refers to a group of closely spaced values rather than a single value. The mode is used more commonly for qualitative data than for quantitative data, as neither the mean nor the median can be used with qualitative data.

TABLE 4.1	Five Science Fiction Movie Series
Series	**Number of movies (as of 2012)**
Alien	4
Planet of the Apes	7
Star Trek	11
Star Wars	6
Terminator	4

Note: Counts only major releases in each series; does not include *Prometheus* in the *Alien* series.

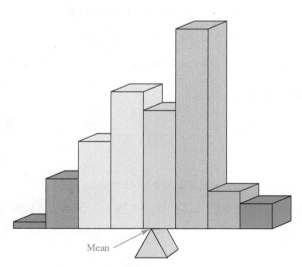

Figure 4.1   A histogram made from blocks would balance at the position of its mean.

Definitions—Measures of Center in a Distribution

The **mean** is what we most commonly call the average value. It is found as follows:

$$\text{mean} = \frac{\text{sum of all values}}{\text{total number of values}}$$

The **median** is the middle value in the sorted data set (or halfway between the two middle values if the number of values is even).

The **mode** is the most common value (or group of values) in a data set.

When rounding, we will use the following rule for all the calculations discussed in this chapter.

Rounding Rule for Statistical Calculations

In general, you should express answers with *one more* decimal place of precision than is found in the raw data. For example, if the data are given as whole numbers, you should round their mean to the nearest tenth; if the data are given to the nearest tenth, you should round their mean to the nearest hundredth; and so on. *As always, round only the final answer and not any intermediate values used in your calculations.*

Notice how we applied this rule in the movie example. The data in Table 4.1 consist of whole numbers, so we stated the mean as 6.4. If the calculation happens to end up with the same number of significant digits as the raw data, then keeping an extra decimal place is optional.

EXAMPLE 1   Price Data

Eight grocery stores sell the PR energy bar for the following prices:

$1.09 $1.29 $1.29 $1.35 $1.39 $1.49 $1.59 $1.79

Find the mean, median, and mode for these prices.

SOLUTION   The *mean* price is $1.41:

$$\text{mean} = \frac{\$1.09 + \$1.29 + \$1.29 + \$1.35 + \$1.39 + \$1.49 + \$1.59 + \$1.79}{8}$$

$$= \$1.41$$

To find the *median*, we first sort the data in ascending order:

$1.09, $1.29, $1.29, $1.35, $1.39, $1.49, $1.59, $1.79

3 values below   2 middle values   3 values above

⏻ USING TECHNOLOGY—**MEAN, MEDIAN, AND MODE**

Excel Excel provides the built-in function AVERAGE for calculating a mean and separate functions for MEDIAN and MODE. The screen shot below shows the use of these functions for the data from Example 1. Column B shows the functions and Column C shows the results.

◇	A	B	C
1	Data	1.09	
2		1.29	
3		1.29	
4		1.35	
5		1.39	
6		1.49	
7		1.59	
8		1.79	
9	Mean	=AVERAGE(B1:B8)	1.41
10	Median	=MEDIAN(B1:B8)	1.37
11	Mode	=MODE(B1:B8)	1.29
12			

Note: If you have a Windows version of Excel, you can get even more information by installing the Data Analysis Toolpak; to find it, use the Help feature and search for "Data Analysis." Once installed, click on **Data**, select **Data Analysis**, then select **Descriptive Statistics** in the pop-up window, and click **OK**. In the dialog box, enter the input range (such as A1:A8 for 8 values in column A), click on **Summary Statistics**, then click **OK**. Results will include the mean and median, as well as other statistics to be discussed in the following sections.

Alternatively, the XLSTAT add-in that is a supplement to this book can be used with both Windows and Mac computers. Enter the data as described above, click on XLSTAT, click on Visualizing Data, then select Descriptive Statistics. Enter the range of the data, such as A1:A8. (If the first row is the name of the data, be sure to click on the box next to "Sample labels."

STATDISK Enter the data in the Data Window or open an existing data set. Click on **Data** and select **Descriptive Statistics**. Now click on **Evaluate** to get the various descriptive statistics, including the mean and median, as well as other statistics to be discussed in the following sections.

TI-83/84 PLUS First enter the data in list L1 by pressing **STAT**, then selecting **Edit** and pressing the **ENTER** key. After the data values have been entered, press **STAT** and select **CALC**, then select **1-Var Stats** and press the **ENTER** key twice. The display will include the mean and median, as well as other statistics to be discussed in the following sections. Use the down-arrow key ⌄ to view the results that don't fit on the initial display.

Because there are eight prices (an even number), there are two values in the middle of the list: $1.35 and $1.39. Therefore the median lies halfway between these two values, which we calculate by adding them and dividing by 2:

$$\text{median} = \frac{\$1.35 + \$1.39}{2} = \$1.37$$

Using the rounding rule, we could express the mean and median as $1.410 and $1.370, respectively, though the extra zeros are optional in this case.

The *mode* is $1.29 because this price occurs more times than any other price.   ⋅⋅●

Effects of Outliers

To explore the differences among the mean, median, and mode, imagine that the five graduating seniors on a college basketball team receive the following first-year contract offers to play in the National Basketball Association (zero indicates that the player did not receive a contract offer):

0 0 0 0 $10,000,000

The mean contract offer is

$$\text{mean} = \frac{0 + 0 + 0 + 0 + \$10,000,000}{5} = \$2,000,000$$

Is it therefore fair to say that the *average* senior on this basketball team received a $2 million contract offer?

TABLE 4.2   **Comparison of Mean, Median, and Mode**

Measure	Definition	How common?	Existence	Takes every value into account?	Affected by outliers?	Advantages
Mean	$\dfrac{\text{sum of all values}}{\text{total number of values}}$	most familiar "average"	always exists	yes	yes	commonly understood; works well with many statistical methods
Median	middle value	common	always exists	no (aside from counting the total number of values)	no	when there are outliers, may be more representative of an "average" than the mean
Mode	most frequent value	sometimes used	may be no mode, one mode, or more than one mode	no	no	most appropriate for qualitative data

BY THE WAY

A survey once found that geography majors from the University of North Carolina had a far higher mean starting salary than geography majors from other schools. The reason for the high mean turned out to be a single outlier—the basketball superstar and geography major named Michael Jordan.

Not really. The problem is that the single player receiving the large offer makes the mean much larger than it would be otherwise. If we ignore this one player and look only at the other four, the mean contract offer is zero. Because this one value of $10,000,000 is so extreme compared with the others, we say that it is an **outlier** (or *outlying value*). As our example shows, an outlier can pull the mean significantly upward (or downward), thereby making the mean unrepresentative of the data set as a whole.

> **Definition**
> An **outlier** in a data set is a value that is much higher or much lower than almost all other values.

While the outlier pulls the mean contract offer upward, it has no effect on the median contract offer, which remains zero for the five players. In general, the value of an outlier has no effect on the median, because outliers don't lie in the middle of a data set. Outliers do not affect the mode either. Table 4.2 summarizes the characteristics of the mean, median, and mode, including the effects of outliers on each measure.

> TIME ◯UT TO THINK
> Is it fair to use the median as the average contract offer for the five players? Why or why not?

Deciding how to deal with outliers is one of the more important issues in statistics. Sometimes, as in our basketball example, an outlier is a legitimate value that must be understood in order to interpret the mean and median properly. Other times, outliers may indicate mistakes in a data set. Deciding when outliers are important and when they may simply be mistakes can be very difficult.

EXAMPLE ② Mistake?

A track coach wants to determine an appropriate heart rate for her athletes during their workouts. She chooses five of her best runners and asks them to wear heart monitors during a workout. In the middle of the workout, she reads the following heart rates for the five athletes: 130, 135, 140, 145, 325. Which is a better measure of the average in this case—the mean or the median? Why?

SOLUTION   Four of the five values are fairly close together and seem reasonable for mid-workout heart rates. The high value of 325 is an outlier. This outlier seems likely to be a mistake (perhaps caused by a faulty heart monitor), because anyone with such a high heart rate should be in cardiac arrest. If the coach uses the mean as the average, she will be including this outlier—which means she will be including any mistake made when it was recorded. If she uses the median as the average, she'll have a more reasonable value, because the median won't be affected by the outlier.   ··●

"Average" Confusion

The different meanings of *average* can lead to confusion. Sometimes this confusion arises because we are not told whether the average is the mean or the median, and other times because we are not given enough information about how the average was computed. The following examples illustrate two such situations.

EXAMPLE 3   Wage Dispute

A newspaper surveys wages for workers in regional high-tech companies and reports an average of $22 per hour. The workers at one large firm immediately request a pay raise, claiming that they work as hard as employees at other companies but their average wage is only $19. The management rejects their request, telling them that they are *overpaid* because their average wage, in fact, is $23. Can both sides be right? Explain.

SOLUTION   Both sides can be right if they are using different definitions of *average*. In this case, the workers may be using the median while the management uses the mean. For example, imagine that there are only five workers at the company and their wages are $19, $19, $19, $19, and $39. The median of these five wages is $19 (as the workers claimed), but the mean is $23 (as management claimed).   ··●

EXAMPLE 4   Which Mean?

All 100 first-year students at a small college take three courses in the Core Studies program. Two courses are taught in large lectures, with all 100 students in a single class. The third course is taught in 10 classes of 10 students each. Students and administrators get into an argument about whether classes are too large. The students claim that the mean size of their Core Studies classes is 70. The administrators claim that the mean class size is only 25. Can both sides be right? Explain

SOLUTION   The students calculated the mean size of the classes in which each student is personally enrolled. Each student is taking two classes with enrollments of 100 and one class with an enrollment of 10, so the mean size of each student's classes is

$$\frac{\text{total enrollment in student's classes}}{\text{number of classes student is taking}} = \frac{100 + 100 + 10}{3} = 70$$

The administrators calculated the mean enrollment in all classes. There are two classes with 100 students and 10 classes with 10 students, making a total enrollment of 300 students in 12 classes. The mean enrollment per class is

$$\frac{\text{total enrollment}}{\text{number of classes}} = \frac{300}{12} = 25$$

The two claims about the mean are both correct, but the two sides are talking about different means. The students calculated the mean *class size per student*, while the administrators calculated the mean number of *students per class*.   ··●

Figures won't lie, but liars will figure.

—Charles H. Grosvenor

TIME OUT TO THINK

In Example 4, could the administrators redistribute faculty assignments so that all classes have 25 students each? How? Discuss the advantages and disadvantages of such a change.

Weighted Mean

Suppose your course grade is based on four quizzes and one final exam. Each quiz counts as 15% of your final grade, and the final counts as 40%. Your quiz scores are 75, 80, 84, and 88, and your final exam score is 96. What is your overall score?

Because the final exam counts more than the quizzes, a simple mean of the five scores does not give your final score. Instead, we must assign a *weight* (indicating the relative importance) to each score. In this case, we assign weights of 15 (for the 15%) to each of the quizzes and 40 (for the 40%) to the final. We then find the **weighted mean** by adding the products of each score and its weight and then dividing by the sum of the weights:

$$\text{weighted mean} = \frac{(75 \times 15) + (80 \times 15) + (84 \times 15) + (88 \times 15) + (96 \times 40)}{15 + 15 + 15 + 15 + 40}$$

$$= \frac{8745}{100} = 87.45$$

BY THE WAY

Sports statistics that rate players or teams according to their performance in many different categories are usually weighted means. Examples include the earned run average (ERA) and slugging percentage in baseball, the quarterback rating in football, and computerized rankings of college teams.

The weighted mean of 87.45 properly accounts for the different weights of the quizzes and the exam. Following the rounding rule, we round this score to 87.5.

Weighted means are appropriate whenever the data values vary in their degree of importance. You can always find a weighted mean using the following formula.

Definitions

A **weighted mean** accounts for variations in the relative importance of data values. Each data value is assigned a weight and the weighted mean is

$$\text{weighted mean} = \frac{\text{sum of (each data value} \times \text{its weight)}}{\text{sum of all weights}}$$

TIME OUT TO THINK

Because the weights are percentages in the course grade example, we could think of the weights as 0.15 and 0.40 rather than 15 and 40. Calculate the weighted mean by using the weights of 0.15 and 0.40. Do you still find the same answer? Why or why not?

EXAMPLE 5   GPA

Randall has 38 credits with a grade of A, 22 credits with a grade of B, and 7 credits with a grade of C. What is his grade point average (GPA)? Base the GPA on values of 4.0 points for an A, 3.0 points for a B, and 2.0 points for a C.

SOLUTION   The grades of A, B, and C represent data values of 4.0, 3.0, and 2.0, respectively. The numbers of credits are the weights. The As represent a data value of 4 with a weight of 38, the Bs represent a data value of 3 with a weight of 22, and the Cs represent a data value of 2 with a weight of 7. The weighted mean is

$$\text{weighted mean} = \frac{(4 \times 38) + (3 \times 22) + (2 \times 7)}{38 + 22 + 7} = \frac{232}{67} = 3.46$$

Following our rounding rule, we round Randall's GPA from 3.46 to 3.5. $\cdots\bullet$

EXAMPLE 6 Stock Voting

Voting in corporate elections is usually weighted by the amount of stock owned by each voter. Suppose a company has five stockholders who vote on whether the company should embark on a new advertising campaign. The votes (Y = yes, N = no) are as follows:

Stockholder	Shares owned	Vote
A	225	Y
B	170	Y
C	275	Y
D	500	N
E	90	N

According to the company's bylaws, the measure needs 60% of the vote to pass. Does it pass?

SOLUTION   We can regard a yes vote as a value of 1 and a no vote as a value of 0. The number of shares is the weight for the vote of each stockholder, so Stockholder A's vote represents a value of 1 with a weight of 225, stockholder B's vote represents a value of 1 with a weight of 170, and so on. The weighted mean vote is

$$\text{weighted mean} = \frac{(1 \times 225) + (1 \times 170) + (1 \times 275) + (0 \times 500) + (0 \times 90)}{225 + 170 + 275 + 500 + 90}$$

$$= \frac{670}{1260} \approx 0.53$$

The weighted vote is 53% (or 0.53) in favor, which is short of the required 60%, so the measure does not pass. $\cdots$ ●

Means with Summation Notation (Optional Section)

Many statistical formulas, including the formula for the mean, can be written compactly with a mathematical notation called *summation notation*. The symbol Σ (the Greek capital letter *sigma*) is called the *summation sign* and indicates that a set of numbers should be added. We use the symbol x to represent *each* value in a data set, so we write the sum of all the data values as

$$\text{sum of all values} = \Sigma x$$

For example, if a sample consists of 25 exam scores, Σx represents the sum of all 25 scores. Similarly, if a sample consists of the incomes of 10,000 families, Σx represents the total dollar value of all 10,000 incomes.

We use n to represent the total number of values in the sample. Thus, the general formula for the mean is

$$\bar{x} = \text{sample mean} = \frac{\text{sum of all values}}{\text{total number of values}} = \frac{\Sigma x}{n}$$

The symbol $\bar{x}$ is the standard symbol for the mean of a sample. When dealing with the mean of a population rather than a sample, statisticians instead use the Greek letter μ (*mu*).

Summation notation also makes it easy to express a general formula for the weighted mean. Again we use the symbol x to represent each data value, and we let w represent the weight of each data value. The sum of the products of each data value and its corresponding weight is $\Sigma(x \times w)$. The sum of the weights is Σw. Therefore, the formula for the weighted mean is

$$\text{weighted mean} = \frac{\Sigma(x \times w)}{\Sigma w}$$

TECHNICAL NOTE

Summations are often written with the use of an *index* that specifies how to step through the sum. For example, the symbol x_i indicates the *i*th data value in the set; the letter *i* is the index. We then write the sum of all values as

$$\sum_{i=1}^{n} x_i$$

We read this expression as "the sum of the x_i values, starting with $i = 1$ and continuing to $i = n$, where n is the total number of data values in the set." With this notation, the mean is written

$$\bar{x} = \frac{1}{n} \sum_{i=1}^{n} x_i$$

Measures of Center for Frequency Tables (Unbinned)

There may be times that we are presented with a frequency table and not a listing of the original data. Fortunately, it is still possible to find the measures of center. The frequency table that follows represents the number of keys that employees had for their workplace.

Number of Keys	Frequency
0	3
1	2
2	7
3	7
4	9

You can think of this frequency table as shorthand for the list of data values:
0, 0, 1, 1, 2, 2, 2, 2, 2, 2, 2, 3, 3, 3, 3, 3, 3, 3, 4, 4, 4, 4, 4, 4, 4, 4, 4

To find the median, you could look at the list of the data and locate the value that is at the middle. Because there are 28 data values (an even number), there are two values that share the center. The values that share the center are both 3. So, the median is 3.

To find the mean, you would sum up all the data values and divide by the number of data values.

The sum of the data values is 73, and there are 28 data values. So, the mean is 73 divided by 28 is approximately 2.6 keys. (Remember that we round to one more place value than the original data).

Although 28 data values is pretty many, it was possible to do this problem by listing out the data values. However, would you want to do that for 128 data values? 1,128 data values? For large data sets, It is helpful to have a technique for finding measures of center for frequency tables that doesn't require listing out all the values.

Recall that multiplication is simply repeated addition. So, instead of adding $2 + 2 + 2 + 2 + 2 + 2 + 2$, we could rewrite this as 2 multiplied by 7. In keeping with this strategy, we could find the sum of the data values by multiplying each data value by its frequency. Let's now find the mean number of keys using this technique. You may find it helpful to do this by inserting another column at the right side of the frequency table.

Number of Keys	Frequency	Number of Keys × Frequency
0	3	$0 \times 3 = 0$
1	2	$1 \times 2 = 2$
2	7	$2 \times 7 = 14$
3	7	$3 \times 7 = 21$
4	9	$4 \times 9 = 36$

Sum up the values in the last column to determine the sum of the data values. Add up the frequencies to determine the total number of pieces of data.

Number of Keys	Frequency	Number of Keys × Frequency
0	3	$0 \times 3 = 0$
1	2	$1 \times 2 = 2$
2	7	$2 \times 7 = 14$
3	7	$3 \times 7 = 21$
4	9	$4 \times 9 = 36$
Sample size = 28		Sum of Data Values = 0 + 2 + 14 + 21 + 36 = 73

As we did in the listing method, we can now find the mean by dividing 73 by 28.

The mean number of keys is 2.6 keys.

With 28 values, the median is between the 14th and 15th values. So, that would fall within the row with 3 keys since $3 + 2 + 7 = 12$ people had 2 or fewer keys and the next 7 people (including the 14th and 15th) had 3 keys.

The mode is 4 keys since that value has the highest frequency.

Measures of Center for Dotplots

You may also want to find measures of center when you have data presented graphically in the form of dotplots or bar charts. We will do an example for dotplots here. The process for bar charts is similar.

The dotplot that follows represents the responses to a survey at a grocery store about the number of people that live in a customer's household. We want to find the measures of center from this dotplot.

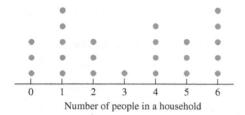

Number of people in a household

Let's transfer the data from a dotplot to a frequency table, and follow the steps outlined in a previous example for the frequency table.

Number of People in a Household	Frequency	Household size * Frequency
0	3	$0 \times 3 = 0$
1	5	$1 \times 5 = 5$
2	3	$2 \times 3 = 6$
3	1	$3 \times 1 = 3$
4	4	$4 \times 4 = 16$
5	3	$5 \times 3 = 15$
6	5	$6 \times 5 = 30$
	Sample size = 24	Sum of Data Values: 75

The mean is $\dfrac{75}{24} = 3.1$ people per household.

The median is located between the 12th and 13th values. This falls between the rows with a household size of 3 and 4. The median is halfway between these values, $\dfrac{3 + 4}{2} = \dfrac{7}{2} = 3.5$. The median is 3.5 people in a household.

There are two modes since 1 and 6 share the same frequency of 5 occurrences each. The modes are 1 and 6 people per household.

Means and Medians with Binned Data (Optional Section)

The ideas of this section can be extended to binned data simply by assuming that the middle value in the bin represents all the data values in the bin. For example, consider the following table of 50 binned integer data values:

Bin	Frequency
0–6	10
7–13	10
14–20	10
21–27	20

The middle value of the first bin is 3, so we assume that the value of 3 occurs 10 times. Continuing this way, the sum of the 50 values in the table is

$$(3 \times 10) + (10 \times 10) + (17 \times 10) + (24 \times 20) = 780$$

The mean is therefore 780/50 = 15.6. With 50 values, the median is between the 25th and 26th values. These values fall within the bin 14–20, so we call this bin the **median class** for the data. The mode is the bin with the highest frequency—the bin 21–27 in this case.

Measures of Center with Binned Data Histograms

We can further extend the explanation for the binned data frequency table to binned data histograms. The following histogram summarizes the responses to a survey that was asked at an airport shoe store. The survey collected data on how many pairs of shoes each customer owned.

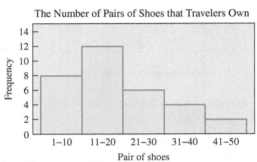

The Number of Pairs of Shoes that Travelers Own

Suppose we want to find the mean number of pairs that travelers owned. However, we only have the histogram without any access to the original data values. Can we find the actual mean? No. However, we can come up with an estimate. Look at the first bar of the histogram labeled 1 - 10. There were 8 respondents that indicated that they own between 1 and 10 pairs of shoes. From the histogram, we don't know the exact number of pairs of shoes that each of these individuals own. If we think about it, we may soon discover that the best estimate would be the middle of those values. So, we will estimate that these 8 respondents each had $\frac{1 + 10}{2} = \frac{11}{2} = 5.5$ pairs of shoes. We will do similar calculations for each grouping. You may want to organize the information as a frequency table and insert additional columns to keep your calculations organized.

Pairs of Shoes	Frequency	Estimated Value for Each Bin	Frequency × Estimated Value
1 − 10	8	5.5	44
11 − 20	12	15.5	186
21 − 30	6	25.5	153
31 − 40	4	35.5	142
41 − 50	2	45.5	91
	Sum = 32		Sum = 616

Now, we will complete another column that represents the frequencies times the respective estimated values. Then, find the sum of this column, which works out to 616. This value of 616 is now the estimated value for the sum of all your data values. We also need to know the sample size. By adding the values in the frequency column, we find a sample size of 32. So, our best estimate for the mean is $\frac{616}{32} = 19.3$ pairs of shoes.

With 32 values, the median is between the 16th and 17th values. These values fall within the bin 11–20; so, we call this grouping the median class for the data. You could also indicate that 15.5 pairs of shoes is the best estimated value for the median.

The modal bin (class) is 11 − 20 pairs of shoes.

Section 4.2 Exercises

Statistical Literacy and Critical Thinking

1. **Average and Mean.** Do the terms "average" and "mean" have the same meaning? Explain.

2. **Mean and Median.** A statistics class consists of 24 students, all but one of whom are unemployed or are employed in low-paying part-time jobs. One student works as an executive secretary earning $75,000 per year. Which does a better job of describing the income of a typical student in the class: the mean or the median? Why?

3. **Outlier.** For the same statistics class described in Exercise 2, is the executive secretary's salary an outlier? Why or why not? In general, is an outlier defined in an exact way so that it can be clearly and objectively identified?

4. **Mean Income.** An economist wants to find the mean annual income for all adults in the United States. She knows that it is not practical to survey each member of the adult population, so she refers to an almanac and finds the mean income listed for each of the 50 states. She adds the 50 state means and divides by 50. Is the result the mean income for the United States? Why or why not?

Does It Make Sense? For Exercises 5–8, decide whether the statement makes sense (or is clearly true) or does not make sense (or is clearly false). Explain clearly; not all of these statements have definitive answers, so your explanation is more important than your chosen answer.

5. **Mean.** The number on the jersey of each New York Giants football player is recorded, then the mean of those numbers is computed.

6. **Mode.** A data set of incomes has modes of $50,000 and $80,000.

7. **Mean, Median, and Mode.** A researcher studying an income distribution obtains the same value of $75,000 for the mean, median, and mode.

8. **Weighted Mean.** A professor calculates final grades using a weighted mean in which the final exam counts twice as much as the midterm.

Appropriate Average. Exercises 9–12 list "averages" that someone might want to know. In each case, state whether the mean or median would give a better description of the "average." Explain your reasoning.

9. **Height.** The average height of all active professional basketball players

10. **Salary.** The average salary of all active professional basketball players

11. **Ages.** The following ages (years) of survey respondents: 22, 19, 21, 27, "over 65," "over 80"

12. **Pulse Rates.** The average resting pulse rate of 500 randomly selected female statistics students

Concepts and Applications

Mean, Median, and Mode. Exercises 13–20 each list a set of numbers. In each case, find the mean, median, and mode of the listed numbers.

13. **Number of Words.** Pages from *Merriam-Webster's Collegiate Dictionary*, 11th edition, were randomly selected. Here are the numbers of words defined on those pages:

51 63 36 43 34 62 73 39 53 79

14. **Space Shuttle Flights.** Listed below are the durations (in hours) of a sample of all flights of NASA's Space Transport System (space shuttle):

73   95 235 192 165 262 191 376
259 235 381 331 221 244   0

15. **Perception of Time.** Actual times (in seconds) recorded when statistics students participated in an experiment to test their ability to determine when one minute (60 seconds) had passed:

53 52 75 62 68 58 49 49

16. **Body Temperatures.** Body temperatures (in degrees Fahrenheit) of randomly selected normal and healthy adults:

98.6   98.6   98.0   98.0   99.0
98.4   98.4   98.4   98.4   98.6

17. **Blood Alcohol.** Blood alcohol concentrations of drivers involved in fatal crashes and then given jail sentences (based on data from the U.S. Department of Justice):

0.27   0.17   0.17   0.16   0.13   0.24
0.29   0.24   0.14   0.16   0.12   0.16

18. **Old Faithful Geyser.** Time intervals (in minutes) between eruptions of Old Faithful geyser in Yellowstone National Park:

98   92   95   87   96   90
65   92   95   93   98   94

19. **Weights of M&Ms.** Weights (in grams) of randomly selected M&M plain candies:

0.957   0.912   0.842   0.925   0.939   0.886
0.914   0.913   0.958   0.947   0.920

20. **Quarters.** Weights (in grams) of quarters in circulation:

5.60   5.63   5.58   5.56   5.66   5.58   5.57   5.59
5.67   5.61   5.84   5.73   5.53   5.58   5.52   5.65
5.57   5.71   5.59   5.53   5.63   5.68

21. Alphabetic States. The following table gives the total area in square miles (land and water) of the seven states with names beginning with the letters A through C.

State	Area
Alabama	52,200
Alaska	615,200
Arizona	114,000
Arkansas	53,200
California	158,900
Colorado	104,100
Connecticut	5,500

  a. Find the mean area and median area for these states.

  b. Which state is an outlier on the high end? If you eliminate this state, what are the new mean and median areas for this data set?

  c. Which state is an outlier on the low end? If you eliminate this state, what are the new mean and median areas for this data set?

22. Outlier Coke. Cans of regular Coca-Cola vary slightly in weight. Here are the measured weights of seven cans, in pounds:

    0.8161   0.8194   0.8165   0.8176
    0.7901   0.8143   0.8126

  a. Find the mean and median of these weights.

  b. Which, if any, of these weights would you consider to be an outlier? Explain.

  c. What are the mean and median weights if the outlier is excluded?

23. Raising Your Grade. Suppose you have scores of 80, 84, 87, and 89 on quizzes in a mathematics class.

  a. What is the mean of these scores?

  b. What score would you need on the next quiz to have an overall mean of 88?

  c. If the maximum score on a quiz is 100, is it possible to have a mean of 90 after the fifth quiz? Explain.

24. Raising Your Grade. Suppose you have scores of 60, 70, 65, 85, and 85 on exams in a sociology class.

  a. What is the mean of these scores?

  b. What score would you need on the next exam to have an overall mean of 75?

  c. If the maximum score on an exam is 100, what is the maximum mean score that you could possibly have after the next exam? Explain.

25. Comparing Averages. Suppose that school district officials claim that the average reading score for fourth-graders in the district is 73 (out of a possible 100). As a principal, you know that your fourth-graders had the following scores: 55, 60, 68, 70, 87, 88, 95. Would you be justified in claiming that your students scored above the district average? Explain.

26. Comparing Averages. Suppose the National Basketball Association (NBA) reports that the average height of basketball players is 6'8". As a coach, you know that the players on your starting lineup have heights of 6'5", 6'6", 6'6", 7'0", and 7'2". Would you be justified in claiming that your starting lineup has above average height for the NBA? Explain.

27. Average Peaches. A grocer has three baskets of peaches. One holds 50 peaches and weighs 18 pounds, one holds 55 peaches and weighs 22 pounds, and the third holds 60 peaches and weighs 24 pounds. What is the mean weight of all of the peaches combined? Explain.

28. Average Confusion. An instructor has a first-period class with 25 students, and they had a mean score of 86% on the midterm exam. The second-period class has 30 students, and they had a mean score of 84% on the same exam. Does it follow that the mean score for both classes combined is 85%? Explain.

29. Different Means? Each of the 300 students at a high school takes the same four courses. Three of the courses are each taught in 15 classes of 20 students each. The fourth course is taught in 3 classes of 100 students each. Find the mean class size experienced by each student. Find the mean class size in the 48 courses. Are the two means the same?

30. Final Grade. Your course grade is based on one midterm that counts as 15% of your final grade, one class project that counts as 20% of your final grade, a set of homework assignments that counts as 40% of your final grade, and a final exam that counts as 25% of your final grade. Your midterm score is 75, your project score is 90, your homework score is 85, and your final exam score is 72. What is your overall final score?

31. Batting Average. A batting average in baseball is determined by dividing the total number of hits by the total number of at-bats (neglecting walks, sacrifices, and a few other special cases). A player goes 2 for 4 (2 hits in 4 at-bats) in the first game, 0 for 3 in the second game, and 3 for 5 in the third game. What is his batting average? In what way is this number an "average"?

32. Averaging Averages. Suppose a player has a batting average over many games of 0.200 (he's not very good). In his next game, he goes 2 for 4, which is a batting average of 0.500 for the game. Does it follow that his new batting average is $(0.200 + 0.500)/2 = 0.350$? Explain.

33. Batteries. A manufacturer uses two different production sites to make batteries for cell phones. There is a defect rate of 2% at one of the sites, and the defect rate at the other site is 4%. Does it follow that when the batteries from the two sites are combined, the overall rate of defects is 3%? Explain.

34. Slugging Average. In addition to the batting average, another measure of hitting performance in baseball is called the slugging average. In finding a slugging average, a single is worth 1 point, a double is worth 2 points, a triple is worth 3 points, and a home run is worth 4 points. A player's slugging average is the total number of points divided by the total number of at-bats (neglecting walks, sacrifices, and a few other special cases). A player has three singles in five at-bats in the first game, a triple and a single in four at-bats in the second game, and a double and a home run in five at-bats in the third game.

   a. What is his batting average?

   b. What is his slugging average?

   c. Is it possible for a slugging average to be more than 1? Explain.

35. Stockholder Voting. A small company has four stockholders. One stockholder has 400 shares, a second stockholder has 300 shares, a third stockholder has 200 shares, and the fourth stockholder has 100 shares. In a vote on a new advertising campaign, the first stockholder votes yes, and the other three stockholders vote no. Explain how the outcome of the vote can be expressed as a weighted mean. What is the outcome of the vote?

36. GPA. One common system for computing a grade point average (GPA) assigns 4 points to an A, 3 points to a B, 2 points to a C, 1 point to a D, and 0 points to an F. What is the GPA of a student who gets an A in a 4-credit course, a B in each of two 3-credit courses, and a C in a 1-credit course?

37. Phenotypes of Peas. An experiment was conducted to determine whether a deficiency of carbon dioxide in soil affects the phenotypes of peas. Listed below are the phenotype codes, where 1 = smooth yellow, 2 = smooth geen, 3 = wrinkled yellow, and 4 = wrinkled green. Can the measures of center be obtained for these values? Do the results make sense?

2	1	1	1	1	1	1	4	1	2	2	1	2
3	3	2	3	1	3	1	3	1	3	2	2

38. U.S. Population Center. Imagine taking a huge flat map of the United States and placing weights on it to represent where people live. The point at which the map would balance is called the mean center of population. Figure 4.2 shows how the location of the mean center of population has shifted from 1790 to 2010. Briefly explain the pattern shown on this map.

PROJECTS FOR THE INTERNET & BEYOND

39. Salary Data. Many Web sites offer data on salaries in different careers. Find salary data for a career you are considering. What are the mean and median salaries for this career? How do these salaries compare with those of other careers that interest you?

40. Is the Median the Message? Read the article "The Median Isn't the Message," by Stephen Jay Gould, which is posted on the Web. Write a few paragraphs in which you describe the message that Gould was trying to get across. How is this message important to other patients diagnosed with cancer?

41. Navel Data. Bin the data collected in Exercise 23 of Section 3.1. Then make a frequency table, and draw a histogram of the distribution. What is the mean of the distribution? What is the median of the distribution? An old theory says that, on average, the navel ratio of humans is the golden ratio: $\left(1 + \sqrt{5}\right)/2$. Does this theory seem accurate based on your observations?

IN THE NEWS

42. Daily Averages. Cite three examples of averages that you deal with in your own life (such as grade point average or batting average). In each case, explain whether the average is a mean, a median, or some other type of average. Briefly describe how the average is useful to you.

43. Averages in the News. Find three recent news articles that refer to some type of average. In each case, explain whether the average is a mean, a median, or some other type of average.

Figure 4.2 Mean center of population.
Source: Statistical Abstract of the United States.

4.3 SHAPES OF DISTRIBUTIONS

In the previous section we discussed how to describe the center of a quantitative data distribution with measures such as the mean and median. We now turn our attention to the overall *shape* of a distribution, which we often describe with three characteristics: its number of modes, its symmetry or skewness, and its variation. Although these three characteristics carry less information than a complete graph of the distribution, they are still useful.

Note that, because we are interested in the *general* shapes of distributions, it's often easier to examine graphs that show smooth curves to fit the original data sets. Figure 4.3 shows three examples of this idea, two in which the distributions are shown as histograms and one in which the distribution is shown as a line chart. In each case, the smooth curves make good approximations to the original distributions.

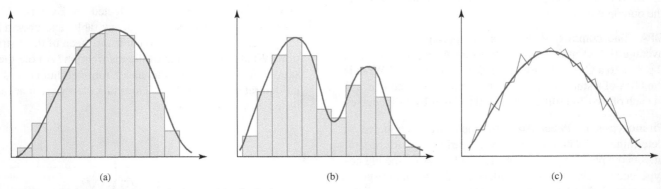

(a)   (b)   (c)

Figure 4.3 The smooth curves approximate the shapes of the distributions.

Number of Modes

One simple way to describe the shape of a distribution is by its number of peaks, or modes. Figure 4.4a shows a distribution, called a **uniform distribution**, that has no mode because all data values have the same frequency. Figure 4.4b shows a distribution with a single peak as its mode. It is called a **single-peaked**, or **unimodal**, distribution. By convention, any peak in a distribution is considered a mode, even if not all peaks have the same height. For example, the distribution in Figure 4.4c is said to have two modes, even though the second peak is lower than the first; it is a *bimodal* distribution. Similarly, the distribution in Figure 4.4d is said to have three modes; it is a *trimodal* distribution.

EXAMPLE 1 Number of Modes

How many modes would you expect for each of the following distributions? Why? Make a rough sketch for each distribution, with clearly labeled axes.

a. Heights of 1,000 randomly selected adult women

b. Hours spent watching football on TV in January for 1,000 randomly selected adult Americans

c. Weekly sales throughout the year at a retail clothing store for children

d. The number of people with particular last digits (0 through 9) in their Social Security numbers

SOLUTION   Figure 4.5 shows sketches of the distributions.

a. The distribution of heights of women is single-peaked because many women are at or near the mean height, with fewer and fewer women at heights much greater or less than the mean.

b. The distribution of times spent watching football on TV for 1,000 randomly selected adult Americans is likely to be bimodal (two modes). One mode represents the mean watching time of men, and the other represents the mean watching time of women.

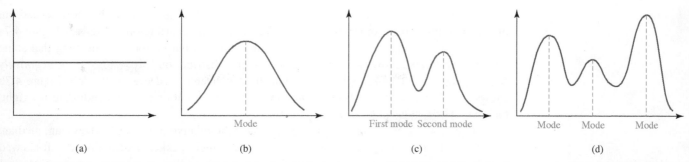

Figure 4.4 (a) A uniform distribution has no mode. (b) A single-peaked distribution has one mode. (c) A bimodal distribution has two modes. (d) A trimodal distribution has three modes.

c. The distribution of weekly sales throughout the year at a retail clothing store for children is likely to have several modes. For example, it will probably have a mode in spring for sales of summer clothing, a mode in late summer for back-to-school sales, and another mode in winter for holiday sales.

d. The last digits of Social Security numbers are essentially random, so the number of people with each different last digit (0 through 9) should be about the same. That is, about 10% of all Social Security numbers end in 0, 10% end in 1, and so on. It is therefore a uniform distribution with no mode.

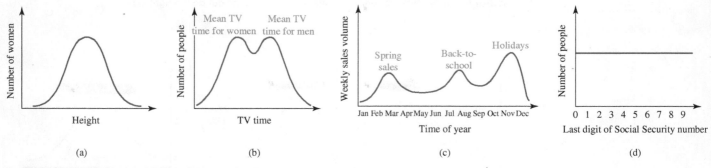

Figure 4.5 Sketches for Example 1.

Symmetry or Skewness

A second simple way to describe the shape of a distribution is in terms of its symmetry or skewness. A distribution is **symmetric** if its left half is a mirror image of its right half. The distributions in Figure 4.6 are all symmetric. The symmetric distribution in Figure 4.6a, with a single peak and a characteristic bell shape, is known in statistics as a *normal distribution*; it is so important that we will devote Chapter 5 to its study.

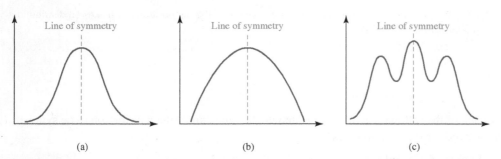

Figure 4.6 These distributions are all symmetric because their left halves are mirror images of their right halves. Note that (a) and (b) are single-peaked (unimodal), whereas (c) is triple-peaked (trimodal).

A distribution that is not symmetric must have values that tend to be more spread out on one side than on the other. In this case, we say that the distribution is **skewed.** Figure 4.7a shows a distribution in which the values are more spread out on the left, meaning that some values are outliers at low values. We say that such a distribution is **left-skewed** (or *negatively* skewed), because it looks as if it has a tail that has been pulled toward the left. Figure 4.7b shows a distribution in which the values are more spread out on a tail extending to the right, making it **right-skewed** (or *positively* skewed).

Figure 4.7 also shows how skewness affects the relative positions of the mean, median, and mode. By definition, the mode is at the peak in a single-peaked distribution. A left-skewed distribution pulls both the mean and median to the left of the mode, meaning to values less than the mode. In addition, outliers at the low end of the data set make the mean less than the median (see Table 4.2 on page 138). Similarly, a right-skewed distribution pulls the mean and median to the right of the mode), and the outliers at the high end of the data set make the mean greater than the median. When the distribution is symmetric and single-peaked, both the mean and the median are equal to the mode.

TECHNICAL NOTE

A left-skewed distribution is also called *negatively skewed*, and a right-skewed distribution is also called *positively skewed*. A symmetric distribution has *zero skewness*.

> **Definitions**
>
> A distribution is **symmetric** if its left half is a mirror image of its right half.
>
> A distribution is **left-skewed** if its values are more spread out on the left side.
>
> A distribution is **right-skewed** if its values are more spread out on the right side.

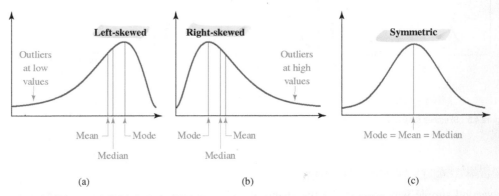

Figure 4.7 (a) Skewed to the left (left-skewed): The mean and median are less than the mode. (b) Skewed to the right (right-skewed). The mean and median are greater than the mode. (c) Symmetric distribution: The mean, median, and mode are the same.

> **TIME OUT TO THINK**
>
> Which is a better measure of "average" (or of the *center* of the distribution) for a skewed distribution: the median or the mean? Why?

BY THE WAY

Median family income in the United States is about $50,000, which is substantially lower than the *mean* family income of about $68,000 (Data for 2011).

EXAMPLE 2 Skewness

For each of the following situations, state whether you expect the distribution to be symmetric, left-skewed, or right-skewed. Explain.

a. Heights of a sample of 100 women

b. Family income in the United States

c. Speeds of cars on a road where a visible patrol car is using radar to detect speeders

SOLUTION

a. The distribution of heights of women is symmetric, because roughly equal numbers of women are shorter and taller than the mean and extremes of height are rare on either side of the mean.

b. The distribution of family incomes is right-skewed. Most families are middle-class, so the mode of this distribution is a middle-class income. But a few very high-income families pull the mean to a considerably higher value, stretching the distribution to the right (high-income) side.

c. Drivers usually slow down when they are aware of a patrol car looking for speeders. Few if any drivers will be exceeding the speed limit, but some drivers tend to slow to well below the speed limit. Thus, the distribution of speeds is therefore left-skewed, with a mode near the speed limit but a few cars going well below the speed limit.   · · ●

> **TIME OUT TO THINK**
>
> In ordinary English, the term *skewed* is often used to mean something that is distorted or depicted in an unfair way. How is this use of *skew* related to its meaning in statistics?

Variation

A third way to describe a distribution is by its **variation**, which is a measure of how much the data values are spread out. A distribution in which most data are clustered together has a low variation. As shown in Figure 4.8a, such a distribution has a fairly sharp peak. The variation is higher when the data are distributed more widely around the center, which makes the peak broader. Figure 4.8b shows a distribution with a moderate variation and Figure 4.8c shows a distribution with a high variation. We'll discuss methods for describing the variation quantitatively in the next section.

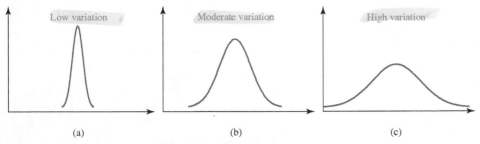

Low variation	Moderate variation	High variation
(a)	(b)	(c)

Figure 4.8   From left to right, these three distributions have increasing variation.

> **Definitions**
>
> **Variation** describes how widely data are spread out about the center of a data set.

EXAMPLE ③ Variation in Marathon Times

How would you expect the variation to differ between times in the Olympic marathon and times in the New York City marathon? Explain.

SOLUTION   The Olympic marathon invites only elite runners, whose times are likely to be clustered relatively near world-record times. The New York City marathon allows runners of all abilities, whose times are spread over a very wide range (from near the world record of just over two hours to many hours). Therefore, the variation among the times should be greater in the New York City marathon than in the Olympic marathon.   · · ●

Section 4.3 Exercises

Statistical Literacy and Critical Thinking

1. Symmetry. In the United States, there are many people with little or no accumulated wealth, and there are a few people with very large amounts of wealth. What does this suggest about the symmetry of the distribution of wealth?

2. Distribution. When the digits 0 through 9 are selected for a state lottery, the digits are selected in a way that they are all equally likely. Which term best describes the distribution of selected digits: skewed, bimodal, uniform, or unimodal?

3. IQ Scores. Consider the IQ scores of professors who teach statistics courses compared with the IQ scores of adults randomly selected from the general population. Which of these two sets of IQ scores has less variation? What effect does the lower variation have on a graph of the distribution of those IQ scores?

4. Skewness. What is skewness in a graph?

Does It Make Sense? For Exercises 5–8, decide whether the statement makes sense (or is clearly true) or does not make sense (or is clearly false). Explain clearly; not all of these statements have definitive answers, so your explanation is more important than your chosen answer.

5. Symmetry. Because a data set has three modes, it must have a skewed distribution.

6. Symmetry. Examination of the data set reveals that it is symmetric with a mean of 98.2 and a median of 98.2.

7. Distribution. Examination of a data set reveals that its distribution is left-skewed and unimodal.

8. Uniform Distribution. Examination of a data set reveals that the mean and median are both equal to 98.2, so the distribution must be uniform.

Concepts and Applications

9. Old Faithful. The histogram in Figure 4.9 shows the times between eruptions of Old Faithful geyser in Yellowstone National Park for a sample of 300 eruptions (with 299 times between eruptions). Over the histogram, draw a smooth curve that captures its general features. Then classify the distribution according to its number of modes and its symmetry or skewness. In words, summarize the meaning of your results.

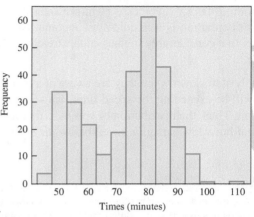

Times Between Eruptions of Old Faithful

Figure 4.9 *Source:* Hand et al., *Handbook of Small Data Sets.*

10. Chip Failures. The histogram in Figure 4.10 shows the time until failure for a sample of 108 computer chips. Over the histogram, draw a smooth curve that captures its general features. Then classify the distribution according to its number of modes and its symmetry or skewness. In words, summarize the meaning of your results.

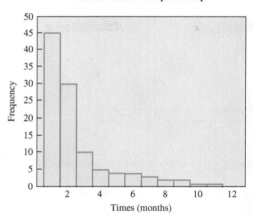

Failure Time of Computer Chips

Figure 4.10 *Source:* Hand et al., *Handbook of Small Data Sets.*

11. Rugby Weights. The histogram in Figure 4.11 shows the weights of a sample of 391 rugby players. Over the histogram, draw a smooth curve that captures its general features. Then classify the distribution according to its number of modes and its symmetry or skewness. In words, summarize the meaning of your results.

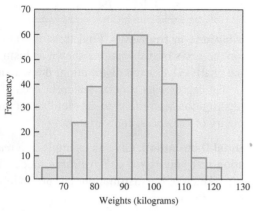

Figure 4.11 *Source:* Hand et al., *Handbook of Small Data Sets.*

12. Penny Weights. The histogram in Figure 4.12 shows the weights (in grams) of 72 pennies. Over the histogram, draw a smooth curve that captures its general features. Then classify the distribution according to its number of modes and its symmetry or skewness. What feature of the graph reflects the fact that 35 of the pennies were made before 1983 and consist of 95% copper and 5% zinc whereas the other 37 pennies were made after 1983 and are 2.5% copper and 97.5% zinc?

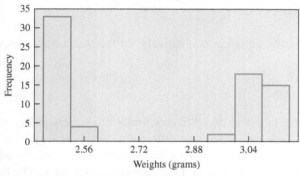

Figure 4.12 *Source: Measurements* by Mario F. Triola.

13. Baseball Salaries. In a recent year, the 817 professional baseball players had salaries with the following characteristics:

- The mean was $3,250,178.

- The median was $1,152,000.

- The salaries ranged from a low of $400,000 to a high of $33,000,000.

a. Describe the shape of the distribution of salaries. Is the distribution symmetric? Is it left-skewed? Is it right-skewed?

b. About how many players had salaries of $1,152,000 or higher?

14. Boston Rainfall. The daily rainfall amounts (in inches) for Boston in a recent year consist of 365 values with these properties:

- The mean daily rainfall amount is 0.083 inch.

- The median of the daily rainfall amounts is 0 inches.

- The minimum daily rainfall amount is 0 inches and the maximum is 1.48 inches.

a. How is it possible that the minimum of the 365 values is 0 inches and the median is also 0 inches?

b. Describe the distribution as symmetric, left-skewed, or right-skewed.

c. Can you determine the exact number of days that it rained? Can you conclude anything about the number of days that it rained? Explain.

Describing Distributions. For each distribution described in Exercises 15–26, answer the following questions:

a. How many modes would you expect for the distribution?

b. Would you expect the distribution to be symmetric, left-skewed, or right-skewed?

15. Incomes. The annual incomes of all those in a statistics class, including the instructor

16. Reaction Times. The reaction times of 500 randomly selected drivers, measured under standard conditions

17. Heights. The heights of 250 randomly selected male attorneys

18. Heights. The heights of 500 male students, half of whom are adults while the other half are eight years of age

19. Weights of Cola. The weights of the cola in 1000 randomly selected cans of Coke

20. Vehicle Weights. The weights of cars in a fleet consisting of 50 compact cars and 50 delivery trucks

21. Patients. The ages of 1,000 randomly selected patients being treated for dementia

22. Speeds. The speeds of drivers on a highway in Montana

23. Patron Ages. The ages of adults who visit the National Air and Space Museum

24. Patron Ages. The ages of people who visit Disneyworld

25. Incomes. The incomes of people sitting in luxury boxes at the Super Bowl

26. Times. The amounts of time that 5000 randomly selected individual taxpayers used to prepare their federal tax returns

PROJECTS FOR THE INTERNET & BEYOND

27. **New York Marathon.** The Web site for the New York City marathon gives frequency data for finish times in the most recent marathon. Study the data, make a rough sketch of the distribution, and describe the shape of the distribution in words.

28. **Tax Stats.** The IRS Web site provides statistics collected from tax returns on income, refunds, and much more. Choose a set of statistics from this Web site and study the distribution. Describe the distribution in words, and discuss anything you learn that is relevant to national tax policies.

29. **Social Security Data.** Survey a sample of fellow students, asking each to indicate the last digit of her or his Social Security number. Also ask each participant to indicate the fifth digit. Draw one graph showing the distribution of the last digits and another graph showing the distribution of the fifth digits. Compare the two graphs. What notable difference becomes apparent?

IN THE NEWS

30. **Distributions in the News.** Find three recent examples in the news of distributions shown as histograms or line charts. Over each distribution, draw a smooth curve that captures its general features. Then classify the distribution according to its number of modes, symmetry or skewness, and variation.

31. **Trimodal Distribution.** Give an example of a real distribution that you expect to have *three* modes. Make a rough sketch of the distribution; be sure to label the axes on your sketch.

32. **Skewed Distribution.** Give an example of a real distribution that you would expect to be either right- or left-skewed. Make a rough sketch of the distribution; be sure to label the axes on your sketch.

4.4 MEASURES OF VARIATION

In Section 4.3, we saw how to describe variation qualitatively. In this section we describe quantitative measures of variation.

Why Variation Matters

We mortals cross the ocean of this world,
Each in his average cabin of a life.

—Robert Browning

Imagine customers waiting in line for tellers at two different banks. Customers at Big Bank can enter any one of three different lines leading to three different tellers. Best Bank also has three tellers, but all customers wait in a single line and are called to the next available teller. The following values are waiting times, in minutes, for 11 customers at each bank. The times are arranged in ascending order.

Big Bank (three lines): 4.1 5.2 5.6 6.2 6.7 7.2 7.7 7.7 8.5 9.3 11.0

Best Bank (one lines): 6.6 6.7 6.7 6.9 7.1 7.2 7.3 7.4 7.7 7.8 7.8

You'll probably find more unhappy customers at Big Bank than at Best Bank, but this is *not* because the average wait is any longer. In fact, you should verify for yourself that the mean and median waiting times are 7.2 minutes at both banks. The difference in customer satisfaction comes from the *variation* at the two banks. The waiting times at Big Bank vary over a fairly wide range, so a few customers have long waits and are likely to become annoyed. In contrast, the variation of the waiting times at Best Bank is small, so all customers feel they are being treated roughly equally. Figure 4.13 shows the difference in the two variations with histograms in which the data values are binned to the nearest minute.

TIME OUT TO THINK

Explain *why* Big Bank, with three separate lines, should have a greater variation in waiting times than Best Bank. Then consider several places where you commonly wait in lines, such as a grocery store, a bank, a theme park ride, or a fast food restaurant. Do these places use a single customer line that feeds multiple clerks or multiple lines? If a place uses multiple lines, do you think a single line would be better? Explain.

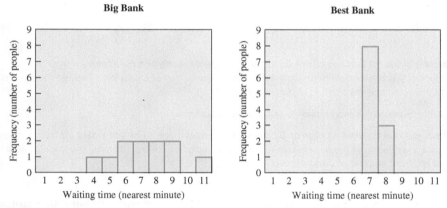

Figure 4.13 Histograms for the waiting times at Big Bank and Best Bank, shown with data binned to the nearest minute.

BY THE WAY

The idea of waiting in line (or *queuing*) is important not only for people but also for data, particularly for data streaming through the Internet. Major corporations often employ statisticians to help them make sure that data move smoothly and without bottlenecks through their servers and Web pages.

Range

The simplest way to describe the variation of a data set is to compute its **range**, defined as the difference between the highest (maximum) and lowest (minimum) values. For the example of the two banks, the waiting times for Big Bank vary from 4.1 to 11.0 minutes, so the range is $11.0 - 4.1 = 6.9$ minutes. The waiting times for Best Bank vary from 6.6 to 7.8 minutes, so the range is $7.8 - 6.6 = 1.2$ minutes. The range for Big Bank is much larger, reflecting its greater variation.

> **Definitions**
>
> The **range** of a set of data values is the difference between its highest and lowest data values:
>
> range = highest value (max) − lowest value (min)
>
> Although the range is easy to compute and can be useful, it occasionally can be misleading, as the next example shows.

EXAMPLE ❶ Misleading Range

Consider the following two sets of quiz scores for nine students. Which set has the greater range? Would you also say that this set has the greater variation?

$$Quiz\ 1:\quad 1\quad 10\quad 10\quad 10\quad 10\quad 10\quad 10\quad 10\quad 10$$
$$Quiz\ 2:\quad 2\quad 3\quad 4\quad 5\quad 6\quad 7\quad 8\quad 9\quad 10$$

SOLUTION The range for Quiz 1 is $10 - 1 = 9$ points, which is greater than the range for Quiz 2 of $10 - 2 = 8$ points. However, aside from a single low score (an outlier), Quiz 1 has no variation at all because every other student got a 10. In contrast, no two students got the same score on Quiz 2, and the scores are spread throughout the list of possible scores. Quiz 2 therefore has greater variation even though Quiz 1 has greater range. ⋅⋅●

Quartiles and the Five-Number Summary

A better way to describe variation is to consider a few intermediate data values in addition to the high and low values. A common way involves looking at the **quartiles**, or values that divide the data distribution into quarters. The following list repeats the waiting times at the two banks, with the quartiles shown in bold. Note that the middle quartile, which divides the data set in half, is simply the median.

	Lower quartile (Q_1) ↓		Median (Q_2) ↓		Upper quartile (Q_3) ↓	

Big Bank: 4.1   5.2   **5.6**   6.2   6.7   **7.2**   7.7   7.7   **8.5**   9.3   11.0

Best Bank: 6.6   6.7   **6.7**   6.9   7.1   **7.2**   7.3   7.4   **7.7**   7.8   7.8

Definitions

The **lower quartile** (or **first quartile** or Q_1 divides the lowest fourth of a data set from the upper three-fourths. It is the median of the data values in the *lower half* of a data set. (Exclude the middle value in the data set if the number of data points is odd.)

The **middle quartile** (or **second quartile** or Q_2 is the overall median.

The **upper quartile** (or **third quartile** or Q_3 divides the lowest three-fourths of a data set from the upper fourth. It is the median of the data values in the *upper half* of a data set. (Exclude the middle value in the data set if the number of data points is odd.)

Once we know the quartiles, we can describe a distribution with a **five-number summary**, consisting of the low value, the lower quartile, the median, the upper quartile, and the high value. For the waiting times at the two banks, the five-number summaries are as follows:

Big Bank:		*Best Bank:*	
low	= 4.1	low	= 6.6
lower quartile	= 5.6	lower quartile	= 6.7
median	= 7.2	median	= 7.2
upper quartile	= 8.5	upper quartile	= 7.7
high	= 11.0	high	= 7.8

The Five-Number Summary

The **five-number summary** for a data distribution consists of the following five numbers:

  low value   lower quartile   median   upper quartile   high value

We can display the five-number summary with a graph called a **boxplot** (or *box-and-whisker plot*). Using a number line for reference, we enclose the values from the lower to the upper quartiles in a box. We then draw a line through the box at the median and add two "whiskers," extending from the box to the low and high values. Figure 4.14 shows boxplots for the bank waiting times. Both the box and the whiskers for Big Bank are broader than those for Best Bank, indicating that the waiting times have greater variation at Big Bank.

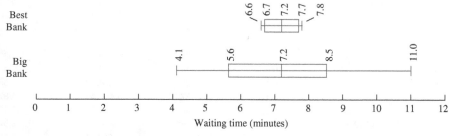

Figure 4.14 Boxplots show that the variation of the waiting times is greater at Big Bank than at Best Bank.

Drawing a Boxplot

Step 1. Draw a number line that spans all the values in the data set.

Step 2. Enclose the values from the lower to the upper quartile in a box. (The thickness of the box has no meaning.)

Step 3. Draw a line through the box at the median.

Step 4. Add "whiskers" extending to the low and high values.

TECHNICAL NOTE

The boxplots shown in this text are called *skeletal boxplots*. Some boxplots are drawn with outliers marked by an asterisk (∗) or a dot and the whiskers extending only to the smallest and largest *non*outliers; these types of boxplots are called *modified boxplots*.

⏻ USING TECHNOLOGY—BOXPLOTS

Excel Although Excel itself is not designed to generate a boxplot, it can be generated using XLSTAT that is a supplement to this book. Load XLSTAT (the Excel add-in), then enter or copy the data into a column of the spreadsheet. Click on **XLSTAT,** click on **Visualizing Data,** then select **Univariate plots.** Enter the range of cells containing the data, such as A1:A11. (If the first cell includes the name of the data, click on the box next to "Sample labels.") Click **OK** to continue. The result will be a boxplot with two features: (1) The boxplot will be vertical, and (2) the exact values of the quartiles are likely to be somewhat different from those found using the procedure described above.

STATDISK Enter the data in the Data Window, then click on **Data,** then **Boxplot.** Click on the columns that you want to include, then click on **Plot.**

TI-83/84 PLUS Enter the sample data in list L1 or enter the data and assign them to a list name. Now select **STAT PLOT** by pressing **2ND** **Y=**. Press **ENTER**, then select the option of **ON**. For a simple boxplot as described in Part 1 of this section, select the boxplot type that is positioned in the middle of the second row; for a modified boxplot as described in Part 2 of this section, select the boxplot that is positioned at the far left of the second row. The Xlist should indicate L1 and the Freq value should be 1. Now press **ZOOM** and select option 9 for **ZoomStat.** Press **ENTER** and the boxplot should be displayed. You can use the arrow keys to move right or left so that values can be read from the horizontal scale.

EXAMPLE ② Passive and Active Smoke

One way to study exposure to cigarette smoke is by measuring blood levels of *serum cotinine*, a metabolic product of nicotine that the body absorbs from cigarette smoke. Table 4.3 lists serum cotinine levels from samples of 50 smokers ("active smoke") and 50 nonsmokers who are exposed to cigarette smoke at home or at work ("passive smoke"). Compare the two data sets (smokers and nonsmokers) with five-number summaries and boxplots, and discuss your results.

BY THE WAY

Passive smoke is particularly harmful to young children. Apparently, the toxins in cigarette smoke have a greater effect on developing bodies than on full-grown adults. A similar effect is found for most other toxins, which is why it is especially important to limit children's exposure to toxic chemicals.

TABLE 4.3	Serum Cotinine Levels (nanograms per milliliter of blood) in Samples of 50 Smokers and 50 Nonsmokers Exposed to Passive Smoke, with Data Values Listed in Ascending Order				
Order number	Smokers	Nonsmokers	Order number	Smokers	Nonsmokers
1	0.08	0.03	26	34.21	0.82
2	0.14	0.07	27	36.73	0.97
3	0.27	0.08	28	37.73	1.12
4	0.44	0.08	29	39.48	1.23
5	0.51	0.09	30	48.58	1.37
6	1.78	0.09	31	51.21	1.40
7	2.55	0.10	32	56.74	1.67
8	3.03	0.11	33	58.69	1.98
9	3.44	0.12	34	72.37	2.33
10	4.98	0.12	35	104.54	2.42
11	6.87	0.14	36	114.49	2.66
12	11.12	0.17	37	145.43	2.87
13	12.58	0.20	38	187.34	3.13
14	13.73	0.23	39	226.82	3.54
15	14.42	0.27	40	267.83	3.76
16	18.22	0.28	41	328.46	4.58
17	19.28	0.30	42	388.74	5.31
18	20.16	0.33	43	405.28	6.20
19	23.67	0.37	44	415.38	7.14
20	25.00	0.38	45	417.82	7.25
21	25.39	0.44	46	539.62	10.23
22	29.41	0.49	47	592.79	10.83
23	30.71	0.51	48	688.36	17.11
24	32.54	0.51	49	692.51	37.44
25	32.56	0.68	50	983.41	61.33

Note: The column "Order number" is included to make it easier to read the table.
Source: National Health and Nutrition Examination Survey, National Institutes of Health.

SOLUTION   The two data sets are already in ascending order, making it easy to construct the five-number summary. Each has 50 data points, so the median lies halfway between the 25th and 26th values. For the smokers, the 25th and 26th values are 32.56 and 34.21, respectively, so the median is

$$\frac{32.56 + 34.21}{2} = 33.385$$

For the nonsmokers, the 25th and 26th values are 0.68 and 0.82, respectively, so the median is

$$\frac{0.68 + 0.82}{2} = 0.75$$

The lower quartile is the median of the *lower half* of the values, which is the 13th value in each set. The upper quartile is the median of the *upper half* of the values, which is the 38th value in each set. The five-number summaries for the two data sets are as follows:

Active smoke:

low = 0.08 ng/ml
lower quartile = 12.58 ng/ml
median = 33.385 ng/ml
upper quartile = 187.34 ng/ml
high = 983.41 ng/ml

Passive smoke:

low = 0.03 ng/ml
lower quartile = 0.20 ng/ml
median = 0.75 ng/ml
upper quartile = 3.13 ng/ml
high = 61.33 ng/ml

Figure 4.15 shows boxplots for the two data sets. The boxplots make it easy to see some key features of the data sets. For example, it is immediately clear that the active smokers have a higher median level of serum cotinine, as well as a greater variation in levels. We conclude that smokers absorb considerably more nicotine than do nonsmokers exposed to passive smoke. Nevertheless, the levels in the passive smokers are much higher than those found in people who had no exposure to cigarette smoke (as demonstrated by other data, not shown here). Indeed, the nonsmoker with the high value for passive smoke has absorbed more nicotine than

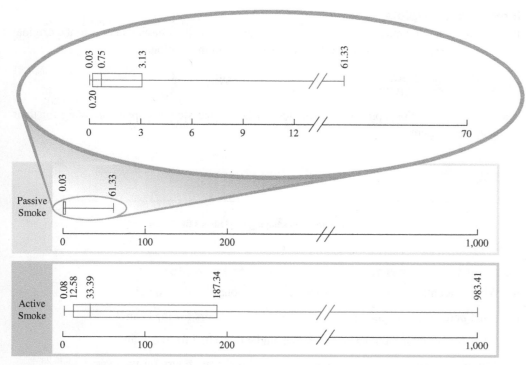

Figure 4.15 Boxplots for the data in Table 4.3.

the median smoker. We conclude that passive smoke can expose nonsmokers to significant amounts of nicotine. Given the known dangers of cigarette smoke, these results give us reason to be concerned about possible health effects from passive smoke.   ·· ●

The Interquartile Range

Another measure of variation that can also be used is the **interquartile range**, or the difference between the upper quartile and the lower quartile.

> **Definitions**
>
> The **interquartile range** (or IQR) is the difference between the upper quartile (Q_3) and the lower quartile (Q_1).
>
> IQR = upper quartile – lower quartile

The advantage of the IQR over the range is that it is not influenced by outliers. Even though the interquartile range requires a bit more effort to calculate than the range, it is still relatively straightforward to determine. The interquartile range is also much easier to calculate than the upcoming measure of variation, standard deviation. Finally, the IQR is also easily calculated from the given values with a boxplot.

If we revisit the serum cotinine levels example, we can calculate the interquartile range for active smoke and for passive smoke

Active Smoke:	**Passive smoke:**
Lower quartile= 12.58 ng/ml	Lower quartile = 0.20 ng/ml
Upper quartile = 187.34 ng/ml	upper quartile = 3.13 ng/ml
IQR = 187.34 – 12.58 = 174.76 ng/ml	IQR = 3.13 – 0.20 = 2.93 ng/ml

In comparing these two interquartile ranges, we can see that the serum cotinine levels vary a lot more for smokers than for nonsmokers. That is, the levels are more consistent for passive smokers. You can see this clearly in the boxplots in figure 4.15 as the box is a lot narrower for the passive smoke than for the active smoke.

Interpreting Boxplots

It is possible that you may encounter boxplots in research without having access to the original data. So, you may want to interpret the information given in boxplots.

EXAMPLE 3 Interpreting Boxplots

The following boxplot represents the number of hours that students spend studying for their Statistics final exam.

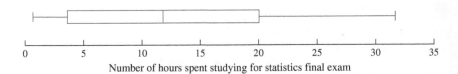

Number of hours spent studying for statistics final exam

Answer the following questions about the boxplot.

a. What percentage of students studied 12 or less hours for the exam?

b. What percentage of students studied more than 20 hours for the exam?

c. What is maximum number of hours that students studied for the exam?

d. The middle 50% of students studied between how many hours for the exam?

e. What is the range of hours that students studied for the exam?

SOLUTION

a. Since 12 is the value that corresponds with the line in the middle of the box, 12 hours is the median value. So, 50% of students studied 12 or less hours for the exam.

b. The value of 20 is the value on the right side of the box. Therefore, 20 hours is the upper quartile. That is, approximately 75% of students studied less than 20 hours and 25% students more than that. So, 25% of students studied more than 20 hours for the exam.

c. The maximum value is located at vertical line that is at the right end of the box plot. In this boxplot, the right whisker ends at the value of 32. So, the maximum number of hours that a student studied is 32 hours.

d. The middle 50% is precisely what the interquartile range represents. So, this is denoted by the box within the boxplot. So, the middle 50% of students studied between 4 and 20 hours.

e. We calculate the range by subtracting the minimum value from the maximum value. We already found the maximum value of 32 in part c. The minimum value is represented by the value at the vertical line at the left end of the whisker, which in this example is 1. So, the range is the difference between 32 and 1. The range is 31 hours.   ·· ●

TECHNICAL NOTE

As with quartiles, statisticians and various statistics software packages may use slightly different procedures to calculate percentiles, resulting in slightly different values.

Percentiles

Quartiles divide a data set into 4 segments. It is possible to divide a data set even more. For example, *quintiles* divide a data set into 5 segments, and *deciles* divide a data set into 10 segments. It is particularly common to divide data sets into 100 segments using **percentiles.** Roughly speaking, the 35th percentile, for example, is a value that separates the bottom 35% of

Definitions

The **nth percentile** of a data set divides the bottom n% of data values from the top $(100 - n)$%. A data value that lies between two percentiles is often said to lie *in* the lower percentile. You can approximate the percentile of any data value with the following formula:

$$\text{percentile of data value} = \frac{\text{number of values less than this data value}}{\text{total number of values in data set}} \times 100$$

the data values from the top 65%. (More precisely, the 35th percentile is greater than or equal to at least 35% of the data values and less than or equal to at least 65% of the data values.)

If a data value lies between two percentiles, it is common to say that the data value lies *in* the lower percentile. For example, if you score higher than 84.7% of all people taking a college entrance examination, we say that your score is in the 84th percentile.

There are different procedures for finding a data value corresponding to a given percentile, but one approximate approach is to find the Lth value, where L is the product of the percentile (in decimal form) and the sample size. For example, with 50 sample values, the 12th percentile is around the $0.12 \times 50 = 6th$ value.

EXAMPLE ④ Smoke Exposure Percentiles

Answer the following questions concerning the data in Table 4.3.

a. What is the percentile for the data value of 104.54 ng/ml for smokers?

b. What is the percentile for the data value of 61.33 ng/ml for nonsmokers?

c. What data value marks the 36th percentile for the smokers? For the nonsmokers?

SOLUTION   The following results are approximate.

a. The data value of 104.54 ng/ml for smokers is the 35th data value in the set, which means that 34 data values lie below it. Thus, its percentile is

$$\frac{\text{number of values less than 104.54 ng/ml}}{\text{total number of values in data set}} = \times 100 = \frac{34}{50} \times 100 = 68$$

In other words, the 35th data value marks the 68th percentile.

b. The data value of 61.33 ng/ml for nonsmokers is the 50th and highest data value in the set, which means that 49 data values lie below it. Thus, its percentile is

$$\frac{\text{number of values less than 61.33 ng/ml}}{\text{total number of values in data set}} \times 100 = \frac{49}{50} \times 100 = 98$$

In other words, the highest data value in this set lies in the 98th percentile.

c. Because there are 50 data values in the set, the 36th percentile is around the $0.36 \times 50 = 18th$ value. For smokers this value is 20.16 ng/ml, and for nonsmokers it is 0.33 ng/ml.   ··●

Standard Deviation

The five-number summary characterizes variation well, but statisticians often prefer to describe variation with a single number. The single number most commonly used to describe variation is called the **standard deviation.**

The standard deviation is a measure of how widely data values are spread around the mean of a data set. To calculate a standard deviation, we first find the mean and then find how much each data value "deviates" from the mean. Consider our bank data sets, in which the mean waiting time was 7.2 minutes for both Big Bank and Best Bank. For a waiting time of 8.2 minutes, the **deviation** from the mean is equal to 8.2 minutes − 7.2 minutes = 1.0 minute, meaning that it is 1.0 minute greater than the mean. For a waiting time of 5.2 minutes, the deviation from the mean is equal to 5.2 minutes − 7.2 minutes = −2 minutes (*negative* 2 minutes), because it is 2.0 minutes *less* than the mean.

In essence, the standard deviation is a measure of the average of all the deviations from the mean. However, because the mean of the deviations is always zero (because the positive deviations exactly balance the negative deviations), we calculate the standard deviation by first finding a mean of the *squares* of the deviations (because squares are always positive) and taking a square root in the end. For technical reasons, we divide the sum of the squares by the total number of data values *minus* 1.

TECHNICAL NOTE

The standard deviation formula given here, in which we divide the sum of the squared deviations by the total number of data values *minus* 1, is technically valid only for data from *samples*. When dealing with *populations*, we do not subtract the 1. In this text, we use only the sample formula.

We divide by $n - 1$ because there are only $n - 1$ independent sample values. With a given mean, only $n - 1$ values can be freely assigned any number before the last value is determined. Here, we say that we have $n - 1$ *degrees of freedom*.

TECHNICAL NOTE

The result of Step 4 is called the *variance* of the distribution. In other words, the standard deviation is the square root of the variance. Although the variance is used in many advanced statistical computations, we will not use it in this text.

Calculating the Standard Deviation

To calculate the standard deviation for any data set:

Step 1.   Compute the mean of the data set. Then find the deviation from the mean for every data value by subtracting the mean from the data value. That is, for every data value,

$$\text{deviation from mean} = \text{data value} - \text{mean}$$

Step 2.   Find the squares (second power) of all the deviations from the mean.

Step 3.   Add all the squares of the deviations from the mean.

Step 4.   Divide this sum by the total number of data values *minus* 1.

Step 5.   The standard deviation is the square root of this quotient. Overall, these steps produce the standard deviation formula:

$$\text{standard deviation} = \sqrt{\frac{\text{sum of (deviations from the mean)}^2}{\text{total number of data values} - 1}}$$

Note that, because we square the deviations in Step 3 and then take the square root in Step 5, the units of the standard deviation are the same as the units of the data values. For example, if the data values have units of minutes, the standard deviation also has units of minutes.

The standard deviation formula is easy to use in principle, but the calculations become tedious for all but the smallest data sets. As a result, it is usually calculated with the aid of a calculator or computer. Nevertheless, you'll find the standard deviation formula easier to understand if you try a few examples in which you work through the calculations in detail.

EXAMPLE 5   Calculating Standard Deviation

Calculate the standard deviations for the waiting times at Big Bank and Best Bank.

SOLUTION   We follow the five steps to calculate the standard deviations. Table 4.4 shows how to organize the work in the first three steps. The first column for each bank lists the waiting times (in minutes). The second column lists the deviations from the mean (Step 1), which we already know to be 7.2 minutes for both banks. The third column lists the squares of the deviations (Step 2). We add all the squared deviations to find the sum at the bottom of the third column (Step 3). For Step 4, we divide the sums from Step 3 by the total number of data values *minus* 1. Because there are 11 data values, we divide by 10:

$$Big\ Bank:\quad \frac{38.46}{10} = 3.846$$

$$Best\ Bank:\quad \frac{1.98}{10} = 0.198$$

Finally, Step 5 tells us that the standard deviations are the square roots of the numbers from Step 4:

$$Big\ Bank:\quad \text{standard deviation} = \sqrt{3.846} \approx 1.96\ \text{minutes}$$

$$Best\ Bank:\quad \text{standard deviation} = \sqrt{0.198} \approx 0.44\ \text{minutes}$$

We conclude that the standard deviation of the waiting times is about 1.96 minutes at Big Bank and 0.44 minute at Best Bank. As we expected, the waiting times showed greater variation at Big Bank, which is why the lines at Big Bank annoyed more customers than did those at Best Bank.

TABLE 4.4   Calculating Standard Deviation

Big Bank			Best Bank		
Time	Deviation (Time − Mean)	(Deviation)^2	Time	Deviation (Time − Mean)	(Deviation)^2
4.1	$4.1 - 7.2 = -3.1$	$(-3.1)^2 = 9.61$	6.6	$6.6 - 7.2 = -0.6$	$(-0.6)^2 = 0.36$
5.2	$5.2 - 7.2 = -2.0$	$(-2.0)^2 = 4.00$	6.7	$6.7 - 7.2 = -0.5$	$(-0.5)^2 = 0.25$
5.6	$5.6 - 7.2 = -1.6$	$(-1.6)^2 = 2.56$	6.7	$6.7 - 7.2 = -0.5$	$(-0.5)^2 = 0.25$
6.2	$6.2 - 7.2 = -1.0$	$(-1.0)^2 = 1.00$	6.9	$6.9 - 7.2 = -0.3$	$(-0.3)^2 = 0.09$
6.7	$6.7 - 7.2 = -0.5$	$(-0.5)^2 = 0.25$	7.1	$7.1 - 7.2 = -0.1$	$(-0.1)^2 = 0.01$
7.2	$7.2 - 7.2 = 0.0$	$(0.0)^2 = 0.0$	7.2	$7.2 - 7.2 = 0.0$	$(0.0)^2 = 0.0$
7.7	$7.7 - 7.2 = 0.5$	$(0.5)^2 = 0.25$	7.3	$7.3 - 7.2 = 0.1$	$(0.1)^2 = 0.01$
7.7	$7.7 - 7.2 = 0.5$	$(0.5)^2 = 0.25$	7.4	$7.4 - 7.2 = 0.2$	$(0.2)^2 = 0.04$
8.5	$8.5 - 7.2 = 1.3$	$(1.3)^2 = 1.69$	7.7	$7.7 - 7.2 = 0.5$	$(0.5)^2 = 0.25$
9.3	$9.3 - 7.2 = 2.1$	$(2.1)^2 = 4.41$	7.8	$7.8 - 7.2 = 0.6$	$(0.6)^2 = 0.36$
11.0	$11.0 - 7.2 = 3.8$	$(3.8)^2 = 14.44$	7.8	$7.8 - 7.2 = 0.6$	$(0.6)^2 = 0.36$
		Sum = 38.46			**Sum = 1.98**

USING TECHNOLOGY—**STANDARD DEVIATION**

Excel The built-in Excel function STDEV automates the calculation of standard deviation, so that all you have to do is enter the data and then use the function. The screen shot below shows the process for the Big Bank data, with the functions shown in Column B and the results in Column C.

◇	A	B	C
1		**Big Bank**	
2	Data	4.1	
3		5.2	
4		5.6	
5		6.2	
6		6.7	
7		7.2	
8		7.7	
9		7.7	
10		8.5	
11		9.3	
12		11	
13	Mean	=AVERAGE(B2:B12)	7.2
14	St. Dev.	=STDEV(B2:B12)	1.96
15			

Note: Alternatively, the procedures given in Section 4.2 using the Analysis Tookit or XLSTAT will give results that include the value of the standard deviation

Statdisk or **TI 83/84**: Use the same procedures given in Section 4.2, and the results will include the value of the standard deviation.

TIME (🕐)UT TO THINK

Look closely at the individual deviations in Table 4.4 in Example 4. Do the standard deviations for the two data sets seem like reasonable "averages" for the deviations? Explain.

Interpreting the Standard Deviation

A good way to develop a deeper understanding of the standard deviation is to consider an approximation called the **range rule of thumb**, summarized in the following box.

TECHNICAL NOTE

Another way of interpreting the standard deviation uses a mathematical rule called *Chebyshev's Theorem*. It states that, for any data distribution, at least 75% of all data values lie within two standard deviations of the mean, and at least 89% of all data values lie within three deviations of the mean.

The Range Rule of Thumb

The standard deviation is *approximately* related to the range of a distribution by the **range rule of thumb**:

$$\text{standard deviation} \approx \frac{\text{range}}{4}$$

If we know the range of a distribution (range = high − low), we can use this rule to estimate the standard deviation. Alternatively, if we know the standard deviation, we can use this rule to estimate the low and high values as follows:

$$\text{low value} \approx \text{mean} - (2 \times \text{standard deviation})$$

$$\text{high value} \approx \text{mean} + (2 \times \text{standard deviation})$$

The range rule of thumb does not work well when the high or low values are outliers.

The range rule of thumb works reasonably well for data sets in which values are distributed fairly evenly. It does not work well when the high or low values are extreme outliers. You must therefore use judgment in deciding whether the range rule of thumb is applicable in a particular case, and in all cases remember that the range rule of thumb yields rough approximations, not exact results.

EXAMPLE 6   Using the Range Rule of Thumb

Use the range rule of thumb to estimate the standard deviations for the waiting times at Big Bank and Best Bank. Compare the estimates to the actual values found in Example 5.

SOLUTION   The waiting times for Big Bank vary from 4.1 to 11.0 minutes, which means a range of 11.0 − 4.1 = 6.9 minutes. The waiting times for Best Bank vary from 6.6 to 7.8 minutes, for a range of 7.8 − 6.6 = 1.2 minutes. Thus, the range rule of thumb gives the following estimates for the standard deviations:

$$Big~Bank: \quad \text{standard derivation} \approx \frac{6.9}{4} = 1.7$$

$$Best~Bank: \quad \text{standard derivation} \approx \frac{1.2}{4} = 0.3$$

The actual standard deviations calculated in Example 5 are 1.96 and 0.44, respectively. For these two cases, the estimates from the range rule of thumb slightly underestimate the actual standard deviations. Nevertheless, the estimates put us in the right ballpark, showing that the rule is useful. $\cdots \bullet$

EXAMPLE 7   Estimating a Range

Studies of the gas mileage of a Prius under varying driving conditions show that it gets a mean of 45 miles per gallon with a standard deviation of 4 miles per gallon. Estimate the minimum and maximum typical gas mileage amounts that you can expect under ordinary driving conditions.

SOLUTION   From the range rule of thumb, the low and high values for gas mileage are approximately

$$\text{low value} \approx \text{mean} - (2 \times \text{standard deviation}) = 45 - (2 \times 4) = 37$$

$$\text{high value} \approx \text{mean} + (2 \times \text{standard deviation}) = 45 + (2 \times 4) = 53$$

The range of gas mileage for the car is roughly from a minimum of 37 miles per gallon to a maximum of 53 miles per gallon. $\cdots \bullet$

BY THE WAY

Technologies such as catalytic converters have helped reduce the amounts of many pollutants emitted by cars (per mile driven), but burning less gasoline is the only way to reduce carbon dioxide emissions that cause global warming. This is a major reason why auto manufacturers are developing high-mileage hybrid vehicles and zero-emission vehicles that run on electricity or fuel cells.

Standard Deviation with Summation Notation (Optional Section)

The summation notation introduced earlier makes it easy to write the standard deviation formula in a compact form. Recall that x represents the individual values in a data set and $\bar{x}$ represents the mean of the data set. We can therefore write the deviation from the mean for any data value as

$$\text{deviation} = \text{data value} - \text{mean} = x - \bar{x}$$

We can now write the sum of all squared deviations as

$$\text{sum of all squared deviations} = \sum (x - \bar{x})^2$$

The remaining steps in the calculation of the standard deviation are to divide this sum by $n - 1$ and then take the square root. You should confirm that the following formula summarizes the five steps in the earlier box:

$$s = \text{standard deviation} = \sqrt{\frac{\sum (x - \bar{x})^2}{n - 1}}$$

The symbol s is the conventional symbol for the standard deviation of a sample. For the standard deviation of a population, statisticians use the Greek letter σ (sigma), and the term $n - 1$ in the formula is replaced by N (the population size). Consequently, you will get slightly different results for the standard deviation depending on whether you assume the data represent a sample or a population.

> **TECHNICAL NOTE**
>
> The formula for the *variance* is
>
> $$s^2 = \frac{\sum (x - \bar{x})^2}{n - 1}$$
>
> The standard symbol for the variance, s^2, reflects the fact that it is the square of the standard deviation.

Section 4.4 Exercises

Statistical Literacy and Critical Thinking

1. **Range.** How is the range computed for a set of sample data? Is the range a measure of variation? What is a major disadvantage of the range?

2. **Standard Deviation.** Assume that you are manufacturing aspirin tablets that are supposed to contain 325 mg of aspirin. If the standard deviation of the amounts of aspirin is calculated, which value would you prefer: a standard deviation of 20 mg or a standard deviation of 10 mg? Why?

3. **Correct Statement?** In the book *How to Lie with Charts,* the author writes that "the standard deviation is usually shown as plus or minus the difference between the high and the mean, and the low and the mean. For example, if the mean is 1, the high is 3, and the low is −1, the standard deviation is ±2." Is that statement correct? Why or why not?

4. **Quartiles.** For the salaries paid to the 817 professional baseball players in a recent year, the first quartile is $4,355,101. What do we mean when we say that $4,355,101 is the first quartile?

Does It Make Sense? For Exercises 5–8, decide whether the statement makes sense (or is clearly true) or does not make sense (or is clearly false). Explain clearly; not all of these statements have definitive answers, so your explanation is more important than your chosen answer.

5. **SAT Score.** Jennifer received an SAT score that was equal to the first quartile and the 35th percentile.

6. **Lengths.** The house key lengths of 15 statistics students are measured and rounded to the nearest centimeter, and all 15 values are the same, so the standard deviation is 0 cm.

7. **Baseball Salaries.** For a recent year, the 817 salaries paid to professional baseball players have a median of $1,152,000 and a second quartile with the same value of $1,152,000.

8. **Baseball Salaries.** If the range of salaries paid to baseball players in the American League is less than the range of salaries paid to baseball players in the National League, then the American League salaries must have a smaller standard deviation than the National League salaries.

Concepts and Applications

Range and Standard Deviation. Exercises 9–16 each list a set of numbers. In each case, find the range and standard deviation. (The same sets of numbers were used in Exercises 13–20 in Section 4.2.)

9. **Number of Words.** Pages from *Merriam-Webster's Collegiate Dictionary*, 11th edition, were randomly selected. Here are the numbers of words defined on those pages:

    51   63   36   43   34   62   73   39   53   79

10. **Space Shuttle Flights.** Listed below are the durations (in hours) of a sample of all flights of NASA's Space Transport System (space shuttle):

    73   95   235   192   165   262   191   376
    259   235   381   331   221   244   0

11. **Perception of Time.** Actual times (in seconds) recorded when statistics students participated in an experiment to test their ability to determine when one minute (60 seconds) had passed:

    53   52   75   62   68   58   49   49

12. **Body Temperatures.** Body temperatures (in degrees Fahrenheit) of randomly selected normal and healthy adults:

    98.6   98.6   98.0   98.0   99.0
    98.4   98.4   98.4   98.4   98.6

13. **Blood Alcohol.** Blood alcohol concentrations of drivers involved in fatal crashes and then given jail sentences (based on data from the U.S. Department of Justice):

    0.27   0.17   0.17   0.16   0.13   0.24
    0.29   0.24   0.14   0.16   0.12   0.16

14. **Old Faithful Geyser.** Time intervals (in minutes) between eruptions of Old Faithful geyser in Yellowstone National Park:

    98   92   95   87   96   90
    65   92   95   93   98   94

15. **Weights of M&Ms.** Weights (in grams) of randomly selected M&M plain candies:

    0.957   0.912   0.842   0.925   0.939   0.886
    0.914   0.913   0.958   0.947   0.920

16. **Quarters.** Weights (in grams) of quarters in circulation:

    5.60   5.63   5.58   5.56   5.66   5.58   5.57   5.59
    5.67   5.61   5.84   5.73   5.53   5.58   5.52   5.65
    5.57   5.71   5.59   5.53   5.63   5.68

Comparing Variation. In Exercises 17–20, find the range and standard deviation for each of the two samples and then compare the two sets of results.

17. **It's Raining Cats.** Statistics are sometimes used to compare or identify authors of different works. The lengths of the first 20 words in the foreword by Tennessee Williams in *Cat on a Hot Tin Roof* are listed along with the lengths of the first 20 words in *The Cat in the Hat* by Dr. Seuss. Does there appear to be a difference in variation?

    Cat on a Hot Tin Roof:

    2   6   2   2   1   4   4   2   4   2
    3   8   4   2   2   7   7   2   3   11

    The Cat in the Hat:

    3   3   3   3   5   2   3   3   3   2
    4   2   2   3   2   3   5   3   4   4

18. **BMI for Miss America.** The trend of thinner Miss America winners has generated charges that the contest encourages unhealthy diet habits among young women. Listed below are body mass indexes (BMI) for Miss America winners from two different time periods. Does there appear to be a difference in variation?

    BMI (from the 1920s and 1930s):

    20.4 21.9 22.1 22.3 20.3 18.8 18.9 19.4 18.4 19.1

    BMI (from recent winners):

    19.5 20.3 19.6 20.2 17.8 17.9 19.1 18.8 17.6 16.8

19. **Weather Forecast Accuracy.** In an analysis of the accuracy of weather forecasts, the actual high temperatures are compared with the high temperatures predicted one day earlier and the high temperatures predicted five days earlier. Listed below are the errors between the predicted temperatures and the actual high temperatures for consecutive days in Dutchess County, New York. Do the standard deviations suggest that the temperatures predicted one day in advance are more accurate than those predicted five days in advance, as we might expect?

    (*actual high*) − (*high predicted one day earlier*):

    2   2   0   0   −3   −2   1
    −2   8   1   0   −1   0   1

    (*actual high*) − (*high predicted five days earlier*):

    0   −3   2   5   −6   −9   4
    −1   6   −2   −2   −1   6   −4

20. **Treatment Effect.** Researchers at Pennsylvania State University conducted experiments with poplar trees. Listed below are weights (in kilograms) of poplar trees given no treatment and poplar trees treated with fertilizer and irrigation. Does there appear to be a difference between the two standard deviations?

    No treatment:

    0.15   0.02   0.16   0.37   0.22

    Fertilizer and irrigation:

    2.03   0.27   0.92   1.07   2.38

21. **Calculating Percentiles.** A statistics professor with too much time on his hands weighed each M&M candy in a bag of 465 plain M&M candies.

   a. One of the M&Ms weighed 0.776 gram and it was heavier than 25 of the other M&Ms. What is the percentile of this particular value?

   b. One of the M&Ms weighed 0.876 gram and it was heavier than 322 of the other M&Ms. What is the percentile of this particular value?

   c. One of the M&Ms weighed 0.856 gram and it was heavier than 224 of the other M&Ms. What is the percentile of this particular value?

22. **Calculating Percentiles.** A data set consists of the 85 ages of women at the time that they won an Oscar in the category of best actress.

   a. One of the actresses was 40 years of age, and she was older than 63 of the other actresses at the time that they won Oscars. What is the percentile of the age of 40?

   b. One of the actresses was 54 years of age, and she was older than 76 of the other actresses at the time that they won Oscars. What is the percentile of the age of 54?

   c. One of the actresses was 60 years of age, and she was older than 77 of the other actresses at the time that they won Oscars. What is the percentile of the age of 60?

23. **Understanding Standard Deviation.** The following four sets of 7 numbers all have a mean of 9.

   $$\{9, 9, 9, 9, 9, 9, 9,\} \quad \{8, 8, 9, 9, 9, 10, 10\}$$
   $$\{8, 8, 8, 9, 10, 10, 10\} \quad \{6, 6, 6, 9, 12, 12, 12\}$$

   a. Make a histogram for each set.

   b. Give the five-number summary and draw a boxplot for each set.

   c. Compute the standard deviation for each set.

   d. Based on your results, briefly explain how the standard deviation provides a useful single-number summary of the variation in these data sets.

24. **Understanding Standard Deviation.** The following four sets of 7 numbers all have a mean of 6.

   $$\{6, 6, 6, 6, 6, 6, 6\}, \quad \{5, 5, 6, 6, 6, 7, 7\}$$
   $$\{5, 5, 5, 6, 7, 7, 7\}, \quad \{3, 3, 3, 6, 9, 9, 9\}$$

   a. Make a histogram for each set.

   b. Give the five-number summary and draw a boxplot for each set.

   c. Compute the standard deviation for each set.

   d. Based on your results, briefly explain how the standard deviation provides a useful single-number summary of the variation in these data sets.

Comparing Variations. For each of Exercises 25–28, do the following:

   a. Find the mean, median, and range for each of the two data sets.

   b. Give the five-number summary and draw a boxplot for each of the two data sets.

   c. Find the standard deviation for each of the two data sets.

   d. Apply the range rule of thumb to estimate the standard deviation of each of the two data sets. How well does the rule work in each case? Briefly discuss why it does or does not work well.

   e. Based on all your results, compare and discuss the two data sets in terms of their center and variation.

25. The following data sets give the ages in years of a sample of cars in a faculty parking lot and a student parking lot at the College of Portland.

   Faculty:

   2   3   1   0   1   2   4   3   3   2   1

   Student:

   5   6   8   2   7   10   1   4   6   10   9

26. The following data sets give the driving speeds in miles per hour of the first nine cars to pass through a school zone and the first nine cars to pass through a downtown intersection.

   School:

   20   18   23   21   19   18   17   24   25

   Downtown:

   29   31   35   24   31   26   36   31   28

27. The following data sets show the ages of the first seven U.S. Presidents (Washington through Jackson) and seven recent U.S. Presidents (Ford through Obama) at the time of inauguration.

   First 7:

   57   61   57   57   58   57   61

   Last 7:

   61   52   69   64   46   54   47

28. The following data sets give the approximate lengths of Beethoven's nine symphonies and Mahler's nine symphonies (in minutes).

   Beethoven:

   28   36   50   33   30   40   38   26   68

   Mahler:

   52   85   94   50   72   72   80   90   80

29. **Manufacturing.** You are in charge of a manufacturing process that produces car batteries that are supposed to provide 12 volts of power. Manufacturing occurs at two different sites. The first site produces batteries with a mean of 12.1 volts and a standard deviation of 0.5 volt, while the second site produces batteries with a mean of 12.2 volts and a standard deviation of 0.1 volt. Which site has better quality? Why?

30. **Managing Complaints.** You manage a small ice cream shop in which your employees scoop the ice cream by hand. Each night, you total your sales and the total volume of ice cream sold. You find that on nights when an

employee named Ben is working, the mean price of the ice cream sold is $1.75 per pint with a standard deviation of $0.05. On nights when an employee named Jerry is working, the mean price of the ice cream sold is $1.70 per pint with a standard deviation of $0.35. Which employee is more likely to be generating complaints of "too small" servings? Explain.

31. **Portfolio Standard Deviation.** The book *Investments*, by Zvi Bodie, Alex Kane, and Alan Marcus, claims that the annual percentage returns for investment portfolios with a single stock have a standard deviation of 0.55, while the annual percentage returns for portfolios with 32 stocks have a standard deviation of 0.325. Explain how the standard deviation measures the risk in these two types of portfolios.

32. **Batting Standard Deviation.** For the past 100 years, the mean batting average in the major leagues has remained fairly constant at about 0.260. However, the standard deviation of batting averages has decreased from about 0.049 in the 1870s to 0.031 in the present. What does this tell us about the batting averages of players? Based on these facts, would you expect batting averages above 0.350 to be more or less common today than in the past? Explain.

PROJECTS FOR THE INTERNET & BEYOND

33. **Secondhand Smoke.** At the Web sites of the American Lung Association and the U.S. Environmental Protection Agency, find statistical data concerning the health effects of secondhand (passive) smoke. Write a short summary of your findings and your opinions about whether and how this health issue should be addressed by government.

34. **Kids and the Media.** A recent study by the Kaiser Family Foundation looked at the role of media (for example, television, books, computers) in the lives of children. The report, which is on the Kaiser Family Foundation Web site, gives many data distributions concerning, for example, how much time children spend daily with each medium. Study at least three of the distributions in the report that you find particularly interesting. Summarize each distribution in words, and discuss your opinions of the social consequences of the findings.

35. **Measuring Variation.** The range and standard deviation use different approaches to measure variation in a data set. Construct two different data sets configured so that the range of the first set is *greater than* the range of the second set (suggesting that the first set has more variation) but the standard deviation of the first set is *less than* the standard deviation of the second set (suggesting that the first set has less variation).

IN THE NEWS

36. **Ranges in the News.** Find two examples of data distributions in recent news reports; they may be given either as tables or as graphs. In each case, state the range of the distribution and explain its meaning in the context of the news report. Estimate the standard deviation by applying the range rule of thumb.

37. **Summarizing a News Data Set.** Find an example of a data distribution given in the form of a table in a recent news report. Make a five-number summary and a boxplot for the distribution.

CHAPTER REVIEW EXERCISES

1. **Nicotine in Cigarettes**. Listed below are the nicotine amounts (in mg per cigarette) for samples of filtered and non-filtered cigarettes. Do filters appear to be effective in reducing the amount of nicotine?

    Non-filtered: 1.1 1.7 1.7 1.1 1.1 1.4 1.1 1.4 1.0 1.2

    Filtered: 0.4 1.0 1.2 0.8 0.8 1.0 1.1 1.1 1.1 0.78

   a. Find the mean and median for each of the two data sets.

   b. Find the range and standard deviation for each of the two data sets.

   c. Give the five-number summary and construct a boxplot for each of the two data sets.

   d. Apply the range rule of thumb to estimate the standard deviation of each of the two data sets. How well does the rule work in each case? Briefly discuss why it does or does not work well.

   e. Based on all your results, compare and discuss the two data sets in terms of their center and variation. Does there appear to be a difference between the amounts of nicotine in non-filtered cigarettes and filtered cigarettes?

2. Combine the two samples from Review Exercise 1 and find the following:

   a. The percentile for the amount of 1.4 mg

   b. The mode

3. **a.** What is the standard deviation for a sample of 50 values, all of which are the same?

   b. Which of the following two car batteries would you prefer to buy, and why?

   - One taken from a population with a mean life of 48 months and a standard deviation of 2 months

   - One taken from a population with a mean life of 48 months and a standard deviation of 6 months

   c. If an outlier is included with a sample of 50 values, what is the effect of the outlier on the mean?

   d. If an outlier is included with a sample of 50 values, what is the effect of the outlier on the median?

   e. If an outlier is included with a sample of 50 values, what is the effect of the outlier on the range?

   f. If an outlier is included with a sample of 50 values, what is the effect of the outlier on the standard deviation?

CHAPTER QUIZ

1. When you add the pulse rates of 65, 74, 88, 77, and 92, then divide by the number of values, the result is 79.2. Which term best describes this value: average, mean, median, mode, or standard deviation?

2. Find the median of the pulse rates given in Exercise 1.

3. What is the range of the pulse rates given in Exercise 1?

4. The standard deviation of the pulse rates given in Exercise 1 is 10.9. What characteristic does that value measure?

5. A histogram is constructed for a large set of pulse rates of adult males, and it is found that the distribution is symmetric and unimodal. What does this imply about the values of the mean and median?

6. Indicate whether the given statement could apply to a data set consisting of 1,000 values that are all different.

   a. The 20th percentile is greater than the 30th percentile.

   b. The median is greater than the first quartile.

   c. The third quartile is greater than the first quartile.

   d. The mean is equal to the median.

   e. The range is zero.

7. A standard test for braking reaction time of drivers is designed so that the mean is 2.00 sec and the standard deviation is 0.25 sec. Based on the range rule of thumb, what are the likely low and high values?

8. Use the range rule of thumb to estimate the standard deviation of the pulse rates given in Exercise 1. How does the result compare to the actual standard deviation of 10.9?

9. Find the standard deviation of these body temperatures (°F): 98.2, 98.2, 98.2, 98.2, and 98.2.

10. Identify the components that constitute the five-number summary for a data set.

FOCUS ON

THE STOCK MARKET

What's Average About the Dow?

As "averages" go, this one is extraordinary. You can't watch the news without hearing what happened to it, and many people spend hours tracking it each day. It is by far the most famous indicator of stock market performance. We are talking, of course, about the Dow Jones Industrial Average, or DJIA for short. But what exactly is it?

The easiest way to understand the DJIA is by looking at its history. As the modern industrial era got under way in the late 19th century, most people considered stocks to be dangerous and highly speculative investments. One reason was a lack of regulation that made it easy for wealthy speculators, unscrupulous managers, and corporate raiders to manipulate stock prices. But another reason was that, given the complexities of daily stock trading, even Wall Street professionals had a hard time figuring out whether stocks in general were going up (a "bull market") or down (a "bear market"). Charles H. Dow, the founder (along with Edward D. Jones) and first editor of the *Wall Street Journal*, believed he could rectify this problem by creating an "average" for the stock market as a whole. If the average was up, the market was up, and if the average was down, the market was down.

To keep the average simple, Dow chose 12 large corporations to include in his average. On May 26, 1896, he added the stock prices of these 12 companies and divided by 12, finding a mean stock price of $40.94. This was the first value for the DJIA. As Dow had hoped, it suddenly became easy for the public to follow the market's direction just by comparing his average from day to day, month to month, or year to year.

The basic idea behind the DJIA is still the same, although the list now includes 30 stocks rather than 12; the list is selected by the editors of the *Wall Street Journal*, who occasionally change the stocks on the list. However, the DJIA is no longer the mean price of its 30 stocks. Instead, it is calculated by adding the prices of its 30 stocks and dividing by a special divisor. Because of this divisor, we now think of the DJIA as an index that helps us keep track of stock values, rather than as an actual average of stock prices.

The divisor is designed to preserve continuity in the underlying value represented by the DJIA, and it therefore must change whenever the list of 30 stocks changes or when a company on the list has a stock split. A simple example shows why the divisor must change when the list changes. Suppose the DJIA consisted of only 2 stocks (rather than 30): Stock A with a price of $100 and Stock B with a price of $50. The mean price of these two stocks is ($100 + $50)/2 = $75. Now, suppose that we change the list by replacing Stock B with Stock C and that Stock C's price is $200. The new mean is ($100 + $200)/2 = $150, so merely replacing one stock on the list would raise the mean price from $75 to $150. Therefore, to keep the "value" of the DJIA constant when we change this list, we must divide the new mean of $150 by 2. In this way, the DJIA remains 75 both before and after the list change, but we can no longer think of this 75 as a mean price in dollars.

To see why a stock split changes the divisor, again suppose the index consists of just two stocks: Stock X at $100 and Stock Y at $50, for a mean price of $75. Now, suppose Stock X undergoes a 2-for-1 stock split, so that its new price is $50. With both stocks now priced at $50, the mean price after the stock split would also be $50. In other words, even though a stock split does not affect a company's total value (it only changes the number and prices of its shares), we'd find a drop in the mean price from $75 to $50. In this case, we can preserve continuity by dividing the new mean of 50 by 2/3 (which is equivalent to multiplying by 3/2) so that the DJIA holds at 75 both before and after the stock split.

Just as in these simple examples, the real divisor changes with every list change or stock split, so it has changed many times since Charles Dow first calculated the DJIA as an actual mean. The current value of the divisor is published daily in the *Wall Street Journal*.

Given that there are now well over 10,000 actively traded stocks, it might seem remarkable that a sample of only 30 could reflect overall market activity. But today, when computers make it easy to calculate stock market "averages" in many other ways, we can look at historical data and see that the DJIA has indeed been a reliable indicator of overall market performance. Figure 4.16 shows the historical performance of the DJIA

If you study Figure 4.16 carefully, you may be tempted to think that you can see patterns that would allow you to forecast precise values of the market in the future. Unfortunately, no

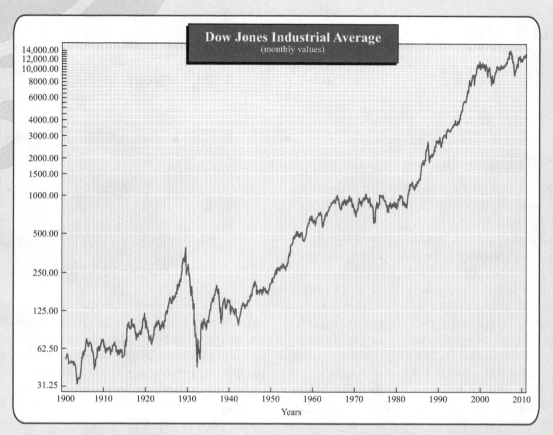

Figure 4.16 Historical values of the Dow Jones Industrial Average, 1900 through 2011 Note that the vertical axis uses an exponential scale in which the value doubles with each equivalent increment in height; this makes it easier to see the changes that occurred when the DJIA was low compared with its value today. Chart courtesy of StockCharts.com.

one has ever found a way to make reliable forecasts, and most economists now believe that such forecasts are impossible.

The futility of trying to forecast the market is illustrated by the story of the esteemed Professor Benjamin Graham, often called the father of "value investing." In the spring of 1951, one of his students came to him for some investment advice. Professor Graham noted that the DJIA then stood at 250, but that it had fallen below 200 at least once during every year since its inception in 1896. Because it had not yet fallen below 200 in 1951, Professor Graham advised his student to hold off on buying until it did. Professor Graham presumably followed his own advice, but the student did not. Instead, the student invested his "about 10 thousand bucks" in the market right away. As it turned out, the market never did fall below 200 in 1951 or any time thereafter. And the student, named Warren Buffet, became a billionaire many times over.

QUESTIONS FOR DISCUSSION

1. The stock market is still considered a riskier investment than, say, bank savings accounts or bonds. Nevertheless, financial advisors almost universally recommend holding at least some stocks, which is quite different from the situation that prevailed a century ago. What role do you think the DJIA played in building investors' confidence in the stock market?

2. The DJIA is only one of many different stock market indices in wide use today. Briefly look up a few other indices, such as the S&P 500, the Russell 2000, and the NASDAQ. How do these indices differ from the DJIA? Do you think that any of them should be considered more reliable indicators of the overall market than the DJIA? Why or why not?

3. The 30 stocks in the DJIA represent a sample of the more than 10,000 actively traded stocks, but it is not a *random* sample because it is chosen by particular editors for particular reasons that may include personal biases. Suppose that you chose a random sample of 30 stocks and tracked their prices. Do you think that such a random sample would track the market as well as the stocks in the DJIA? Why or why not?

4. Create your own "portfolio" of 10 stocks that you'd like to own, and assume you own 100 shares of each. Calculate the total value of your portfolio today, and track price changes over the next month. At the end of the month, calculate the percent change in the value of your portfolio. How did the performance of your portfolio compare to the performance of the DJIA during the month? If you really owned these stocks, would you continue to hold them or would you sell? Explain.

F🔭CUS ON
ECONOMICS

Are the Rich Getting Richer?

The media love to report on the lavish spending of the super-rich, making it seem that the rich keep getting richer while the rest of us are left behind. But is it true?

If we wish to draw general conclusions about how the average person is faring compared to the rich, we must look at the overall income distribution. Economists have developed a number, called the **Gini Index,** that is used to describe the level of equality or inequality in the income distribution. The Gini Index is defined so that it can range only between 0 and 1. A Gini Index of 0 indicates perfect income equality, in which every person has precisely the same income. A Gini Index of 1 indicates perfect inequality, in which a single person has all the income and no one else has anything. Figure 4.17 shows the Gini Index in the United States since 1947. Note that the Gini Index fell from 1947 to 1968, indicating that the income distribution became more uniform during this period. The Gini Index has generally risen ever since, indicating that the rich are, indeed, getting richer.

Although the Gini Index provides a simple single-number summary of income inequality, the number itself is fairly difficult to interpret (and to calculate). An alternative way to look at the income distribution is to study income quintiles, which divide the population into fifths by income. Often, the highest quintile is further broken down to show how the top 5% of income earners compares with others.

Figure 4.18 shows the share of total income received by each quintile and the top 5% in the United States in different decades. The height of each bar (the number on top of it) represents the share of total income. For example, the 3.3 on the bar for the lowest quintile in 2010 means that the poorest 20% of the population received only 3.3% of the total income in the United States. Similarly, the 50.2 on the bar for the top quintile in 2010 means that the richest 20% of the population received 50.2% of the income. Note also that the richest 5% received 21.3% of the income—nearly double the total income of the poorest 40% of the population. If you study this graph carefully, you'll see that the share of income earned by the first four quintiles—which means all but the richest 20% of the population—dropped since 1970. Meanwhile, the share earned by the richest 20% rose substantially, as did the share of the top 5%. In other words, this graph also confirms that the rich have been getting richer compared to most of the population.

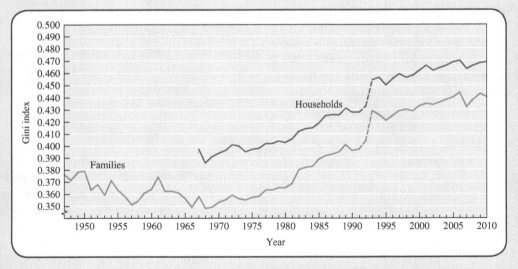

Figure 4.17 Gini Index for families and households, 1947–2010. Household data, which include single people and households in which the members are not part of the same family, have been taken only since 1967. The dashed segments in 1993 indicate a change in the methodology for data collection, so the corresponding rise in the Gini Index may be partially or wholly due to this change rather than a real change in income inequality. *Source:* Adapted from data by the U.S. Census Bureau.

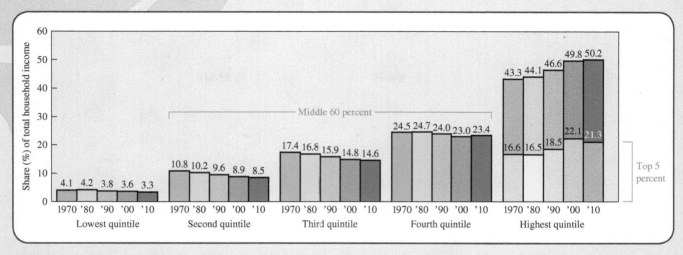

Figure 4.18 Share of total household income by quintile (and top 5%) at 10-year intervals. *Source:* U.S. Census Bureau.

Now that we've established that the rich are getting richer, the next question is whether it matters. Most people, including most economists, have traditionally assumed that rising income inequality is bad for democracies. But a few economists from both the left and the right of the political spectrum argue that the change in recent decades is different. For one thing, the change meets a widely accepted ethical condition called the *Pareto criterion*, after the Italian economist Vilfredo Pareto (for whom Pareto charts are also named): Any change is good if it makes someone better off without making anyone else worse off. The Pareto criterion appears to be satisfied because overall growth in the U.S. economy has been helping nearly everyone. In other words, most people may have a smaller percentage of total income than they had in the past, but they still have more absolute income and therefore are living better than they did in the past.

Secondly, today's rich differ from the rich in the past. For example, as recently as 1980, 60% of the "Forbes 400" (the richest 400 people) had inherited most of their wealth. Today, less than 20% of the Forbes 400 represents old money. The implication is that while you had to be born rich in the past, today you can *become* rich by getting educated and working hard. Surely, it is a good thing to encourage education and hard work.

Finally, while overall income inequality has increased, the income inequality among different races and between men and women has decreased. In other words, it is now easier than it was in the past for African Americans, Hispanics, and women to earn as much as white males. Again, this is surely a good thing for our democratic values, even if we still have a long way to go before the inequalities are completely eliminated.

QUESTIONS FOR DISCUSSION

1. Compare several different ways of looking at the data shown in Figure 4.17 and Figure 4.18. For example, does one seem to indicate a larger change in income inequality than the other? Can you think of other possible ways to display income data that might give a different picture than those shown here?

2. Do you agree that the Pareto criterion is a good way to evaluate the ethics of economic change? Why or why not?

3. Overall, do you think the increase in income inequality has been a good or bad thing for the United States? Will it be good if the trend continues? Defend your opinion.

4. Although economic data suggest that the vast majority of Americans are better off today than they were a few decades ago, the poorest Americans still live in difficult economic conditions. What do you think can or should be done to help improve the lives of the poor? Can your suggestion be implemented without harming the overall economy? Explain.

5

A Normal World

When you walk into a store, how do you know if a sale price is really a good price? When you exercise and your heart rate rises, how do you know if it has risen enough, but not too much, for a good workout? If your 12-year-old daughter runs a mile in 5 minutes, is she a future Olympic hopeful? These questions seem very different, but from a statistical standpoint they are very similar: Each one asks whether a particular number (price, heart rate, running time) is somehow unusual. In this chapter, we will discuss how we can answer such questions with the aid of the bell-shaped *normal distribution*.

Nothing in life is to be feared.
It is only to be understood.

—Marie Curie

LEARNING GOALS

5.1 What Is Normal?
Understand the normal distribution and identify situations in which a normal distribution is likely to arise.

5.2 Properties of the Normal Distribution
Know how to interpret the normal distribution in terms of the 68-95-99.7 rule, standard scores, and percentiles.

FOCUS TOPICS

p. 199 Focus on Education: What Can We Learn from SAT Trends?

p. 201 Focus on Psychology: Are We Smarter than Our Parents?

WHAT IS NORMAL?

Suppose a friend is pregnant and due to give birth on June 30. Would you advise her to schedule an important business meeting for June 16, two weeks before the due date? Answering this question requires knowing whether the baby is likely to arrive more than 14 days before the due date. For that, we need to examine data concerning due dates and actual birth dates.

Figure 5.1 is a histogram for a distribution of 300 natural births at Providence Memorial Hospital; the data are hypothetical, but based on how births would be distributed without medical intervention. The horizontal axis shows how many days before or after the due date a baby was born. Negative numbers represent births *prior* to the due date, zero represents a birth on the due date, and positive numbers represent births *after* the due date. The left vertical axis shows the number of births for each 4-day bin. For example, the frequency of 35 for the highest bar corresponds to the bin from −2 days to 2 days; it shows that out of the 300 total births in the sample, 35 births occurred within 2 days of the due date.

To answer our question about whether a birth is likely to occur more than 14 days early, it is more useful to look at the *relative frequencies*. Recall that the relative frequency of any data value is its frequency divided by the total number of data values (see Section 3.1). Figure 5.1 shows relative frequencies on the right vertical axis. For example, the bin for −14 days to −10 days (shaded dark blue) has a relative frequency of about 0.07, or 7%. That is, about 7% of the 300 births occurred between 14 days and 10 days before the due date.

We can find the proportion of births that occurred more than 14 days before the due date simply by adding the relative frequencies for the bins to the left of −14; you can measure the graph to confirm that these bins have a total relative frequency of about 0.21, which means that about 21% of the births in this data set occurred more than 14 days before the due date. Based on these data, your friend has about a 1 in 5 chance of her baby being born on or before the date of the business meeting. If the meeting is important, it might be good to schedule it earlier.

BY THE WAY

The Scottish politician John Sinclair (1754–1835) was one of the first collectors of economic, demographic, and agricultural data. He is credited with introducing the words *statistics* and *statistical* into the English language, having heard them used in Germany to refer to matters of state.

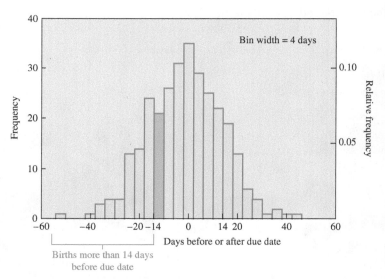

Figure 5.1   Histogram of frequencies (left vertical axis) and relative frequencies (right vertical axis) for birth dates relative to due date. (These data are hypothetical.) Negative numbers refer to births before the due date; positive numbers refer to births after the due date. The width of each bin is 4 days. For example, the bin shaded dark blue represents births occurring between 10 and 14 days early.

TIME OUT TO THINK

Suppose the friend plans to take a three-month maternity leave after the birth. Based on the data in Figure 5.1 and assuming a due date of June 30, should she promise to be at work on October 10?

The Normal Distribution

The distribution of the birth data has a fairly distinctive shape, which is easier to see if we overlay the histogram with a smooth curve (Figure 5.2). For our present purposes, the shape of this smooth distribution has three very important characteristics:

- The distribution is *single-peaked.* Its mode, or most common birth date, is the due date.
- The distribution is *symmetric* around its single peak; therefore, its median and mean are the same as its mode. The median is the due date because equal numbers of births occur before and after this date. The mean is also the due date because, for every birth before the due date, there is a birth the same number of days after the due date.
- The distribution is spread out in a way that makes it resemble the shape of a bell, so we call it a "bell-shaped" distribution.

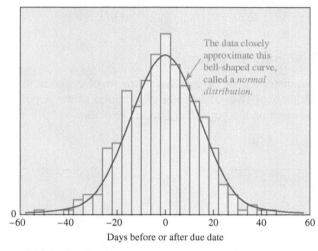

The data closely approximate this bell-shaped curve, called a *normal distribution.*

Days before or after due date

Figure 5.2 A smooth normal distribution curve is drawn over the histogram of Figure 5.1.

TIME OUT TO THINK

The histogram in Figure 5.2, which is based on natural births, is fairly symmetric. Today, doctors usually induce birth if a woman goes too far past her due date. How would the shape of the histogram change if it included induced births?

The smooth distribution in Figure 5.2, with these three characteristics, is called a **normal distribution**. All normal distributions have the same characteristic bell shape, but they can differ in their mean and in their variation. Figure 5.3 shows two different normal distributions. Both have the same mean, but distribution (a) has greater variation. As we'll discuss in the next section, knowing the *standard deviation* (see Section 4.4) of a normal distribution tells us everything we need to know about its variation. Therefore, a normal distribution can be fully described with just two numbers: its mean and its standard deviation.

TECHNICAL NOTE

Although we will not use it in this text, the following algebraic function describes a normal distribution with mean μ and standard deviation σ:

$$y = \frac{e^{-\frac{1}{2}[(x-\mu)/\sigma]^2}}{\sigma\sqrt{2\pi}}$$

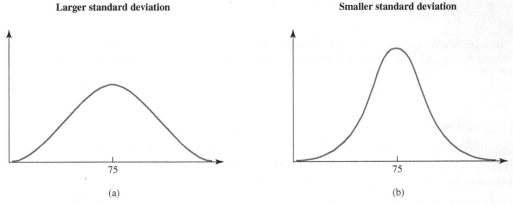

Figure 5.3 Both distributions are normal and have the same mean of 75, but the distribution on the left has a larger standard deviation.

> **Definition**
>
> The **normal distribution** is a symmetric, bell-shaped distribution with a single peak. Its peak corresponds to the mean, median, and mode of the distribution. Its variation can be characterized by the standard deviation of the distribution.

BY THE WAY

Using data taken from French and Scottish soldiers, the Belgian social scientist Adolphe Quetelet realized in the 1830s that human characteristics such as height and chest circumference are normally distributed. This observation led him to coin the term "the average man." Quetelet was the first foreign member of the American Statistical Association.

EXAMPLE ❶ Normal Distributions?

Figure 5.4 shows two distributions: (a) a famous data set of the chest sizes of 5,738 Scottish militiamen collected in about 1846 and (b) the distribution of the population densities of the 50 states. Is either distribution a normal distribution? Explain.

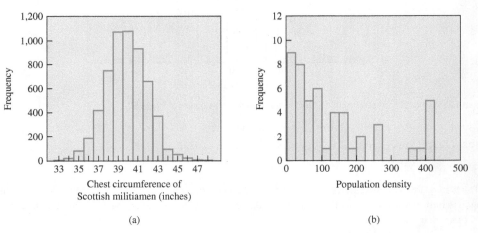

Figure 5.4 *Source of* (a): Adolphe Quetelet, *Lettres à S. A. R. le Duc Régnant de Saxe-Cobourg et Gotha*, 1846.

SOLUTION   The distribution in Figure 5.4a is nearly symmetric, with a mean between 39 and 40 inches. Values far from the mean are less common, giving it the bell shape of a normal distribution. The distribution in Figure 5.4b shows that most states have low population densities, but a few have much higher densities. This fact makes the distribution right-skewed, so it is not a normal distribution.   • • ●

It is also possible to visually inspect a normal distribution and come up with an estimate for the standard deviation. In order to do this, we must first briefly introduce two concepts, concavity and points of inflection.

Definition

- A graph of a normal distribution is **concave upward** at a point on the curve if you can draw a line (or put a ruler) on that point without touching the curve immediately next it and that line (ruler) would be below (holding up) the normal curve.

- A graph of a normal distribution is concave downward at a point on the curve if you could draw a line (or put a ruler) on that point without touching the curve immediately next it and that line (ruler) would be above (resting on) the normal curve.

- A point of inflection is a point on a curve where the curve switches from concave upward to concave downward or vice versa.

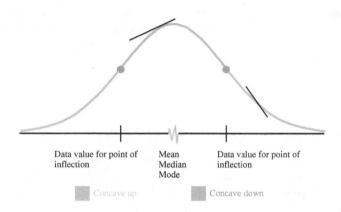

Data value for point of inflection | Mean Median Mode | Data value for point of inflection

Concave up | Concave down

Every normal curve will have two points of inflection. Since normal distributions are symmetric, the point of inflection below the mean and the point of inflection above the mean are equidistant from the mean. That is, each point of inflection is the same distance from the mean and that distance happens to be the standard deviation.

We can visually estimate the standard deviation by looking at any normal curve. The distance on the horizontal axis from the lowest point of inflection to the peak is a good visual estimate of standard deviation. So, if you want to estimate the standard deviation from a figure of a normal distribution, you can follow these steps. 1) Locate the value that corresponds with the peak. This is the mean. 2) Locate the value that corresponds with the lower point of inflection. This value occurs one standard deviation below the mean. 3) Subtract. The standard deviation is the mean – lower point of inflection.

EXAMPLE 2 Heart Rates during an Exam

The following normal distribution represents the heart rates of students during a statistics final exam.

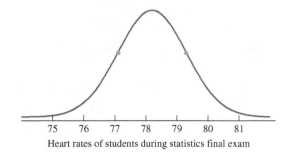

Heart rates of students during statistics final exam

Answer the following questions using the normal distribution.

a. What is the mean heart rate?

b. What is the median heart rate?

c. What is the approximate value for standard deviation?

SOLUTION

a. The mean heart rate can be found by locating the value that is directly below the peak. The value below the peak is 78. So, the mean heart rate is 78 beats per minute.

b. The median for any normal curve is the same as the mean and is located directly beneath the peak. Therefore, the median is 78 beats per minute.

c. First we locate the left point of inflection. This appears to be occurring at about 77. So, the standard deviation can be estimated by subtracting 77 from the mean of 78. Our best estimate for standard deviation is 78 − 77 = 1 beat per minute.   ·· ●

The Normal Distribution and Relative Frequencies

Recall that the total relative frequency for any data set must be 1 (see Section 3.1). Now consider the smooth curve for the normal distribution in Figure 5.2, which is repeated in Figure 5.5. Although we no longer show individual bars, we can still associate the height of the normal curve with the relative frequency. The fact that the relative frequencies must sum to 1 becomes the condition that the area under the normal curve must be 1.

The key idea is this: *The relative frequency for any range of data values is the area under the curve covering that range of values.* For example, a precise calculation shows that the shaded region to the left of −14 days in Figure 5.5 represents about 18% of the total area under the curve. We therefore conclude that the relative frequency is about 0.18 for data values less than −14 days, which means that about 18% of births are more than 14 days early. Similarly, the shaded region to the right of 18 days represents about 12% of the total area under the curve. We therefore conclude that the relative frequency is about 0.12 for data values greater than 18 days, which means that about 12% of births are more than 18 days late. Altogether, we see that 18% + 12% = 30% of all births are either more than 14 days early or more than 18 days late.

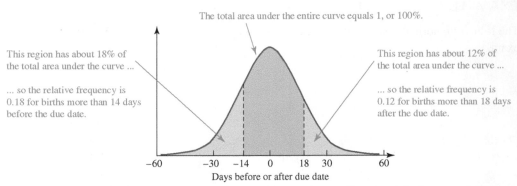

Figure 5.5 The percentage of the total area in any region under the normal curve tells us the relative frequency of data values in that region.

Relative Frequencies and the Normal Distribution

• The area that lies under the normal distribution curve corresponding to a range of values on the horizontal axis is the relative frequency of those values.

• Because the total relative frequency must be 1, the total area under the normal distribution curve must equal 1, or 100%.

EXAMPLE 3 Estimating Areas

Look again at the normal distribution in Figure 5.5.

a. Estimate the percentage of births occurring between 0 and 60 days after the due date.

b. Estimate the percentage of births occurring between 14 days before and 14 days after the due date.

SOLUTION

a. About half of the total area under the curve lies in the region between 0 days and 60 days. This means that about 50% of the births in the sample occur between 0 and 60 days after the due date.

b. Figure 5.5 shows that about 18% of the births occur more than 14 days before the due date. Because the distribution is symmetric, about 18% must also occur more than 14 days after the due date. Therefore, a total of about 18% + 18% = 36% of births occur either more than 14 days before or more than 14 days after the due date. The question asked about the remaining region, which means *between* 14 days before and 14 days after the due date, so this region must represent 100% − 36% = 64% of the births.   ·· •

TIME ⏰UT TO THINK
About what percentage of births in Figure 5.5 occur between 14 days early and 18 days late? Explain. (Hint: Remember that the total area under the curve is 100%.)

When Can We Expect a Normal Distribution?

We can better appreciate the importance of the normal distribution if we understand why it is so common. Consider a human characteristic such as height, which closely approximates a normal distribution. Most men or women have heights clustered near the mean height (for their sex), so a data set of heights has a peak at the mean height. But as we consider heights increasingly far from the mean on either side, we find fewer and fewer people. This "tailing off" of heights far from the mean produces the two tails of the normal distribution.

On a deeper level, any quantity that is influenced by many factors is likely to follow a normal distribution. Adult heights are the result of many genetic and environmental factors. Scores on SAT tests or IQ tests tend to be normally distributed because each test score is determined from many individual test questions. Sports statistics, such as batting averages, tend to be normally distributed because they involve many people with many different levels of skill. More generally, we can expect a data set to have a nearly normal distribution if it meets the following conditions.

BY THE WAY
The normal distribution curve is often called a *Gaussian curve* in honor of the 19th-century German mathematician Carl Friedrich Gauss. The American logician Charles Peirce introduced the term *normal distribution* in about 1870.

> **Conditions for a Normal Distribution**
>
> A data set that satisfies the following four criteria is likely to have a nearly normal distribution:
>
> 1. Most data values are clustered near the mean, giving the distribution a well-defined single peak.
>
> 2. Data values are spread evenly around the mean, making the distribution symmetric.
>
> 3. Larger deviations from the mean become increasingly rare, producing the tapering tails of the distribution.
>
> 4. Individual data values result from a combination of many different factors, such as genetic and environmental factors.By the Way

EXAMPLE 4 Is It a Normal Distribution?

Which of the following variables would you expect to have a normal or nearly normal distribution?

a. Scores on a very easy test

b. Shoe sizes of a random sample of adult women

c. The number of apples in each of 100 full bushel baskets

SOLUTION

a. Tests have a maximum possible score (100%) that limits the size of data values. If the test is very easy, the mean will be high and many scores will be near the maximum. The fewer lower scores can be spread out well below the mean. We therefore expect the distribution to be left-skewed and non-normal.

b. Foot length is a human trait determined by many genetic and environmental factors. We therefore expect lengths of women's feet to cluster near a mean and become less common farther from the mean, giving the distribution a bell shape, so the lengths have a nearly normal distribution.

c. The number of apples in a bushel basket varies with the size of the apples. We expect that in the distribution there will be a single mode that should be close to the mean number of apples per basket. The number of baskets with more than the mean number of apples should be close to the number of baskets with fewer than the mean number of apples. We therefore expect the number of apples per basket to have a nearly normal distribution.   ·· ●

> **TIME OUT TO THINK**
>
> Would you expect scores on a moderately difficult exam to have a normal distribution? Suggest two more quantities that you would expect to be normally distributed.

Section 5.1 Exercises

Statistical Literacy and Critical Thinking

1. **Normal Distribution.** When we refer to a "normal" distribution, does the word *normal* have the same meaning as in ordinary language, or does it have a special meaning in statistics? What exactly is a normal distribution?

2. **Normal Distribution.** A normal distribution is informally and loosely described as a probability distribution that is "bell-shaped" when graphed. Draw a rough sketch of the bell shape that characterizes normal distributions.

3. **Random Digits.** Many states have lotteries that involve the random selection of digits 0, 1, 2, …, 9. Is the distribution of those digits a normal distribution? Why or why not?

4. **Areas.** Birth weights in the United States are normally distributed with a mean (in grams) of 3420 g and a standard deviation of 495 g. If you graph this normal distribution, the area to the right of 4000 g is 0.12. What is the area to the left of 4000 g?

Does It Make Sense? For Exercises 5–8, decide whether the statement makes sense (or is clearly true) or does not make sense (or is clearly false). Explain clearly; not all of these have definitive answers, so your explanation is more important than your chosen answer.

5. **Heights of Women.** A sample of 2,000 women is randomly selected, and it is found that the heights of the women are normally distributed with a mean of 63.6 in.

6. **Brains.** As part of a study of the relationship between brain size and IQ, a random sample of 250 adult males is obtained and their brain volumes are measured and found to be normally distributed.

7. **IQ Scores.** The mean of a normally distributed set of IQ scores is 100, and 60% of the scores are over 105.

8. **Salaries.** An economist plans to obtain the current salaries of all professional football players, and she predicts that those salaries will have a normal distribution.

Concepts and Applications

9. **What Is Normal?** Identify the distribution in Figure 5.6 that is not normal. Of the two normal distributions, which has the larger standard deviation?

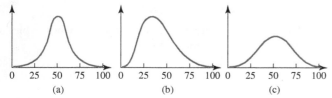

Figure 5.6

10. **What Is Normal?** Identify the distribution in Figure 5.7 that is not normal. Of the two normal distributions, which has the larger standard deviation?

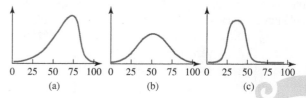

Figure 5.7

Normal Variables. For each of the data sets in Exercises 11–18, state whether you would expect it to be normally distributed. Explain your reasoning.

11. **Weights of Quarters.** The exact weights of a random sample of quarters manufactured in 2012 by the U.S. Mint.

12. **Incomes.** The incomes of randomly selected adults in the United States.

13. **Lottery.** The numbers selected in the Pennsylvania "Match 6" lottery, in which players attempt to match six randomly selected numbers between 1 and 49.

14. **SAT Scores.** All of the SAT scores from last year.

15. **White Blood Cell Counts.** The measured white blood cell counts of 500 randomly selected adult women.

16. **Flight Delays.** The lengths of time that commercial aircraft are delayed before departing.

17. **Waiting Times.** The waiting times at a bus stop if the bus comes once every 10 minutes and you arrive at random times.

18. **Parking Ticket Fines.** The amounts of the fines from parking tickets found on a random sample of 1,000 parked cars.

19. **Movie Lengths.** Figure 5.8 shows a histogram for the lengths of 60 movies. The mean movie length is 110.5 minutes. Is this distribution close to normal? Should this variable have a normal distribution? Why or why not?

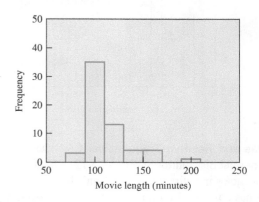

Figure 5.8

20. Pulse Rates. Figure 5.9 shows a histogram for the pulse rates of 98 students. The mean pulse rate is 71.2 beats per minute. Is this distribution close to normal? Should this variable have a normal distribution? Why or why not?

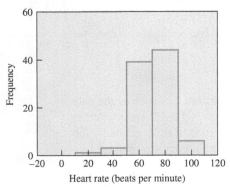

Figure 5.9

21. Quarter Weights. Figure 5.10 shows a histogram for the weights of 50 randomly selected quarters. The mean weight is 5.62 grams. Is this distribution close to normal? Should this variable have a normal distribution? Why or why not?

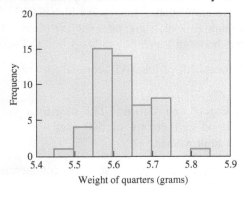

Figure 5.10

22. Aspirin Weights. Figure 5.11 shows a histogram for the weights of 30 randomly selected aspirin tablets. The mean weight is 665.4 milligrams. Is this distribution close to normal? Should this variable have a normal distribution? Why or why not?

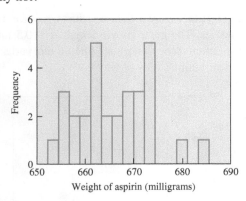

Figure 5.11

23. Areas and Relative Frequencies. Consider the graph of the normal distribution in Figure 5.12, which gives relative frequencies in a distribution of men's heights. The distribution has a mean of 69.6 inches and a standard deviation of 2.8 inches.

a. What is the total area under the curve?

b. Estimate (using area) the relative frequency of values less than 67.

c. Estimate the relative frequency of values greater than 67.

d. Estimate the relative frequency of values between 67 and 70.

e. Estimate the relative frequency of values greater than 70.

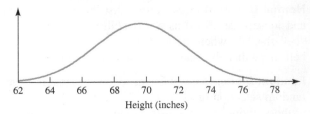

Figure 5.12

24. Areas and Relative Frequencies. Consider the graph of the normal distribution in Figure 5.13, which shows the relative frequencies in a distribution of IQ scores. The distribution has a mean of 100 and a standard deviation of 16.

a. What is the total area under the curve?

b. Estimate (using area) the relative frequency of values less than 100.

c. Estimate the relative frequency of values greater than 110.

d. Estimate the relative frequency of values less than 110.

e. Estimate the relative frequency of values between 100 and 110.

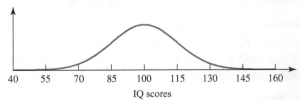

Figure 5.13

25. Estimating Areas. Consider the graph of the normal distribution in Figure 5.14, which illustrates the relative frequencies in a distribution of systolic blood pressures for a sample of female students. The distribution has a standard deviation of 14.

a. What is the mean of the distribution?

b. Estimate (using area) the percentage of students whose blood pressure is less than 100.

c. Estimate the percentage of students whose blood pressure is between 110 and 130.

d. Estimate the percentage of students whose blood pressure is greater than 130.

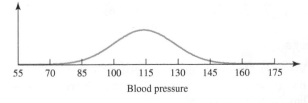

Figure 5.14

26. Estimating Areas. Consider the graph of the normal distribution in Figure 5.15, which gives the relative frequencies in a distribution of body weights for a sample of male students.

a. What is the mean of the distribution?

b. Estimate (using area) the percentage of students whose weight is less than 140.

c. Estimate the percentage of students whose weight is greater than 170.

d. Estimate the percentage of students whose weight is between 140 and 160.

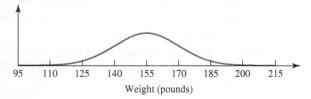

Figure 5.15

PROJECTS FOR THE INTERNET & BEYOND

27. SAT Score Distributions. The College Board Web site gives the distribution of SAT scores (usually in 50-point bins). Collect these data and construct a histogram for each part of the test. Discuss the validity of the claim that SAT scores are normally distributed.

28. Finding Normal Distributions. Using the guidelines given in the text, choose a variable that you think should be nearly normally distributed. Collect at least 30 data values for the variable and make a histogram. Comment on how closely the distribution fits a normal distribution. In what ways does it differ from a normal distribution? Try to explain the differences.

29. Movie Lengths. Collect data to support or refute the claim that movies have gotten shorter over the decades. Specifically, make a histogram of movie lengths for each decade from the 1940s through the present, find the mean movie length for each sample, and comment on whether these distributions are normal. Discuss your results and give plausible reasons for any trends that you observe.

IN THE NEWS

30. Normal Distributions. Rarely does a news article refer to the actual distribution of a variable or state that a variable is normally distributed. Nevertheless, variables mentioned in news reports must have some distribution. Find two variables in news reports that you suspect have nearly normal distributions. Explain your reasoning.

31. Non-normal Distributions. Find two variables in news reports that you suspect *do not* have nearly normal distributions. Explain your reasoning.

5.2 PROPERTIES OF THE NORMAL DISTRIBUTION · · · · · · · · · · · · · · · ·

Consider a *Consumer Reports* survey in which participants were asked how long they owned their last TV set before they replaced it. The variable of interest in this survey is *replacement time for television sets*. Based on the survey, the distribution of replacement times has a mean of about 8.2 years, which we denote as μ (the Greek letter *mu*). The standard deviation of the distribution is about 1.1 years, which we denote as σ (the Greek letter *sigma*). Making the reasonable assumption that the distribution of TV replacement times is approximately normal, we can picture it as shown in Figure 5.16.

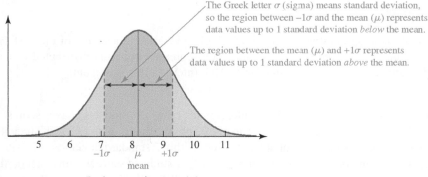

The Greek letter σ (sigma) means standard deviation, so the region between -1σ and the mean (μ) represents data values up to 1 standard deviation *below* the mean.

The region between the mean (μ) and $+1\sigma$ represents data values up to 1 standard deviation *above* the mean.

Replacement time (years)

Figure 5.16 Normal distribution for replacement times for TV sets with a mean of $\mu = 8.2$ years and a standard deviation of $\sigma = 1.1$ years.

TECHNICAL NOTE

A normal distribution can have any value for the mean and any positive value for the standard deviation. The term *standard normal distribution* specifically refers to a normal distribution with a mean of 0 and a standard deviation of 1.

Because all normal distributions have the same bell shape, knowing the mean and standard deviation of a distribution allows us to know much about where the data values lie. For example, if we measure areas under the curve in Figure 5.16, we find that about two-thirds of the area lies within 1 standard deviation of the mean, which in this case is between $8.2 - 1.1 = 7.1$ years and $8.2 + 1.1 = 9.3$ years. Therefore, the TV replacement time is between 7.1 and 9.3 years for about two-thirds of the people surveyed. Similarly, about 95% of the area lies within 2 standard deviations of the mean, which in this case is between $8.2 - 2.2 = 6.0$ years and $8.2 + 2.2 = 10.4$ years. We conclude that the TV replacement time is between 6.0 and 10.4 years for about 95% of the people surveyed.

A simple rule, called the **68-95-99.7 rule**, gives precise guidelines for the percentage of data values that lie within 1, 2, and 3 standard deviations of the mean for any normal distribution. The following box states the rule in words, and Figure 5.17 shows it visually.

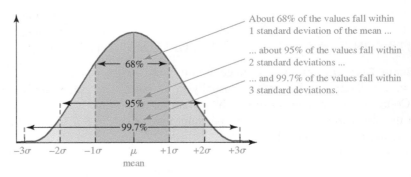

Figure 5.17   Normal distribution illustrating the 68-95-99.7 rule.

The 68-95-99.7 Rule for a Normal Distribution

- About 68% (more precisely, 68.3%), or just over two-thirds, of the data values fall within 1 standard deviation of the mean.

- About 95% (more precisely, 95.4%) of the data values fall within 2 standard deviations of the mean.

- About 99.7% of the data values fall within 3 standard deviations of the mean.

EXAMPLE ❶ SAT Scores

The tests that make up the verbal (critical reading) and mathematics parts of the SAT (and the GRE, LSAT, and GMAT) are designed so that their scores are normally distributed with a mean of $\mu = 500$ and a standard deviation of $\sigma = 100$. Interpret this statement.

TECHNICAL NOTE

As discussed in the "Focus on Psychology" section at the end of the chapter, the mean score on a particular component of the SAT may differ from 500 depending on the test and the year it is given.

SOLUTION   From the 68-95-99.7 rule, about 68% of students have scores within 1 standard deviation (100 points) of the mean of 500 points; that is, about 68% of students score between 400 and 600. About 95% of students score within 2 standard deviations (200 points) of the mean, or between 300 and 700. And about 99.7% of students score within 3 standard deviations (300 points) of the mean, or between 200 and 800. Figure 5.18 shows this interpretation graphically; note that the horizontal axis shows both actual scores and distance from the mean in standard deviations.

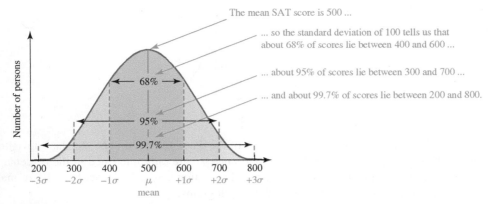

Figure 5.18 Normal distribution for scores on components of the SAT, showing the percentages associated with 1, 2, and 3 standard deviations.

EXAMPLE ② Detecting Counterfeits

Vending machines can be adjusted to reject coins above and below certain weights. The weights of legal U.S. quarters have a normal distribution with a mean of 5.67 grams and a standard deviation of 0.0700 gram. If a vending machine is adjusted to reject quarters that weigh more than 5.81 grams and less than 5.53 grams, what percentage of legal quarters will be rejected by the machine?

SOLUTION A weight of 5.81 is 0.14 gram, or 2 standard deviations, above the mean. A weight of 5.53 is 0.14 gram, or 2 standard deviations, below the mean. Therefore, by accepting only quarters within the weight range 5.53 to 5.81 grams, the machine accepts quarters that are within 2 standard deviations of the mean and rejects those that are more than 2 standard deviations from the mean. By the 68-95-99.7 rule, 95% of legal quarters will be accepted and 5% of legal quarters will be rejected. ⋯●

EXAMPLE ③ Birth Weight

The birth weight of male babies is normally distributed. The mean birth weight of male babies born to mothers taking a vitamin supplement was 3.67 kilograms with a standard deviation of 0.66 kilograms (based on data from the New York State Department of Health).

Answer the following questions based on this information.

a. What percentage of the male babies in the study weigh more than 3.67 kilograms?

b. What percentage of male babies in the study weigh between 3.67 and 4.33 kilograms?

c. What percentage of male babies in the study weigh more than 4.33 kilograms?

SOLUTION

a. Since 3.67 kilograms is the value of the mean, we are trying to find out what percentage of the data values lie to the right of the mean. If we look at the relevant area under the normal curve, we see that 50% of the area lies to the right of the mean.

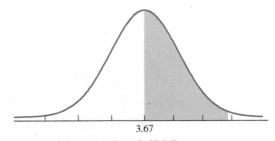

So, 50% of male babies weigh more than 3.67 kilograms.

b. The mean is 3.67 kilograms. The value of 4.33 is one standard deviation above the mean since 4.33 − 3.67 = 0.66. So, we are trying to find out what percentage of the data values lie between the mean and one standard deviation above the mean. This can be found using the 68-95-99.7 rule.

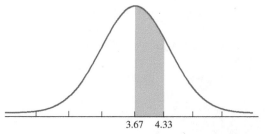

3.67   4.33

The rule tells us that approximately 68% of the data falls within one standard deviation of the mean. We only need half of that or 34% since we are only interested in the percentage of data that fall within the mean and one standard deviation above the mean. So, 34% of male babies in the study weigh between 3.67 and 4.33 kilograms.

c. As in part b, the value of 4.33 is one standard deviation above the mean. For this part, we are trying to find out what percentage of the data values lie to the right of one standard deviation above the mean. This can be found using the 68-95-99.7 rule.

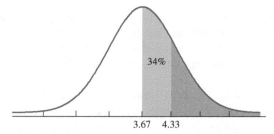

3.67   4.33

We are interested in finding the area in red. From part b, we know that 34% of male baby weights are between the mean (3.67 kilograms) and one standard deviation above the mean (4.33 kilograms). From part a, we know that 50% of male babies in the study weigh above 3.67 kilograms. To find the area in red, we can subtract the area between 3.67 and 4.33 from 50%. Therefore, 50% - 34% = 16% of male babies weigh more than 4.33 kilograms.   ⋯●

Applying the 68-95-99.7 Rule

We can apply the 68-95-99.7 rule to answer many questions about the frequencies (or relative frequencies) of data values in a normal distribution. Consider an exam taken by 1,000 students for which the scores are normally distributed with a mean of $\mu = 75$ and a standard deviation of $\sigma = 7$. How many students scored above 82?

A score of 82 is 7 points, or 1 standard deviation, above the mean of 75. The 68-95-99.7 rule tells us that about 68% of the scores are *within* 1 standard deviation of the mean. Therefore, about $100\% - 68\% = 32\%$ of the scores are *more than* 1 standard deviation from the mean. Half of this 32%, or 16%, of the scores are more than 1 standard deviation *below* the mean; the other 16% of the scores are more than 1 standard deviation *above* the mean (Figure 5.19a). We conclude that about 16% of 1,000 students, or 160 students, scored above 82.

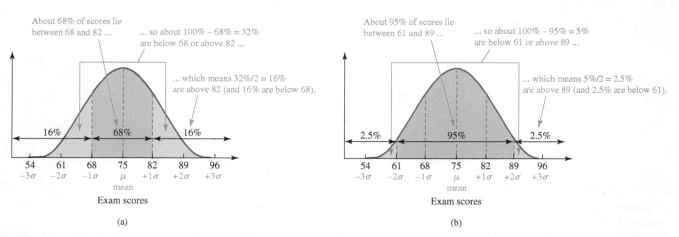

Figure 5.19 A normal distribution of test scores with a mean of 75 and a standard deviation of 7. (a) 68% of the scores lie within 1 standard deviation of the mean. (b) 95% of the scores lie within 2 standard deviations of the mean.

Similarly, suppose we want to know how many students scored below 61. A score of 61 is 14 points, or 2 standard deviations, below the mean of 75. The 68-95-99.7 rule tells us that about 95% of the scores are *within* 2 standard deviations of the mean, so about 5% of the scores are *more than* 2 standard deviations from the mean. Half of this 5%, or 2.5%, of the scores are more than 2 standard deviations *below* the mean (Figure 5.19b), so we conclude that about 2.5% of 1,000 students, or 25 students, scored below 61.

Because 95% of the scores fall between 61 and 89, we sometimes say the scores outside this range are *unusual* because they are relatively rare.

Identifying Unusual Results

In statistics, we often need to distinguish values that are typical, or "usual," from values that are "unusual." By applying the 68-95-99.7 rule, we find that about 95% of all values from a normal distribution lie within 2 standard deviations of the mean. This implies that, among all values, 5% lie more than 2 standard deviations away from the mean. We can use this property to identify values that are relatively "unusual": **Unusual values** are values that are more than 2 standard deviations away from the mean.

EXAMPLE 4 Traveling and Pregnancy

Consider again the question of whether you should advise a pregnant friend to schedule an important business meeting 2 weeks before her due date. Actual data suggest that the number of days between the birth date and the due date is normally distributed with a mean of $\mu = 0$ days and a standard deviation of $\sigma = 15$ days. How would you help your friend make the decision? Would a birth 2 weeks before the due date be considered "unusual"?

SOLUTION Your friend is assuming that she will *not* have given birth 14 days, or roughly 1 standard deviation, before her due date. But because this outcome is well within 2 standard deviations of the mean, it is *not* unusual. By the 68-95-99.7 rule, the day of birth for 68% of pregnancies is within 1 standard deviation of the mean, or between -15 days and 15 days from the due date. This means that about $100\% - 68\% = 32\%$ of births occur either more than 15 days early or more than 15 days late. Therefore, half of this 32%, or 16%, of all births are more than 15 days early (Figure 5.20). You should tell your friend that about 16% of all births occur more than 15 days before the due date. If your friend likes to think in terms of probability, you could say that there is a 0.16 (about 1 in 6) chance that she will give birth on or before her meeting date.

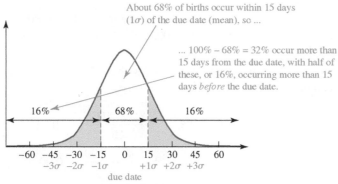

Figure 5.20 About 16% of births occur more than 15 days before the due date.

EXAMPLE 5 Normal Heart Rate

You measure your resting heart rate at noon every day for a year and record the data. You discover that the data have a normal distribution with a mean of 66 and a standard deviation of 4. On how many days was your heart rate below 58 beats per minute?

SOLUTION   A heart rate of 58 is 8 (or 2 standard deviations) below the mean. According to the 68-95-99.7 rule, about 95% of the data values are within 2 standard deviations of the mean. Therefore, 2.5% of the data values are more than 2 standard deviations *below* the mean, and 2.5% of the data values are more than 2 standard deviations *above* the mean. On 2.5% of 365 days, or about 9 days, your measured heart rate was below 58 beats per minute.   ·· ●

> **TIME OUT TO THINK**
>
> As Example 5 suggests, multiple measurements of the resting heart rate of a *single* individual are normally distributed. Would you expect the average resting heart rates of *many* individuals to be normally distributed? Which distribution would you expect to have the larger standard deviation? Why?

Standard Scores

The 68-95-99.7 rule applies only to data values that are exactly 1, 2, or 3 standard deviations from the mean. For other cases, we can generalize this rule if we know precisely how many standard deviations from the mean a particular data value lies. The number of standard deviations a data value lies above or below the mean is called its **standard score** (or *z-score*), often abbreviated by the letter z. For example:

- The standard score of the mean is $z = 0$, because it is 0 standard deviations from the mean.
- The standard score of a data value 1.5 standard deviations *above* the mean is $z = 1.5$.
- The standard score of a data value 2.4 standard deviations *below* the mean is $z = -2.4$.

The following box summarizes the computation of standard scores.

> **Computing Standard Scores**
>
> The number of standard deviations a data value lies above or below the mean is called its standard score (or z-score), defined by
>
> $$z = \text{standard score} = \frac{\text{data value} - \text{mean}}{\text{standard deviation}}$$
>
> The standard score is positive for data values above the mean and negative for data values below the mean.

EXAMPLE 6 Standard IQ Scores

The Stanford-Binet IQ test is scaled so that scores have a mean of 100 and a standard deviation of 16. Find the standard scores for IQs of 85, 100, and 125.

SOLUTION   We calculate the standard scores for these IQs by using the standard score formula with a mean of 100 and standard deviation of 16.

$$\textit{standard score for 85: } z = \frac{85 - 100}{16} = -0.94$$

$$\textit{standard score for 100: } z = \frac{100 - 100}{16} = 0.00$$

$$\textit{standard score for 125: } z = \frac{125 - 100}{16} = 1.56$$

We can interpret these standard scores as follows: 85 is 0.94 standard deviation *below* the mean, 100 is equal to the mean, and 125 is 1.56 standard deviations *above* the mean. Figure 5.21 shows these values on the distribution of IQ scores.

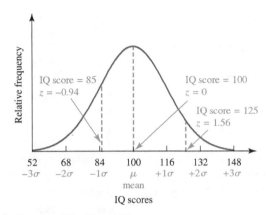

Figure 5.21   Standard scores for IQ scores of 85, 100, and 125.

Standard Scores and Percentiles

Once we know the standard score of a data value, the properties of the normal distribution allow us to find its **percentile** in the distribution. You are probably familiar with the idea of percentiles. For example, if you scored in the 45th percentile on the SAT, 45% of the SAT scores were lower than yours.

> **Percentiles**
>
> The *n*th percentile of a data set is the smallest value in the set with the property that n% of the data values are less than or equal to it. A data value that lies between two percentiles is said to lie in the lower percentile.

We can convert standard scores to percentiles with a *standard score table*, such as Table 5.1 (or see Appendix A for a more detailed table), or with computer software. For each of many standard scores in a normal distribution, the table gives the percentage of values in the distribution *less than or equal to* that value. For example, the table shows that 55.96% of the values in a normal distribution have a standard score less than or equal to 0.15. In other words, a data value with a standard score of 0.15 lies in the 55th percentile.

> ⏻ USING TECHNOLOGY—**STANDARD SCORES IN EXCEL**
>
> Excel's built-in function STANDARDIZE returns the standard score for any data value, given the mean and standard deviation of the distribution. Enter the data in the form "=STANDARDIZE(data value, mean, standard deviation)." The screen shot below shows this function with a table for the data value, mean, and standard deviation from Example 5; the function references the cells (B1, B2, B3) containing those data. Column C shows the results.
>
>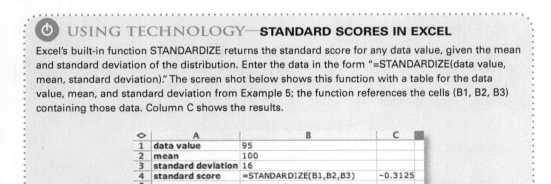
>
> | ◇ | A | B | C |
> |---|---|---|---|
> | 1 | data value | 95 | |
> | 2 | mean | 100 | |
> | 3 | standard deviation | 16 | |
> | 4 | standard score | =STANDARDIZE(B1,B2,B3) | -0.3125 |
> | 5 | | | |

TABLE 5.1		**Standard Scores and Percentiles for a Normal Distribution (cumulative values from the *left*)**					
Standard score	**%**	**Standard score**	**%**	**Standard score**	**%**	**Standard score**	**%**
−3.5	0.02	−1.0	15.87	0.0	50.00	1.1	86.43
−3.0	0.13	−0.95	17.11	0.05	51.99	1.2	88.49
−2.9	0.19	−0.90	18.41	0.10	53.98	1.3	90.32
−2.8	0.26	−0.85	19.77	0.15	55.96	1.4	91.92
−2.7	0.35	−0.80	21.19	0.20	57.93	1.5	93.32
−2.6	0.47	−0.75	22.66	0.25	59.87	1.6	94.52
−2.5	0.62	−0.70	24.20	0.30	61.79	1.7	95.54
−2.4	0.82	−0.65	25.78	0.35	63.68	1.8	96.41
−2.3	1.07	−0.60	27.43	0.40	65.54	1.9	97.13
−2.2	1.39	−0.55	29.12	0.45	67.36	2.0	97.72
−2.1	1.79	−0.50	30.85	0.50	69.15	2.1	98.21
−2.0	2.28	−0.45	32.64	0.55	70.88	2.2	98.61
−1.9	2.87	−0.40	34.46	0.60	72.57	2.3	98.93
−1.8	3.59	−0.35	36.32	0.65	74.22	2.4	99.18
−1.7	4.46	−0.30	38.21	0.70	75.80	2.5	99.38
−1.6	5.48	−0.25	40.13	0.75	77.34	2.6	99.53
−1.5	6.68	−0.20	42.07	0.80	78.81	2.7	99.65
−1.4	8.08	−0.15	44.04	0.85	80.23	2.8	99.74
−1.3	9.68	−0.10	46.02	0.90	81.59	2.9	99.81
−1.2	11.51	−0.05	48.01	0.95	82.89	3.0	99.87
−1.1	13.57	0.0	50.00	1.0	84.13	3.5	99.98

Note: The table shows percentiles for standard scores between −3.5 and +3.5, though much lower and higher standard scores are possible. (Appendix A has a more detailed standard score table.) The % column gives the percentage of values in the distribution less than the corresponding standard score.

EXAMPLE 7 Cholesterol Levels

Cholesterol levels in men 18 to 24 years of age are normally distributed with a mean of 178 and a standard deviation of 41.

a. What is the percentile for a 20-year-old man with a cholesterol level of 190?

b. What cholesterol level corresponds to the 90th percentile, the level at which treatment may be necessary?

SOLUTION

a. The *standard score* for a cholesterol level of 190 is

$$z = \text{standard score} = \frac{\text{data value} - \text{mean}}{\text{standard deviation}} = \frac{190 - 178}{41} \approx 0.29$$

Table 5.1 shows that a standard score of 0.29 corresponds to about the 61st percentile.

b. Table 5.1 shows that 90.32% of all data values have a standard score less than 1.3. That is, the 90th percentile is about 1.3 standard deviations above the mean. Given the mean cholesterol level of 178 and the standard deviation of 41, a cholesterol level 1.3 standard deviations above the mean is

$$\underbrace{178}_{\text{mean}} + \underbrace{(1.3 \times 41)}_{\substack{1.3 \text{ standard} \\ \text{deviations}}} = 231.3$$

The 90th percentile begins at a cholesterol level of about 231, so anyone with this level or higher may be in need of treatment.   • • ●

USING TECHNOLOGY—STANDARD SCORES AND PERCENTILES

Excel The built-in function NORMDIST saves you the work of using a table like Table 5.1. Find a data value's percentile in a normal distribution by entering "=NORMDIST (data value, mean, standard deviation, TRUE)"; the fourth input (TRUE) is necessary to get a percentile result. The screen shot below shows the calculation of the standard score and percentile for the data in Example 6a. Column C shows the results; note that the percentile is displayed as 0.615, so you need to multiply by 100 to express it as a percentage (61.5%).

◇	A	B	C
1	data value	190	
2	mean	178	
3	standard deviation	41	
4	standard score	=STANDARDIZE(B1,B2,B3)	0.29
5	percentile	=NORMDIST(B1,B2,B3,TRUE)	0.615

STATDISK STATDISK can be used in place of Table 5.1. Select **Analysis, Probability Distributions, Normal Distribution**. Either enter the z score to find corresponding areas, or enter the cumulative area from the left to find the z score. After entering a value, click on the **Evaluate** button. The display will include the area to the left of the z score as well as the area to the right of the z score.

TI-83/84 Plus

- *Finding Area:* To find the area between two values, press **2ND**, then press **VARS** to get to the **DISTR** (distribution) menu. Select **normalcdf**. Enter the two values, the mean, and the standard deviation, all separated by commas, as in this format: (left value, right value, mean, standard deviation). *Hint:* If there is no left value, enter the left value as −999999, and if there is no right value, enter the right value as 999999. For example, **normalcdf(80, 85, 100, 15)** returns a value of 0.0674 (rounded), indicating that for a normally distributed population with mean 100 and standard deviation 15, 6.74% of the values are between 80 and 85.

- *Finding x Value:* To find a value corresponding to a known area, press **2ND**, then press **VARS** to get to the **DISTR** (distribution) menu. Select **invNorm**, and proceed to enter the total area to the left of the value, the mean, and the standard deviation in this format with the commas included: (total area to the left, mean, standard deviation). For example, **invNorm(0.4, 100, 15)** returns a value of 96.2 (rounded), indicating that for a normally distributed population with mean 100 and standard deviation 15, the value of 96.2 has an area of 0.4 (or 40%) to its left.

EXAMPLE 8 IQ Scores

IQ scores are normally distributed with a mean of 100 and a standard deviation of 16 (see Example 6). What are the IQ scores for people in the 75th and 40th percentiles on IQ tests?

SOLUTION   Table 5.1 shows that the 75th percentile falls *between* standard scores of 0.65 and 0.70; we can estimate that it has a standard score of about 0.67. This corresponds to an IQ that is 0.67 standard deviation, or about $0.67 \times 16 = 11$ points, above the mean of 100. Therefore, a person in the 75th percentile has an IQ of 111. The 40th percentile corresponds to a standard score of approximately −0.25, or a score that is $0.25 \times 16 = 4$ points *below* the mean of 100. So a person in the 40th percentile has an IQ of 96.   ·· ●

EXAMPLE 9 Women in the Army

The heights of American women ages 18 to 24 are normally distributed with a mean of 65 inches and a standard deviation of 2.5 inches. In order to serve in the U.S. Army, women must be between 58 inches and 80 inches tall. What percentage of women are ineligible to serve based on their height?

SOLUTION   The standard scores for the army's minimum and maximum heights of 58 inches and 80 inches are

$$For\ 58\ inches:\ z = \frac{58 - 65}{2.5} = -2.8$$

$$For\ 80\ inches:\ z = \frac{80 - 65}{2.5} = 6.0$$

Table 5.1 shows that a standard score of −2.8 corresponds to the 0.26 percentile. A standard score of 6.0 does not appear in Table 5.1, which means it is above the 99.98th percentile (the highest percentile shown in the table). We conclude that 0.26% of all women are too

short to serve in the army and fewer than 0.02% of all women are too tall to serve in the army. Altogether, fewer than about 0.28% of all women, or about 1 out of every 400 women, are ineligible to serve in the army based on their height.   ··●

Toward Probability

Suppose you pick a baby at random and ask whether the baby was born more than 15 days prior to his or her due date. Because births are normally distributed around the due date with a standard deviation of 15 days, we know that 16% of all births occur more than 15 days prior to the due date (see Example 4). For an individual baby chosen at random, we can therefore say that there's a 0.16 chance (about 1 in 6) that the baby was born more than 15 days early. In other words, the properties of the normal distribution allow us to make a *probability statement* about an individual. In this case, our statement is that the probability of a birth occurring more than 15 days early is 0.16.

This example shows that the properties of the normal distribution can be restated in terms of ideas of probability. In fact, much of the work we will do throughout the rest of this text is closely tied to ideas of probability. For this reason, we will devote the next chapter to studying fundamental ideas of probability. But first, in the next section, we will use the basic ideas we have discussed so far to introduce one of the most important concepts in statistics.

Section 5.2 Exercises

Statistical Literacy and Critical Thinking

1. **Standard Score.** Men's heights are normally distributed with a mean of 69.0 in. and a standard deviation of 2.8 in. What is the standard z-score for a man with a height of 69.0 in.?

2. **Standard Score.** The standard score for the height of a male is $z = -2$. Is the height of this male above or below the mean height of all males? How many standard deviations away from the mean is this?

3. **Distributions.** For rolling a die, the mean outcome is 3.5. Can we apply the 68-95-99.7 rule and conclude that 95% of all outcomes fall within 2 standard deviations of 3.5? Why or why not?

4. **z-Scores and Percentages.** Table 5.1 includes standard scores and percentiles. Can a z-score be a negative value? Can a percentile be a negative value? Explain.

Does It Make Sense? For Exercises 5–8, decide whether the statement makes sense (or is clearly true) or does not make sense (or is clearly false). Explain clearly; not all of these have definitive answers, so your explanation is more important than your chosen answer.

5. **Test Scores.** Scores on a statistics test are normally distributed with a mean of 75 and a standard deviation of 75.

6. **Birth Weights.** Birth weights (in grams) in Lichtenstein are normally distributed with a mean of 3,420 g and a standard deviation of 0 g.

7. **Depth Perception Scores.** Scores on a standard test of depth perception are normally distributed with two different modes.

8. **SAT Scores.** SAT scores are normally distributed with a mean of 1518 and a standard deviation of 325.

Concepts and Applications

9. **Using the 68-95-99.7 Rule.** A test of depth perception is designed so that scores are normally distributed with a mean of 50 and a standard deviation of 10. Use the 68-95-99.7 rule to find the following values.

   a. Percentage of scores less than 50

   b. Percentage of scores less than 60

   c. Percentage of scores greater than 70

   d. Percentage of scores greater than 40

   e. Percentage of scores between 40 and 70

10. **Using the 68-95-99.7 Rule.** Assume the resting pulse rates for a sample of individuals are normally distributed with a mean of 70 and a standard deviation of 15. Use the 68-95-99.7 rule to find the following quantities.

   a. Percentage of pulse rates less than 70

   b. Percentage of pulse rates greater than 55

   c. Percentage of pulse rates between 55 and 70

   d. Percentage of pulse rates between 55 and 100

   e. Percentage pulse of rates between 70 and 100

11. **Applying the 68-95-99.7 Rule.** In a study of facial behavior, people in a control group are timed for eye contact in a 5-minute period. Their times are normally distributed with a mean of 184.0 seconds and a standard deviation of 55.0 seconds (based on data from "Ethological Study of Facial Behavior

in Nonparanoid and Paranoid Schizophrenic Patients," by Pittman, Olk, Orr, and Singh, *Psychiatry*, Vol. 144, No. 1). Use the 68-95-99.7 rule to find the indicated quantity.

a. Find the percentage of times within 55.0 seconds of the mean of 184.0 seconds.

b. Find the percentage of times within 110.0 seconds of the mean of 184.0 seconds.

c. Find the percentage of times within 165.0 seconds of the mean of 184.0 seconds.

d. Find the percentage of times between 184.0 seconds and 294 seconds.

12. Applying the 68-95-99.7 Rule. When designing the placement of a CD player in a new model car, engineers must consider the forward grip reach of the driver. Women have forward grip reaches that are normally distributed with a mean of 27.0 inches and a standard deviation of 1.3 inches (based on anthropometric survey data from Gordon, Churchill et al.). Use the 68-95-99.7 rule to find the indicated quantity.

a. Find the percentage of women with forward grip reaches between 24.4 inches and 29.6 inches.

b. Find the percentage of women with forward grip reaches less than 30.9 inches.

c. Find the percentage of women with forward grip reaches between 27.0 inches and 28.3 inches.

IQ Scores. For Exercises 13–24, use the normal distribution of IQ scores, which has a mean of 100 and a standard deviation of 16. Use Table 5.1 (on page 192) to find the indicated quantities. Note: Table 5.1 shows standard scores from −3.5 to +3.5. In these problems, for standard scores above 3.5, use a percentile of 99.99%; for all standard scores below −3.5, use a percentile of 0.01%.

13. Percentage of scores greater than 100

14. Percentage of scores less than 116

15. Percentage of scores less than 68

16. Percentage of scores greater than 108

17. Percentage of scores less than 132

18. Percentage of scores less than 92

19. Percentage of scores greater than 76

20. Percentage of scores greater than 148

21. Percentage of scores between 84 and 116

22. Percentage of scores between 68 and 132

23. Percentage of scores between 52 and 116

24. Percentage of scores between 76 and 108

Heights of Women. For Exercises 25–36, use the normal distribution of heights of adult women, which has a mean of 162 centimeters and a standard deviation of 6 centimeters. Use Table 5.1 to find the indicated quantities. Note: Table 5.1 shows standard scores from −3.5 to +3.5. In these problems, for standard scores above 3.5, use a percentile of 99.99%; for all standard scores below −3.5, use a percentile of 0.01%.

25. The percentage of heights greater than 162 centimeters

26. The percentage of heights less than 168 centimeters

27. The percentage of heights greater than 156 centimeters

28. The percentage of heights greater than 171 centimeters

29. The percentage of heights less than 177 centimeters

30. The percentage of heights less than 147 centimeters

31. The percentage of heights less than 144 centimeters

32. The percentage of heights greater than 179 centimeters

33. The percentage of heights between 156 centimeters and 168 centimeters

34. The percentage of heights between 159 centimeters and 165 centimeters

35. The percentage of heights between 148 centimeters and 170 centimeters

36. The percentage of heights between 146 centimeters and 156 centimeters

37. Coin Weights. Consider the following table, showing the official mean weight and estimated standard deviation for five U.S. coins. Suppose a vending machine is designed to reject all coins with weights more than 2 standard deviations above or below the mean. For each coin, find the range of weights that is acceptable to the vending machine. In each case, what percentage of legal coins is rejected by the machine?

Coin	Weight (grams)	Estimated standard deviation (grams)
Cent	2.500	0.03
Nickel	5.000	0.06
Dime	2.268	0.03
Quarter	5.670	0.07
Half dollar	11.340	0.14

38. Pregnancy Lengths. Lengths of pregnancies are normally distributed with a mean of 268 days and a standard deviation of 15 days.

a. What is the percentage of pregnancies that last less than 250 days?

b. What is the percentage of pregnancies that last more than 300 days?

c. If a birth is considered premature if the pregnancy lasts less than 238 days, what is the percentage of premature births?

39. SAT Scores. Based on data from the College Board, SAT scores are normally distributed with a mean of 1518 and a standard deviation of 325.

   a. Find the percentage of SAT scores greater than 2000.

   b. Find the percentage of SAT scores less than 1500.

   c. Find the percentage of SAT scores between 1600 and 2100.

40. GRE Scores. Assume that the scores on the Graduate Record Exam (GRE) are normally distributed with a mean of 497 and a standard deviation of 115.

   a. A graduate school requires a GRE score of 650 for admission. To what percentile does this correspond?

   b. A graduate school requires a GRE score in the 95th percentile for admission. To what actual score does this correspond?

41. Calibrating Barometers. Researchers for a manufacturer of barometers (devices to measure atmospheric pressure) read each of 50 barometers at the same time of day. The mean of the readings is 30.4 (inches of mercury) with a standard deviation of 0.23 inch, and the readings appear to be normally distributed.

   a. What percentage of the barometers read over 31?

   b. What percentage of the barometers read less than 30?

   c. The company decides to reject barometers that read more than 1.5 standard deviations above or below the mean. What is the critical reading below which barometers will be rejected? What is the critical reading above which barometers will be rejected?

   d. What would you take as the actual atmospheric pressure at the time the barometers were read? Explain.

42. Spelling Bee Scores. At the district spelling bee, the 60 girls have a mean score of 71 points with a standard deviation of 6, while the 50 boys have a mean score of 66 points with a standard deviation of 5 points. Those students with a score greater than 75 are eligible to go to the state spelling bee. What percentage of those going to the state bee will be girls?

43. Being a Marine. According to data from the National Health Survey, the heights of adult men are normally distributed with a mean of 69.0 inches and a standard deviation of 2.8 inches. The U.S. Marine Corps requires that men have heights between 64 inches and 78 inches. What percentage of American men are eligible for the Marines based on height?

44. Movie Lengths. Based on a random sample of movie lengths, the mean length is 110.5 minutes with a standard deviation of 22.4 minutes. Assume that movie lengths are normally distributed.

   a. What fraction of movies are more than 2 hours long?

   b. What fraction of movies are less than $1\frac{1}{2}$ hours long?

   c. What is the probability that a randomly selected movie will be less than $2\frac{1}{2}$ hours long?

PROJECTS FOR THE INTERNET & BEYOND

45. Normal Distribution Demonstrations on the Web. Do an Internet search on the keywords "normal distribution" and find an animated demonstration of the normal distribution. Describe how the demonstration works and the useful features that you observed.

46. Estimating a Minute. Ask survey subjects to estimate 1 minute without looking at a watch or clock. Each subject should say "go" at the beginning of the minute and then "stop" when

1. For each of the following situations, state whether the distribution of values is likely to be a normal distribution. Give a brief explanation justifying your choice.

   a. Numbers resulting from spins of a roulette wheel. (There are 38 equally likely slots with numbers 0, 00, 1, 2, 3, ..., 36.)

   b. Weights of 12-year old girls

   c. Scores on a test designed to measure knowledge of current events

2. The College of Portland uses a diagnostics test to correctly place students in math courses. Scores on the test are normally distributed with a mean of 400 and a standard deviation of 50.

   a. Using the 68-95-99.7 rule, find the percentage of scores within 50 of the mean of 400.

   b. Using the 68-95-99.7 rule, find the percentage of scores between 300 and 500.

   c. Is a score of 550 unusual? Why or why not?

3. Assume that body temperatures of healthy adults are normally distributed with a mean of 98.20°F and a standard deviation of 0.62°F (based on data from University of Maryland researchers).

   a. If you have a body temperature of 99.00°F, what is your percentile score?

   b. Convert 99.00°F to a standard score (or z-score).

   c. Is a body temperature of 99.00°F "unusual"? Why or why not?

   d. Fifty adults are randomly selected. What is the likelihood that the mean of their body temperatures is 97.98°F or lower?

   e. A person's body temperature is found to be 101.00°F. Is this result "unusual"? Why or why not? What should you conclude?

   f. What body temperature is the 95th percentile?

   g. What body temperature is the 5th percentile?

   h. Bellevue Hospital in New York City uses 100.6°F as the lowest temperature considered to indicate a fever. What percentage of normal and healthy adults would be considered to have a fever? Does this percentage suggest that a cutoff of 100.6°F is appropriate?

   i. If, instead of assuming that the mean body temperature is 98.20°F, we assume that the mean is 98.60°F (as many people believe), what is the chance of randomly selecting 106 people and getting a mean of 98.20°F or lower? (Continue to assume that the standard deviation is 0.62°F.) University of Maryland researchers did get such a result. What should we conclude?

CHAPTER QUIZ

1. Which of the following statements are correct?

   a. A normal distribution is any distribution that typically occurs.

   b. The graph of a normal distribution is bell-shaped.

   c. The graph of a normal distribution has one mode.

   d. In a normal distribution, the mean and median are equal.

   e. In a normal distribution, the standard deviation is 0.

2. Car seat belts are tested for strength, and it is found that the results are normally distributed with a mean of 2,400 lb and a standard deviation of 400 lb. Using the 68-95-99.7 rule, find the percentage of scores between 1,600 lb and 3,200 lb.

3. Car seat belts are tested for strength, and it is found that the results are normally distributed with a mean of 2,400 lb and a standard deviation of 400 lb. Use Table 5.1 to find the percentage of scores between 1,600 lb and 3,200 lb.

4. A population is normally distributed with a mean of 850 and a standard deviation of 49, and samples of size 100 are randomly selected. What is the mean of the sample means?

5. A population is normally distributed with a mean of 850 and a standard deviation of 49, and samples of size 100 are randomly selected. What is the standard deviation of the sample means?

6. A population is normally distributed with a mean of 850 and a standard deviation of 49. What is the standard z-score corresponding to 801?

7. A population is normally distributed with a mean of 850 and a standard deviation of 49. What percentage of scores are greater than 801?

8. A population is normally distributed with a mean of 850 and a standard deviation of 49. If 2.28% of the scores are less than 752, what percentage of scores are greater than 752?

9. A population is normally distributed with a mean of 850 and a standard deviation of 49. Find the percentage of scores between 801 and 948.

10. Which of the following is likely to have a distribution that is closest to a normal distribution?

   a. The outcomes that occur when a single die is rolled many times

   b. The outcomes that occur when two dice are rolled many times and the mean is computed each time

   c. The outcomes that occur when five dice are rolled many times and the mean is computed each time

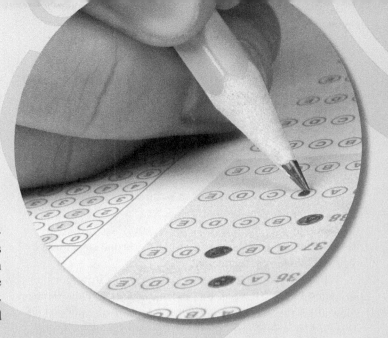

FOCUS ON EDUCATION

What Can We Learn from SAT Trends?

The Scholastic Aptitude Test (SAT) has been taken by college-bound high school students since 1941, when 11,000 students took the first test. Today it is taken by more than 2 million students each year. Until 2006, there were only two parts to the SAT: a "verbal" test and a mathematics test. In 2006, the verbal test was changed to become the "critical reading" test and writing was added as a third test.

The scores on each part of the SAT were originally scaled to have a mean of 500 and a standard deviation of 100. The maximum and minimum scores on each part are 800 and 200, respectively, which are 3 standard deviations above and below the mean. (Scores more than 3 standard deviations above or below the mean are assigned the maximum 800 or minimum 200.)

The mean does not stay at 500 from year to year, however. Each year's test shares some common questions with prior years' tests, and the College Board (which designs the test) uses these common questions to compare each year's test results to those from prior years. The intent is for a score of 500 to represent the same level of achievement at all times, so scores can be compared from one year to the next. For example, if the mean score in a particular year is higher than 500, it implies students performed better on average than did students at the time that the average was set to 500.

Trends in SAT scores are widely used to assess the general state of American education. Figure 5.22 shows the average scores on the verbal/critical reading (meaning the verbal test prior to 2006 and the critical reading test since) and math parts of the SAT between 1972 and 2010; results for the writing test are not shown, because there are not yet enough data to look for trends over time.

The trends show that if the scores from year to year are truly comparable, then students taking the SAT in recent years have significantly poorer verbal skills than students of a few decades ago, though somewhat better mathematical skills. But before we accept this conclusion, we must answer two important questions:

1. Are trends among the *sample* of high school students who take the SAT representative of trends for the *population* of all high school students?

2. Aside from the small number of common questions that link one year to the next, the test changes every year. Can test scores from one year legitimately be compared to scores in other years?

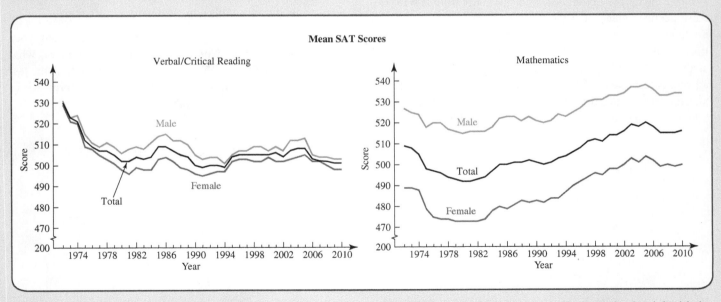

Figure 5.22 Verbal/critical reading and mathematics SAT scores, 1972–2010. Scores for years before 1996 are shown at their "recentered" values, rather than their original values. *Source:* The College Board.

Unfortunately, neither question can be answered with a clear yes. For example, only about a third of high school graduates took the SAT in the 1970s, while more than 50% of high school graduates take it today. If these samples represent the top tier of high school students, the decline in verbal scores might simply reflect the fact that a greater range of student abilities is represented in later samples.

The second question is even more difficult. Even if some test questions stay the same from one year to the next, different material may be emphasized in high schools, thereby changing the likelihood that students will answer the same questions correctly from one year to the next.

Further complications arise when the test undergoes major changes. For example, in 1994 the use of calculators was allowed for the first time on the mathematics section, and additional time was allotted for the entire test (the verbal test also underwent significant changes that year). Is it a coincidence that mathematics scores began an upward trend starting that year, or could it be that the test became "easier" as a result of the changes? Similarly, in 2006 the combined critical reading and mathematics scores suffered their largest decline in more than 30 years. Critics attributed the decline to the fact that the SAT became longer and harder as a result of adding the writing test, while the College Board attributed the decline to a decrease in the number of repeat test-takers. (Repeat test-takers tend to raise the average score, because individual students make significant gains in their scores when they take the test a second or third time.) Clearly, changes in the structure of the test make it difficult to determine whether changes in average scores reflect real changes in education.

Perhaps even more significantly, the calibration of the SAT test underwent a major change in 1996. By that time, scores had declined significantly from the originally planned mean of 500: The mean verbal score had fallen to about 420, while the mean mathematics score had fallen to about 470. Because the range of possible scores goes only from 200 to 800, these declines meant that the minimum and maximum scores no longer represented the same number of standard deviations from the mean, which created difficulties with statistical analysis. The College Board therefore decided to "recenter" all scores to a mean of 500 in 1996. The recentering affected different percentiles differently, but it effectively added about 80 points to the mean of the verbal scores and 30 points to the mean of the mathematics scores. The scores shown in Figure 5.22 are the "recentered" scores. For example, Figure 5.22 shows a mean verbal score of almost exactly 500 in 1994, but if you look back at news reports from that time, you'll see that the actual mean verbal score was about 420 in 1994.

The College Board argues that its statistical analysis has been done with great care, and that despite recentering and changes to the test, trends in the SAT reflect real changes in education. Critics generally agree that the statistical analysis has been done well, but argue that other factors, such as the change in the test-taking population and changes in our education system, make the comparisons invalid. For students, however, the key fact is that many colleges continue to use SAT scores as a part of their decision on whether to admit applicants. As long as that remains the case, the SAT will remain one of the nation's most important tests—and the debate over its merits will surely continue.

QUESTIONS FOR DISCUSSION

1. Do you think that comparisons of SAT scores over two years are meaningful? Over 10 years? Do you agree that the long-term trends indicate that students today have poorer verbal skills but better mathematical skills than those of a few decades ago? Defend your opinions.

2. The downward trend in verbal skills was a major reason why the College Board added the writing test in 2006. The hope was that adding the new test would cause students to focus more on writing in high school and therefore improve both in writing and in overall verbal abilities. What do you think of this rationale? Do you think it will be successful?

3. Notice that scores for males have been consistently higher than scores for females. Why do you think this is the case? Do you think that changes in our education system could eliminate this gap? Defend your opinions.

4. Discuss personal experiences with the SAT among your classmates. Based on these personal experiences, what do you think the SAT is measuring? Do you think the test is a reasonable way to predict students' performance in college? Why or why not?

• • • • • • • • • • • • • •

Are We Smarter than Our Parents?

Most kids tend to think that they're smarter than their parents, but is it possible that they're right? If you believe the results of IQ tests, not only are we smarter than our parents, on average, but our parents are smarter than our grandparents. In fact, almost all of us would have ranked as geniuses if we'd lived a hundred years ago. Of course, before any of us start touting our Einstein-like abilities, it would be good to investigate what lies behind this startling claim.

The idea of an IQ, which stands for *intelligence quotient*, was invented by French psychologist Alfred Binet (1857–1911). Binet created a test that he hoped would identify children in need of special help in school.[*] He gave his test to many children and then calculated each child's IQ by dividing the child's "mental age" by his or her physical age (and multiplying by 100). For example, a 5-year-old child who scored as well as an average 6-year-old was said to have a mental age of 6, and therefore an IQ of (6 ÷ 5) × 100, or 120. Note that, by this definition, IQ tests make sense only for children. However, later researchers, especially psychologists for the U.S. Army, extended the idea of IQ so that it could be applied to adults as well.

Today, IQ is defined by a normal distribution with a mean of 100 and a standard deviation of 16. Traditionally, psychologists have classified people with an IQ below 70 (about 2 standard deviations below the mean of 100) as "intellectually deficient," and people who score above 130 (about 2 standard deviations above the mean) as "intellectually superior."

You're probably aware of the controversy that surrounds IQ tests, which boils down to two key issues:

- Do IQ tests measure intelligence or something else?
- If they do measure intelligence, is it something that is innate and determined by heredity or something that can be molded by environment and education?

A full discussion of these issues is too involved to cover here, but a surprising trend in IQ scores sheds light on these issues. As we'll see shortly, the trend is quite pronounced, but it was long hidden because of the way IQ tests are scored. There are several different, competing versions of IQ tests, and most of them are regularly changed and updated. But in all cases, the scores are adjusted to fit a normal distribution with a mean of 100 and standard deviation of 16. In other words, the scoring of

[*]Binet himself assumed that intelligence could be molded and warned against taking his tests as a measure of any innate or inherited abilities. However, many later psychologists concluded that IQ tests could measure innate intelligence, which led to their being used for separating school children, military recruits, and many other groups of people according to supposed intellectual ability.

an IQ test is essentially done in the same way that an instructor might grade an exam "on a curve." Because of this adjustment, the mean on IQ tests is *always* 100, which makes it impossible for measured IQ scores to rise and fall with time.

Nevertheless, a few IQ tests have not been changed and updated substantially over time, and even tests that have changed considerably often still repeat some old questions. In the early 1980s, a political science professor named Dr. James Flynn began to look at the raw, unadjusted scores on unchanged tests and questions. The results were astounding.

Dr. Flynn found that raw scores have been steadily rising, although the precise amount of the rise varies somewhat with the type of IQ test. The highest rates of increase are found on tests that purport to measure abstract reasoning abilities (such as the "Raven's" tests). For these tests, Dr. Flynn found that the unadjusted IQ scores of people in industrialized countries have been rising at a rate of about 6 points per decade. In other words, a person who scored 100 on a test given in 2010 would have scored about 106 on a test in 2000, 112 on a test in 1990, and so on. Over a hundred years, this would imply a rise of some 60 points, suggesting that someone who scores an "intellectually deficient" IQ of 70 today would have rated an "intellectually superior" IQ of 130 a century ago.

This long-term trend toward rising scores on IQ tests is now called the *Flynn effect*. It is present for all types of IQ tests, though not always to the same degree as with abstract reasoning tests. For example, Figure 5.23 shows how results changed on one of the most widely used IQ tests (the Stanford-Binet test) between 1932 and 1997. Note that, in terms of unadjusted scores, the mean rose by 20 points during that time period. In other words, if people who scored an IQ of 100 on a 1997 test were instead scored on a 1932 test, they would rate an IQ of 120. As the figure shows, about one-fourth of the 1997 test-takers would have rated "intellectually superior" on the 1932 test. There is some evidence that the rise in scores may have begun to slow or halt in more recent years, though the data are still subject to debate.

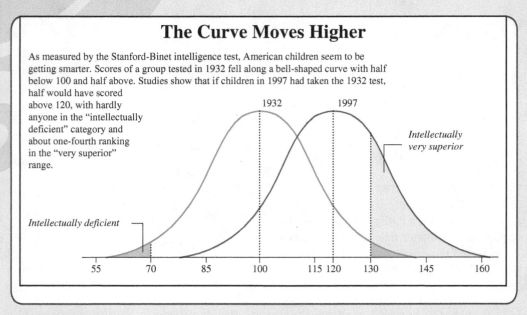

The Curve Moves Higher

As measured by the Stanford-Binet intelligence test, American children seem to be getting smarter. Scores of a group tested in 1932 fell along a bell-shaped curve with half below 100 and half above. Studies show that if children in 1997 had taken the 1932 test, half would have scored above 120, with hardly anyone in the "intellectually deficient" category and about one-fourth ranking in the "very superior" range.

1932   1997

Intellectually very superior

Intellectually deficient

55   70   85   100   115   120   130   145   160

Figure 5.23   *Source:* Adapted from the *New York Times,* based on data from Neisser, Ulric (ed.). *The Rising Curve: Long-Term Gains in IQ and Related Measures.* American Psychological Association, 1998.

Many other scientists have investigated the Flynn effect, and there is general agreement that the long-term trend is real. The implication is clear: Whatever IQ tests measure, people today really *do* have more of it than people just a few decades ago. If IQ tests measure intelligence, then it means we really are smarter than our parents (on average), who in turn are smarter than our grandparents (on average).

Of course, if IQ tests don't measure "intelligence" but only measure some type of skill, then the rise in scores may indicate only that today's children have more practice at that skill than past children. The fact that the greatest rise is seen on tests of abstract thinking lends some support to this idea. These tests often involve such problems as solving puzzles and looking for patterns among sets of shapes, and these types of problems are now much more common in games than they were in the past.

While the Flynn effect does not answer the question of whether IQ tests measure intelligence, it may tell us one important thing: If IQs really have been rising as the Flynn effect suggests, then IQ cannot be an entirely inherited trait, because inherited traits cannot change that much in just a few decades. That is, if IQ tests are measuring intelligence, then intelligence can be molded by environmental as well as hereditary factors.

Dr. Flynn's discovery has already changed the way psychologists look at IQ tests, and it is sure to remain an active topic of research. Moreover, given the many uses to which modern society has put IQ tests, the Flynn effect is likely to have profound social and political consequences as well. So back to our starting question: Are we smarter than our parents? We really can't say, but we can certainly hope so, because it will take a lot of brainpower to solve the problems of the future.

QUESTIONS FOR DISCUSSION

1. Which explanation do you favor for the Flynn effect: that people are getting smarter or that people are getting more practice at the skills measured on IQ tests? Defend your opinion.

2. The rise in performance on IQ tests contrasts sharply with a steady decline in performance over the past few decades on many tests that measure factual knowledge, such as the SAT. Think of several possible ways to explain these contrasting results, and form an opinion as to the most likely explanation.

3. Results on IQ tests tend to differ among different ethnic groups. Some people have used this fact to argue that some ethnic groups tend to be intellectually superior to others. Can such an argument still be supported in light of the Flynn effect? Defend your opinion.

4. Discuss some of the common uses of IQ tests. Do you think that IQ tests *should* be used for these purposes? Does the Flynn effect alter your thoughts about the uses of IQ tests? Explain.

Probability in Statistics

Most statistical studies seek to learn something about a *population* from a much smaller *sample*. Therefore, a key question in any statistical study is whether it is valid to generalize from a sample to the population. To answer this question, we must understand the likelihood, or probability, that what we've learned about the sample also applies to the population. In this chapter, we will focus on a few basic ideas of probability that are commonly used in statistics. As you will see, these ideas of probability also have many applications in their own right.

Probability is the very guide of life.

—Cicero (106–43 BC)

6.1   SETS AND VENN DIAGRAMS

We've seen that propositions come in many forms. The only general requirement is that a proposition must make a clear claim (assertion or denial). In this section, we focus on propositions that claim a relationship between two categories of things. For example, the proposition *all whales are mammals* makes the claim that the category *whales* is entirely contained within the category *mammals*.

Propositions of this type are most easily studied with the aid of two key ideas. The first is the idea of a *set,* which is really just another word for a collection. The second is the idea of a *Venn diagram,* which is a simple visual way of illustrating relationships among sets. Both ideas are very useful for organizing information and hence are important tools of critical thinking.

BY THE WAY

The four military services are organized under the United States Department of Defense. The United States Coast Guard is often grouped with these services, but it is administered by the Department of Home land Security.

Relationships Among Sets

A **set** is a collection of objects, living or nonliving. The **members** of a set are the specific objects within it. For example:

- The members of the set *days of the week* are the individual days Sunday, Monday, Tuesday, Wednesday, Thursday, Friday, and Saturday.
- The members of the set *American military services* are the Army, Navy, Air Force, and Marine Corps.
- The members of the set *Academy Award winning actresses* are the individual actresses who have won Academy Awards.

Set Notation

Sets are often described by listing all their individual members within a pair of braces, { }. For example, the set *American military services* can be written as

$$\{ \text{Army, Navy, Air Force, Marine Corps} \}$$

Every member of the set is listed within the braces, with each member separated from the next by a comma.

Some sets have so many members that it would be difficult or impossible to list all of them. In that case, we can use three dots, "...," to indicate that the list continues in the same basic manner. (The three dots are called an *ellipsis,* but most people just say "dot-dot-dot" when reading them.) If the dots come at the end of a list, they indicate that the list continues indefinitely. For example, we can write the set *dog breeds* as

$$\{ \text{Rottweiler, German Shepherd, Poodle, . . .} \}$$

The three dots indicate that the list continues as you would expect—in this case, with the names of all other dog breeds. It does not matter how many members you list, as long as the pattern is clear. Listing three members, as in the dog breed list, is usually enough to make the point.

In other cases, the dots may come in the middle of the list, representing members that were not explicitly written. For example, the set

$$\{ A, B, C, ..., Z \}$$

represents the entire alphabet in capital letters. The dots are simply a convenience, saving us from having to write every letter.

Although it is less common, the three dots can also come at the beginning of a list. For example, the set

$$\{ ..., -3, -2, -1 \}$$

represents all negative integers. Here, the dots indicate that the list continues to the left, to ever smaller (more negative) numbers.

The whole is more than the sum of its parts.

—Aristotle, Metaphysica

> **Definitions**
>
> A **set** is a collection of objects; the individual objects are the **members** of the set. We write sets by listing their members within a pair of braces, { }. If there are too many members to list, we use three dots, "…," to indicate a continuing pattern.

> TIME 🕐UT TO THINK
>
> How would you use braces to describe the set of students in your mathematics class? How about the set of countries you have visited? Describe one more example of a set that affects you personally, and write it with braces notation.

EXAMPLE 1 Set Notation

Use braces to write the contents of each of the following sets:

a. the set of *countries larger in land area than the United States*

b. the set of *years of the Cold War*, generally taken to have started in 1945 and ended in 1991

c. the set of *natural numbers greater than 5*

SOLUTION

a. The set of *countries larger in land area than the United States* is {Russia, Canada}.

b. The set of *years of the Cold War* is {1945, 1946, 1947,…, 1991}; the dots indicate that the list includes all the years between 1947 and 1991, even though they are not listed explicitly.

c. The set of *natural numbers greater than 5* is {6, 7, 8,…}; the dots indicate that the list continues to ever-higher numbers.   ··●

Illustrating Relationships with Venn Diagrams

The English logician John Venn (1834–1923) invented a simple visual way of describing relationships among sets. His diagrams, now called **Venn diagrams,** use circles to represent sets. Venn diagrams are fairly intuitive and best learned through examples.

Consider the sets *whales* and *mammals*. Because every member of the set *whales* is also a member of the set *mammals*, we say that the set *whales* is a **subset** of the set *mammals*. We represent this relationship in a Venn diagram by drawing the circle for whales *inside* the circle for mammals (Figure 6.1). Notice that the diagram illustrates only the relationship between the sets. The sizes of the circles do not matter

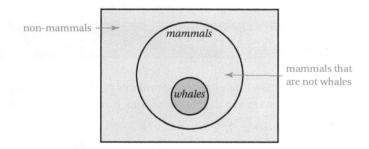

Figure 6.1 The set *whales* is a subset of the set *mammals*.

The circles are enclosed by a rectangle, so this diagram has three regions:

• The inside of the whales circle represents all whales.

• The region outside the *whales* circle but inside the *mammals* circle represents mammals that are not whales (such as cows, bears, and people).

- The region outside the *mammals* circle represents non-mammals; from the context, we interpret this region to represent animals (or living things) that are not mammals, such as birds, fish, and insects.

Next, consider the sets *dogs* and *cats*. A pet can be either a dog or a cat, but not both. We draw the Venn diagram with separated circles that do not touch, and we say that *dogs* and *cats* are **disjoint sets** (Figure 6.2). Again, we enclose the circles in a rectangle. This time, the context suggests that the region outside both circles represents pets that are neither dogs nor cats, such as birds and hamsters.

For our last general case, consider the sets *nurses* and *women*. As shown in Figure 6.3, these are **overlapping sets** because it is possible for a person to be both a woman and a nurse. Because of the overlapping region, this diagram has four regions:

- The overlapping region represents people who are both women and nurses—that is, female nurses.
- The non-overlapping region of the *nurses* circle represents nurses who are not women—that is, male nurses.

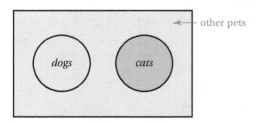

Figure 6.2 The set *dogs* is disjoint from the set *cats*.

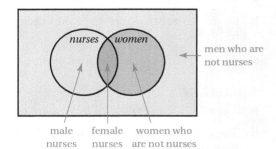

Figure 6.3 The sets *nurses* and *women* are overlapping.

- The non-overlapping region of the *women* circle represents women who are not nurses.
- From the context, we interpret the region outside both circles to represent people who are neither nurses nor women—that is, men who are not nurses.

Note that the sizes of the regions are not important. For example, the small size of the overlapping region does not imply that female nurses are less common than male nurses. In fact, it is possible that some of the regions might have *no* members. For example, imagine that Figure 6.3 represents a single clinic where all four nurses are male. In that case, the overlapping region, which represents female nurses, would have no members. Speaking more generally, we use overlapping circles whenever two sets *might* have members in common.

BRIEF REVIEW: COMMON FRACTIONS

In mathematics, we commonly work with the following important sets of numbers.

The set of **natural numbers** (*or counting numbers*) is

$\{1, 2, 3, \ldots \}$

We can represent the natural numbers on a *number line* with equally spaced dots beginning at 1 and continuing to the right forever.

The set of **whole numbers** is the same as the set of natural numbers except it includes zero. Its members are

$\{0, 1, 2, 3, \ldots \}$

We can represent the whole numbers on a number line with equally spaced dots beginning at 0 and continuing to the right forever.

(*Continued*)

The set of **integers** includes the whole numbers and their negatives. Its members are

$$\{ \ldots, -3, -2, -1, 0, 1, 2, 3, \ldots \}$$

On the number line, the integers extend forever both to the left and to the right.

$$\ldots \; -5 \; -4 \; -3 \; -2 \; -1 \; 0 \; 1 \; 2 \; 3 \; 4 \; 5 \ldots$$

The set of **rational numbers** includes the integers and the fractions that can be made by dividing one integer by another, as long as we don't divide by zero. (The word *rational* refers to a *ratio* of integers.) In other words, rational numbers can be expressed in the form

$\dfrac{x}{y}$, where x and y are integers and $y \neq 0$

(Recall that the symbol $\neq$ means "is not equal to.")

When expressed in decimal form, rational numbers are either terminating decimals with a finite number of digits (such as 0.25, which is $\frac{1}{4}$) or repeating decimals in which a pattern repeats over and over (such as $0.333\ldots$, which is $\frac{1}{3}$).

Irrational numbers are numbers that *cannot* be expressed in the form x/y, where x and y are integers. When written as decimals, irrational numbers neither terminate nor have a repeating pattern. For example, the number $\sqrt{2}$ is irrational because it cannot be expressed exactly in a form x/y; as a decimal, we can write it as $1.414213562\ldots$, where the dots mean that the digits continue

forever with no pattern. The number π is also an irrational number, which as a decimal is written $3.14159265\ldots$.

The set of **real numbers** consists of both rational and irrational numbers; hence, it is represented by the entire number line. Each point on the number line has a corresponding real number, and each real number has a corresponding point on the number line. In other words, the real numbers are the integers and "everything in between." A few selected real numbers are shown on the number line below.

$$-\sqrt{2} \qquad \sqrt{2} \qquad \pi$$
$$-2 \; -\tfrac{3}{2} \; -1 \; -\tfrac{1}{2} \; 0 \; \tfrac{1}{2} \; 1 \; \tfrac{3}{2} \; 2 \; \tfrac{5}{2} \; 3 \; \tfrac{7}{2} \; 4$$
$$\sqrt{3}$$

Examples:

- The number 25 is a natural number, which means it is also a whole number, an integer, a rational number, and a real number.

- The number -6 is an integer, which means it is also a rational number and a real number.

- The number $\frac{2}{3}$ is a rational number, which means it is also a real number.

- The number $7.98418\ldots$ is an irrational number; the dots indicate that the digits continue forever with no particular pattern. It is also a real number.

Set Relationships and Venn Diagrams

Two sets A and B may be related in three basic ways:

- may be a **subset** of B (or vice versa), meaning that all members of A are also members of B. The Venn diagram for this case shows the circle for A inside the circle for B

- may be **disjoint** from B, meaning that the two sets have no members in common. The Venn diagram for this case consists of separated circles that do not touch.

- A and B may be **overlapping** sets, meaning that the two sets share some of the same members. The Venn diagram for this case consists of two overlapping circles. We also use overlapping circles for cases in which the two sets might share common members.

> **TECHNICAL NOTE**
>
> Mathematically, there is a fourth way that two sets can be related: They can be *equal*, meaning that they have precisely the same members.

EXAMPLE 2 Venn Diagrams

Describe the relationship between the given pairs of sets, and draw a Venn diagram showing this relationship. Interpret all the regions of the Venn diagram.

a. *Democrats* and *Republicans* (party affiliations)

b. *Nobel Prize winners* and *Pulitzer Prize winners*

SOLUTION

a. A person can be registered for only one political party, so the sets *Democrats* and *Republicans* are disjoint. Figure 6.4a shows the Venn diagram. The region outside both circles represents people who are neither Democrats nor Republicans—that is, people who are registered for other political parties, who are independent, or who are not registered.

b. It is possible for a person to win both a Nobel Prize and a Pulitzer Prize, so these are overlapping sets. Figure 6.4b shows the Venn diagram. The region outside both circles represents people who have not won either prize, which means most of humanity.

independents and members of other political parties

everyone else

Democrats

Republicans

Nobel winners

Pulitzer winners

winners of Nobel only

winners of both prizes

winners of Pulitzer only

(a)

(b)

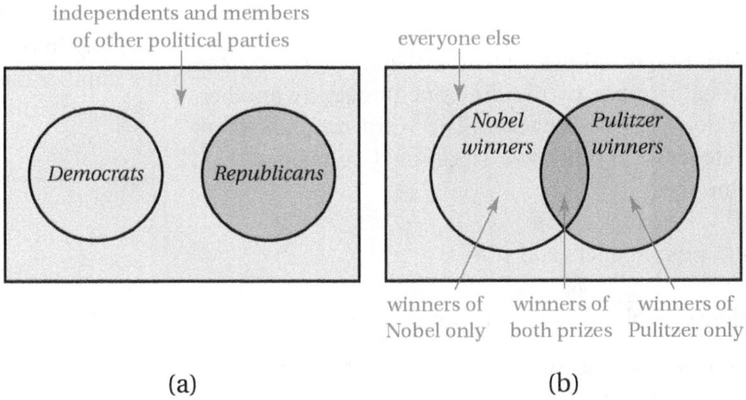

Figure 6.4

EXAMPLE 3 Sets of Numbers

Draw a Venn diagram showing the relationships among the sets of *natural numbers, whole numbers, integers, rational numbers,* and *real numbers.* Where are irrational numbers found in this diagram? (If you've forgotten the meanings of these number sets, see *Brief Review* on p. 206.)

SOLUTION Natural numbers are also whole numbers, which means that the natural numbers are a subset of the whole numbers. Similarly, all whole numbers are integers, so the whole numbers are a subset of the integers. The integers, in turn, are a subset of the rational numbers, and the rational numbers are a subset of the real numbers. Figure 6.5 shows these relationships with a set of nested circles. Because irrational numbers are real numbers that are not rational, they are represented by the region outside the *rational numbers* circle but inside the *real numbers* circle.

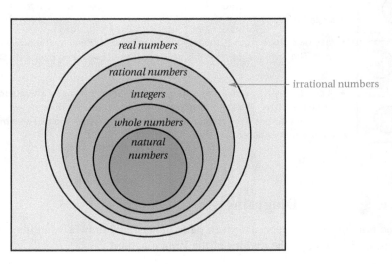

real numbers

rational numbers

integers

whole numbers

natural numbers

irrational numbers

Figure 6.5

Categorical Propositions

Now that we have discussed general relationships between sets, we are ready to study propositions that make claims about sets. For example, the proposition *all whales are mammals* makes a very specific claim—namely, that the set *whales* is a subset of the set *mammals.* Propositions of this type are called **categorical propositions** because they claim a particular relationship between two categories or sets.

Like all propositions, categorical propositions must have the structure of a complete sentence. Categorical propositions also have another important general feature. Of the two sets in a categorical proposition, one set appears in the subject of the sentence and the other appears in the predicate. For example, in the proposition *all whales are mammals,* the set *whales* is the **subject set** and the set *mammals* is the **predicate set.** We usually use the letter S to represent the subject set and P for the predicate set, so we can rewrite *all whales are mammals* as

all S are P, where S = whales and P = mammals

Categorical propositions come in the following four standard forms.

The Four Standard Categorical Propositions

Form	Example	Subject Set (S)	Predicate Set (P)
All S are P	All whales are mammals	whales	mammals
No S are P	No fish are mammals	fish	mammals
Some S are P	Some doctors are women	doctors	women
Some S are not P	Some teachers are not men	teachers	men

Venn Diagrams for Categorical Propositions

We can use Venn diagrams to make visual representations of categorical propositions. Figures 6.6 to 6.9 show the diagrams for each of the four sample propositions in the box above. Note the following key features of these diagrams:

- Figure 6.6 shows the Venn diagram for the proposition *all whales are mammals.* The circle for the set S = *whales* is drawn inside the circle for the set P = *mammals,* because S is a subset of P in this case. All propositions of the form *all S are P* have the same basic Venn diagram.

- Figure 6.7 shows the Venn diagram for the proposition *no fish are mammals.* In this case, the sets S = *fish* and P = *mammals* have no common members (they are disjoint). The Venn diagram therefore shows two separated circles.

- Figure 6.8 shows the Venn diagram for the proposition *some doctors are women,* which requires overlapping circles for S = *doctors* and P = *women.* However, the overlapping circles alone do not represent the proposition, because they don't tell us which regions have members. In this case, the proposition asserts that there *are* some people (at least one) who are both doctors and women. We indicate this fact by putting an X in the overlapping region of the diagram. Note that the proposition does not tell us whether there are also doctors who are not women, nor does it tell us whether there are women who are not doctors. Without further information, we do not know whether the non-overlapping regions contain any members.

- Figure 6.9 shows the Venn diagram for the proposition *some teachers are not men,* which also requires overlapping circles. This proposition asserts that there are some people (at least one) who are in the S = *teachers* circle but not in the P = *men* circle. Therefore, we put an X in the non-overlapping region of the *teachers* circle. Note that no claim is made about whether there are teachers who are also men or men who are not teachers.

Mathematics is, in its way, the poetry of logical ideas.

—Albert Einstein

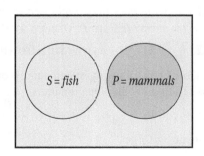

Figure 6.6 The Venn diagram for *all S are P*.   **Figure 6.7** The Venn diagram for *no S are P*.

The X indicates that the overlapping region has at least one member.

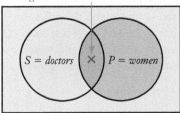

Figure 6.8 The Venn diagram for *some S are P.*

The X indicates the region claimed to have at least one member.

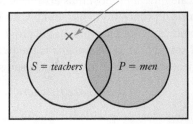

Figure 6.9 The Venn diagram for *some S are not P.*

EXAMPLE ④ Interpreting the Venn Diagrams

Answer the following questions based *only* on the information provided in the Venn diagrams. That is, don't consider any prior knowledge you have about the sets.

a. Based on Figure 6.6, can you conclude that some mammals are not whales?

b. Based on Figure 6.7, is it possible that some mammals are fish?

c. Based on Figure 6.8, is it possible that all doctors are women?

d. Based on Figure 6.9, is it possible that no men are teachers?

SOLUTION

a. No. The diagram shows only that all members of the set $S = whales$ are also members of the set $P = mammals$, but it does not tell us whether there are any mammals that lie outside the whales circle.

b. No. The sets for $S = fish$ and $P = mammals$ are disjoint, meaning they cannot have common members.

c. Yes. The X in the overlap region tells us that some women are definitely doctors. But there are no Xs elsewhere, so it is possible that all other regions have no members, in which case *all* women would be doctors.

d. Yes. The X is outside the men circle, so we have no information on whether any men are teachers.   ··●

> ## TIME ◯UT TO THINK
> The principal of an elementary school states that at her school some teachers are not men. Can you conclude that some of the teachers *are* men? Why or why not? Can you conclude that *none* of the teachers are men? Why or why not?

Putting Categorical Propositions in Standard Form

Many statements in everyday speech make claims about relationships between two categories, but don't look precisely like one of the four standard forms for categorical propositions. It's often useful to rephrase such statements in one of the standard forms. For example, the statement *all diamonds are valuable* can be rephrased to read *all diamonds are things of value.* Now the statement has the form *all S are P,* where $S = diamonds$ and $P = things\,of\,value.$

EXAMPLE ⑤ Rephrasing in Standard Form

Rephrase each of the following statements in one of the four standard forms for categorical propositions. Then draw the Venn diagram.

a. Some birds can fly.

b. Elephants never forget.

SOLUTION

a. *Some birds can fly* can be rephrased as *some birds are animals that can fly.* It now has the form *some S are P* where $S = $ *birds* and $P = $ *animals that can fly.* Figure 6.10a shows the Venn diagram, with an X in the overlapping region to indicate the claim that there *are* some birds that can fly.

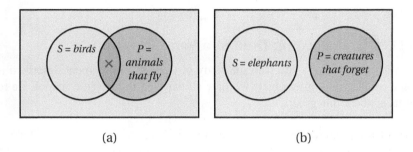

(a)   (b)

Figure 6.10

b. *Elephants never forget* can be rephrased as *no elephants are creatures that forget.* This proposition has the form *no S are P* shown in Figure 6.10b, where $S = $ *elephants* and $P = $ *creatures that forget.*   •• ●

Venn Diagrams with Three Sets

Venn diagrams are particularly useful for dealing with three sets that may overlap one another. For example, suppose you are conducting a study to learn how teenage employment rates differ between boys and girls and between honor students and others. For each teenager in your study, you need to record the answers to these three questions:

- Is the teenager a boy or a girl?
- Is the teenager an honor student or not?
- Is the teenager employed or not?

Figure 6.11 shows a Venn diagram that can help you organize this information. Notice that it has three circles, representing the sets *boys, honor students,* and *employed.* Because the circles overlap one another, they form a total of eight regions (including the region outside all three circles). Be sure that you understand the labels shown for each region.

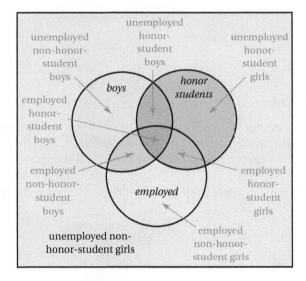

Figure 6.11   A Venn diagram for three overlapping sets has $2^3 = 8$ regions.

TIME (Ⓞ)UT TO THINK

Could the information in Figure 6.11 be recorded in a diagram in which the three circles represented the sets *girls* (rather than boys), *honor students*, and *employed*? Could it be recorded in a diagram with the three circles representing the sets *girls, boys,* and *unemployed*? Explain.

EXAMPLE ❻ Recording Data in a Venn Diagram

You hire an assistant to help you with the study of teenage employment described above. He focuses on a small group of teenagers who are all enrolled in the same school. He reports the following facts about this group:

• Some of the honor-student boys are unemployed.
• Some of the non-honor-student girls are employed.

Put Xs in the appropriate places in Figure 6.11 to indicate the regions that you can be sure have members. Based on this report, do you know whether any of the school's honor-student girls are unemployed? Why or why not?

SOLUTION   Figure 6.12 shows the Xs in the correct regions of the diagram (compare with the labels in Figure 6.11). The region corresponding to unemployed honor-student girls is the pink region of the *honor students* circle. There is no X in this region because the given information does not tell us whether this region has members. Therefore, among the teenagers in the school, we do not know whether any honor-student girls are unemployed.   • • ●

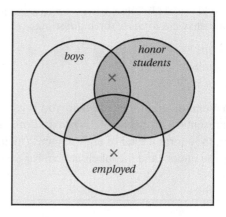

Figure 6.12   The Xs mark regions known to have members.

EXAMPLE ❼ Color Monitors

Color television and computer monitors make all the colors you see by combining *pixels* (short for *picture elements*) that display just three colors: red, green, and blue. In pairs, these combinations of colors give the following results (with colors at equal strength):

Combination	Result
Red-green	Yellow
Red-blue	Purple (or magenta)
Blue-green	Light blue (or cyan)

White is made by combining all three colors, and black is made by using none of the colors. Draw a Venn diagram to represent all this color information.

SOLUTION   The Venn diagram in Figure 6.13 represents the color combinations with three overlapping circles. The basic colors (red, green, and blue) appear in regions where there is no overlap. The red-green, red-blue, and blue-green combinations appear in regions where two circles overlap. White appears in the central region, where all three colors are present, while black appears outside all three circles, where no colors are present. A real monitor can make a much wider range of colors by varying the relative strengths of the colors.   ·· ●

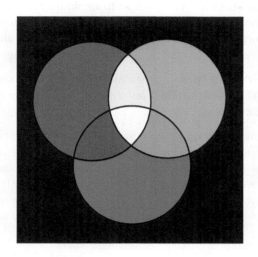

Figure 6.13 The color combinations possible from red, green, and blue (in equal strength).

TIME ◯UT TO THINK

If you have a magnifying glass, hold it close to your television to see the individual red, blue, and green dots. How do you think a high-resolution monitor (such as a monitor for HDTV) differs from a lower-resolution one?

Venn Diagrams with Numbers

So far, we have used Venn diagrams only to describe relationships, such as whether two sets overlap or whether overlapping sets share common members. Venn diagrams can be even more useful when we add specific information, such as the number of members in each set or overlapping region. The following examples illustrate some of the ways in which Venn diagrams can be used with numbers.

EXAMPLE 8   Two-Way Tables

Consider the study summarized in Table 6.1, which is an example of a **two-way table**. This study was designed to learn whether a pregnant mother's status as a smoker or nonsmoker affects whether she delivers a low or normal birth weight baby. The table shows four numbers, which correspond to the four possible combinations of the baby's birth weight status and the mother's smoking status.

TABLE 6.1	Distribution of 350 Births by Birth Weight Status and Mother's Smoking Status		
		Baby's Birth Weight Status	
		Low Birth Weight	Normal Birth Weight
Mother's Smoking Status	Smoker	18	132
	Nonsmoker	14	186

Source: U.S. National Center for Health Statistics.

BY THE WAY

More than 400,000 premature or low birth weight babies are born each year in the United States. These babies are much more likely than others to suffer health problems and often require weeks or months of intensive high-technology outpatient care.

a. Make a list summarizing the four key facts shown in the table.

b. Draw a Venn diagram to represent the table data.

c. Based on the Venn diagram, briefly summarize the results of the study.

SOLUTION

a. The four cells in the table tell us the following key facts:

- 18 babies were born with low birth weight to smoking mothers.
- 132 babies were born with normal birth weight to smoking mothers.
- 14 babies were born with low birth weight to nonsmoking mothers.
- 186 babies were born with normal birth weight to nonsmoking mothers.

b. Figure 6.14 shows one way of making the Venn diagram. The circles represent the sets *smoking mothers* and *low birth weight babies*. The labels show how each region corresponds to one of the entries in Table 6.1.

c. The Venn diagram makes it easy to see how smoking affected babies in the study. Notice that normal birth weight babies were much more common than low birth weight babies among both smokers and nonsmokers. However, the smoking mothers had a lower proportion of normal birth weight babies and a higher proportion of low birth weight babies. This suggests that smoking increases the risk of having a low birth weight baby, a fact that has been borne out by careful statistical analysis of this and other studies.

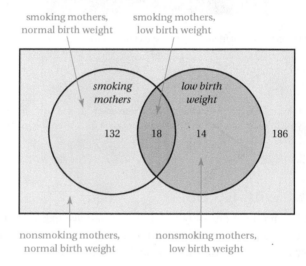

Figure 6.14   Venn diagram for the data in Table 6.1.

TIME ( ) UT TO THINK

Explain why the Venn diagram in Example 8 also could be drawn with circles for the sets *nonsmoking mothers* and *normal birth weight babies*. Draw the diagram for this case, and put the four numbers in the right places.

EXAMPLE 9   Three Sets with Numbers—Blood Types

Human blood is often classified according to whether three antigens, A, B, and Rh, are present or absent. Blood type is stated first in terms of the antigens A and B: Blood containing only A is called type A, blood containing only B is called type B, blood containing both A and B is called type AB, and blood containing neither A nor B is called type O. The presence or absence of Rh is indicated by adding the word *positive* (present) or *negative* (absent) or its symbol. Table 6.2 shows the eight blood types that result and the percentage of people with each type in the U.S. population. Draw a Venn diagram to illustrate these data.

SOLUTION   We can think of the three antigens as three sets *A*, *B*, and *Rh* (positive). We therefore draw a Venn diagram with three overlapping circles. Figure 6.15 shows the eight regions, each labeled with its type and percentage of the population. For example, the central region corresponds to the presence of all three antigens (AB positive), so it is labeled with 3%. You should check that all eight regions are labeled according to the data from Table 6.2.

TABLE 6.2	Blood Types in U.S. Population
Blood Type	**Percentage of Population**
A positive	34%
B positive	8%
AB positive	3%
O positive	35%
A negative	8%
B negative	2%
AB negative	1%
O negative	9%

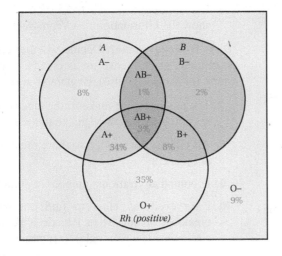

Figure 6.15   Venn diagram for blood types.

Section 6.1 Exercises

Quick Quiz

Choose the best answer to each of the following questions. Explain your reasoning with one or more complete sentences.

1. Consider the set {Alabama, Alaska, Arizona, ..., Wyoming}. The "..." represents

   a. the fact that we don't know the other members of the set.

   b. the other 46 states of the United States.

   c. Colorado, California, Florida, and Mississippi.

2. Which of the folloawing is not a member of the set of integers?

   a. -107 **b.** 481   **c.** $3\frac{1}{2}$

3. Based on the Venn diagram below, we conclude that

   a. C is a subset of D.

   b. D is a subset of C.

   c. C is disjoint from D.

4. Suppose that A represents the set of all boys and B represents the set of all girls. The correct Venn diagram for the relationship between these sets is

a. **b.** **c.**

5. Suppose that A represents the set of all apples and B represents the set of all fruit. The correct Venn diagram for the relationship between these sets is

a. **b.** **c.**

6. Suppose that A represents the set of all high school cross country runners and B represents the set of all high school swimmers. The correct Venn diagram for the relationship between these sets is

a. **b.** **c.**

7. In the Venn diagram below, the X tells us that

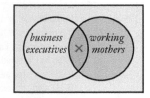

a. some working mothers are business executives.

b. no working mothers are business executives.

c. some working mothers are not business executives.

8. The region with the X in the Venn diagram below represents

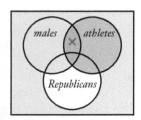

a. male Republican athletes.

b. male Republicans who are not athletes.

c. male athletes who are not Republicans.

9. Consider again the Venn diagram from Exercise 8. The central region of the diagram represents people who are

a. male and Republican and athletes.

b. male or Republican or athletes.

c. neither male nor Republican nor athletes.

10. Look at the data in Table 6.1 (p. 213). The total number of babies born with low birth weight was

a. 14.

b. 18.

c. 32.

Exercises

Review Questions

1. What is a set? Describe the use of braces for listing the members of a set.

2. What is a Venn diagram? How do we show that one set is a subset of another in a Venn diagram? How do we show disjoint sets? How do we show overlapping sets?

3. List the four standard categorical propositions. Give an example of each type, and draw a Venn diagram for each of your examples.

4. Briefly discuss how you can put a categorical proposition into one of the standard forms if it is not in such a form already.

5. Explain how to draw a Venn diagram for three overlapping sets. Discuss the types of information that can be shown in such diagrams.

6. Explain how to read a table such as Table 6.1 and how to show the information in a Venn diagram.

Does It Make Sense? Decide whether each of the following statements makes sense (or is clearly true) or does not make sense (or is clearly false). Explain your reasoning.

7. The payments we make to the electric company are a subset of the payments we make to the satellite TV company.

8. All jabbers are wocks, so there must be no wocks that are not jabbers.

9. I counted an irrational number of students in my class.

10. I surveyed my class to find out whether students ate breakfast or not. Then I made a Venn diagram with one circle (inside a rectangle) to summarize the results.

11. My professor asked me to draw a Venn diagram for a categorical proposition, but I couldn't do it because the proposition was clearly false.

12. I used a Venn diagram to prove that your opinion is false.

Basic Skills & Concepts

13–28: Classifying Numbers. Choose the first set in the list *natural numbers, whole numbers, integers, rational numbers, and real numbers* that describes the following numbers.

13. 23

14. −45

15. 2/3

16. −5/2

17. 1.2345

18. 0

19. π

20. $\sqrt{8}$

21. −34.25

22. $\sqrt{98}$

23. $\pi/4$

24. −123/456

25. −13/3

26. −145.01

27. $\pi/129$

28. 13,579,023

29–36: Set Notation. Use set notation (braces) to write the members of the following sets, or state that the set has no members. You may use "…" to indicate patterns.

29. The months of the year

30. The even numbers between, but not including, 12 and 100

31. The states that share a border with Texas

32. Every third number between 4 and 20 beginning with 4

33. The perfect squares between 5 and 26

34. The queens of America

35. Odd numbers between 2 and 30 that are multiples of 3

36. The vowels of the English alphabet

37–44: Venn Diagrams for Two Sets. Draw Venn diagrams with two circles showing the relationship between the following pairs of sets. Provide an explanation of the diagram you drew.

37. attorneys and men

38. nurses and skydivers

39. water and liquids

40. reptiles and bacteria

41. novelists and athletes

42. atheists and Catholic bishops

43. rational numbers and irrational numbers

44. limericks and poems

45–52: Categorical Propositions. For the given categorical propositions, do the following.

  a. If necessary, rephrase the statement in standard form.

  b. State the subject and predicate sets.

  c. Draw a Venn diagram for the proposition, and label all regions of the diagram.

  d. Based only on the Venn diagram (not on any other knowledge you have), answer the question that follows each proposition.

45. All widows are women. Can you conclude that some women are not widows?

46. No worms are birds. Is it possible that some birds are worms?

47. All U.S. Presidents have been over 30 years old. Can you conclude that no one under 30 years old has been President?

48. Every child can sing. Can you conclude that some singers are adults?

49. Monkeys don't gamble. Is it possible that some gamblers are monkeys?

50. Plumbers don't cheat. Is it possible that at least one plumber cheats?

51. Winners smile. Is it true that no frowners are winners?

52. Some movie stars are redheads. Can you conclude that there are blond movie stars?

53–58: Venn Diagrams for Three Sets. Draw Venn diagrams with three overlapping circles (eight regions) for the following groups of three sets. Describe the members of each region, or state that a region has no members.

53. women, dentists, and kindergarten teachers

54. hockey players, figure skaters, and women

55. published works, novels, and songs

56. oceans, bodies of salt water, and bodies of fresh water

57. words that begin with *s*, verbs, and words with fewer than four letters

58. teachers, swimmers, and tall people

59–62: Two-Circle Venn Diagram with Numbers. Use the Venn diagram to answer the following questions.

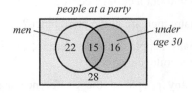

people at a party

59. **a.** How many women at the party are under 30?

  b. How many men at the party are not under 30?

  c. How many women are at the party?

  d. How many people are at the party?

60. **a.** How many men at the party are under 30?

  b. How many women at the party are over 30?

  c. How many men are at the party?

  d. How many people at the party are not under 30?

61. **Election Results.** The following table gives popular vote counts (in millions) for the two leading candidates in the 2012 U.S. presidential election. Draw a two-circle Venn diagram that represents the results.

	Obama	Romney
Women voters	36.25	26.80
Men voters	29.66	31.67

62. **Tomatoes and Cancer.** A study by the Harvard Medical School (*Journal of the National Cancer Institute*, February 17, 1999) reviewed 72 previous studies of the effect of tomatoes on cancer. The data showed convincingly that "high consumers of tomatoes and tomato products are at substantially decreased risk of numerous cancers, although probably not all cancers." Consider the following table that shows the incidence of oral cancer for a group of people who ate an average of one tomato a day and another group of people who ate fewer than three tomatoes per week. Draw a Venn diagram for the data.

	No oral cancer	Oral cancer
One tomato per day	191	9
Fewer than three tomatoes per week	164	16

TV/radio only	20	TV/radio and Internet only	12
Internet only	29	TV/radio and newspapers only	18
Newspapers only	15	Internet and newspapers only	22
None	6	All three sources	8

63–66: Three-Circle Venn Diagram with Numbers. Use the Venn diagram to answer the following questions.

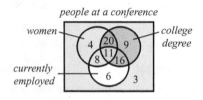

63. a. How many people at the conference are unemployed women with a college degree?

b. How many people at the conference are employed men?

c. How many people at the conference are employed women without a college degree?

d. How many men are at the conference?

64. a. How many people at the conference are employed men without a college degree?

b. How many people at the conference are unemployed women?

c. How many people at the conference are unemployed men without a college degree?

d. How many people are at the conference?

65. Hospital Drug Use. Patients in a (hypothetical) hospital on a single day were taking antibiotics (A), blood pressure medication (BP), and pain medication (P) in the following numbers:

A only	12	A and BP only	15
BP only	8	A and P only	24
P only	22	BP and P only	16
None	2	All three	20

a. Draw a three-circle Venn diagram that summarizes the results in the table.

b. How many patients took antibiotics or blood pressure medication?

c. How many patients took blood pressure medication but not pain medication?

d. How many patients took (at least) pain medication?

e. How many patients took antibiotics and blood pressure medicine but not pain medication?

f. How many patients took antibiotics or blood pressure medicine or pain medication?

66. Readership Survey. A (hypothetical) survey revealed the following results about the news sources that a sample of 130 people use:

a. Draw a three-circle Venn diagram that summarizes the results of the survey.

b. How many people use (at least) TV/radio and newspapers?

c. How many people use TV/radio or Internet?

d. How many people use TV/radio or Internet but not newspapers?

e. How many people use Internet but not TV/radio?

f. How many people use TV/radio but not newspapers?

Further Applications

67–70: Venn Diagram Analysis.

67. Of the 45 theater performances that a critic reviewed, 23 were comedies. She gave favorable reviews to 8 of the comedies and unfavorable reviews to 12 of the non-comedies.

a. Make a two-way table summarizing the reviews.

b. Make a Venn diagram from the table in part (a).

c. How many comedies received unfavorable reviews?

d. How many non-comedies received favorable reviews?

68. All cyclists who competed in a race were given a drug test. Of the 18 who tested positive, 3 finished in the top 10. Twenty-five cyclists tested negative.

a. Make a two-way table summarizing the results of the drug test.

b. Make a Venn diagram from the table in part (a).

c. How many cyclists who tested negative did not finish in the top 10?

d. How many cyclists were tested?

69. One hundred people who grew up in either New York or Los Angeles were surveyed to determine whether they preferred hip-hop music or rock music (*both* and *neither* were not acceptable responses). Of those who grew up in Los Angeles, 20 preferred hip-hop and 40 preferred rock. Of those who grew up in New York, 30 preferred hip-hop.

a. Make a two-way table summarizing the survey.

b. Make a Venn diagram from the table in part (a).

c. How many New Yorkers preferred rock?

70. In a trial of a new allergy medicine, 120 people were given the medicine and 80 were given a placebo. Of those given the medicine, 90 showed improvement in their allergies. Of those given the placebo, 20 did not show improvement.

a. Make a two-way table summarizing the results.

b. Make a Venn diagram from the table in part (a).

c. How many people who received medicine did not improve?

d. How many people who received the placebo improved?

71. Coffee and Gallstones. A study on the effect of coffee on gallstones (*Journal of the American Medical Association,* June 9, 1999) resulted (in small part) in the data shown below. The category *Coffee* means more than four cups of caffeinated coffee per day. The category *No coffee* means no caffeinated coffee. Draw a Venn diagram for the data.

	Gallstone disease	No disease
No coffee	385	14,068
Coffee	91	4,806

72–73: Completing Two-Way Tables. Fill in the remaining entries in the following two-way tables.

72. A car insurance company issued a monthly report showing the following numbers of claims filed by clients.

	Women	Men	Total
No claims			50
At least one claim		40	
Total	50	60	

73. A survey of 120 patrons at a restaurant gave the following preferences for entrees and drinks.

	Vegetarian	Meat/fish	Total
Wine	20		60
No wine		15	
Total			120

74. Health Clinic Data. The records for a student health clinic show that during one month

- Of the 120 men who visited with flu or anemia, 60 had flu only and 10 had flu and anemia.

- Of the 150 women who visited with flu or anemia, 80 had flu only and 50 had anemia only.

a. Fill in the following table.

	Women	Men
Flu		
Anemia		
Both		
Total		

b. Draw a three-circle Venn diagram that represents the data. Which two regions of the diagram have no members?

75–78: More Than Three Sets. Draw a Venn diagram that illustrates the relationships among the following sets. The diagram should have one circle for each set. In this case, a circle may lie entirely inside of other circles, it may overlap other circles, or it may be completely separate from other circles.

75. animals, house pets, dogs, cats, canaries

76. athletes, women, professional soccer players, amateur golfers, sedentary doctors

77. things that fly, birds, jets, hang gliders, eagles

78. painters, artists, musicians, pianists, violinists, abstract painters

79. Obama Vote Breakdown. The popular vote received by Barack Obama in the 2012 presidential election can be divided according to gender and party as follows (vote counts in millions are approximate).

	Women	Men
Democrats	24.4	21.6
Republicans	1.3	1.2
Independents and others	9.1	8.1

a. Show how a three-circle Venn diagram can be used to display the data in the table. Which regions of the diagram are not used? Label the regions, and insert the numbers in the correct regions.

b. Show how all regions of the diagram below can be used to display the data in the table. Label the regions, and insert the numbers in the correct regions.

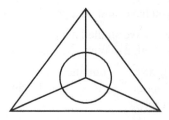

80–82: Organizing Propositions. Draw a Venn diagram that represents the information in the following statements. Use the diagram (and no other information) to answer the questions that follow. Explain your reasoning.

80. All hairy animals are mammals. No mammals are fish. Some mammals can swim. No fish can walk on land.

Questions: Could there be hairy fish? Could there be hairy animals that swim? Could there be walking mammals? Could there be hairy animals that walk on land?

81. All meat has protein. All dairy products have protein. Some beans have protein. All beans, but no meat or dairy products, are plants.

Questions: Could there be beans that are dairy products? Could there be meat that is a dairy product? Could there be dairy products that are plants? Could there be plants with protein?

82. No Republicans are Democrats. No Republicans are Green Party members. All Republicans are conservative. Some liberals are Democrats. No liberals are conservatives.

Questions: Could there be conservative Democrats? Could there be liberal Green Party members? Could there be liberal Republicans?

83. Organizing Politicos. You are at a conference attended by men and women of various political parties. The conference organizer tells you that none of the women are Republicans and some (but not all) of the Democrats are women.

a. Draw a Venn diagram to organize the given information.

b. Based on the given information, is it possible to meet a woman who is neither a Republican nor a Democrat?

c. Based on the given information, is it possible that there are any male Republicans?

84. Organizing Literature. In reviewing for an exam in your literature survey course, you notice the following facts about the writers that you studied:

- Some of the novelists are also poets.
- None of the novelists are playwrights.
- All of the novelists were born in the 20th century.
- All of the writers born in the 19th century are playwrights.

a. Organize these facts in a Venn diagram.

b. Could you have studied a novelist born in the 19th century?

c. Could you have studied a poet born in the 19th century?

d. Could you have studied a writer born in the 20th century who was both a playwright and a poet?

85. *N*-set Diagrams. A computer store offers a basic computer with four options A, B, C, and D, any or none of which buyers can select.

a. How many different sets of options can buyers choose? For example, one choice is A and C, another choice is no options, and another choice is all options.

b. Consider the four-circle Venn diagram below. Label the regions with the various sets of options.

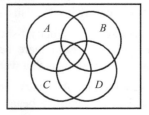

c. Does the diagram in part (b) represent all the sets of options? If not, which sets of options are missing?

d. Suppose the computer store offered five options A, B, C, D, and E. How many different sets of options would be available?

e. Generalizing from parts (a–d), how many different sets of options are available if the store offers N options, where $N = 2, 3, 4, \ldots,$?

In Your World

86. Categorical Propositions. Find at least three examples of categorical propositions in news articles or advertisements. State the sets involved in each proposition, and draw a Venn diagram for each proposition.

87. Venn Diagrams in Your Life. Describe a situation in your own life that could be described or organized using a Venn diagram.

88. Quantitative Diagram. Find a news article or research report that can be summarized with a table similar to Table 6.1 or Table 6.2. Draw a Venn diagram to represent the data in the table.

89. State Politics. Determine how many states have a Republican majority in the State House and how many states have a Republican majority in the State Senate. Draw a Venn diagram to illustrate the situation.

90. U.S. Presidents. Collect the following facts about each past American President:

- Bachelor or married (classify as married if married for part of the term)
- Inaugurated before or after age 50
- Served one term (or less) or more than one term

Make a three-circle Venn diagram to represent your results.

6.2 NOTATION FOR DESCRIBING OUTCOMES······························

Often when interpreting data, we will want to investigate the possibility of several outcomes at once.

For instance, we could study the following frequency table which represents the number of credit cards that 55 students had in their wallets.

Number of Credit Cards	Frequency
0	5
1	22
2	13
3	7
4	3
5	5

We can answer such straightforward questions such as "How many students have exactly 3 credit cards in their wallets?" by looking at the relevant row and responding with the corresponding frequency of 7.

However, sometimes we would like to investigate the likelihood of an array of values.

The Language for Using Several Rows in a Frequency Table

EXAMPLE **At Least Three Credit Cards**

Number of Credit Cards	Frequency
0	5
1	22
2	13
3	7
4	3
5	5

Students that had at least three credit cards could have had either 3, 4, or 5 credit cards in their wallet. To answer this question, we need to add up the frequencies from several rows.

$$7 + 3 + 5 = 15$$

There are 15 students that have at least 3 credit cards in their wallets.

EXAMPLE **2** **More than Three Credit Cards**

"How many students have **more than** 3 credit cards in their wallets?"

Number of Credit Cards	Frequency
0	5
1	22
2	13
3	7
4	3
5	5

Students that had more than three credit cards could have had either 4 or 5 credit cards in their wallets. Notice how more than does not include the value of 3.

To answer this question, we need to sum up the frequencies from two rows.

$$3 + 5 = 8$$

There are 8 students that have more than 3 credit cards in their wallets.

EXAMPLE ③ Less than Three Credit Cards

"How many students have **less than** 3 credit cards in their wallets?"

Number of Credit Cards	Frequency
0	5
1	22
2	13
3	7
4	3
5	5

Students that had less than three credit cards could have had either 0, 1, or 2 credit cards in their wallets.

$$5 + 22 + 13 = 40$$

There are 40 students that have less than 3 credit cards in their wallets.

You may want to carefully review the examples with **at least** and **less than** as those two phrases are often mistakenly interchanged.

We will handle the two more possibilities in the next two examples.

EXAMPLE ④ No More than Three Credit Cards

Number of Credit Cards	Frequency
0	5
1	22
2	13
3	7
4	3
5	5

There are $5 + 22 + 13 + 7$ or 47 students that have no more than 3 credit cards in their wallet.

EXAMPLE ⑤ Three or More Credit Cards

Number of Credit Cards	Frequency
0	5
1	22
2	13
3	7
4	3
5	5

There are $7 + 3 + 5$ or 15 students that have 3 or more credit cards in their wallets.

In the above examples, we went over several questions that could be asked of the same data. Sometimes, we will want to translate these phrases into mathematical symbols. This will come particularly handy when we start learning probability.

Translating to Inequalities

EXAMPLE 6

Let's say that the cards for a game are numbered 0, 1, 2, 3, 4, 5, 6, 7, 8, 9. We will use this scenario to practice translating.

Let x represent the unknown value on a card.

Find the cards that have a value of _____.

In Words	In Symbols	Cards that Fit Description
At least 1 1 or more	$x \geq 1$	1, 2, 3, 4, 5, 6, 7, 8, 9
Less than 1 Fewer than 1	$x < 1$	0
More than 1 Greater than 1	$x > 1$	2, 3, 4, 5, 6, 7, 8, 9
No more than 1 1 or less	$x \leq 1$	0, 1
Exactly 1	$x = 1$	1

EXAMPLE 7

When we learn probability, we will be discussing the likelihood of success. For this example, we will be flipping a quarter 5 times and observing whether the coin lands heads up or tails up each time. Let h represent the number times that the quarter lands on heads.

Translate the following phrases into symbols:

a. Getting at least 3 heads.

Translation: $h \geq 3$

b. Getting no heads.

Translation: $h = 0$

c. Getting less than 2 heads.

Translation: $h < 2$

All the examples so far have dealt with values that were discrete. However, the concept we have been discussion also is relevant for continuous data.

EXAMPLE 8

Translate the following expressions into symbols.

a. A dog weighs at least 22 pounds.

Translation: $d \geq 22$

b. A child less than 42 inches tall cannot ride an amusement ride.

Translation: $c < 42$

c. An alligator that is more than 72 inches long.

Translation: $a > 72$

Concepts and Applications

1. Number of Pets. The following table shows the number of household pets for a sample of 50 second graders.

Number of Pets	Frequency
0	15
1	22
2	8
3	2
4	3

a. How many second graders had exactly 1 pet?

b. How many second graders had more than 1 pet?

c. How many second graders had at least 3 pets?

d. How many second graders had less than 3 pets?

2. Prize Drawing. At the end of the school day, there will be a random prize drawing for all kids that were well behaved that day. There were 12 well behaved kids on May 5, and those kids were each given one of 12 tickets numbered 1–12. List the values that meet the following conditions.

a. Tickets with a value of no more than 3

b. Tickets with a value of more than 3

c. Tickets with a value greater than 3

3. Playing Ball. A baseball player can be put into play for any of the games in the 13 game season.

Let g represent the number of games that an athlete can be put into play during the season. Match the phrase with the correct inequality translation.

a. Playing at least 10 games
   1. $g \geq 10$

b. Playing exactly 10 games
   2. $g \leq 10$

c. Playing less than 10 games
   3. $g > 10$

d. Playing no more than 10 games
   4. $g < 10$

e. Playing more than 10 games
   5. $g = 10$

4. Quiz. There are 10 true/false questions on a quiz. Let c represent the number of correctly answered questions on the quiz. Translate the following statements into symbols.

a. Correctly answering at least 7 questions on the quiz

b. Correctly answering no more than 5 questions on the quiz

c. Correctly answering less than 7 questions on the quiz

d. Correctly answering exactly 9 questions on the quiz

6.3 BASICS OF PROBABILITY

Basics of Probability

In considering probability, we deal with procedures (such as answering a multiple-choice test question or undergo-ing a test for drug use) that produce outcomes.

> **Definitions**
>
> An **event** is any collection of results or outcomes of a procedure.
>
> A **simple event** is an outcome or an event that cannot be further broken down into simpler components.
>
> The **sample space** for a procedure consists of all possible *simple* events. That is, the sample space consists of all outcomes that cannot be broken down any further.

Example 1 illustrates the concepts defined above.

EXAMPLE 1

In the following display, we use "b" to denote a baby boy and "g" to denote a baby girl.

Procedure	Example of Event	Sample Space (List of Simple Events)
Single birth	1 girl (simple event)	{b, g}
3 births	2 boys and 1 girl (bbg, bgb, and gbb are all simple events resulting in 2 boys and 1 girl)	{bbb, bbg, bgb, bgg, gbb, gbg, ggb, ggg}

With one birth, the result of 1 female is a *simple event* because it cannot be broken down any further. With three births, the event of "2 girls and 1 boy" is *not a simple event* because it can be broken down into simpler events, such as ggb, gbg, or bgg. With three births, the *sample space* consists of the eight simple events listed above. With three births, the outcome of ggb is considered a simple event, because it is an outcome that cannot be broken down any further. We might incorrectly think that ggb can be further broken down into the individual results of g, g, and b, but g, g, and b are not individual outcomes from three births. With three births, there are exactly eight outcomes that are simple events: bbb, bbg, bgb, bgg, gbb, gbg, ggb, and ggg.

Mathematically, we express probabilities as numbers between 0 and 1. For example, the probability of a coin landing on heads is one-half, or 0.5. If an event is impossible, such as the event of being in two places at the same time, we assign it a probability of 0. At the other extreme, an event that is certain to occur, such as the event of the Sun being above the horizon in the daytime, is given a probability of 1. Figure 6.16 shows the scale of probability values, along with common expressions of likelihood.

It's helpful to have some special notation for probability. We write P(event) to mean the probability of an event, and often denote events by letters or symbols. For example, if we use H to represent the event of a head on a coin toss, then we write the probability of heads as $P(\text{H}) = 0.5$.

> **Expressing Probability**
> The probability of an event, expressed as P(event), is always between 0 and 1 (inclusive). A probability of 0 means that the event is impossible and a probability of 1 means that the event is certain.

Theoretical Probabilities

There are three basic techniques for finding probabilities, called the *theoretical method*, the *relative frequency method*, and the *subjective method*. We'll begin with the theoretical method.

When we say that the probability of heads on a coin toss is 1/2, we are assuming that the coin is fair and is equally likely to land on heads or tails. In essence, the probability is based on a theory of how the coin behaves, so we say that the probability of 1/2 comes from the theoretical method. As another example, consider rolling a single die. Because there are six equally likely outcomes (Figure 6.17), the theoretical probability for each outcome is 1/6.

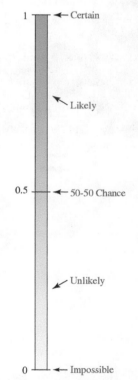

Figure 6.16 The scale shows various degrees of certainty as expressed by probabilities.

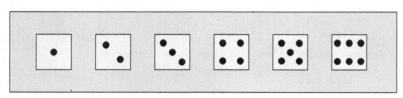

Figure 6.17 The six possible outcomes for a roll of one six-sided die.

As long as all outcomes are equally likely, we can use the following procedure to calculate theoretical probabilities.

Theoretical Method for Equally Likely Outcomes

Step 1.   Count the total number of possible outcomes.

Step 2.   Among all the possible outcomes, count the number of ways the event of interest, *A*, can occur.

Step 3.   Determine the probability, *P(A)*, from

$$P(A) = \frac{\text{number of ways } A \text{ can occur}}{\text{total number of outcomes}}$$

EXAMPLE 2   Guessing Birthdays

You select a person at random from a large group at a conference. What is the probability that the person selected has a birthday in July? Assume 365 days in a year.

SOLUTION   If we assume that all birthdays are equally likely, we can use the three-step theoretical method.

Step 1.   Each possible birthday represents an outcome, so there are 365 possible outcomes.

Step 2.   July has 31 days, so 31 of the 365 possible outcomes represent the event of a July birthday.

Step 3.   The probability that a randomly selected person has a birthday in July is

$$P(\text{July birthday}) = \frac{31}{365} \approx 0.0849$$

which is slightly more than 1 in 12.

Counting Outcomes

Suppose we toss two coins and want to count the total number of outcomes. The toss of the first coin has two possible outcomes: heads (H) or tails (T). The toss of the second coin also has two possible outcomes. The two outcomes for the first coin can each occur with either of the two outcomes for the second coin, making a total of $2 \times 2 = 4$ possible outcomes for the two coins together. The tree diagram of Figure 6.18a shows an easy way to identify the four outcomes: HH, HT, TH, and TT.

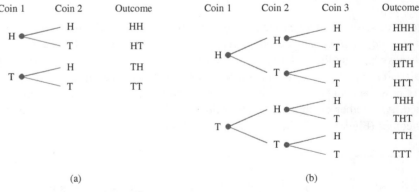

Figure 6.18   Tree diagrams showing the outcomes of tossing (a) two and (b) three coins.

TIME OUT TO THINK

Are the outcomes for tossing one coin twice in a row the same as those for tossing two coins at the same time? Explain.

We can now extend this thinking. If we toss three coins, there are $2 \times 2 \times 2 = 8$ possible outcomes, all shown in Figure 6.18b. This idea is the basis for the following counting rule.

Counting Outcomes

Suppose process A has a possible outcomes and process B has b possible outcomes. Assuming the outcomes of the processes do not affect each other, the number of different outcomes for the two processes combined is $a \times b$. This idea extends to any number of processes. For example, if a third process C has c possible outcomes, the number of possible outcomes for the three processes combined is $a \times b \times c$.

EXAMPLE 3 Dice Counting

a. How many outcomes are there if you roll two fair dice?

b. What is the probability of rolling two 1's (snake eyes) when two fair dice are rolled?

SOLUTION

a. Rolling a single die has six equally likely outcomes (see Figure 6.3). Therefore, when two fair dice are rolled, there are $6 \times 6 = 36$ different outcomes.

b. Of the 36 possible outcomes for rolling two fair dice, only one is the event of interest (two 1's). Therefore, the probability of rolling two 1's is

$$P(\text{two 1's}) = \frac{\text{number of ways two 1's can occur}}{\text{total number of outcomes}} = \frac{1}{36} = 0.0278 \quad \cdots \bullet$$

EXAMPLE 4 Counting Children

What is the probability that a randomly selected family with three children has two girls and one boy? Assume that births of boys and girls are equally likely.

SOLUTION   We apply the three-step theoretical method.

Step 1.   There are two possible outcomes for each birth: boy (B) or girl (G). For a family with three children, the total number of possible outcomes (birth orders) is $2 \times 2 \times 2 = 8$: BBB, BBG, BGB, BGG, GBB, GBG, GGB, GGG.

Step 2.   Of these eight possible outcomes, three of them have two girls and one boy: BGG, GBG, and GGB.

Step 3.   Therefore, the probability that a family with three children has two girls and one boy is

$$P(\text{two girls}) = \frac{\text{number of outcomes with two girls}}{\text{total number of outcomes}} = \frac{3}{8} = 0.375 \quad \cdots \bullet$$

TIME OUT TO THINK

How many different four-child families are possible if birth order is taken into account? What is the probability of a couple having a four-child family with four girls?

BY THE WAY

Births of boys and girls are *not* equally likely. Naturally, there are approximately 105 male births for every 100 female births. However, male death rates are higher than female death rates, so female adults outnumber male adults.

Relative Frequency Probabilities

A second way to determine probabilities is to *approximate* the probability of an event *A* by making many observations and counting the number of times event *A* occurs. This approach is called the **relative frequency method** (or *empirical* method). For example, if we observe that it rains an average of 100 days per year, we might say that the probability of rain on a randomly selected day is 100/365. We apply this method as follows.

Relative Frequency Method

Step 1. Repeat or observe a process many times and count the number of times the event of interest, *A*, occurs.

Step 2. Estimate *P(A)* by

$$P(A) = \frac{\text{number of times } A \text{ occurred}}{\text{total number of observations}}$$

EXAMPLE 5   500-Year Flood

Geological records indicate that a river has crested above a particular high flood level four times in the past 2,000 years. What is the relative frequency probability that the river will crest above the high flood level next year?

SOLUTION   Based on the data, the probability of the river cresting above this flood level in any single year is

$$\frac{\text{number of years with flood}}{\text{total number of years}} = \frac{4}{2,000} = \frac{1}{500}$$

Because a flood of this magnitude occurs on average once every 500 years, it is called a "500-year flood." The probability of having a flood of this magnitude in any given year is 1/500, or 0.002.   ⋯●

Subjective Probabilities

The third method for determining probabilities is to estimate a **subjective probability** using experience or intuition. For example, you could make a subjective estimate of the probability that a friend will be married in the next year or of the probability that a good grade in statistics will help you get the job you want.

BY THE WAY

Another approach to finding probabilities, called the *Monte Carlo method*, uses computer simulations. This technique essentially finds relative frequency probabilities; in this case, observations are made by causing a computer to behave in a way that is essentially the same as the actual event.

Three Approaches to Finding Probability

A **theoretical probability** is based on assuming that all outcomes are equally likely. It is determined by dividing the number of ways an event can occur by the total number of possible outcomes.

A **relative frequency probability** is based on observations or experiments. It is the relative frequency of the event of interest.

A **subjective probability** is an estimate based on experience or intuition.

EXAMPLE 6   Which Method?

Identify the method that resulted in the following statements.

a. The chance that you'll get married in the next year is zero.

b. Based on government data, the chance of dying in an automobile accident is about 1 in 8,000 (per year).

c. The chance of rolling a 7 with a 12-sided die is 1/12.

SOLUTION

a. This is a subjective probability because it is based on a feeling at the current moment.

b. This is a relative frequency probability because it is based on observed data on past automobile accidents.

c. This is a theoretical probability because it is based on assuming that a fair twelve-sided die is equally likely to land on any of its 12 sides. $\cdots\bullet$

Probability of an Event *Not* Occurring

Suppose we are interested in the probability that a particular event or outcome does *not* occur. For example, consider the probability of a wrong answer on a multiple-choice question with five possible answers. The probability of answering correctly with a random guess is 1/5, so the probability of *not* answering correctly is 4/5. Notice that the sum of the two probabilities must be 1, because the answer must be either right or wrong. We can generalize this idea.

BY THE WAY

Theoretical methods are also called *a priori* methods. The words *a priori* are Latin for "before the fact" or "before experience."

> **Probability of an Event *Not* Occurring**
>
> Suppose the probability of an event A is $P(A)$. Then the probability that event A does *not* occur is $P(\text{not } A) = 1 - P(A)$. Note: The event *not A* is called the **complement** of the event A; the "not" is often designated by a bar, so $\bar{A}$ means *not A*.

EXAMPLE 7 **Is Scanner Accuracy the Same for Specials?**

In a study of checkout scanning systems, samples of purchases were used to compare the scanned prices to the posted prices. Table 6.3 summarizes results for a sample of 819 items. Based on these data, what is the probability that a regular-priced item has a scanning error? What is the probability that an advertised-special item has a scanning error?

BY THE WAY

A *lot* is a person's portion or allocation. The term came to be used for any object or marker that identified a person in a selection by chance. The casting of lots was used in the Trojan Wars to determine who would throw the first spear and in the Old Testament to divide conquered lands.

TABLE 6.3   Scanner Accuracy

	Regular-priced items	Advertised-special items
Undercharge	20	7
Overcharge	15	29
Correct price	384	364

Source: Ronald Goodstein, "UPC Scanner Pricing Systems: Are They Accurate?" *Journal of Marketing*, Vol. 58.

SOLUTION   We can let R represent a regular-priced item being scanned correctly. Because 384 of the 419 regular-priced items are correctly scanned,

$$P(R) = \frac{384}{419} = 0.916$$

The event of a scanning error is the complement of the event of a correct scan, so the probability of a regular-priced item being subject to a scanning error (either undercharged or overcharged) is

$$P(\text{not } R) = 1 - 0.916 = 0.084$$

Now let A represent an advertised-special item being scanned correctly. Of the 400 advertised-special items in the sample, 364 are scanned correctly. Therefore,

$$P(A) = \frac{364}{400} = 0.910$$

TABLE 6.4	Tossing Two Coins
Event	Probability
2 heads, 0 tails	0.25
1 head, 1 tail	0.50
0 heads, 2 tails	0.25
Total	1

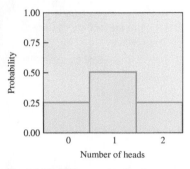

Figure 6.19 Histogram showing the probability distribution for the results of tossing two coins.

The probability of an advertised-special item being scanned incorrectly is

$$P(\text{not } A) = 1 - 0.910 = 0.090$$

The error rates are nearly equal. However, Table 6.3 also shows that the errors differed in their effects on customers: Most of the errors made with advertised-special items were overcharges, while most of the errors with regular-priced items were undercharges. $\cdots\bullet$

Probability Distributions

In Chapters 3 through 5, we worked with frequency and relative frequency distributions—for example, distributions of age or income. One of the most fundamental ideas in probability and statistics is that of a *probability distribution*. As the name suggests, a probability distribution is a distribution in which the variable of interest is associated with a probability.

Suppose you toss two coins simultaneously. As we found earlier (see Figure 6.18a), there are a total of four possible outcomes for the two coins: HH, HT, TH, and TT. Notice, however, that these four outcomes represent only three different events: one outcome represents 2 heads (HH), one outcome represents 2 tails (TT), and two outcomes (HT, TH) represent 1 head and 1 tail. Therefore, the probability of two heads is $P(\text{HH}) = 1/4 = 0.25$; the probability of two tails is $P(\text{TT}) = 1/4 = 0.25$; and the probability of one head and one tail is $P(\text{H and T}) = 2/4 = 0.50$. We can display this **probability distribution** as a table (Table 6.4) or a histogram (Figure 6.19). Note that the sum of all the probabilities must be 1 (because exactly one of the possible results must occur).

> **Making a Probability Distribution**
>
> A **probability distribution** represents the probabilities of all possible events. Do the following to make a display of a probability distribution:
>
> Step 1. List all possible *outcomes*. Use a table or figure if it is helpful.
>
> Step 2. Identify outcomes that represent the same *event*. Find the probability of each event.
>
> Step 3. Make a table in which one column lists each event and another column lists each probability. The sum of all the probabilities must be 1.

EXAMPLE 8 Tossing Three Coins

Make a probability distribution for the number of heads that occurs when three coins are tossed simultaneously.

SOLUTION   We apply the three-step process.

Step 1.   The number of different outcomes when three coins are tossed is $2 \times 2 \times 2 = 8$ (see Figure 6.18b): HHH, HHT, HTH, HTT, THH, THT, TTH, and TTT.

Step 2.   The eight outcomes represent four possible events: 0 heads, 1 head, 2 heads, and 3 heads. Notice that only one outcome represents the event of 0 heads, so its probability is 1/8; the same is true for the event of three heads (0 tails). The remaining events of 1 head (and 2 tails) or 2 heads (and 1 tail) each occur three times, so their probabilities are each 3/8.

Step 3.   Table 6.5 shows the probability distribution, with the four events listed in the left column and their probabilities in the right column.

TABLE 6.5	Tossing Three Coins
Result	Probability
3 heads (0 tails)	1/8
2 heads (1 tail)	3/8
1 head (2 tails)	3/8
0 heads (3 tails)	1/8
Total	1

$\cdots\bullet$

TIME UT TO THINK

How many different *outcomes* are possible when you toss four coins? If you are interested in the number of heads, how many different *events* are possible?

EXAMPLE 9 Two Dice Distribution

Make a probability distribution for the sum of the dice when two dice are rolled.

SOLUTION There are six ways for each die to land (see Figure 6.17), so there are $6 \times 6 = 36$ possible outcomes for a roll of two dice. Table 6.6 shows all 36 outcomes by listing one die along the rows and the other along the columns, with each cell showing for the two dice.

TABLE 6.6	Outcomes and Sums for the Roll of Two Dice					
	1	**2**	**3**	**4**	**5**	**6**
1	1 + 1 = 2	1 + 2 = 3	1 + 3 = 4	1 + 4 = 5	1 + 5 = 6	1 + 6 = 7
2	2 + 1 = 3	2 + 2 = 4	2 + 3 = 5	2 + 4 = 6	2 + 5 = 7	2 + 6 = 8
3	3 + 1 = 4	3 + 2 = 5	3 + 3 = 6	3 + 4 = 7	3 + 5 = 8	3 + 6 = 9
4	4 + 1 = 5	4 + 2 = 6	4 + 3 = 7	4 + 4 = 8	4 + 5 = 9	4 + 6 = 10
5	5 + 1 = 6	5 + 2 = 7	5 + 3 = 8	5 + 4 = 9	5 + 5 = 10	5 + 6 = 11
6	6 + 1 = 7	6 + 2 = 8	6 + 3 = 9	6 + 4 = 10	6 + 5 = 11	6 + 6 = 12

Notice that the possible sums, which are the *events* in this case, are 2 through 12. We find the probability of each sum by counting the number of times it occurs and dividing by the total of 36 possible outcomes. For example, the five highlighted outcomes in the table have a sum of 8, so the probability of a sum of 8 is 5/36. Table 6.7 shows the complete probability distribution, which is also shown as a histogram in Figure 6.20.

BY THE WAY

As early as 3600 BC, rounded bones called *astragali* were used much like dice for games of chance in the Middle East. Our familiar cubical dice appeared about 2000 BC in Egypt and in China. Playing cards were invented in China in the 10th century and brought to Europe in the 14th century.

TABLE 6.7	Probability Distribution for the Sum of Two Dice											
Event (sum)	2	3	4	5	6	7	8	9	10	11	12	**Total**
Probability	$\frac{1}{36}$	$\frac{2}{36}$	$\frac{3}{36}$	$\frac{4}{36}$	$\frac{5}{36}$	$\frac{6}{36}$	$\frac{5}{36}$	$\frac{4}{36}$	$\frac{3}{36}$	$\frac{2}{36}$	$\frac{1}{36}$	**1**

Figure 6.20 Histogram showing the probability distribution for the sum of two dice.

Section 6.3 Exercises

Statistical Literacy and Critical Thinking

1. **Notation.** If *A* denotes the event that you answer a particular true/false test question correctly, what do each of the following represent: $P(A)$, $P(not\ A)$, $P(\overline{A})$, and what are their values?

2. **Probability of Life.** A student reasons that there is a probability of 1/2 that there is life on Neptune, because there are two possible events: There is life or there is not life. Is this reasoning correct? Why or why not?

3. **Interpreting Probability.** What do we mean when we say that "the probability of getting 20 babies of the same gender when 20 random babies are born is 1/524,288? Is such an event *unusual*? Why or why not?

4. **Subjective Probability.** Use subjective judgment to estimate the probability that the next time you ride an elevator, it gets stuck between floors.

Does It Make Sense? For Exercises 5–10, decide whether the statement makes sense (or is clearly true) or does not make sense (or is clearly false). Explain clearly; not all of these have definitive answers, so your explanation is more important than your chosen answer.

5. **Certain Event.** When randomly selecting a day of the week, it is certain that you will select a day containing the letter *y*, so $P(y) = 1$.

6. **Impossible Event.** Because it is impossible for Thanksgiving to fall on Tuesday, the probability of Thanksgiving falling on Tuesday is 0.

7. **Complementary Events.** If there is a 0.9 probability that it will rain sometime today, then there is a probability of 0.1 that it will not rain sometime today.

8. **Car Crash.** An insurance company states that the probability that a particular car will be involved in a car crash this year is 0.6 and the probability that the car will not be involved in a car crash this year is 0.3.

9. **Lightning.** Jack estimates that the subjective probability of his being struck by lightning sometime next year is 1/2.

10. **Lightning.** Jill estimates that the subjective probability of her being struck by lightning sometime next year is 1/1,000,000.

Concepts and Applications

Theoretical Probabilities. For Exercises 11–18, use the theoretical method to determine the probability of the given outcome or event. State any assumptions that you need to make.

11. **Die.** Rolling a die and getting an outcome that is greater than 2.

12. **Test Question.** Making a correct random guess for an answer to a particular multiple-choice question with possible answers of a, b, c, d, e, one of which is correct.

13. **Roulette.** Getting an outcome of a red slot when a roulette wheel is spun (A roulette wheel has slots of 0, 00, 1, 2, 3, ..., 36, and 18 of those slots are red.).

14. **Birthday.** Finding that the next President of the United States was born on Saturday.

15. **Birthday.** Finding that the next person you meet has the same birthday as yours (Ignore leap years.).

16. **Births.** Finding that the next baby born in Alaska is a girl.

17. **Births.** Finding that the next baby born to a couple is a girl, given that the couple already has two children and they are both boys.

18. **Dice.** Rolling a pair of dice and getting an outcome (sum) of 12.

Complementary Events. Exercises 19–26 involve complementary events. In each exercise, find the probability of the given event. State any assumptions that you use.

19. **Die.** What is the probability of rolling a fair die and not getting an outcome less than 7?

20. **Die.** What is the probability of rolling a fair die and not getting an outcome that is greater than 6?

21. **Week Days.** What is the probability of randomly selecting a day of the week and not getting Monday?

22. **Birthday.** What is the probability of finding that the next President of the United States was not born on Saturday?

23. **Basketball.** What is the probability that a 55% free-throw shooter will miss her next free throw?

24. **Testing.** What is the probability of guessing incorrectly when making a random guess on a multiple-choice test question with possible answers of a, b, c, d, and e, one of which is correct?

25. **Baseball.** What is the probability that a 0.280 hitter in baseball will not get a hit on his next at-bat?

26. **Defects.** What is the probability of not getting a defective fuse when one fuse is randomly selected from an assembly line and 1% of the fuses are defective?

Theoretical Probabilities. For Exercises 27–30, use the theoretical method to determine the probability of the given outcome or event. State any assumptions that you need to make.

27. **M&Ms.** A bag contains 10 red M&Ms, 15 blue M&Ms, and 20 yellow M&Ms. What is the probability of drawing a red M&M? A blue M&M? A yellow M&M? Something besides a yellow M&M?

28. Test Questions. The New England College of Medicine uses an admissions test with multiple-choice questions, each with five possible answers, only one of which is correct. If you guess randomly on every question, what score might you expect to get? (Express the answer as a percentage.)

29. Three-Child Family. Suppose you randomly select a family with three children. Assume that births of boys and girls are equally likely. What is the probability that the family has each of the following?

a. Three girls

b. Two boys and a girl

c. A girl, a boy, and a boy, in that order

d. At least one girl

e. At least two boys

30. Four-Child Family. Suppose you randomly select a family with four children. Assume that births of boys and girls are equally likely.

a. How many birth orders are possible? List all of them.

b. What is the probability that the family has four boys? Four girls?

c. What is the probability that the family has a boy, a girl, a boy, and a girl, in that order?

d. What is the probability that the family has two girls and two boys in any order?

Relative Frequency Probabilities. Use the relative frequency method to estimate the probabilities in Exercises 31–34.

31. Weather Forecast. After recording the forecasts of your local weatherman for 30 days, you conclude that he gave a correct forecast 18 times. What is the probability that his next forecast will be correct?

32. Flood. What is the probability of a 100-year flood this year?

33. Basketball. Halfway through the season, a basketball player has hit 86% of her free throws. What is the probability that her next free throw will be successful?

34. Surgery. In a clinical trial of 73 carpal tunnel syndrome patients treated with surgery, 67 had successful treatments (based on data from "Splinting vs. Surgery in the Treatment of Carpal Tunnel Syndrome" by Gerritsen et al., *Journal of the American Medical Association*, Vol. 288, No. 10). What is the probability that the next surgery treatment will be successful?

35. Senior Citizen Probabilities. In the year 2000, there were 34.7 million people over 65 years of age out of a U.S. population of 281 million. In the year 2050, it is estimated that there will be 78.9 million people over 65 years of age out of a U.S. population of 394 million. Would your chances of meeting a person over 65 at random be greater in 2000 or in 2050? Explain.

36. Age at First Marriage. The following table gives percentages of women and men married for the first time in several age categories (U.S. Census Bureau).

	Under 20	20–24	25–29	30–34	35–44	45–64	Over 65
Women	16.6	40.8	27.2	10.1	4.5	0.7	0.1
Men	6.6	36.0	34.3	14.8	7.1	1.1	0.1

a. What is the probability that a randomly encountered married woman was married, for the first time, between the ages of 35 and 44?

b. What is the probability that a randomly encountered married man was married, for the first time, before he was 20 years old?

c. Construct a bar chart consisting of side-by-side bars representing men and women.

37. Four-Coin Probability Distribution.

a. Construct a table similar to Table 6.2, showing all possible outcomes of tossing four coins at once.

b. Construct a table similar to Table 6.3, showing the probability distribution for the events 4 heads, 3 heads, 2 heads, 1 head, and 0 heads when you toss four coins at once.

c. What is the probability of getting 2 heads and 2 tails when you toss four coins at once?

d. What is the probability of tossing anything except 4 heads when you toss four coins at once?

e. Which of the five possible events (4 heads, 3 heads, 2 heads, 1 head, 0 heads) is most likely to occur?

38. Colorado Lottery Distribution. The histogram in Figure 6.22 shows the distribution of 5,964 Colorado lottery numbers (possible values range from 1 to 42).

a. Assuming the lottery drawings are random, what would you expect the probability of any number to be?

b. Based on the histogram, what is the relative frequency probability of the most frequently appearing number?

c. Based on the histogram, what is the relative frequency probability of the least frequently appearing number?

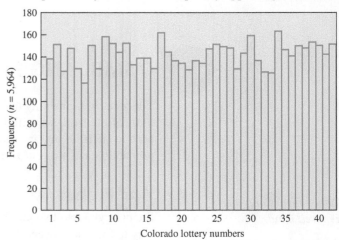

Figure 6.22 Colorado lottery distribution.

d. Comment on the deviations of the empirical probabilities from the expected probabilities. Would you say these deviations are significant?

PROJECTS FOR THE INTERNET & BEYOND

39. Blood Groups. The four major blood groups are designated A, B, AB, and O. Within each group there are two Rh types: positive and negative. Using library resources or the Internet, find data on the relative frequency of blood groups, including the Rh types. Construct a table showing the probability of meeting someone in each of the eight combinations of blood group and Rh type.

40. Age and Gender. The proportions of men and women in the population change with age. Using current data from a Web site, construct a table showing the probability of meeting a male or a female in each of these age categories: 0–5, 6–10, 11–20, 21–30, 31–40, 41–50, 51–60, 61–70, 71–80, over 80.

41. Thumb Tack Probabilities. Find a standard thumb tack and practice tossing it onto a flat surface. Notice that there are two different outcomes: The tack can land point down or point up.

  a. Toss the tack 50 times and record the outcomes.

  b. Give the relative frequency probabilities of the two outcomes based on these results.

  c. If possible, ask several other people to repeat the process. How well do your probabilities agree?

42. Three-Coin Experiment. Toss three coins at once 50 times and record the outcomes in terms of the number of heads. Based on your observations, give the relative frequency probabilities of the outcomes. Do they agree with the theoretical probabilities? Explain and discuss your results.

43. Randomizing a Survey. Suppose you want to conduct a survey involving a sensitive question that not all participants may choose to answer honestly (for example, a question involving cheating on taxes or drug use). Here is a way to conduct the survey and protect the identity of respondents. We will assume that the sensitive question requires a *yes* or *no* answer. First, ask all respondents to toss a fair coin. Then give the following instructions:

- If you toss a head, then answer the decoy question (yes/no): Were you born on an even day of the month?

- If you toss a tail, then answer the real survey question (yes/no).

After all participants have answered *yes* or *no* to the question they were assigned, count the total numbers of *yes* and *no* responses.

  a. Choose a question that may not produce totally honest responses and conduct a survey in your class using this technique.

  b. Given only the total numbers of *yes* and *no* responses to both questions, explain how you can estimate the number of people who answered *yes* and *no* to the real question.

  c. Will the results computed in part b be exact? Explain.

  d. Suppose the decoy question was replaced by these instructions: If you toss a head, then answer *yes*. Can you still determine the number of people who answered *yes* and *no* to the real question?

IN THE NEWS

44. Theoretical Probabilities. Find a news article or research report that cites a theoretical probability. Provide a one-paragraph discussion.

45. Relative Frequency Probabilities. Find a news article or research report that makes use of a relative frequency (or empirical) probability. Provide a one-paragraph discussion.

46. Subjective Probabilities. Find a news article or research report that refers to a subjective probability. Provide a one-paragraph discussion.

47. Probability Distributions. Find a news article or research report that cites or makes use of a probability distribution. Provide a one-paragraph discussion.

6.4 COMBINING PROBABILITIES

The ideas of probability that we have discussed to this point in the chapter will be sufficient for most of the work we will do in this book. However, probability has many more applications, both in statistics and in other areas of life. In this section, we investigate a few more ideas of probability and a few of their many applications.

And Probabilities

Chance favors only the prepared mind.

—Louis Pasteur, 19th-century scientist

Suppose you toss two fair dice and want to know the probability that *both* will come up 4. One way to find the probability is to consider the two tossed dice as a *single* toss of two dice. Then we can find the probability using the *theoretical* method (see Section 6.3). Because "double 4's" is 1 of 36 possible outcomes, its probability is 1/36.

Alternatively, we can consider the two dice individually. For each die, the probability of a 4 is 1/6. We find the probability that both dice show a 4 by multiplying the individual probabilities:

$$P(double\ 4's) = P(4) \times P(4) = \frac{1}{6} \times \frac{1}{6} = \frac{1}{36}$$

By either method, the probability of rolling double 4's is 1/36. In general, we call the probability of event *A and* event *B* occurring an **and probability** (or *joint probability*).

The advantage of the multiplication technique is that it can easily be extended to situations involving more than two events. For example, we might want to find the probability of getting 10 heads on 10 coin tosses or of having a baby *and* getting a pay raise in the same year. However, there is an important distinction that must be made when working with *and* probabilities. We must distinguish between events that are *independent* and events that are *dependent*. Let's investigate each case.

Independent Events

The repeated roll of a single die produces **independent events** because the outcome of one roll does not affect the probabilities of the other rolls. Similarly, coin tosses are independent because one coin toss does not affect others. For independent events, we calculate the *and* probability by multiplying.

> ### *And* Probability for Independent Events
>
> Two events are **independent** if the outcome of one event does not affect the probability of the other event. Consider two independent events *A* and *B* with probabilities *P(A)* and *P(B)*. The probability that *A and B* occur together is
>
> $$P(A \text{ and } B) = P(A) \times P(B)$$
>
> This principle can be extended to any number of independent events. For example, the probability of *A*, *B*, and a third independent event *C* is
>
> $$P(A \text{ and } B \text{ and } C) = P(A) \times P(B) \times P(C)$$

EXAMPLE 1   Three Coins

Suppose you toss three fair coins. What is the probability of getting three tails?

SOLUTION   Because coin tosses are independent, we multiply the probability of tails on each individual coin:

$$P(3 \text{ tails}) = \underbrace{P(\text{tails})}_{\text{coin 1}} \times \underbrace{P(\text{tails})}_{\text{coin 2}} \times \underbrace{P(\text{tails})}_{\text{coin 3}} = \frac{1}{2} \times \frac{1}{2} \times \frac{1}{2} = \frac{1}{8}$$

The probability that three tossed coins all land on tails is 1/8 (which we also determined in Example 8 of Section 6.3 with much more work).   ··●

Dependent Events

A batch of 15 memory chips contains 5 defective chips. If you select a chip at random from the batch, the probability of getting a defect is 5/15. Now, suppose that you select a defect on the first selection and put it in your pocket. What is the probability of getting a defect on the second selection?

Because you've removed one defective chip from the batch, the batch now contains only 14 chips, of which 4 are defective. Thus, the probability of getting a defective chip on the second draw is 4/14. This probability is less than the 5/15 probability on the first selection because the first selection changed the contents of the batch. Because the outcome of the first event affects the probability of the second event, these are **dependent events**.

Calculating the probability for dependent events still involves multiplying the individual probabilities, but we must take into account how prior events affect subsequent events. In the case of the batch of memory chips, we find the probability of getting two defective chips in a row by multiplying the 5/15 probability for the first selection by the 4/14 probability for the second selection.

$$P(2 \text{ defectives}) = \underbrace{P(\text{defective})}_{\substack{\text{first selectio}}} \times \underbrace{P(\text{defective})}_{\substack{\text{second selectic} \\ \text{if first selectio} \\ \text{defective}}} = \frac{5}{15} \times \frac{4}{14} = 0.0952$$

The probability of drawing two defective chips in a row is 0.0952, which is slightly less than $(5/15) \times (5/15) = 0.111$, the probability we get if we replace the first chip before the second selection.

TECHNICAL NOTE

$P(B$ given $A)$ is called a *conditional probability*. In some texts, it is denoted $P(B|A)$.

> ### *And* Probability for Dependent Events
>
> Two events are **dependent** if the outcome of one event affects the probability of the other event. The probability that dependent events A and B occur together is
>
> $$P(A \text{ and } B) = P(A) \times P(B \text{ given } A)$$
>
> where $P(B$ given $A)$ means the probability of event B given the occurrence of event A.
>
> This principle can be extended to any number of individual events. For example, the probability of dependent events A, B, and C is
>
> $$P(A \text{ and } B \text{ and } C) = P(A) \times P(B \text{ given } A) \times P(C \text{ given } A \text{ and } B)$$

EXAMPLE 2 Bingo

The game of bingo involves drawing labeled buttons from a bin at random, without replacement. There are 75 buttons, 15 for each of the letters B, I, N, G, and O. What is the probability of drawing two B buttons in the first two selections?

SOLUTION Bingo involves dependent events because selected buttons are not replaced, so removing a button changes the contents of the bin. The probability of drawing a B on the first draw is 15/75. If this occurs, 74 buttons remain in the bin, of which 14 are Bs. Therefore, the probability of drawing a B button on the second draw is 14/74. The probability of drawing two B buttons in the first two selections is

$$P(B \text{ and } B) = \underbrace{P(B)}_{\text{first draw}} \times \underbrace{P(B)}_{\substack{\text{second draw} \\ \text{given B on} \\ \text{first draw}}} = \frac{15}{75} \times \frac{14}{74} = 0.0378$$

· · ●

> ### TIME ⏱ UT TO THINK
>
> Suppose you have a standard deck of cards (which has 13 hearts among the 52 cards). For your first experiment, you draw three cards from the deck without replacing any of the selected cards. For your second experiment, you draw a card, look at it, and then replace it and reshuffle the deck before drawing again. Without doing any calculations, is the probability of drawing 3 hearts in a row larger in the first experiment or the second? Explain.

EXAMPLE 3 Polling Probability

A polling organization has a list of 1,000 people for a telephone survey. The pollsters know that 433 people out of the 1,000 are members of the Democratic Party. Assuming that a person cannot be called more than once, what is the probability that the first two people called will be members of the Democratic Party?

SOLUTION This problem involves an *and* probability for dependent events: Once a person is called, that person cannot be called again. The probability of calling a member of the Democratic Party on the first call is 433/1,000. With that person removed from the calling pool, the probability of calling a member of the Democratic Party on the second call is 432/999. Therefore, the probability of calling two members of the Democratic Party on the first two calls is

The importance of probability can only be derived from the judgment that it is rational to be guided by it in action.

—John Maynard Keynes

$$\frac{433}{1,000} \times \frac{432}{999} = 0.1872$$

In this case, it's worth noting what would happen if we were to treat the two calls as independent events (because a selected person is not removed from the list). In that case, the probability of calling a member of the Democratic Party would be 433/1,000 on both calls, and the probability of calling two members of the Democratic Party would be

$$\frac{433}{1,000} \times \frac{433}{1,000} = 0.1875$$

Notice that this result is nearly identical to the result we found when correctly doing the calculation with dependent events. In general, if relatively few items or people are selected from a large pool (in this case, 2 people out of 1,000), then dependent events can be treated as independent events with very little error. A common guideline is that we can treat the events as being independent when the sample size is less than 5% of the population size. This practice is commonly used by polling organizations. ·· ●

Either/Or Probabilities

Suppose we want to know the probability that *either* of two events occurs, rather than the probability that both of two events occurs. In that case, we are looking for an **either/or probability**, such as the probability of having either a blue-eyed *or* a green-eyed baby or the probability of losing your home either to a fire *or* to a hurricane. As with *and* probabilities, there are two cases to consider; we call them *overlapping* and *non-overlapping* events.

Non-Overlapping Events

A coin can land on either heads *or* tails, but it can't land on both heads *and* tails at the same time. When two events cannot possibly occur at the same time, they are said to be **non-overlapping** (or *mutually exclusive*). We can represent non-overlapping events with a Venn diagram in which each circle represents an event. If the circles do not overlap, it means that the corresponding events cannot occur together. For example, we show the possibilities of heads and tails in a coin toss as two non-overlapping circles because a coin cannot land on both heads and tails at the same time (Figure 6.23). We can calculate either/or probabilities for non-overlapping events with the following rule.

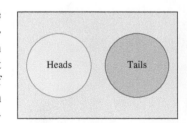

Figure 6.23 Venn diagram for non-overlapping events.

> *Either/Or* **Probability for Non-Overlapping Events**
>
> Two events are **non-overlapping** if they cannot occur at the same time. If *A* and *B* are non-overlapping events, the probability that either *A* or *B* occurs is
>
> $$P(A \text{ or } B) = P(A) + P(B)$$
>
> This principle can be extended to any number of non-overlapping events. For example, the probability that either event *A*, event *B*, or event *C* occurs is
>
> $$P(A \text{ or } B \text{ or } C) = P(A) + P(B) + P(C)$$
>
> provided that *A, B,* and *C* are all non-overlapping events.

EXAMPLE 4 *Either/Or* **Dice**

Suppose you roll a single die. What is the probability of rolling either a 2 or a 3?

SOLUTION   The outcomes of 2 and 3 are non-overlapping because a single die can yield only one result. Each probability is 1/6 (because there are 6 ways for the die to land), so the combined probability is

$$P(2 \text{ or } 3) = P(2) + P(3) = \frac{1}{6} + \frac{1}{6} = \frac{2}{6} = \frac{1}{3}$$

The probability of rolling a 2 or a 3 is 1/3.   ·· ●

TABLE 6.8	Tourism Committee	
	Men	Women
American	2	6
French	4	8

Overlapping Events

To improve tourism between France and the United States, the two governments form a committee consisting of 20 people: 2 American men, 4 French men, 6 American women, and 8 French women (Table 6.8). If you meet one of these people at random, what is the probability that the person will be *either* a woman *or* a French person?

Twelve of the 20 people are French, so the probability of meeting a French person is 12/20. Similarly, 14 of the 20 people are women, so the probability of meeting a woman is 14/20. The sum of these two probabilities is

$$\frac{12}{20} + \frac{14}{20} = \frac{26}{20}$$

This cannot be the correct probability of meeting either a woman or a French person, because probabilities cannot be greater than 1. The Venn diagram in Figure 6.24 shows why simple addition was wrong in this situation. The left circle contains the 12 French people, the right circle contains the 14 women, and the American men are in neither circle. We see that there are 18 people who are either French or women (or both). Because the total number of people in the room is 20, the probability of meeting a person who is *either* French *or* a woman is 18/20 = 9/10.

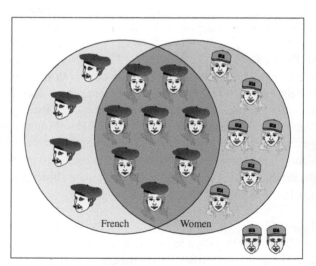

Figure 6.24 Venn diagram for overlapping events.

As the Venn diagram shows, simple addition was incorrect because the region in which the circles overlap contains 8 people who are *both* French *and* women. If we add the two individual probabilities, these 8 people get counted twice: once as women and once as French people. The probability of meeting one of these French women is 8/20. We can correct the double counting error by subtracting out this probability. Thus, the probability of meeting a person who is either French or a woman is

$$P(\text{woman or French}) = \underbrace{\frac{14}{20}}_{\substack{\text{probability} \\ \text{of a woman}}} + \underbrace{\frac{12}{20}}_{\substack{\text{probability of} \\ \text{a French person}}} - \underbrace{\frac{8}{20}}_{\substack{\text{probability of a} \\ \text{French woman}}} = \frac{18}{20} = \frac{9}{10}$$

which agrees with the result found by counting.

We say that meeting a woman and meeting a French person are **overlapping** (or *non–mutually exclusive*) events because both can occur at the same time. Generalizing the procedure we used in this example, we find the following rule.

> *Either/Or* **Probability for Overlapping Events**
>
> Two events A and B are **overlapping** if they can occur together. For overlapping events, the probability that either A or B occurs is
>
> $$P(A \text{ or } B) = P(A) + P(B) - P(A \text{ and } B)$$

The last term, $P(A \text{ and } B)$, corrects for the double counting of events in which A and B both occur together. Note that it is not necessary to use this formula. The correct probability can always be found by counting carefully and avoiding double counting.

> TIME ◷UT TO THINK
>
> Are the events of being born on a Wednesday or being born in Las Vegas overlapping? Are the events of being born on a Wednesday or being born in March overlapping? Are the events of being born on a Wednesday or being born on a Friday overlapping? Explain.

EXAMPLE 5 Minorities and Poverty

Suppose that the town of Pine Creek has 2,350 citizens, of which 1,950 are white and 400 are nonwhite. Further suppose that 11% of the white citizens, or 215 people, live below the poverty level, while 28% of the nonwhite citizens, or 112 people, live below the poverty level. If you visit Pine Creek, what is the probability of meeting (at random) a person who is *either* nonwhite *or* living below the poverty level?

SOLUTION   Meeting a nonwhite citizen and meeting a person living in poverty are overlapping events. It's useful to make a small table such as Table 6.9, showing how many citizens are in each of the four categories.

You should check that the figures in the table are consistent with the given data and that the total in all four categories is 2,350. Because there are 400 nonwhite citizens, the probability of (randomly) meeting a nonwhite citizen is 400/2,350 = 0.170. Because there are 215 + 112 = 327 people living in poverty, the probability of meeting a citizen in poverty is 327/2,350 = 0.139. The probability of meeting a person who is *both* nonwhite and living in poverty is 112/2,350 = 0.0477. According to the rule for overlapping events, the probability of meeting *either* a nonwhite citizen *or* a person living in poverty is

TABLE 6.9	Citizens in Pine Creek	
	In Poverty	Not in Poverty
White	215	1,735
Nonwhite	112	288

$$P(\text{non white or poverty}) = 0.170 + 0.139 - 0.0477 = 0.261$$

The probability of meeting a citizen who is *either* nonwhite or living below the poverty level is about 1 in 4. Notice the importance of subtracting out the term that corresponds to meeting a person who is *both* nonwhite and living in poverty.   ··●

Summary

Table 6.10 provides a summary of the formulas we've used in combining probabilities.

TABLE 6.10	Summary of Combining Probabilities		
And probability: independent events	*And* probability: dependent events	*Either/or* probability: non-overlapping events	*Either/or* probability: overlapping events
$P(A \text{ and } B) =$ $P(A) \times P(B)$	$P(A \text{ and } B) =$ $P(A) \times P(B \text{ given } A)$	$P(A \text{ or } B) =$ $P(A) + P(B)$	$P(A \text{ or } B) =$ $P(A) \times P(B) - P(A \text{ and } B)$

Section 6.4 Exercises

Statistical Literacy and Critical Thinking

1. **Independence.** Let A denote the event of turning on your cell phone and finding that it works, and let B denote the event of turning on your car radio and finding that it works. Are events A and B independent or are they dependent?

2. **Non-overlapping Events.** In your own words, state what it means for two events to be non-overlapping.

3. **Sampling with Replacement?** The professor in a class of 25 students randomly selects a student and then randomly selects a second student. If all 25 students are available for the second selection, is this sampling with replacement or sampling without replacement? Is the second outcome independent of the first?

4. **Complementary Events.** Let A denote some event. Are events A and $\overline{A}$ non-overlapping? Why or why not?

Does It Make Sense? For Exercises 5–8, decide whether the statement makes sense (or is clearly true) or does not make sense (or is clearly false). Explain clearly; not all of these have definitive answers, so your explanation is more important than your chosen answer.

5. **Lottery.** The numbers 5, 17, 18, 27, 36, and 41 were drawn in the last lottery; they should not be bet on in the next lottery because they are now less likely to occur.

6. **Combining Probabilities.** The probability of flipping a coin and getting heads is 0.5. The probability of selecting a red card when one card is drawn from a shuffled deck is also 0.5. When flipping a coin and drawing a card, the probability of getting heads or a red card is $0.5 + 0.5 = 1$.

7. *Either/Or* **Probability.** $P(A) = 0.5$ and $P(A \text{ or } B) = 0.8$.

8. **Lottery.** The probability of your winning the state lottery this week is not affected by whether you won that same lottery last week.

Concepts and Applications

9. **Births.** Assume that boys and girls are equally likely and that the gender of a child is independent of the gender of any brothers or sisters. If a couple already has three girls, find the probability of getting a girl when their fourth baby is born.

10. **Births.** A couple plans to have four children. Find the probability that the first two children are girls and the last two children are boys.

11. **Password.** A new computer owner creates a password consisting of five characters. She randomly selects a letter of the alphabet for the first character and a digit (0, 1, 2, 3, 4, 5, 6, 7, 8, 9) for each of the other four characters; the digits may be reused, so there are 10 possibilities for each of the four characters. What is the probability that her password is A1234?

12. **Wearing Hunter Orange.** A study of hunting injuries and the wearing of hunter orange clothing showed that among 123 hunters injured when mistaken for game, 6 were wearing orange (based on data from the Centers for Disease Control and Prevention). If a follow-up study begins with the random selection of hunters from this sample of 123, find the probability that the first two hunters selected were both wearing orange.

   a. Assume that the first hunter is replaced before the next one is selected.

   b. Assume that the first hunter is not replaced before the second one is selected.

   c. Which makes more sense in this situation: selecting with replacement or selecting without replacement? Why?

13. Radio Tunes. An MP3 player is loaded with 60 musical selections: 30 rock selections, 15 jazz selections, and 15 blues selections. The player is set on "random play," so selections are played randomly and can be repeated. What is the probability of each of the following events?

a. The first four selections are all jazz.

b. The first five selections are all blues.

c. The first selection is jazz and the second is rock.

d. Among the first four selections, none is rock.

e. The second selection is the same song as the first.

14. Polling Calls. A telephone pollster has names and telephone numbers for 45 voters, 20 of whom are registered Democrats and 25 of whom are registered Republicans. Calls are made in random order. Suppose you want to find the probability that the first two calls are to Republicans.

a. Are these independent or dependent events? Explain.

b. If you treat them as *dependent* events, what is the probability that the first two calls are to Republicans?

c. If you treat them as *independent* events, what is the probability that the first two calls are to Republicans?

d. Compare the results of parts b and c.

Probability and Court Decisions. The data in the following table show the outcomes of guilty and not-guilty pleas in 1,028 criminal court cases. Use the data to answer Exercises 15–20.

	Guilty plea	Not-guilty plea
Sent to prison	392	58
Not sent to prison	564	14

Source: Brereton and Casper, "Does It Pay to Plead Guilty? Differential Sentencing and the Functioning of the Criminal Courts," *Law and Society Review,* Vol. 16, No. 1.

15. What is the probability that a randomly selected defendant either pled guilty or was sent to prison?

16. What is the probability that a randomly selected defendant either pled not guilty or was not sent to prison?

17. If two different defendants are randomly selected, what is the probability that they both entered guilty pleas?

18. If two different defendants are randomly selected, what is the probability that they both were sentenced to prison?

19. If a defendant is randomly selected, what is the probability that the defendant entered a guilty plea and was sent to prison?

20. If a defendant is randomly selected, what is the probability that the defendant entered a guilty plea and was not sent to prison?

Pedestrian Deaths. For Exercises 21–26, use the following table, which summarizes data on 985 pedestrian deaths that were caused by accidents (based on data from the National Highway Traffic Safety Administration).

		Pedestrian intoxicated?	
		Yes	No
Driver intoxicated?	Yes	59	79
	No	266	581

21. If one of the pedestrian deaths is randomly selected, find the probability that the pedestrian was intoxicated or the driver was intoxicated.

22. If one of the pedestrian deaths is randomly selected, find the probability that the pedestrian was not intoxicated or the driver was not intoxicated.

23. If one of the pedestrian deaths is randomly selected, find the probability that the pedestrian was intoxicated or the driver was not intoxicated.

24. If one of the pedestrian deaths is randomly selected, find the probability that the driver was intoxicated or the pedestrian was not intoxicated.

25. If two different pedestrian deaths are randomly selected, find the probability that they both involved intoxicated drivers.

26. If two different pedestrian deaths are randomly selected, find the probability that in both cases the pedestrians were intoxicated.

27. Drug Tests. An allergy drug is tested by giving 120 people the drug and 100 people a placebo. A control group consists of 80 people who were given no treatment. The number of people in each group who showed improvement appears in the table below.

	Allergy drug	Placebo	Control	Total
Improvement	65	42	31	138
No improvement	55	58	49	162
Total	120	100	80	300

a. What is the probability that a randomly selected person in the study was given either the drug or the placebo?

b. What is the probability that a randomly selected person either improved or did not improve?

c. What is the probability that a randomly selected person either was given the drug or improved?

d. What is the probability that a randomly selected person was given the drug and improved?

28. Survey Refusals. Refer to the following table summarizing results from a study of people who refused to answer survey questions (based on data from "I Hear You Knocking but You Can't Come In," by Fitzgerald and Fuller, *Sociological Methods and Research,* Vol. 11, No. 1). In each case, assume that one of the subjects is randomly selected.

	Age					
	18–21	22–29	30–39	40–49	50–59	60 and over
Responded	73	255	245	136	138	202
Refused	11	20	33	16	27	49

a. What is the probability that the selected person refused to answer? Does that probability value suggest that refusals are a problem for pollsters? Why or why not?

b. A pharmaceutical company is interested in opinions of the elderly, because they are either receiving Medicare or will receive it soon. What is the probability that the selected subject is someone 60 and over who responded?

c. What is the probability that the selected person responded or is in the 18–21 age bracket?

d. What is the probability that the selected person refused to respond or is over 59 years of age?

29. **Probability Distributions and Genetics.** Many traits are controlled by a dominant gene, denoted by **A**, and a recessive gene, denoted by **a**. Suppose that two parents carry these genes in the proportion 3:1; that is, the probability of either parent giving the **A** gene is 0.75, and the probability of either parent giving the **a** gene is 0.25. Assume that the genes are selected from each parent randomly. To answer the following questions, imagine 100 trial "births."

a. What is the probability that a child receives an **A** gene from both parents?

b. What is the probability that a child receives an **A** gene from one parent and an **a** gene from the other parent? Note that this can occur in two ways.

c. What is the probability that a child receives an **a** gene from both parents?

d. Make a table showing the probability distribution for all events.

e. If the combinations **AA** and **Aa** both result in the same dominant trait (say, brown hair) and **aa** results in the recessive trait (say, blond hair), what is the probability that a child will have the dominant trait?

30. **BINGO.** The game of BINGO involves drawing numbered and lettered buttons at random from a barrel. The B numbers are 1–15, the I numbers are 16–30, the N numbers are 31–45, the G numbers are 46–60, and the O numbers are 61–75. Buttons are not replaced after they have been selected. What is the probability of each of the following events on the initial selections?

a. Drawing a B button

b. Drawing two B buttons in a row

c. Drawing a B or an O

d. Drawing a B, then a G, then an N, in that order

e. Drawing anything but a B on each of the first five draws

At Least Once Problems. A common problem asks for the probability that an event occurs at least once in a given number of trials. Suppose the probability of a particular event is p (for example, the probability of drawing a heart from a deck of cards is 0.25). Then the probability that the event occurs at least once in N trials is

$$1 - (1 - p)^N$$

For example, the probability of drawing at least one heart in 10 draws (with replacement) is

$$1 - (1 - 0.25)^{10} = 0.944$$

Use this rule to solve Exercises 31 and 32.

31. **The Bets of the Chevalier de Mère.** It is said that probability theory was invented in the 17th century to explain the gambling of a nobleman named the Chevalier de Mère.

a. In his first game, the Chevalier bet on rolling at least one 6 with four rolls of a fair die. If played repeatedly, is this a game he should expect to win?

b. In his second game, the Chevalier bet on rolling at least one double-6 with 24 rolls of two fair dice. If played repeatedly, is this a game he should expect to win?

32. **HIV among College Students.** Suppose that 3% of the students at a particular college are known to carry HIV.

a. If a student has 6 sexual partners during the course of a year, what is the probability that at least one of them carries HIV?

b. If a student has 12 sexual partners during the course of a year, what is the probability that at least one of them carries HIV?

c. How many partners would a student need to have before the probability of an HIV encounter exceeded 50%?

PROJECTS FOR THE INTERNET & BEYOND

33. **Simulation.** A classic probability problem involves a king who wants to increase the proportion of women in his kingdom. He decrees that after a mother gives birth to a son, she is prohibited from having any more children. The king reasons that some families will have just one boy whereas other families will have a few girls and one boy, so the proportion of girls will be increased. Use coin tossing to simulate a kingdom that abides by this decree: "After a mother gives birth to a son, she will not have any other children." If this decree is followed, does the proportion of girls increase?

IN THE NEWS

34. A columnist for the *New York Daily News* (Stephen Allensworth) provided tips for selecting numbers in New York State's lottery. He advocated a system based on the use of "cold digits," which are digits that hit once or not at all in a seven-day period. He made this statement: "That [system] produces the combos $5-8-9$, $7-8-9$, $6-8-9$, $0-8-9$, and $3-8-9$. These five combos have an excellent chance of being drawn this week. Good luck to all." Can this system work? Why or why not?

CHAPTER REVIEW EXERCISES

For Exercises 1–7, use the data in the accompanying table (based on data from "Helmet Use and Risk of Head Injuries in Alpine Skiers and Snowboarders" by Sullheim et al., *Journal of the American Medical Association*, Vol. 295, No. 8).

	Head injured	Head not injured
Wore helmet	96	656
No helmet	480	2330

1. If one of the subjects is randomly selected, find the probability of selecting someone with a head injury.

2. If one of the subjects is randomly selected, find the probability of selecting someone who had a head injury or wore a helmet.

3. If one of the subjects is randomly selected, find the probability of selecting someone who did not wear a helmet or was not injured.

4. If one of the subjects is randomly selected, find the probability of selecting someone who wore a helmet and was injured.

5. If one of the subjects is randomly selected, find the probability of selecting someone who did not wear a helmet and was not injured.

6. If two different study subjects are randomly selected, find the probability that they both wore helmets.

7. If one of the subjects is randomly selected, find the probability of selecting someone who did not wear a helmet, given that the subject had head injuries.

8. Use subjective probability to estimate the probability of randomly selecting a car and selecting one that is black.

9. The Binary Computer Company manufactures computer chips used in DVD players. Those chips are made with a 27% yield, meaning that 27% of them are good and the others are defective.

    a. If one chip is randomly selected, find the probability that it is *not* good.

    b. If two chips are randomly selected, find the probability that they are both good.

    c. If five chips are randomly selected, what is the *expected number* of good chips?

    d. If five chips are randomly selected, find the probability that they are all good. If you did get five good chips among the five selected, would you continue to believe that the yield was 27%? Why or why not?

10. For a recent year, the fatality rate from motor vehicle crashes was reported as 15.2 per 100,000 population.

    a. What is the probability that a randomly selected person will die this year as a result of a motor vehicle crash?

    b. If two people are randomly selected, find the probability that they both die this year as the result of motor vehicle crashes, and express the result using three significant digits.

    c. If two people are randomly selected, find the probability that neither of them dies this year as the result of motor vehicle crashes, and express the result using six decimal places.

1. A Las Vegas handicapper can correctly predict the winning professional football team 70% of the time. What is the probability that she is wrong in her next prediction?

2. For the same handicapper described in Exercise 1, find the probability that she is correct in each of her next two predictions.

3. Estimate the probability that a randomly selected prime-time television show will be interrupted with a news bulletin.

4. When conducting a clinical trial of the effectiveness of a gender selection method, it is found that there is a 0.342 probability that the results could have occurred by chance. Does the method appear to be effective?

5. If $P(A) = 0.4$, what is the value of $P(\overline{A})$?

In Exercises 6–10, use the following results:

In the judicial case of *United States v. City of Chicago*, discrimination was charged in a qualifying exam for the position of fire captain. In the table below, Group A is a minority group and Group B is a majority group.

	Passed	Failed
Group A	10	14
Group B	417	145

6. If one of the test subjects is randomly selected, find the probability of getting someone who passed the exam.

7. Find the probability of randomly selecting one of the test subjects and getting someone who is in Group B or passed.

8. Find the probability of randomly selecting two different test subjects and finding that they are both in Group A.

9. Find the probability of randomly selecting one of the test subjects and getting someone who is in Group A and passed the exam.

10. Find the probability of getting someone who passed, given that the selected person is in Group A.

FOCUS ON
SOCIAL SCIENCE

Do Lotteries Harm the Poor?

State-sponsored lotteries are a big business in the United States, generating more than $50 billion in annual sales, of which about one-third ($17 billion) ends up as state revenue. (The rest goes to prizes and expenses.) But are lotteries good social policy?

Lottery proponents point to several positive aspects. For example, lottery revenue helps states to fund education and recreation, while also allowing states to keep tax rates lower than they would be otherwise. Proponents also point out that lottery participation is voluntary and that polls show a large majority of Americans to be in favor of state-sponsored lotteries.

This favorable picture is part of the marketing and public relations of state lotteries. For example, Colorado state lottery officials offer statistics on the age, income, and education of lottery players compared to the general population (Figure 6.25). Within a few percentage points, the age of lottery players parallels that of the population as a whole. Similarly, the histogram for the income of lottery players gives the impression that lottery players as a whole are typical citizens—with the exception of the bars for incomes of $15,000−$25,000 and $25,000−$35,000, which show that the poor tend to play more than we would expect for their proportion of the population.

Despite the apparent benefits of lotteries, critics have long argued that lotteries are merely an unfair form of taxation. To investigate the reality, the *New York Times* conducted a study of data from 48,875 people who had won at least $600 in New Jersey lottery games. (In an ingenious bit of sampling, these winners were taken to be a random sample of all lottery players; after all, lottery winners are determined randomly. However, the sample is not really representative of all lottery players because winners tend to buy more than an average number of tickets.) By identifying the home zip codes of the lottery players, researchers were able to determine whether players came from areas with high or low income, high or low average education, and various other demographic characteristics. The overwhelming conclusion of the *New York Times* study was that lottery spending has a much greater impact *in relative terms* on those players with lower incomes and lower educational backgrounds. For example, the following were among the specific findings:

- People in the state's lowest income areas spend five times as much of their income on lotteries as those in the state's highest income areas (more than $25 per $10,000 of annual

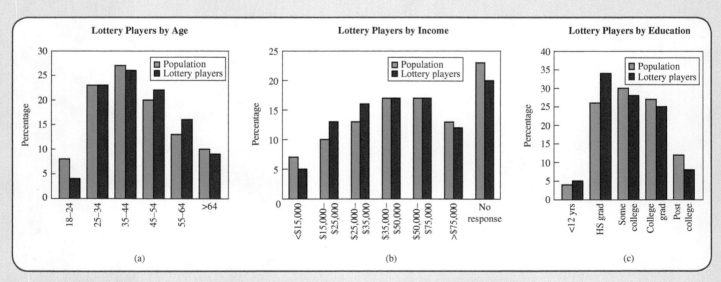

Figure 6.25 Three figures showing (a) age, (b) income, and (c) education of Colorado lottery players compared to population.

income in the lowest income areas, compared to less than $5 per $10,000 of annual income in the highest income areas).

- The number of lottery sales outlets (where lottery tickets can be purchased) is nearly twice as high per 10,000 people in low-income areas as in high-income areas.
- People in areas with the lowest percentage of college education spent over five times as much per $10,000 of annual income as those in areas with the highest percentage of college education.
- Advertising and promotion of lotteries is focused in low-income areas.

Some of the results of the *New York Times* study are summarized in Figure 6.26. It suggests that while New Jersey has a progressive tax system (higher-income people pay a greater percentage of their income in taxes), the "lottery tax" is regressive. Moreover, the study found that the areas that generate the largest percentage of lottery revenues do *not* receive a proportional share of state funding.

Other studies have found similar patterns in other states. The overall conclusions are inescapable: While lotteries provide many benefits to state governments, the revenue they produce comes disproportionately from poorer and less educated individuals.

QUESTIONS FOR DISCUSSION

1. Study Figure 6.25. Do lottery players appear to be a typical cross-section of American society based on age? Based on income? Based on level of education? Explain. How does the "no response" category affect these conclusions?

2. Based on the more than $50 billion in total annual lottery spending and the current U.S. population, about how much does the average person spend on the lottery each year? Now, using the statistics in Figure 6.25 to estimate the percentage of the population that plays the lottery, about how much does the average lottery player spend each year?

3. Find and study a particular lottery advertisement, and determine whether it is misleading in any way.

4. Considering all factors presented in this section and other facts that you can find, do you think lotteries are fair to poor or uneducated people? Should they remain legal? Should they be restricted in any way?

5. An anonymous quote circulated on the Internet read "Lotteries are a tax on people who are bad at math." Comment on the meaning and accuracy of this quote.

• • • • • • • • • • • • •

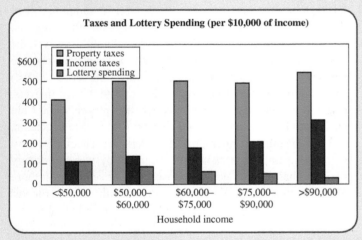

Figure 6.26 Taxes and lottery spending for New Jersey lottery winners (all figures are per $10,000 of income).

Source: New York Times.

FOCUS ON
LAW

Is DNA Fingerprinting Reliable?

DNA fingerprinting (also called DNA profiling or DNA identification) is a major tool of law enforcement, used in criminal cases, in paternity cases, and even in the identification of human remains.

The scientific foundation for DNA identification has been in place for many decades. However, these ideas were not used in the courtroom until 1986. The case involved a 17-year-old boy accused of the rape and murder of two schoolgirls in Narborough, in the Midlands of England. During his interrogation, the suspect asked for a blood test, which was sent to the laboratory of a noted geneticist, Alec Jeffreys, at the nearby University of Leicester. Using methods that he had developed for paternity testing, Jeffreys compared the suspect's DNA to that found in samples from the victims. The tests showed that although both rapes and murders were committed by the same person, the person was *not* the suspect in custody. The following year, after more than 4,500 blood samples were collected, researchers made a positive identification of the murderer using Jeffreys's methods. Word of the British case and Jeffreys's methods spread rapidly. The techniques were swiftly tested, commercialized, and promoted.

To explore the essential roles that probability and statistics play in DNA identification, consider a simple eyewitness analogy. Suppose you are looking for a person who helped you out during a moment of need and you remember only three things about this person:

- The person was female.
- She had green eyes.
- She had long red hair.

If you find someone who matches this profile, can you conclude that this person is the woman who helped you? To answer, you need data telling you the probabilities that randomly selected individuals in the population have these characteristics. The probability that a person is female is about 1/2. Let's say that the probability of green eyes is about 0.06 (6% of the population has green eyes) and the probability of long red hair is 0.0075. If we assume that these characteristics occur independently of one another, then the probability that a randomly selected person has all three characteristics is

$$0.5 \times 0.06 \times 0.0075 = 0.000225$$

or about 2 in 10,000. This may seem relatively low, but it probably is not low enough to draw a definitive conclusion. For example, a profile matched by only 2 in 10,000 people will still be matched by some 200 people in a city with a population of 1 million.

DNA identification is based on a similar idea, but it is designed so that the probability of a profile match is much lower. The DNA of every individual is unique and is the same throughout the individual. A single physical trait is determined by a small piece of DNA called a *gene* at a specific *locus* (location) on a *chromosome* (Figure 6.27); humans have 23 chromosomes and roughly 30,000 genes. A gene can take two or more (often hundreds) of different forms, called *alleles* (pronounced a-leels). Different alleles give rise to variations of a trait (for example, different hair colors or different blood types). Not only can different alleles appear at a locus, but the corresponding piece of DNA can have different lengths in different people (called *variable number of tandem repeats* or VNTRs). The genetic evidence that is collected and analyzed in the lab consists of the allele lengths or allele types at five to eight different loci.

Collecting genetic evidence (from samples of blood, tissues, hair, semen, or even saliva on a postage stamp) and analyzing it are straightforward, at least in theory. Nevertheless, the process is subject to both controversy and sources of error. Suppose, in our analogy, a person is found with "reddish brown" hair instead of "red" hair. Because many characteristics are continuous (not discrete) variables, should you rule this

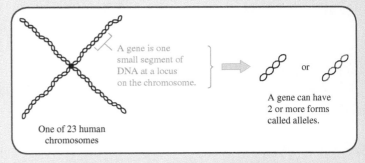

Figure 6.27 Diagram showing the relationship among chromosomes, alleles, genes, and loci.

person out or assume that reddish brown is close enough? For this reason, the issue of *binning* becomes extremely important (see Section 3.1). You might choose to include all people with hair that is any shade of red, or you could choose a narrower bin—say, bright red hair only—which would give a more discriminating test.

The same issue arises in genetic tests. When allele types or lengths are measured in the lab, there is enough variability or error in the measurements that these variables are continuous. Bin widths need to be chosen, and the choice is the source of debate. Bins with a small width give a more refined test, exclude more suspects, and ultimately provide stronger evidence against a defendant.

Other sources of scientific and statistical controversy come from assumptions about the independence of different genetic traits and in the populations chosen for measuring the frequency of different traits. For the former, DNA fingerprinting usually assumes that each genetic trait is independent of other genetic traits—which means that probabilities can be calculated with the multiplication rule for independent events—but some scientists suspect that the presence of a particular trait may affect the probability of other traits. For the latter, consider Figure 6.28, which shows allele data for four different Asian subpopulations. The horizontal axis shows 30 bins for

the different allele measurements, and the vertical axis shows the frequency for each bin. Because of the significant variation in the curves for the different subpopulations, calculations will yield different probabilities for the guilt of a suspect depending on whether the suspect is compared to his own Asian subpopulation, to the population of all Asian Americans, or to the population of all Americans. Fortunately, the calculations today yield small enough probabilities that DNA fingerprinting is considered very reliable, as long as no errors are made in examining the evidence.

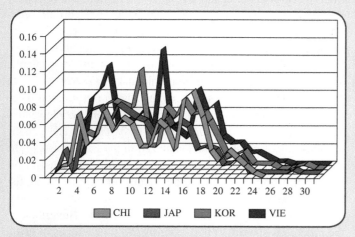

Figure 6.28 Binned frequency data for one allele, showing variability among four ethnic groups.

Source: Kathryn Roeder, "DNA Fingerprinting: A Review of the Controversy," *Statistical Science,* Vol. 9, No. 2, pp. 222–247.

QUESTIONS FOR DISCUSSION

1. The result of a DNA test is considered physical (as opposed to circumstantial) evidence. Yet it is much more sophisticated and difficult to understand than a typical piece of physical evidence, such as a weapon or a piece of clothing. Some people have therefore argued that DNA evidence should not be used in a criminal trial in which jury members may not fully understand how the evidence is collected and analyzed. What do you think of this argument? Defend your opinion.

2. Suppose that an allele has a *greater* frequency in a suspect's subpopulation than in the full population, but that the suspect is compared to the full population. How would this affect the probability of a match between the suspect and a DNA sample from the crime scene?

3. Evidence from blood tests can identify a suspect with a probability of about 1 in 200. Evidence from DNA tests often provides probabilities claimed to be on the order of 1 in 10 million. If you were a juror, would you accept such a probability as positive identification of a suspect?

4. The Innocence Project uses DNA to try to clear suspects wrongfully convicted of crimes. Is innocence easier to establish than guilt through DNA testing? Explain.

5. Discuss a few other ways DNA tests can be useful, such as in settling issues of paternity. Overall, how much do you think DNA evidence affects our society?   248

• • • • • • • • • • • •

Correlation

Does smoking cause lung cancer? Are drivers more dangerous when on their cell phones? Is human activity causing global warming? A major goal of many statistical studies is to search for relationships among different variables so that researchers can then determine whether one factor *causes* another. Once a relationship is discovered, we can try to determine whether there is an underlying cause. In this chapter, we will study relationships known as correlations and explore how they are important to the more difficult task of searching for causality.

The person who knows "how"
will always have a job.
The person who knows "why"
will always be his boss.

—Diane Ravitch

7.1 INTRODUCTION TO GRAPHING

What Graphing Is and Why It Is Important

Many mathematical relationships can be expressed as equations, inequalities, or their graphs. Although lacking the precision of an equation, a graph can clarify at a glance patterns and trends in a relationship, helping us to understand that relationship better.

In the past, the graphing approach to problem solving was usually more time-consuming than the traditional algebraic approach. Today, the use of graphing calculators and computer software packages has made graphing easier. But to utilize these graphing tools, you must first understand the concepts and skills involved in graphing, which are discussed in this chapter.

In this chapter, the relationships that we graph are relatively simple.

Plotting Points

If you were to enter a theater or sports arena with a ticket for row 5, seat 3, you would know exactly where to sit that is, at $(5, 3)$. Such a system of **coordinates** in which we associate a pair of numbers in a given order with a corresponding location is commonplace.

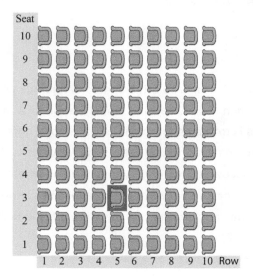

The flat surface on which we draw graphs is called a **coordinate plane**. To create a coordinate plane, we first sketch two perpendicular number lines—one horizontal, the other vertical—that intersect at their zeros. Each number line is called an **axis**. The point where the axes intersect is called the **origin**. It is common practice to refer to the horizontal number line as the ***x*-axis** and the vertical number line as the ***y*-axis**

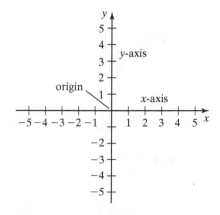

Each point in a coordinate plane is represented by a pair of numbers called an **ordered pair**. For example, the origin is the point (0, 0). The first number in an ordered pair represents a horizontal distance and is called the ***x*-coordinate**. The second number represents a vertical distance and is called the ***y*-coordinate**.

To **plot** a point in the coordinate plane, we find its location represented by its ordered pair. For example, to plot the point (3, 1), we start at the origin and go 3 units *to the right,* then go *up* 1 unit. For this point, we say that $x = 3$ and $y = 1$.

Notice that the two numbers in an ordered pair are written in parentheses, separated by a comma. Do the ordered pairs (3, 1) and (1, 3) correspond to different points? Why?

When an ordered pair has a negative *x*-coordinate, the corresponding point is to the left of the *y*-axis, as shown in the following coordinate plane. Similarly, when an ordered pair's y-coordinate is negative, the point is below the *x*-axis.

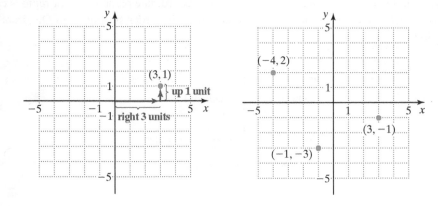

Any ordered pair whose y-coordinate is 0 corresponds to a point that is on the *x*-axis. For instance, the points $(-4, 0)$, $(0, 0)$, and $(3, 0)$ are on the x-axis, as shown in the graph below on the left. Similarly, any ordered pair whose x-coordinate is 0 corresponds to a point that is on the y-axis. For instance, the points $(0, 2)$, $(0, -1)$, and $(0, -4)$ are on the y-axis, as shown in the middle graph below.

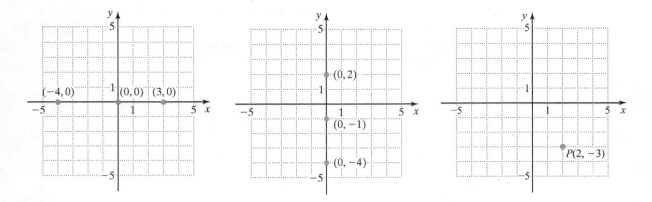

Sometimes we name points with letters. We can refer to a point as *P* or *A* or any other letter that we choose. Generally, a capital letter is used. If we want to emphasize that point *P* has coordinates $(2, -3)$, we can write it as $P(2, -3)$, as shown in the graph above on the right.

If there is a point whose coordinates we do not know, we can refer to it as (x, y) or $P(x, y)$, where *x* and *y* are the unknown coordinates.

Now, let's look at some examples of plotting points.

PRACTICE 1

On a coordinate plane, plot the points corresponding to each ordered pair.

a. $(0, -5)$ b. $(4, 4)$
c. $(-2, 2)$ d. $(5, 0)$
e. $(-3, -2)$ f. $(2, -4)$

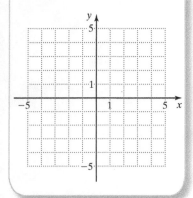

EXAMPLE 1

Plot the following points on a coordinate plane.

a. $(5, 2)$ b. $(3, -4)$ c. $(-1, 1)$

d. $(0, 3)$ e. $(-4, -2)$ f. $(0, 0)$

SOLUTION The points are plotted on the coordinate plane as shown.

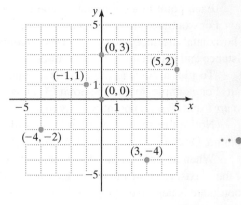

The x- and y-axes are boundaries that separate a coordinate plane into four regions called *quadrants*. These quadrants are named in counterclockwise order starting with Quadrant I, as shown below:

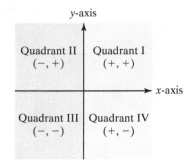

The quadrant in which a point is located tells us something about its coordinates. For instance, any point in Quadrant I is to the right of the y-axis and above the x-axis, so both its coordinates must be positive. Points in this quadrant are of particular interest in applied problems in which all quantities are positive.

Any point in Quadrant II lies to the left of the y-axis and above the x-axis, so its x-coordinate must be negative and its y-coordinate positive. Points in Quadrant III are to the left of the y-axis and below the x-axis, so both coordinates are negative. And finally, any point in Quadrant IV is to the right of the y-axis and below the x-axis, so its x-coordinate must be positive and its y-coordinate negative. Points that lie on an axis are not in any quadrant.

PRACTICE 2

In which quadrant is each point located?

a. $\left(-\dfrac{1}{2}, 3\right)$

b. $(6, -7)$

c. $(-1, -4)$

d. $(2, 9)$

EXAMPLE 2

Determine the quadrant in which each point is located.

a. $(-5, 5)$ b. $(7, 20)$

c. $(1.3, -4)$ d. $(-4, -5)$

SOLUTION

a. $(-5, 5)$ is in Quadrant II.

b. $(7, 20)$ is in Quadrant I.

c. $(1.3, -4)$ is in Quadrant IV.

d. $(-4, -5)$ is in Quadrant III.

Often the points that we are to plot affect how we draw the axes on a coordinate plane. For instance, in the following coordinate planes we choose for each axis an appropriate **scale**—the length between adjacent tick marks—to conveniently plot all points in question.

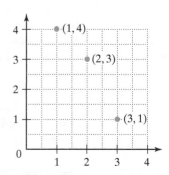

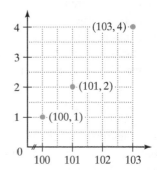

> **TIP**   Depending on the location of the points to be plotted, we can choose to show only part of a coordinate plane.

EXAMPLE 3

A young entrepreneur started a dot-com company that made a profit of $10,000 in its first year of business. In the second year, the company's profit grew to $15,000. In the third year, however, the company lost $5000. Plot points on a coordinate plane to display this information.

SOLUTION   We let x represent the year of business and y represent the company's profit in dollars that year. The three points to be plotted are:

$$(1, 10{,}000),\ (2, 15{,}000),\ \text{and}\ (3, -5000).$$

Notice that in the third year, the company's loss is represented by a negative profit. Because the y-coordinates are large, we use 5000 as the scale on the y-axis. Then, we plot the points on the following coordinate plane.

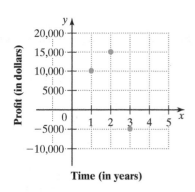

We end this discussion of plotting points with a final comment about variables. On a coordinate plane, the first coordinate of each point is a value of one quantity (or variable), and the second coordinate is a value of another quantity. For instance, in Example 3 we considered the profit that a company makes at various times. One variable represents time and the other variable the profit. Notice that the profit made by the company depends on the time rather than the other way around. So we refer to time as the *independent* variable and the profit as the *dependent* variable. It is customary when plotting points to assign the independent variable to the horizontal axis and the dependent variable to the vertical axis. However, as shown in Practice 3, letters other than x and y can be used to represent quantities.

PRACTICE 3

The following table shows the average monthly temperatures for the first four months of the year (where month 1 represents January) for Chicago, Illinois. (*Source*: U.S. National Climatic Data Center)

Month m	1	2	3	4
Temperature t (°F)	22	27	37	49

On the coordinate plane shown, graph the information displayed in the table.

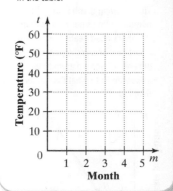

Interpreting Graphs

Points plotted on a coordinate plane are merely dots on a piece of paper. However, their significance comes to life when we understand the information that they convey.

Describing the trend on a coordinate plane tells the story of that trend. When key points are missing, as is frequently the case, the story is incomplete. In such cases, we may want to make a prediction, that is, to extend the observed pattern so as to estimate the missing data. Such predictions, while not certain, at least allow us to make decisions based on the best available evidence. We may also want to speculate about the conditions that underlie an observed pattern of plotted points.

The trend among plotted points on a coordinate plane shows a relationship between the two variables. To highlight the relationship, it is common practice either to draw a line that passes through the plotted points or to connect adjacent points with short line segments.

Consider the following examples that involve interpreting trends on a coordinate plane:

PRACTICE 4

The value V of a new car after t years is displayed on the following graph. Describe the line graph in terms of the changing value of the car.

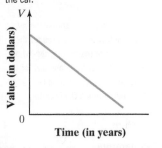

EXAMPLE 4

The graph shows the cost C of parking a car at a lot for time t hr. Describe the trend that you observe in terms of both the coordinate plane and the cost of parking.

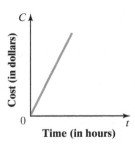

SOLUTION   On the graph, the larger C-values correspond to the larger t-values. In terms of parking, we see that the longer a car is parked in the lot, the more it costs to park the car.

• • ●

PRACTICE 5

The following graph shows the number of times per minute that a runner's heart beats. Describe in a sentence or two the pattern you observe. Use this pattern to write a scenario as to what the runner might be doing.

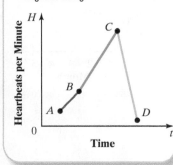

EXAMPLE 5

The following graph shows the cost that a shipping company charges to send a package, depending on the package's weight.

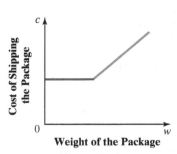

Write a brief story describing the displayed relationship. What business practice does the horizontal line segment reflect?

SOLUTION   From the horizontal line segment, we see that the cost of shipping is constant (that is, a flat rate) for lighter packages up to a certain weight. The horizontal line segment indicates that the company established a minimum cost for sending lightweight packages. Since the slanted line segment goes upward to the right, the cost of shipping increases with the weight of heavier packages.

• • ●

Mathematically Speaking

Fill in each blank with the most appropriate term or phrase from the given list.

above	horizontal	elow
dependent	x-axis	independent
origin	coordinate	center
ordered pair	vertical	y-axis

1. A coordinate plane has two number lines that intersect at a point called the _____.

2. The horizontal number line on a coordinate plane is usually referred to as the _____.

3. Each point in a coordinate plane is represented by a pair of numbers called a(n) _____.

4. The *y*-coordinate of a point on a coordinate plane represents a(n) _____ distance.

5. Points in Quadrant III are to the left of the *y*-axis and _____ the *x*-axis.

6. The _____ variable is usually assigned to the horizontal axis.

A. *On the coordinate plane below, plot the points with the given coordinates.*

7. A(0, 5)   B(−1, −5)   C(1, 4)

D(3, −3)   E(−4, 2)   F(5, 0)

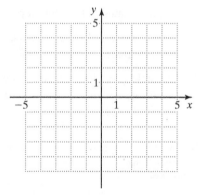

8. A(−2, 4)   B(0, 0)   C(2, −1)

D(−3, 0)   E(3, 4)   F(−4, −2)

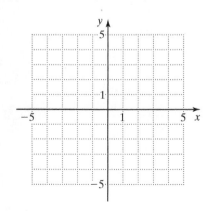

Next to each point, write its coordinates.

9.

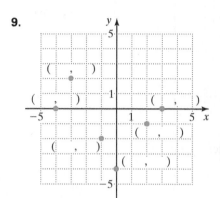

10.

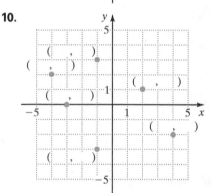

11. (−2, −3)

12. (−13, −24)

13. (−9, 5)

14. (−5.1, 4)

15. $\left(3, -\dfrac{1}{2}\right)$

16. $\left(3\dfrac{1}{2}, -8\right)$

17. (65, 11)

18. (8, 6.2)

Mixed Practice

Solve.

19. Plot the points with the given coordinates on the coordinate plane.

A(3, 2)   B(4, 0)   C(−4, −1)   D(−2, 3)   E(0, −3)

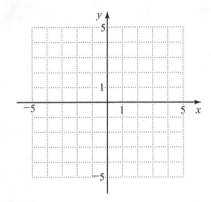

20. Write the coordinates next to each point.

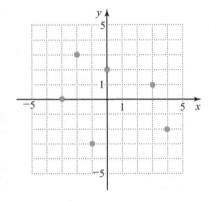

Identify the quadrant in which each point is located.

21. $(-3, 7)$

22. $\left(6, -\dfrac{3}{4}\right)$

23. $(27, 39)$

24. $(-4.2, -3.8)$

Applications

C. *Solve.*

25. College students coded A, B, C, and D took placement tests in mathematics and in English. The following coordinate plane displays their scores.

a. Estimate the coordinates of the plotted points.

b. Which students scored higher in English than in mathematics?

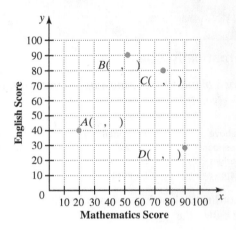

26. Suppose that a financier owns shares of stock in three companies—Dearborn, Inc. (D), Ellsworth Products (E), and Fairfield Publications (F). On the following coordinate plane, the x-value of a point represents the change in value of a share of the indicated stock from the previous day. The y-value stands for the number of shares of that stock owned by the financier.

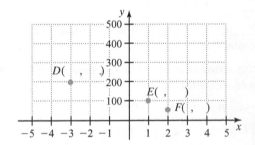

a. Name the coordinates of the plotted points.

b. For each point, explain the significance of the product of the point's coordinates.

27. The following table gives the percent of the U.S. adult population that smoked in various years. (*Source:* cdc.gov)

Year	1980	1990	2000	2010
Percent of the Population That Smoked	33%	26%	23%	20%

Plot this information on the coordinate plane below:

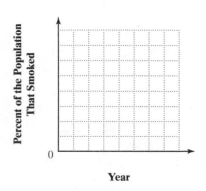

28. The number of electoral votes cast for the winning candidate in recent presidential elections is displayed in the following table:

Year	1996	2000	2004	2008
Electoral Votes	379	271	286	365

(Source: The New York Times)

Plot this information on the coordinate plane below:

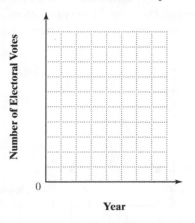

29. A chemist conducts an experiment to measure the melting and boiling points of four substances, as indicated in the following table:

Year	Symbol	Melting Point (°C)	Boiling Point (°C)
Chlorine	Cl	−101	−35
Oxygen	O	−218	−183
Bromine	Br	−7	59
Phosphorous	P	44	280

On the coordinate plane next column, an x-value represents a substance's melting point and a y-value stands for its boiling point, both in degrees Celsius.

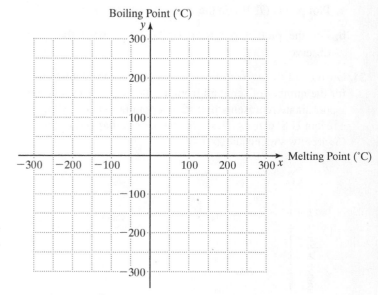

a. Plot points for the four substances. Label each point with the appropriate substance symbol.

b. For each point, which of its coordinates is larger—the x-value or the y-value? In a sentence, explain this pattern.

30. Meteorologists use the windchill index to determine the windchill temperature (how cold it feels outside) relative to the actual temperature when the wind speed is considered. The following table shows the actual temperatures in degrees Fahrenheit and the related windchill temperatures when the wind speed is 5 mph.

Actual Temperature T	−10	−5	0	5	10	15
Windchill Temperature W	−22	−16	−11	−5	1	7

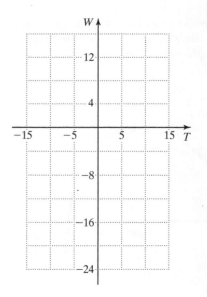

a. Plot points (T, W) on the given coordinate plane.

b. For the plotted points, describe the pattern that you observe.

31. On the following coordinate plane, a y-coordinate stands for the number of senators from a state. The corresponding x-coordinate represents that state's population according to a recent U.S. census. Describe the pattern that you observe. (*Source:* www.census.gov)

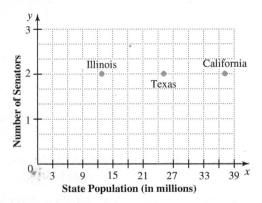

32. Last year's daily closing values (in dollars) of a share of a technology stock are plotted on the graph below. What story is this graph telling?

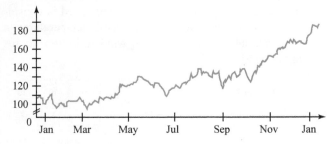

33. A child walks away from a wall, stands still, and then approaches the wall. In a couple of sentences, explain which of the graphs below could describe this motion.

a.

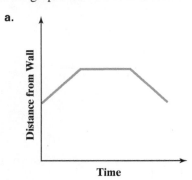

b.

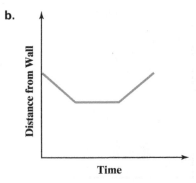

c.

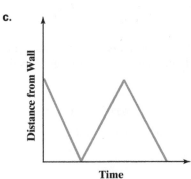

34. The following graph shows the temperature of a patient on a particular day. Describe the overall pattern you observe in the patient's temperature over the time period.

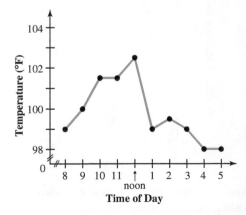

MIND STRETCHERS

Writing

1. Many situations involve using a coordinate system to identify positions. Two such situations are given below:

- a chessboard
- a map

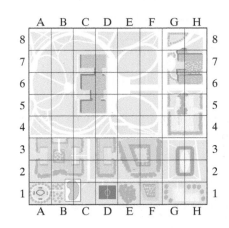

a. Explain to what extent a chessboard and an atlas map are coordinate systems.

b. Identify some other examples of coordinate systems in everyday life.

Critical Thinking

2. The map shows a square section of a city. You want to walk along the horizontal and vertical streets from point $(-2, -2)$ to point $(2, 2)$. One possible route is

$$(-2, -2) \rightarrow (-1, -2) \rightarrow (0, -2) \rightarrow (0, -1) \rightarrow (0, 0) \rightarrow (0, 1) \rightarrow (0, 2) \rightarrow (1, 2) \rightarrow (2, 2)$$

as pictured below.

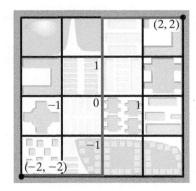
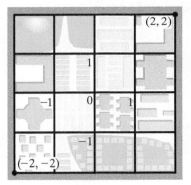

(continued)

This route is 8 blocks long. List four other 8-block routes from $(-2, -2)$ to $(2, 2)$.

$$(-2, -2) \rightarrow (\underline{}, \underline{}) \rightarrow (\underline{}, \underline{}) \rightarrow (\underline{}, \underline{}) \rightarrow (\underline{}, \underline{})$$
$$\rightarrow (\underline{}, \underline{}) \rightarrow (\underline{}, \underline{}) \rightarrow (\underline{}, \underline{}) \rightarrow (2, 2)$$
$$(-2, -2) \rightarrow (\underline{}, \underline{}) \rightarrow (\underline{}, \underline{}) \rightarrow (\underline{}, \underline{}) \rightarrow (\underline{}, \underline{})$$
$$\rightarrow (\underline{}, \underline{}) \rightarrow (\underline{}, \underline{}) \rightarrow (\underline{}, \underline{}) \rightarrow (2, 2)$$
$$(-2, -2) \rightarrow (\underline{}, \underline{}) \rightarrow (\underline{}, \underline{}) \rightarrow (\underline{}, \underline{}) \rightarrow (\underline{}, \underline{})$$
$$\rightarrow (\underline{}, \underline{}) \rightarrow (\underline{}, \underline{}) \rightarrow (\underline{}, \underline{}) \rightarrow (2, 2)$$
$$(-2, -2) \rightarrow (\underline{}, \underline{}) \rightarrow (\underline{}, \underline{}) \rightarrow (\underline{}, \underline{}) \rightarrow (\underline{}, \underline{})$$
$$\rightarrow (\underline{}, \underline{}) \rightarrow (\underline{}, \underline{}) \rightarrow (\underline{}, \underline{}) \rightarrow (2, 2)$$

Groupwork

3. Two points are plotted on a coordinate plane. Discuss with a partner what is special about a third point whose x-coordinate is the average of the first two x-coordinates, and whose y-coordinate is the average of the first two y-coordinates.

CULTURAL NOTE

It was the seventeenth-century French mathematician and philosopher René Descartes (pronounced day-KART) who developed the concepts that underlie graphing. The story goes that one morning Descartes, who liked to stay in bed and meditate, began to eye a fly crawling on his bedroom ceiling. In a flash of insight, he realized that it was possible to express mathematically the fly's position in terms of its distance to the two adjacent walls.

7.2 SLOPE ·

In the previous section, we discussed points on a coordinate plane. Now, let's look at (straight) lines that pass through points. A key characteristic of a line is its slope. In this section, we focus on the slope of a line and its relationship to the corresponding equation.

Slope

On an airplane, would you rather glide downward gradually or drop like a stone? Would you rather ski down a run that drops precipitously or ski across a gently inclined snowfield? These questions relate to *slope*, the extent to which a line is slanted. In other words, slope is a measure of a line's steepness.

Slope, also called **rate of change**, is an important concept in the study of graphing. Examining the slope of a line can tell us if the quantity being graphed increases or decreases, as well as how fast the quantity is changing. For example, in one application, the slope of a line can represent the speed of a moving object. In another application, the slope can stand for the rate at which a share of stock is changing in value.

To understand exactly what slope means, let's suppose that a straight line on a coordinate plane passes through two arbitrary points. We can call the coordinates of the first point (x_1, y_1), read "x sub 1" and "y sub 1," and the coordinates of the second point (x_2, y_2). These coordinates are written with *subscripts* in order to distinguish them from one another. We can plot these two points on a coordinate plane, and then graph the line passing through them.

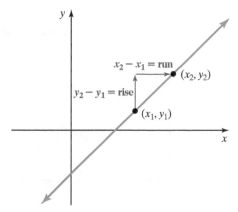

We usually represent the slope of a line by the letter m and define slope to be the ratio of the change in the y-values to the change in the x-values. Using the coordinates of the points (x_1, y_1) and (x_2, y_2) shown in the previous graph gives us the following formula:

$$m = \frac{\text{change in } y\text{-values}}{\text{change in } x\text{-values}} = \frac{y_2 - y_1}{x_2 - x_1}, \quad \text{where } x_1 \neq x_2$$

In this formula, the numerator of the fraction is the vertical change called the *rise* and the denominator is the horizontal change called the *run*. So another way of writing the formula for slope is $m = \dfrac{\text{rise}}{\text{run}}$.

Definition

The **slope** m of a line passing through the points (x_1, y_1) and (x_2, y_2) is defined to be

$$m = \frac{y_2 - y_1}{x_2 - x_1}, \text{ where } x_1 \neq x_2.$$

Can you explain why in the definition of slope, x_1 and x_2 must not be equal?

Note that when using the formula for slope, it does not matter which point is chosen for (x_1, y_1) and which point for (x_2, y_2) as long as the order of subtraction of the coordinates is the same in both the numerator and denominator.

<table>
<tr>
<td>

PRACTICE 1

Find the slope of a line that contains the points, (1,2) and (4, 3) Plot the points, and then sketch the line.

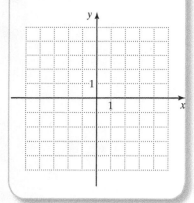

</td>
<td>

EXAMPLE 1

Find the slope of the line that passes through the points $(2, 1)$ and $(4, 2)$. Plot the points, and then sketch the line.

SOLUTION   Let $(2, 1)$ stand for (x_1, y_1) and $(4, 2)$ for (x_2, y_2).

$$
\begin{array}{cc}
(2, 1) & (4, 2) \\
\uparrow\ \uparrow & \uparrow\ \uparrow \\
x_1\ y_1 & x_2\ y_2
\end{array}
$$

Substituting into the formula for slope, we get:

$$m = \frac{y_2 - y_1}{x_2 - x_1} = \frac{2 - 1}{4 - 2} = \frac{1}{2}$$

Now, let's plot $(2, 1)$ and $(4, 2)$, and then sketch the line passing through them. $\cdot\ \cdot\ \bullet$

</td>
</tr>
</table>

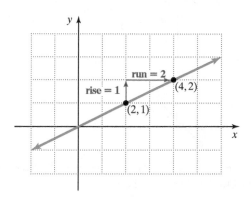

We can also find the slope of a line using its graph. From $(2, 1)$ and $(4, 2)$, we see that the change in y-values (the rise) is $2 - 1$, or 1.

The change in x-values (the run) is $4 - 2$, or 2. So $m = \dfrac{\text{rise}}{\text{run}} = \dfrac{1}{2}$.

Therefore, we get the same answer whether we use the formula $m = \dfrac{y_2 - y_1}{x_2 - x_1}$ or $m = \dfrac{\text{rise}}{\text{run}}$.

$\cdots \bullet$

A line rising to the right as shown in Example 1 has a *positive* slope. We say that such a line is *increasing* because as the x-values gets larger, the corresponding y-values also get larger.

EXAMPLE 2

Sketch the line passing through the points $(-3, 1)$ and $(2, -2)$. Find the slope.

SOLUTION   First, we plot the points $(-3, 1)$ and $(2, -2)$. Then, we draw a line passing through them.

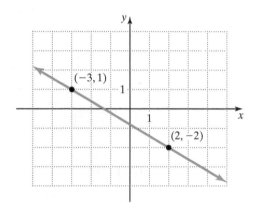

Next, find the slope.

$$
\begin{array}{cccc}
(-3, 1) & & (2, -2) \\
\uparrow \ \uparrow & & \uparrow \ \ \uparrow \\
x_1 \ y_1 & & x_2 \ \ y_2
\end{array}
$$

$$
m = \frac{y_2 - y_1}{x_2 - x_1} = \frac{-2 - 1}{2 - (-3)} = \frac{-3}{5} = -\frac{3}{5}
$$

A line falling to the right as shown in Example 2 has a *negative* slope. We say that such a line is *decreasing* because as the x-values get larger, the corresponding y-values get smaller.

$\cdots \bullet$

EXAMPLE 3

Find the slope of a line that passes through the points $(7, 5)$ and $(-1, 5)$. Plot the points, and then sketch the line.

SOLUTION   First, find the slope of the line.

$$
\begin{array}{cccc}
(7, 5) & & (-1, 5) \\
\uparrow \ \uparrow & & \uparrow \ \uparrow \\
x_1 \ y_1 & & x_2 \ y_2
\end{array}
$$

$$
m = \frac{y_2 - y_1}{x_2 - x_1} = \frac{5 - 5}{-1 - 7} = \frac{0}{-8} = 0
$$

So the slope of this line is 0.

PRACTICE 2

Sketch the line that contains the points (–2, 1) and (3, –5). Find the slope.

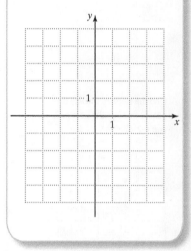

PRACTICE 3

On the following coordinate plane, plot the points (2, –1) and (6, –1). Sketch the line, and then compute its slope.

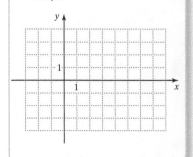

Next, we plot the points, and then sketch the line passing through them.

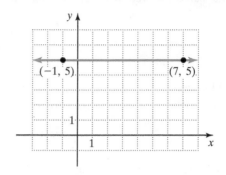

When the slope of a line is 0, its graph is a **horizontal** line as shown in Example 3. All points on a horizontal line have the same y-coordinate, that is, the y-values are constant for all x-values.

EXAMPLE 4

What is the slope of the line pictured on the coordinate plane shown to the right?

PRACTICE 4

Find the slope of the line that passes through the points (2, −7) and (−2, 0).

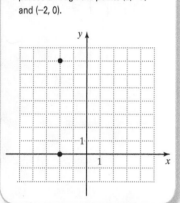

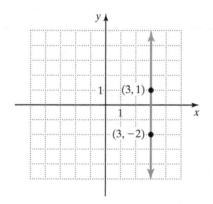

SOLUTION   First, we plot the points $(-3, 1)$ and $(2, -2)$. Then, we draw a line passing through them.

$$
\begin{array}{cc}
(3, -2) & (3, 1) \\
\uparrow\ \ \uparrow & \uparrow\ \uparrow \\
x_1\ \ y_1 & x_2\ y_2
\end{array}
$$

$$
m = \frac{y_2 - y_1}{x_2 - x_1} = \frac{1 - (-2)}{3 - 3} = \frac{3}{0}
$$

Since division by 0 is undefined, the slope of this line is undefined.

When the slope of a line is undefined, its graph is a **vertical line** as shown in Example 4. All points on a vertical line have the same x-coordinate, that is, the x-values are constant for all y-values.

As we have seen in Examples 1 through 4, the sign of the slope of a line tells us a lot about the line. As we continue graphing lines, it will be helpful to keep in mind the following graphs:

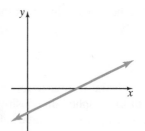

Positive *m*
**The line slants upward
from left to right.**

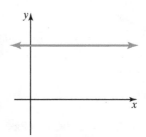

Negative *m*
**The line slants downward
from left to right.**

Zero *m*
The line is horizontal.

Undefined *m*
The line is vertical.

In the next example, we graph two lines on a coordinate plane.

EXAMPLE 5

Calculate the slopes for the lines shown.

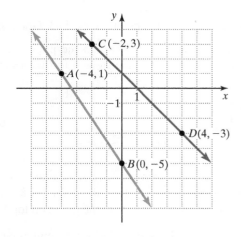

PRACTICE 5

Compute the slopes for the lines shown.

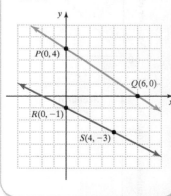

SOLUTION Line AB, written $\overleftrightarrow{AB}$, passes through $A(-4, 1)$ and $B(0, -5)$. Its slope is:

$$m = \frac{y_2 - y_1}{x_2 - x_1} = \frac{1 - (-5)}{(-4) - 0} = \frac{1 + 5}{-4} = \frac{6}{-4} = -\frac{3}{2}$$

For $\overleftrightarrow{CD}$ passing through $C(-2, 3)$ and $D(4, -3)$, the slope is:

$$m = \frac{y_2 - y_1}{x_2 - x_1} = \frac{3 - (-3)}{(-2) - 4} = \frac{3 + 3}{(-2) - 4} = \frac{6}{-6} = -1$$

Note that both lines have negative slopes and slant downward from left to right. • • ●

PRACTICE 6

A doctor is trying to help eliminate an epidemic. Explain, in terms of slope, which scenario would be the most desirable.

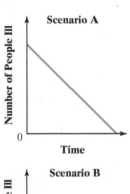

Scenario A

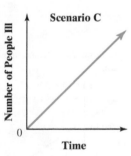

Scenario B

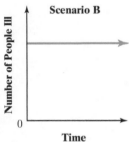

Scenario C

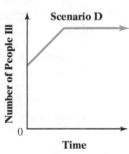

Scenario D

As shown in the next example, how a line slants often helps us to interpret the information given in the graph.

EXAMPLE 6

The following graph shows the amount of money that your dental insurance reimburses you, depending on the amount of your dental bill. Is the slope of the graphed line positive or negative? Explain how you know. What does this mean in terms of insurance reimbursement?

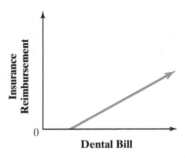

SOLUTION   Since the graphed line slants upward from left to right, its slope is positive. According to this graph, larger x-values correspond to larger y-values. So your dental insurance reimburses you more for larger dental bills.

$\cdots \bullet$

We have already graphed a line by plotting two points and drawing the line passing through them. Now, let's look at graphing a line when given the slope of the line and a point on the line.

EXAMPLE 7

The slope of a line that passes through the point $(2, 5)$ is 3. Graph the line.

SOLUTION   The line in question passes through the point $(2, 5)$. But there are many such lines—which is the right one? We use the slope 3 to find a second point through which the line also passes.

Since 3 can be written as $\frac{3}{1}$, we have:

$$\text{slope} = \frac{\text{rise}}{\text{run}} = \frac{3}{1}$$

We first plot the point $(2, 5)$. Starting at $(2, 5)$, we move 3 units up (for a rise of 3) and then 1 unit to the right (for a run of 1). Arriving at the point $(3, 8)$, we sketch the line passing through the points $(2, 5)$ and $(3, 8)$, as shown in the graph on top left on next page.

Since $\frac{3}{1} = \frac{-3}{-1}$, we could have started at $(2, 5)$ and moved down 3 units (for a rise of -3) and then 1 unit to the left (for a run of -1). In this case, we would arrive at $(1, 2)$, which is another point on the same line, as shown in the graph on top right on next page.

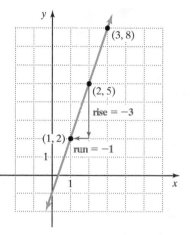

Can you find other points on this line? Explain.   ·· ●

EXAMPLE 8

A family on vacation is driving out of town at a constant speed. At 2 o'clock, they have traveled 110 mi. By 6 o'clock, they have traveled 330 mi.

a. On a coordinate plane, label the axes, and then plot the appropriate points.

b. Compute the slope of the line passing through the points.

c. Interpret the meaning of the slope in this situation.

SOLUTION

a. Label the axes on the coordinate plane. Then, plot the points $(2, 110)$ and $(6, 330)$.

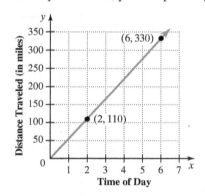

b. The slope of the line through the two points is:

$$m = \frac{y_2 - y_1}{x_2 - x_1}$$

$$= \frac{330 - 110}{6 - 2}$$

$$= \frac{220}{4}$$

$$= 55$$

c. Here the slope is the change in distance divided by the change in time. In other words, the slope is the average speed the family traveled, which is 55 mph.   ·· ●

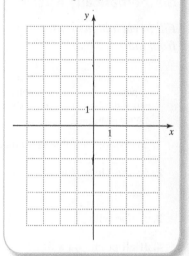

PRACTICE 7

Graph the line with slope 4 that passes through the point (1, −2).

PRACTICE 8

In 1985, the streetcar running along Boston's Arborway Corridor had a daily ridership of 28,000. The streetcar was then replaced by a bus. Twenty-five years later, daily ridership had dropped to 14,000. (*Source:* arborway.org)

a. On a coordinate plane, label the axes, and then plot the appropriate points for daily ridership *r* in *y* years after 1985.

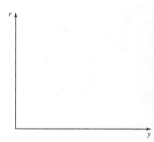

b. Compute the slope of the line that passes through the points.

c. Interpret the meaning of the slope in this situation.

Mathematically Speaking

Fill in each blank with the most appropriate term or phrase from the given list.

y-coordinate	parallel	negative
positive	vertical	x-coordinate
perpendicular	rate of change	run
horizontal	rise	

1. The slope of a line is also called its _____.

2. In the slope formula, the vertical change is called the _____.

3. A line with _____ slope is decreasing.

4. If all points on a line have the same _____, then the line is vertical.

5. A line with zero slope is _____.

6. A line with undefined slope is _____.

7. Two nonvertical lines are _____ if and only if their slopes are equal.

8. Two nonvertical lines are _____ if and only if the product of their slopes is -1.

A. *Compute the slope m of the line that passes through the given points. Plot these points on the coordinate plane, and sketch the line that passes through them.*

9. $(2, 3)$ and $(-2, 0)$, $m =$

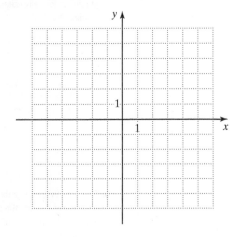

10. $(-1, 4)$ and $(0, 5)$, $m =$

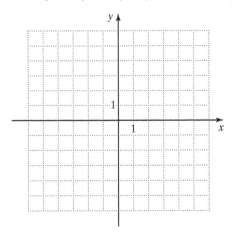

11. $(6, -4)$ and $(6, 1)$, $m =$

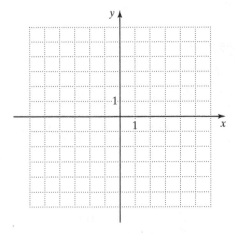

12. $(1, 1)$ and $(1, -3)$, $m =$

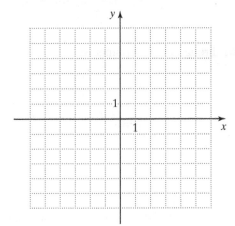

13. $(-2, 1)$ and $(3, -1)$, $m =$

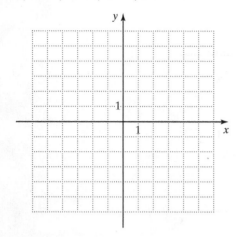

16. $(3, 0)$ and $(5, 0)$, $m =$

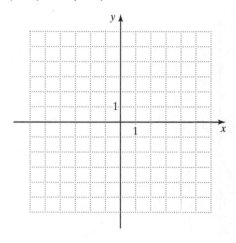

14. $(0, 0)$ and $(-2, 5)$, $m =$

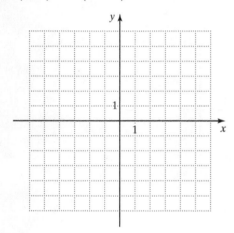

17. $(0.5, 0)$ and $(0, 3.5)$, $m =$

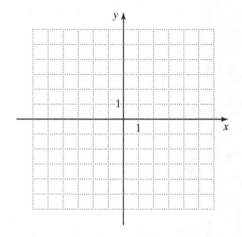

15. $(-1, -4)$ and $(3, -4)$, $m =$

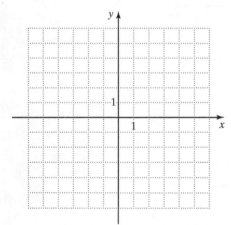

18. $(4, 4.5)$ and $(1, 2.5)$, $m =$

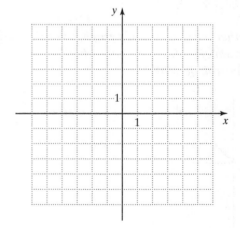

On each graph, calculate the slopes for the lines shown.

19.

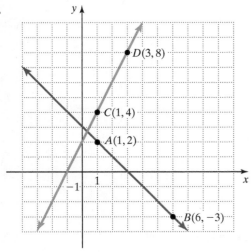

20.

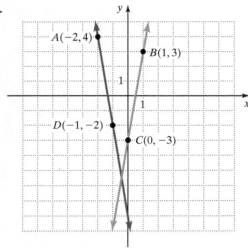

B. *Indicate whether the slope of each graph is positive, negative, zero, or undefined. Then, state whether the line is horizontal, vertical, or neither.*

21.

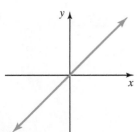

22.

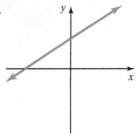

23.

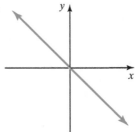

24.

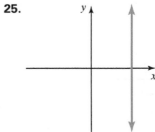

25.

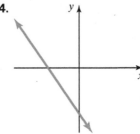

26.

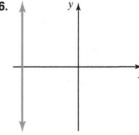

27.

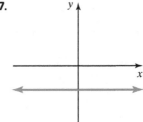

28.

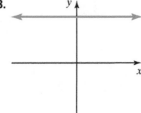

C. *Graph the line on the coordinate plane using the given information.*

29. Passes through $(2, 5)$ and $m = 4$

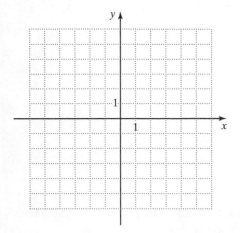

30. Passes through $(-1, 1)$ and $m = \frac{1}{2}$

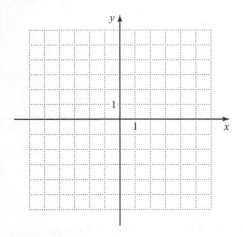

31. Passes through $(2, 5)$ and m $= -\frac{4}{3}$

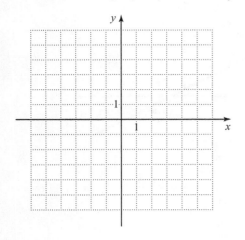

32. Passes through $(1, 5)$ and $m = -3$

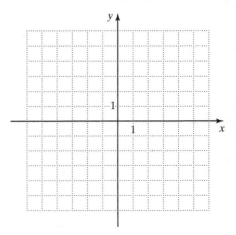

33. Passes through $(0, -6)$ and $m = 0$

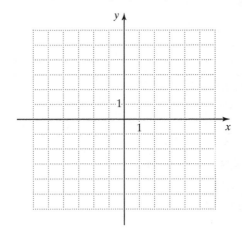

34. Passes through $(0, -2)$ and $m = 0$

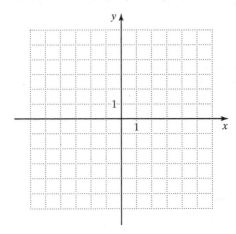

35. Passes through $(-4, 0)$ and the slope is undefined

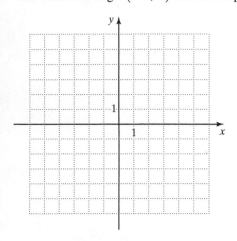

36. Passes through $(-6, 2)$ and the slope is undefined

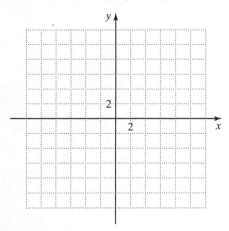

D. *Determine whether* $\overleftrightarrow{PQ}$ *and* $\overleftrightarrow{RS}$ *are parallel or perpendicular.*

37.

	P	Q	R	S
a.	(0, −1)	(1, 3)	(5, 0)	(7, 8)
b.	(9, 1)	(7, 4)	(0, 0)	(6, 4)

38.

	P	Q	R	S
a.	(3, 3)	(7, 7)	(−5, 5)	(2, −2)
b.	(8, 0)	(0, 4)	(0, −4)	(−12, 2)

Mixed Practice

Indicate whether the slope of each graph is positive, negative, zero, or undefined. Then, state whether the line is horizontal, vertical, or neither.

39.

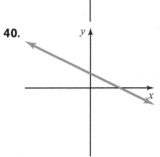

40.

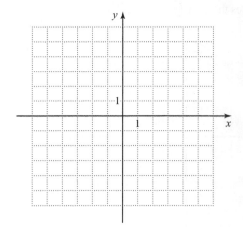

41. Graph the line on the coordinate plane if the line passes through $(-2, 3)$ and $m = 4$.

42. Calculate the slopes for the lines shown in the graph.

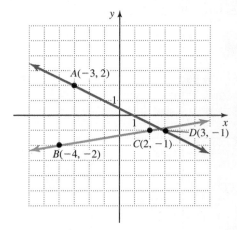

43. Determine whether $\overleftrightarrow{AB}$ and $\overleftrightarrow{CD}$ are parallel or perpendicular.

	P	Q	R	S
a.	(−3, 2)	(5, −2)	(1, −4)	(5, 4)
b.	(−1, 5)	(5, −3)	(2, 2)	(5, −2)

Compute the slope m of the line that passes through the given points. Plot these points on the coordinate plane, and sketch the line that passes through them.

44. $(-4, -5)$ and $(2, -1)$, $m =$

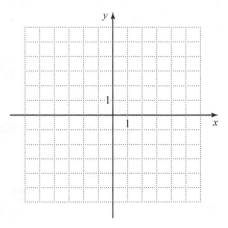

45. $(-3, -2)$ and $(-3, 4)$, $m =$

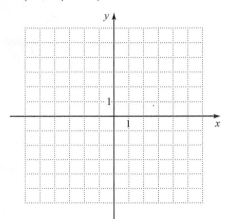

46. $(-4, 4.5)$ and $(-2, -1.5)$, $m =$

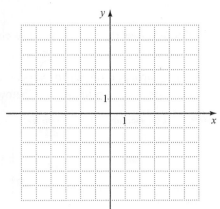

Applications

Solve

47. A chemist conducts an experiment on the gas contained in a sealed tube. The experiment is to heat the gas and then to measure the resulting pressure in the tube. In the lab manual, points are plotted and the line is sketched to show the gas pressure for various temperatures.

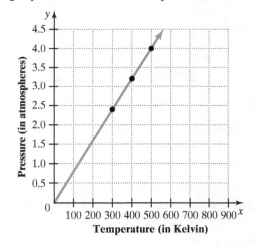

a. Is the slope of this line positive, negative, zero, or undefined?

b. In a sentence, explain the significance of the answer to part (a) in terms of temperature and pressure.

48. To reduce their taxes, many businesses use the straight-line method of depreciation to estimate the change in the value over time of equipment that they own. The graph shows the value of equipment owned from the time of purchase to 7 yr later.

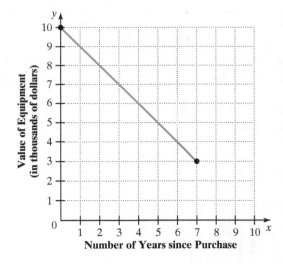

a. Is the slope of this line positive, negative, zero, or undefined?

b. In a sentence or two, explain the significance of the answer to part (a) in terms of the value of the equipment over time.

49. Two motorcyclists leave at the same time, racing down a road. Consider the lines in the graph that show the distance traveled by each motorcycle at various times.

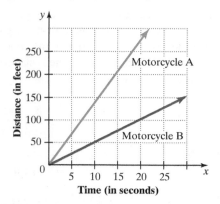

a. Which motorcycle first travels 100 ft?
b. Which motorcycle is traveling more slowly?
c. Explain what the slopes mean in this situation.

50. Most day-care centers charge parents additional fees for arriving late to pick up their children. The following graph shows the late fee for two day-care centers:

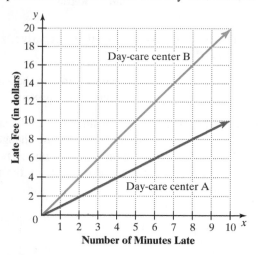

a. Which day-care center charges a higher late fee?
b. Explain what the slopes represent in this situation.

51. The following graph records the amount of garbage deposited in landfills A and B after they are opened.

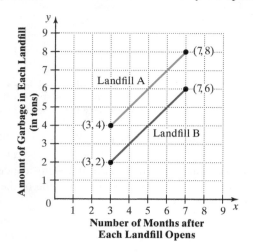

Are the garbage deposits at the two landfills growing at the same rate? Explain in a sentence or two how you know.

52. The weights of a brother and sister from age 3 yr to 7 yr are recorded in the graph. Did their weights increase at the same rate? Explain.

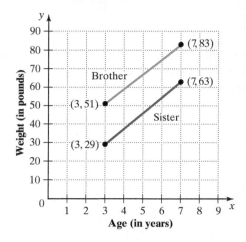

53. After a stock split, the per-share value of the stock increased, as shown in the following table:

Number of Days after the Split	Per-share Stock Value (in dollars)	Point
2	27	$P(2, 27)$
4	51	$Q(4, 51)$
8	79	$R(8, 79)$

a. Choose appropriate scales and label each axis. Plot the points, and then sketch $\overleftrightarrow{PQ}$ and $\overleftrightarrow{QR}$.

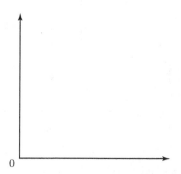

b. Determine whether the rate of increase changed over time. Explain.

54. The position of a dropped object for various times after the object is released is given in the table below:

Time After Release (in seconds)	Position (in feet)	Point
1	−16	$A(1, -16)$
2	−64	$B(2, -64)$
3	−144	$C(3, -144)$

a. Choose appropriate scales and label each axis. Plot the points, and then sketch $\overleftrightarrow{AB}$ and $\overleftrightarrow{BC}$.

b. Compute the slopes of $\overleftrightarrow{AB}$ and $\overleftrightarrow{BC}$.

c. Was the rate of fall for the dropped object constant throughout the experiment? Explain.

55. A hiker is at point A as shown in the graph and wants to take the shortest route through a field to reach a nearby road represented by $\overleftrightarrow{BC}$. The shortest route will be to walk perpendicular to the road. Is $\overrightarrow{AD}$ the shortest route? Explain.

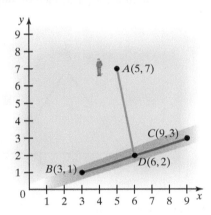

56. The coordinates of the vertices of triangle ABC are shown. Is triangle ABC a right triangle? Explain.

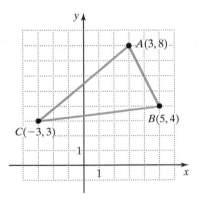

57. On a highway, a driver sets a car's cruise control for a constant speed of 55 mph.

a. Of the following, which graph shows the distance the car travels? Using the slope of the line, explain.

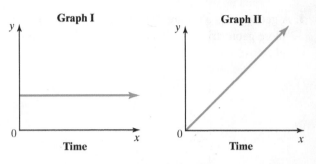

b. Which of the above graphs shows the speed of the car? Using the slope of the line, explain.

58. City leaders consider imposing an income tax on residents whose income is above a certain amount, as pictured below.

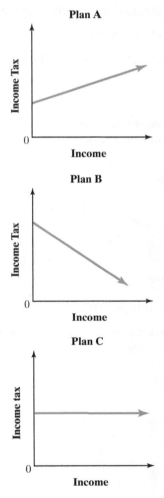

a. Using the slopes of the lines, describe each plan.

b. Which plan do you think is the fairest? Explain.

MIND STRETCHERS

Groupwork

1. A geoboard is a square flat surface with pegs forming a grid pattern. You can stretch rubber bands around the pegs to explore geometric questions such as, "What is the slope of $\overline{AB}$?" Pictured is a geoboard with rubber bands forming a series of steps.

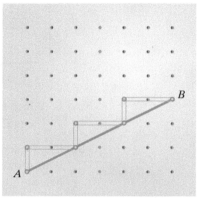

Using a geoboard or graph paper, determine whether the slope of $\overleftrightarrow{AB}$ increases or decreases if:

a. the rise of each step increases by one peg.

b. the run of each step increases by one peg

Writing

2. Describe a real-world situation that each of the following graphs might illustrate. Explain the significance of slope in the situation that you have described.

a. 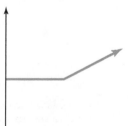   **b.**    **c.**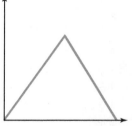

Mathematical Reasoning

3. If the slope of a line is positive, explain why any line perpendicular to it must have a negative slope.

7.3 SEEKING CORRELATION ····················

What does it mean when we say that smoking *causes* lung cancer? It certainly does *not* mean that you'll get lung cancer if you smoke a single cigarette. It does not even mean that you'll definitely get lung cancer if you smoke heavily for many years, as some heavy smokers do not get lung cancer. Rather, it is a *statistical* statement meaning that you are *much more likely* to get lung cancer if you smoke than if you don't smoke.

How did researchers learn that smoking causes lung cancer? The process began with informal observations, as doctors noticed that a surprisingly high proportion of their patients with lung cancer were smokers. These observations led to carefully conducted studies in which researchers compared lung cancer rates among smokers and nonsmokers. These studies showed clearly that heavier smokers were more likely to get lung cancer. In more formal terms, we say that there is a **correlation** between the variables *amount of smoking* and *likelihood of lung cancer*. A correlation is a special type of relationship between variables, in which a rise or fall in one goes along with a corresponding rise or fall in the other.

Smoking is one of the leading causes of statistics.

—Fletcher Knebel

> **Definition**
>
> A **correlation** exists between two variables when higher values of one variable consistently go with higher values of another variable or when higher values of one variable consistently go with lower values of another variable.

Here are a few other examples of correlations:

- There is a correlation between the variables *height* and *weight* for people; that is, taller people tend to weigh more than shorter people.
- There is a correlation between the variables *demand for apples* and *price of apples;* that is, demand tends to decrease as price increases.
- There is a correlation between *practice time* and *skill* among piano players; that is, those who practice more tend to be more skilled.

It's important to realize that establishing a correlation between two variables does *not* mean that a change in one variable *causes* a change in the other. The correlation between smoking and lung cancer did not by itself prove that smoking causes lung cancer. We could imagine, for example, that some gene predisposes a person both to smoking and to lung cancer. Nevertheless, identifying the correlation was the crucial first step in learning that smoking causes lung cancer. We will discuss the difficult task of establishing causality later in this chapter. For now, we concentrate on how we look for, identify, and interpret correlations.

> **BY THE WAY**
>
> Smoking is linked to many serious diseases besides lung cancer, including heart disease and emphysema. Smoking is also linked with many less lethal health conditions, such as premature skin wrinkling and sexual impotence.

> **TIME ⏱ OUT TO THINK**
>
> Suppose there really were a gene that made people prone to both smoking and lung cancer. Explain why we would still find a strong correlation between smoking and lung cancer in that case, but would not be able to say that smoking causes lung cancer.

Scatterplots

Table 7.1 lists data for a sample of gem-store diamonds—their prices and several common measures that help determine their value. Because advertisements for diamonds often quote only their weights (in carats), we might suspect a correlation between the weights and the prices. We can look for such a correlation by making a **scatterplot** (or *scatter diagram*) showing the relationship between the variables *weight* and *price*.

TABLE 7.1   Prices and Characteristics of a Sample of 23 Diamonds from Gem Dealers

Diamond	Price	Weight (carats)	Depth	Table	Color	Clarity
1	$6,958	1.00	60.5	65	3	4
2	$5,885	1.00	59.2	65	5	4
3	$6,333	1.01	62.3	55	4	4
4	$4,299	1.01	64.4	62	5	5
5	$9,589	1.02	63.9	58	2	3
6	$6,921	1.04	60.0	61	4	4
7	$4,426	1.04	62.0	62	5	5
8	$6,885	1.07	63.6	61	4	3
9	$5,826	1.07	61.6	62	5	5
10	$3,670	1.11	60.4	60	9	4
11	$7,176	1.12	60.2	65	2	3
12	$7,497	1.16	59.5	60	5	3
13	$5,170	1.20	62.6	61	6	4
14	$5,547	1.23	59.2	65	7	4
15	$7,521	1.29	59.6	59	6	2
16	$7,260	1.50	61.1	65	6	4
17	$8,139	1.51	63.0	60	6	4
18	$12,196	1.67	58.7	64	3	5
19	$14,998	1.72	58.5	61	4	3
20	$9,736	1.76	57.9	62	8	2
21	$9,859	1.80	59.6	63	5	5
22	$12,398	1.88	62.9	62	6	2
23	$11,008	2.03	62.0	63	8	3

Notes: Weight is measured in carats (1 carat = 0.2 gram). Depth is defined as 100 times the ratio of height to diameter. Table is the size of the upper flat surface. (Depth and table determine "cut.") Color and clarity are each measured on standard scales, where 1 is best. For color, 1 = colorless, and increasing numbers indicate more yellow. For clarity, 1 = flawless, and 6 indicates that defects can be seen by eye.

> **Definition**
>
> A **scatterplot** (or *scatter diagram*) is a graph in which each point represents the values of two variables.

Figure 7.1 shows the scatterplot, which can be constructed with the following procedure.

1. We assign one variable to each axis and label the axis with values that comfortably fit all the data. Sometimes the axis selection is arbitrary, but if we suspect that one variable depends on the other then we plot the *explanatory variable* on the horizontal axis and the *response variable* on the vertical axis. In this case, we expect the diamond price to depend at least in part on its weight; we therefore say that *weight* is the explanatory variable (because it helps

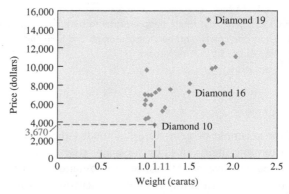

Figure 7.1 Scatterplot showing the relationship between the variables *price* and *weight* for the diamonds in Table 7.1. The dashed lines show how we find the position of the point for Diamond 10.

explain the price) and *price* is the response variable (because it *responds* to changes in the explanatory variable). We choose a range of 0 to 2.5 carats for the *weight* axis and $0 to $16,000 for the *price* axis.

2. For each diamond in Table 7.1, we plot a *single point* at the horizontal position corresponding to its weight and the vertical position corresponding to its price. For example, the point for Diamond 10 goes at a position of 1.11 carats on the horizontal axis and $3,670 on the vertical axis. The dashed lines on Figure 7.1 show how we locate this point.

3. (Optional) We can label some (or all) of the data points, as is done for Diamonds 10, 16, and 19 in Figure 7.1.

Scatterplots get their name because the way in which the points are scattered may reveal a relationship between the variables. In Figure 7.1, we see a general upward trend indicating that diamonds with greater weight tend to be more expensive. The correlation is not perfect. For example, the heaviest diamond is not the most expensive. But the overall trend seems fairly clear.

TIME ◷UT TO THINK
Identify the points in Figure 7.1 that represent Diamonds 3, 7, and 23.

EXAMPLE ❶ Color and Price

Using the data in Table 7.1, create a scatterplot to look for a correlation between a diamond's *color* and *price*. Comment on the correlation.

SOLUTION   We expect price to depend on color, so we plot the explanatory variable *color* on the horizontal axis and the response variable *price* on the vertical axis in Figure 7.2. (You should check a few of the points against the data in Table 7.1.) The points appear much more scattered than in Figure 7.1. Nevertheless, you may notice a weak trend diagonally downward from the upper left toward the lower right. This trend represents a weak correlation in which diamonds with more yellow color (higher numbers for color) are less expensive. This trend is consistent with what we would expect, because colorless diamonds appear to sparkle more and are generally considered more desirable.

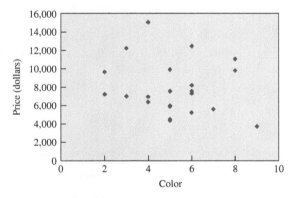

Figure 7.2 Scatterplot for the color and price data in Table 7.1.

TIME ◷UT TO THINK
Thanks to a large bonus at work, you have a budget of $6,000 for a diamond ring. A dealer offers you the following two choices for that price. One diamond weighs 1.20 carats and has color = 4. The other weighs 1.18 carats and has color = 3. Assuming all other characteristics of the diamonds are equal, which would you choose? Why?

Types of Correlation

We have seen two examples of correlation. Figure 7.1 shows a fairly strong correlation between weight and price, while Figure 7.2 shows a weak correlation between color and price. We are now ready to generalize about types of correlation. Figure 7.3 shows eight scatterplots for variables called x and y. Note the following key features of these diagrams:

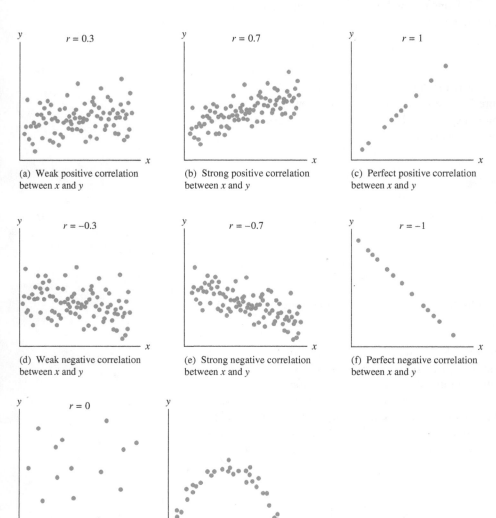

(a) Weak positive correlation between x and y

(b) Strong positive correlation between x and y

(c) Perfect positive correlation between x and y

(d) Weak negative correlation between x and y

(e) Strong negative correlation between x and y

(f) Perfect negative correlation between x and y

(g) No correlation between x and y

(h) Nonlinear relationship between x and y

Figure 7.3 Types of correlation seen on scatterplots.

- Parts a to c show **positive correlations**: The values of y tend to increase with increasing values of x. The correlation becomes stronger as we proceed from a to c. In fact, c shows a perfect positive correlation, in which all the points fall along a straight line.
- Parts d to f show **negative correlations**: The values of y tend to decrease with increasing values of x. The negative correlation becomes stronger as we proceed from d to f. In fact, f shows a perfect negative correlation, in which all the points fall along a straight line.
- Part g shows **no** correlation between x and y: Values of x do not appear to be linked to values of y in any way.
- Part h shows a **nonlinear relationship**: x and y appear to be related but the relationship does not correspond to a straight line. (*Linear* means along a straight line, and *nonlinear* means *not* along a straight line.)

TECHNICAL NOTE

In this text we use the term *correlation* only for *linear* relationships. Some statisticians refer to nonlinear relationships as "nonlinear correlations." There are techniques for working with nonlinear relationships that are similar to those described in this text for linear relationships.

Types of Correlation

Positive correlation: Both variables tend to increase (or decrease) together.

Negative correlation: The two variables tend to change in opposite directions, with one increasing while the other decreases.

No correlation: There is no apparent (linear) relationship between the two variables.

Nonlinear relationship: The two variables are related, but the relationship results in a scatterplot that does not follow a straight-line pattern.

EXAMPLE **2** **Life Expectancy and Infant Mortality**

Figure 7.4 shows a scatterplot for the variables *life expectancy* and *infant mortality* in 16 countries. What type of correlation does it show? Does this correlation make sense? Does it imply causality? Explain.

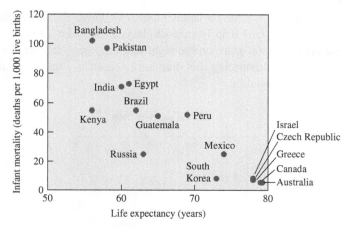

Figure 7.4 Scatterplot for life expectancy and infant mortality data.
Source: United Nations.

SOLUTION   The diagram shows a moderate negative correlation in which countries with *lower* infant mortality tend to have *higher* life expectancy. It is a *negative* correlation because the two variables vary in opposite directions. The correlation makes sense because we would expect that countries with better health care would have both lower infant mortality and higher life expectancy. However, it does *not* imply causality between infant mortality and life expectancy: We would not expect that a concerted effort to reduce infant mortality would increase life expectancy significantly unless it was part of an overall effort to improve health care. (Reducing infant mortality will *slightly* increase life expectancy because having fewer infant deaths tends to raise the mean age of death for the population.) $\cdots\bullet$

Measuring the Strength of a Correlation

For most purposes, it is enough to state whether a correlation is strong, weak, or nonexistent. However, sometimes it is useful to describe the strength of a correlation in more precise terms. Statisticians measure the strength of a correlation with a number called the **correlation coefficient**, represented by the letter r. The correlation coefficient is easy to calculate in principle (see the optional section on p. 282), but the actual work is tedious unless you use a calculator or computer.

We can explore the interpretation of correlation coefficients by studying Figure 7.3, which shows the value of the correlation coefficient r for each scatterplot. Notice that the correlation coefficient is always between -1 and 1. When points in a scatterplot lie close to an ascending straight line, the correlation coefficient is positive and close to 1. When all the points lie close to a descending straight line, the correlation coefficient is negative with a value close to -1. Points that do not fit any type of straight-line pattern or that lie close to a *horizontal* straight line (indicating that the y values have no dependence on the x values) result in a correlation coefficient close to 0.

Properties of the Correlation Coefficient, r

- The correlation coefficient, r, is a measure of the strength of a correlation. Its value can range only from -1 to 1.

- If there is no correlation, the points do not follow any ascending or descending straight-line pattern, and the value of r is close to 0.

- If there is a positive correlation, the correlation coefficient is positive ($0 < r \leq 1$): Both variables increase together. A perfect positive correlation (in which all the points on a scatterplot lie on an ascending straight line) has a correlation coefficient $r = 1$. Values of r close to 1 indicate a strong positive correlation and positive values closer to 0 indicate a weak positive correlation.

- If there is a negative correlation, the correlation coefficient is negative($-1 \leq r < 0$): When one variable increases, the other decreases. A perfect negative correlation (in which all the points lie on a descending straight line) has a correlation coefficient $r = -1$. Values of r close to -1 indicate a strong negative correlation and negative values closer to 0 indicate a weak negative correlation.

TECHNICAL NOTE

For the methods of this section, there is a requirement that the two variables result in data having a "bivariate normal distribution." This basically means that for any fixed value of one variable, the corresponding values of the other variable have a normal distribution. This requirement is usually very difficult to check, so the check is often reduced to verifying that both variables result in data that are normally distributed.

EXAMPLE 3 **U.S. Farm Size**

Figure 7.5 shows a scatterplot for the variables *number of farms* and *mean farm size* in the United States. Each dot represents data from a single year between 1950 and 2000; on this diagram, the earlier years generally are on the right and the later years on the left. Estimate the correlation coefficient by comparing this diagram to those in Figure 7.3 and discuss the underlying reasons for the correlation.

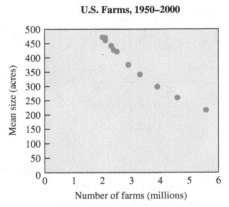

U.S. Farms, 1950–2000

Figure 7.5 Scatterplot for farm size data.
Source: U.S. Department of Agriculture.

SOLUTION The scatterplot shows a strong negative correlation that most closely resembles the scatterplot in Figure 7.3f, suggesting a correlation coefficient around $r = -0.9$. The correlation shows that when there were fewer farms, they tended to have a larger mean size, and when there were more farms, then tended to have a smaller mean size. This trend reflects a basic change in the nature of farming: Prior to 1950, most farms were small family farms. Over time, these small farms were replaced by large farms owned by agribusiness corporations. · · ●

EXAMPLE 4 **Accuracy of Weather Forecasts**

The scatterplots in Figure 7.6 show two weeks of data comparing the actual high temperature for the day with the same-day forecast (part a) and the three-day forecast (part b). Estimate the correlation coefficient for each data set and discuss what these coefficients imply about weather forecasts.

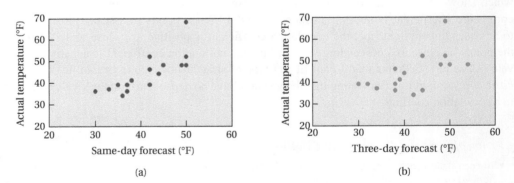

(a)   (b)

Figure 7.6 Comparison of actual high temperatures with (a) same-day and (b) three-day forecasts.

SOLUTION If every forecast were perfect, each actual temperature would equal the corresponding forecasted temperature. This would result in all points lying on a straight line and a correlation coefficient of $r = 1$. In Figure 7.6a, in which the forecasts were made at the beginning of the same day, the points lie fairly close to a straight line, meaning that same-day forecasts are closely related to actual temperatures. By comparing this scatterplot to the diagrams in Figure 7.3, we can reasonably estimate this correlation coefficient to be about $r = 0.8$. The correlation is weaker in Figure 7.6b, indicating that forecasts made three days in advance aren't as close to actual temperatures as same-day forecasts. This correlation coefficient is about $r = 0.6$. These results are unsurprising because we expect longer-term forecasts to be less accurate. · · ●

TIME UT TO THINK

For further practice, visually estimate the correlation coefficients for the data for diamond weight and price (Figure 7.1) and diamond color and price (Figure 7.2).

Calculating the Correlation Coefficient (Optional Section)

The formula for the (linear) correlation coefficient r can be expressed in several different ways that are all algebraically equivalent, which means that they produce the same value. The following expression has the advantage of relating more directly to the underlying rationale for r:

$$r = \frac{\sum \left[\dfrac{(x - \bar{x})(y - \bar{y})}{s_x \qquad s_y} \right]}{n - 1}$$

⏻ USING TECHNOLOGY—SCATTERPLOTS AND CORRELATION COEFFICIENTS

Excel The screen shot below shows the process for making a scatterplot like that in Figure 7.1:

1. Enter the data, which are shown in Columns B (weight) and C (price).

2. Select the columns for the two variables on the scatterplot; in this case, Columns B and C.

3. Choose "XY Scatter" as the chart type, with no connecting lines. You can then use the "chart options" (which comes up with a right-click in the graph) to customize the design, axis range, labels, and more.

4. To calculate the correlation coefficient, shown in row 26, use the built-in function CORREL.

5. [Optional] The straight line on the graph, called a best-fit line, is added by choosing the option to "Add Trendline"; be sure to choose the "linear" option for the trendline. You'll also find options that add the two items shown in the upper left of the graph: the equation of the line and the value R^2, which is the square of the correlation coefficient. Best-fit lines and R^2 are discussed in Section 8.4.

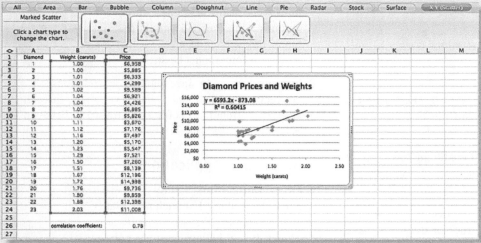

Microsoft Excel 2008 for Mac.

STATDISK Enter the paired data in columns of the STATDISK Data Window. Select **Analysis** from the main menu bar, then select the option **Correlation and Regression**. Select the columns of data to be used, then click on the **Evaluate** button. The STATDISK display will include the value of the linear correlation coefficient r and other. A scatterplot can also be obtained by clicking on the **PLOT** button.

TI-83/84 Plus Enter the paired data in lists L1 and L2, then press **STAT** and select **TESTS**. Using the option of **LinRegTTest** will result in several displayed values, including the value of the linear correlation coefficient r.

   To obtain a scatterplot, press **2ND**, then **Y=** (for STAT PLOT). Press **ENTER ENTER** to turn Plot 1 on, then select the first graph type, which resembles a scatterplot. Set the X list and Y list labels to L1 and L2 and press **ZOOM**, then select **ZoomStat** and press **ENTER**.

In the above expression, division by $n - 1$ (where n is the number of pairs of data) shows that r is a type of average, so it does not increase simply because more pairs of data values are included. The symbol s_x denotes the standard deviation of the x values (or the values of the first variable), and s_y denotes the standard deviation of the y values. The expression $(x - \bar{x})/s_x$ is in the same format as the *standard score* introduced in Section 5.2. By using the standard scores for x and y, we ensure that the value of r does not change simply because a different scale of values is used. The key to understanding the rationale for r is to focus on the product of the standard scores for x and the standard scores for y. Those products tend to be positive when there is a positive correlation, and they tend to be negative when there is a negative correlation. For data with no correlation, some of the products are positive and some are negative, with the net effect that the sum is relatively close to 0.

The following alternative formula for r has the advantage of simplifying calculations, so it is often used whenever manual calculations are necessary. The following formula is also easy to program into statistical software or calculators:

$$r = \frac{n \times \Sigma(x \times y) - (\Sigma x) \times (\Sigma y)}{\sqrt{n \times (\Sigma x^2) - (\Sigma x)^2} \times \sqrt{n \times (\Sigma y^2) - (\Sigma y)^2}}$$

This formula is straightforward to use, at least in principle: First calculate each of the required sums, then substitute the values into the formula. Be sure to note that (Σx^2) and $(\Sigma x)^2$ are *not* equal: (Σx^2) tells you to first square all the values of the variable x and then add them; $(\Sigma x)^2$ tells you to add the x values first and then square this sum. In other words, perform the operation within the parentheses first. Similarly, (Σy^2) and $(\Sigma y)^2$ are not the same.

Section 7.3 Exercises

Statistical Literacy and Critical Thinking

1. **Correlation.** In the context of correlation, what does r measure, and what is it called?

2. **Scatterplot.** What is a scatterplot, and how does it help us investigate correlation?

3. **Correlation.** After computing the correlation coefficient r from 50 pairs of data, you find that $r = 0$. Does it follow that there is no relationship between the two variables? Why or why not?

4. **Scatterplot.** One set of paired data results in $r = 1$ and a second set of paired data results in $r = -1$. How do the corresponding scatterplots differ?

Does It Make Sense? For Exercises 5–8, decide whether the statement makes sense (or is clearly true) or does not make sense (or is clearly false). Explain clearly; not all of these statements have definitive answers, so your explanation is more important than your chosen answer.

5. **Births.** A study showed that for one town, as the stork population increased, the number of births in the town also increased. It therefore follows that the increase in the stork population caused the number of births to increase.

6. **Positive Effect.** An engineer for a car company finds that by reducing the weights of various cars, mileage (mi/gal) increases. Because this is a positive result, we say that there is a positive correlation.

7. **Correlation.** Two studies both found a correlation between low birth weight and weakened immune systems. The second study had a much larger sample size, so the correlation it found must be stronger.

8. **Interpreting r.** In investigating correlations between many different pairs of variables, in each case the correlation coefficient r must fall between -1 and 1.

Concepts and Applications

Types of Correlation. Exercises 9–16, list pairs of variables. For each pair, state whether you believe the two variables are correlated. If you believe they are correlated, state whether the correlation is positive or negative. Explain your reasoning.

9. **Weight/Cost.** The weights and costs of 50 different bags of apples

10. **IQ/Hat Size.** The IQ scores and hat sizes of randomly selected adults

11. **Weight/Fuel Efficiency.** The total weights of airliners flying from New York to San Francisco and the fuel efficiency as measured in miles per gallon

12. **Weight/Fuel Consumption.** The total weights of airliners flying from New York to San Francisco and the total amounts of fuel that they consume

13. **Points and DJIA.** The total number of points scored in Super Bowl football games and the changes in the Dow Jones Industrial stock index in the years following those games

14. **Altitude/Temperature.** The outside air temperature and the altitude of aircraft

15. **Height/SAT Score.** The heights and SAT scores of randomly selected subjects who take the SAT

16. **Golf Score/Prize Money.** Golf scores and prize money won by professional golfers

17. **Crickets and Temperature.** One classic application of correlation involves the association between the temperature and the number of times a cricket chirps in a minute. The scatterplot in Figure 7.7 shows the relationship for eight different pairs of temperature/chirps data. Estimate the correlation coefficient and determine whether there appears to be a correlation between the temperature and the number of times a cricket chirps in a minute.

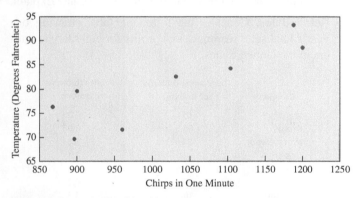

Figure 7.7 Scatterplot for cricket chirps and temperature.
Source: Based on data from *The Song of Insects* by George W. Pierce, Harvard University Press.

18. **Two-Day Forecast.** Figure 7.8 shows a scatterplot in which the actual high temperature for the day is compared with a forecast made two days in advance. Estimate the correlation coefficient and discuss what these data imply about weather forecasts. Do you think you would get similar results if you made similar diagrams for other two-week periods? Why or why not?

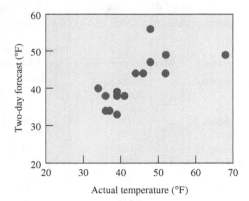

Figure 7.8

19. **Safe Speeds?** Consider the following table showing speed limits and death rates from automobile accidents in selected countries.

Country	Death rate (per 100 million vehicle-miles)	Speed limit (miles per hour)
Norway	3.0	55
United States	3.3	55
Finland	3.4	55
Britain	3.5	70
Denmark	4.1	55
Canada	4.3	60
Japan	4.7	55
Australia	4.9	65
Netherlands	5.1	60
Italy	6.1	75

Source: D. J. Rivkin, *New York Times.*

a. Construct a scatterplot of the data.

b. Briefly characterize the correlation in words (for example, strong positive correlation, weak negative correlation) and estimate the correlation coefficient of the data. (Or calculate the correlation coefficient exactly with the aid of a calculator or software.)

c. In the newspaper, these data were presented in an article titled "Fifty-five mph speed limit is no safety guarantee." Based on the data, do you agree with this claim? Explain.

20. **Population Growth.** Consider the following table showing percentage change in population and birth rate (per 1,000 of population) for 10 states over a period of 10 years.

State	Percentage change in population	Birth rate
Nevada	50.1%	16.3
California	25.7%	16.9
New Hampshire	20.5%	12.5
Utah	17.9%	21.0
Colorado	14.0%	14.6
Minnesota	7.3%	13.7
Montana	1.6%	12.3
Illinois	0%	15.5
Iowa	−4.7%	13.0
West Virginia	−8.0%	11.4

Source: U.S. Census Bureau and Department of Health and Human Services.

a. Construct a scatterplot for the data.

b. Briefly characterize the correlation in words and estimate the correlation coefficient.

c. Overall, does birth rate appear to be a good predictor of a state's population growth rate? If not, what other factor(s) may be affecting the growth rate?

21. **Brain Size and Intelligence.** The table below lists brain sizes (in cm^3) and Wechsler IQ scores of subjects (based on data from "Brain Size, Head Size, and Intelligence Quotient in Monozygatic Twins," by Tramo et al, *Neurology*, Vol. 50, No. 5). Is there sufficient evidence to conclude that there is

a linear correlation between brain size and IQ score? Does it appear that people with larger brains are more intelligent?

Brain Size	IQ	Brain Size	IQ
965	90	1,077	97
1,029	85	1,037	124
1,030	86	1,068	125
1,285	102	1,176	102
1,049	103	1,105	114

a. Construct a scatterplot for the data.

b. Briefly characterize the correlation in words and estimate the correlation coefficient.

c. Do these data suggest that people with larger brains are more intelligent? Explain.

22. Movie Data. Consider the following table showing total box office receipts and total attendance for all American films.

Year	Total Gross Receipts (billions of dollars)	Tickets Sold (billions)
2001	8.4	1.49
2002	9.2	1.58
2003	9.2	1.53
2004	9.4	1.51
2005	8.8	1.38
2006	9.2	1.41
2007	9.7	1.40
2008	9.6	1.34
2009	10.6	1.41
2010	10.6	1.34

Source: Motion Picture Association of America.

a. Construct a scatterplot of the data.

b. Briefly characterize the correlation in words and estimate the correlation coefficient.

23. TV Time. Consider the following table showing the average hours of television watched in households in five categories of annual income.

Household income	Weekly TV hours
Less than $30,000	56.3
$30,000–$40,000	51.0
$40,000–$50,000	50.5
$50,000–$60,000	49.7
More than $60,000	48.7

Source: Nielsen Media Research.

a. Construct a scatterplot for the data. To locate the dots, use the midpoint of each income category. Use a value of $25,000 for the category "less than $30,000," and use $70,000 for "more than $60,000."

b. Briefly characterize the correlation in words and estimate the correlation coefficient.

c. Suggest a reason why families with higher incomes watch less TV. Do you think these data imply that you can increase your income simply by watching less TV? Explain.

24. January Weather. Consider the following table showing January mean monthly precipitation and mean daily high temperature for ten Northern Hemisphere cities (National Oceanic and Atmospheric Administration).

City	Mean daily high temperature for January (°F)	Mean January precipitation (inches)
Athens	54	2.2
Bombay	88	0.1
Copenhagen	36	1.6
Jerusalem	55	5.1
London	44	2.0
Montreal	21	3.8
Oslo	30	1.7
Rome	54	3.3
Tokyo	47	1.9
Vienna	34	1.5

Source: The New York Times Almanac.

a. Construct a scatterplot for the data.

b. Briefly characterize the correlation in words and estimate the correlation coefficient.

c. Can you draw any general conclusions about January temperatures and precipitation from these data? Explain.

25. Retail Sales. Consider the following table showing one year's total sales (revenue) and profits for eight large retailers in the United States.

Company	Total sales (billions of dollars)	Profits (billions of dollars)
Wal-Mart	315.6	11.2
Kroger	60.6	0.98
Home Depot	81.5	5.8
Costco	60.1	1.1
Target	52.6	2.4
Starbuck's	7.8	0.6
The Gap	16.0	1.1
Best Buy	30.8	1.1

Source: Fortune.com.

a. Construct a scatterplot for the data.

b. Briefly characterize the correlation in words and estimate the correlation coefficient.

c. Discuss your observations. Does higher sales volume necessarily translate into greater earnings? Why or why not?

26. Calories and Infant Mortality. Consider the following table showing mean daily caloric intake (all residents) and infant mortality rate (per 1,000 births) for 10 countries.

Country	Mean daily calories	Infant mortality rate (per 1,000 births)
Afghanistan	1,523	154
Austria	3,495	6
Burundi	1,941	114
Colombia	2,678	24
Ethiopia	1,610	107
Germany	3,443	6
Liberia	1,640	153
New Zealand	3,362	7
Turkey	3,429	44
United States	3,671	7

a. Construct a scatterplot for the data.

b. Briefly characterize the correlation in words and estimate the correlation coefficient.

c. Discuss any patterns you observe and any general conclusions that you can reach.

Properties of the Correlation Coefficient. For Exercises 27 and 28, determine whether the given property is true, and explain your answer.

27. Interchanging Variables. The correlation coefficient remains unchanged if we interchange the variables x and y.

28. Changing Units of Measurement. The correlation coefficient remains unchanged if we change the units used to measure x, y, or both.

PROJECTS FOR  THE INTERNET & BEYOND

29. Unemployment and Inflation. Use the Bureau of Labor Statistics Web page to find monthly unemployment rates and inflation rates over the past year. Construct a scatterplot for the data. Do you see any trends?

30. Success in the NFL. Find last season's NFL team statistics. Construct a table showing the following for each team: number of wins, average yards gained on offense per game, and average yards allowed on defense per game. Make scatterplots to explore the correlations between offense and wins and between defense and wins. Discuss your findings. Do you think that there are other team statistics that would yield stronger correlations with the number of wins?

31. Statistical Abstract. Explore the "frequently requested tables" at the Web site for the *Statistical Abstract of the United States*. Choose data that are of interest to you and explore at least two correlations. Briefly discuss what you learn from the correlations.

32. Height and Arm Span. Select a sample of at least eight people and measure each person's height and arm span. (When you measure arm span, the person should stand with arms extended like the wings on an airplane.) Using the paired sample data, construct a scatterplot and estimate or calculate the value of the correlation coefficient. What do you conclude?

33. Height and Pulse Rate. Select a sample of at least eight people and record each person's pulse rate by counting the number of heartbeats in 1 minute. Also record each person's height. Using the paired sample data, construct a scatterplot and estimate or calculate the value of the correlation coefficient. What do you conclude?

IN THE NEWS

34. Correlations in the News. Find a recent news report that discusses some type of correlation. Describe the correlation. Does the article give any sense of the strength of the correlation? Does it suggest that the correlation reflects any underlying causality? Briefly discuss whether you believe the implications the article makes with respect to the correlation.

35. Your Own Positive Correlations. Give examples of two variables that you expect to be positively correlated. Explain why the variables are correlated and why the correlation is (or is not) important.

36. Your Own Negative Correlations. Give examples of two variables that you expect to be negatively correlated. Explain why the variables are correlated and why the correlation is (or is not) important.

7.4 INTERPRETING CORRELATIONS

Researchers sifting through statistical data are constantly looking for meaningful correlations, and the discovery of a new and surprising correlation often leads to a flood of news reports. You may recall hearing about some of these discovered correlations: dark chocolate consumption correlated with reduced risk of heart disease; musical talent correlated with good grades in mathematics; or eating less correlated with increased longevity. Unfortunately, the task of *interpreting* such correlations is far more difficult than discovering them in the first place. Long after the news reports have faded, we may still be unsure of whether the correlations are significant and, if so, whether they tell us anything of practical importance. In this section, we discuss some of the common difficulties associated with interpreting correlations.

Statistics show that of those who contract the habit of eating, very few survive.

—Wallace Irwin

Beware of Outliers

Examine the scatterplot in Figure 7.9. Your eye probably tells you that there is a positive correlation in which larger values of x tend to mean larger values of y. Indeed, if you calculate the correlation coefficient for these data, you'll find that it is a relatively high $r = 0.880$, suggesting a very strong correlation.

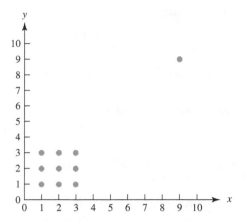

Figure 7.9 How does the outlier affect the correlation?

However, if you place your thumb over the data point in the upper right corner of Figure 7.9, the apparent correlation disappears. In fact, without this data point, the correlation coefficient is zero! In other words, removing this one data point changes the correlation coefficient from $r = 0.880$ to $r = 0$.

This example shows that correlations can be very sensitive to outliers. Recall that an *outlier* is a data value that is extreme compared to most other values in a data set (see Section 4.2). We must therefore examine outliers and their effects carefully before interpreting a correlation. On the one hand, if the outliers are mistakes in the data set, they can produce apparent correlations that are not real or mask the presence of real correlations. On the other hand, if the outliers represent real and correct data points, they may be telling us about relationships that would otherwise be difficult to see.

Note that while we should examine outliers carefully, we should *not* remove them unless we have strong reason to believe that they do not belong in the data set. Even in that case, good research principles demand that we report the outliers along with an explanation of why we thought it legitimate to remove them.

EXAMPLE ① Masked Correlation

You've conducted a study to determine how the number of calories a person consumes in a day correlates with time spent in vigorous bicycling. Your sample consisted of ten women cyclists, all of approximately the same height and weight. Over a period of two weeks, you asked each woman to record the amount of time she spent cycling each day and what she ate on each of those days. You used the eating records to calculate the calories consumed each day. Figure 7.10 shows a scatterplot with each woman's mean time spent cycling on the horizontal axis and mean caloric intake on the vertical axis. Do higher cycling times correspond to higher intake of calories?

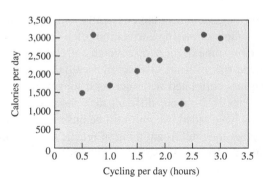

Figure 7.10 Data from the cycling study.

SOLUTION If you look at the data as a whole, your eye will probably tell you that there is a positive correlation in which greater cycling time tends to go with higher caloric intake. But the correlation is very weak, with a correlation coefficient of $r = 0.374$. However, notice that two points are outliers: one representing a cyclist who cycled about a half-hour per day and consumed more than 3,000 calories, and the other representing a cyclist who cycled more than 2 hours per day on only 1,200 calories. It's difficult to explain the two outliers, given that all the women in the sample have similar heights and weights. We might therefore suspect that these two women either recorded their data incorrectly or were not following their usual habits during the two-week study. If we can confirm this suspicion, then we would have reason to delete the two data points as invalid. Figure 7.11 shows that the correlation is quite strong without those two outlier points, and suggests that the number of calories consumed rises by a little more than 500 calories for each hour of cycling. Of course, we should *not* remove the outliers without confirming our suspicion that they were invalid data points, and we should report our reasons for leaving them out.

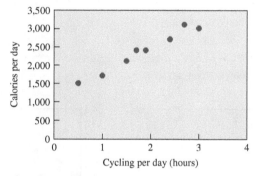

Figure 7.11   The data from Figure 7.10 without the two outliers.

Beware of Inappropriate Grouping

Correlations can also be misinterpreted when data are grouped inappropriately. In some cases, grouping data hides correlations. Consider a (hypothetical) study in which researchers seek a correlation between hours of TV watched per week and high school grade point average (GPA). They collect the 21 data pairs in Table 7.2.

The scatterplot (Figure 7.12) shows virtually no correlation; the correlation coefficient for the data is about $r = -0.063$. The lack of correlation seems to suggest that TV viewing habits are unrelated to academic achievement. However, one astute researcher realizes that some of the students watched mostly educational programs, while others tended to watch comedies, dramas, and movies. She therefore divides the data set into two groups, one for the students who watched mostly educational television and one for the other students. Table 7.3 shows her results with the students divided into these two groups.

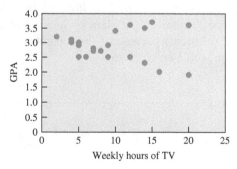

Figure 7.12   The full set of data concerning hours of TV and GPA shows virtually no correlation.

Now we find two very strong correlations (Figure 7.13): a strong positive correlation for the students who watched educational programs ($r = 0.855$) and a strong negative correlation for the other students ($r = -0.951$). The moral of this story is that the original data set hid an important (hypothetical) correlation between TV and GPA: Watching educational TV correlated positively with GPA and watching non-educational TV correlated negatively with GPA. Only when the data were grouped appropriately could this discovery be made.

TABLE 7.2	Hours of TV and High School GPA (hypothetical data)
Hours per week of TV	**GPA**
2	3.2
4	3.0
4	3.1
5	2.5
5	2.9
5	3.0
6	2.5
7	2.7
7	2.8
8	2.7
9	2.5
9	2.9
10	3.4
12	3.6
12	2.5
14	3.5
14	2.3
15	3.7
16	2.0
20	3.6
20	1.9

TABLE 7.3   Hours of TV and High School GPA—Grouped Data (hypothetical data)

Group 1: watched educational programs		Group 2: watched regular TV	
Hours per week of TV	GPA	Hours per week of TV	GPA
5	2.5	2	3.2
7	2.8	4	3.0
8	2.7	4	3.1
9	2.9	5	2.9
10	3.4	5	3.0
12	3.6	6	2.5
14	3.5	7	2.7
15	3.7	9	2.5
20	3.6	12	2.5
		14	2.3
		16	2.0
		20	1.9

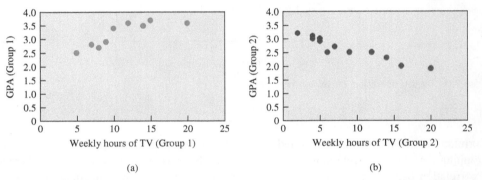

Figure 7.13 These scatterplots show the same data as Figure 7.12, separated into the two groups identified in Table 7.3.

In other cases, a data set may show a stronger correlation than actually exists among subgroups. Consider the (hypothetical) data in Table 7.4, showing the relationship between the weights and prices of selected cars. Figure 7.14 shows the scatterplot.

The data set as a whole shows a strong correlation; the correlation coefficient is $r = 0.949$. However, on closer examination, we see that the data fall into two rather distinct categories corresponding to light and heavy cars. If we analyze these subgroups separately, neither shows any correlation: The light cars alone (top six in Table 7.4) have a correlation coefficient $r = 0.019$ and the heavy cars alone (bottom six in Table 7.4) have a correlation coefficient $r = -0.022$. You can see the problem by looking at Figure 7.14. The apparent correlation of the full data set occurs because of the separation between the two clusters of points; there's no correlation within either cluster.

TABLE 7.4   Car Weights and Prices (hypothetical data)

Weight (pounds)	Price (dollars)
1,500	9,500
1,600	8,000
1,700	8,200
1,750	9,500
1,800	9,200
1,800	8,700
3,000	29,000
3,500	25,000
3,700	27,000
4,000	31,000
3,600	25,000
3,200	30,000

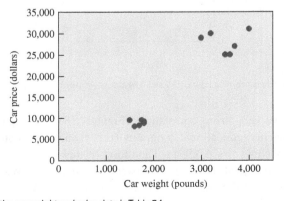

Figure 7.14 Scatterplot for the car weight and price data in Table 7.4.

TIME ⏱ UT TO THINK

Suppose you were shopping for a compact car. If you looked at only the overall data and correlation coefficient from Figure 7.14, would it be reasonable to consider weight as an important factor in price? What if you looked at the data for light and heavy cars separately? Explain.

CASE STUDY **Fishing for Correlations**

Oxford physician Richard Peto submitted a paper to the British medical journal *Lancet* showing that heart-attack victims had a better chance of survival if they were given aspirin within a few hours after their heart attacks. The editors of *Lancet* asked Peto to break down the data into subsets, to see whether the benefits of the aspirin were different for different groups of patients. For example, was aspirin more effective for patients of a certain age or for patients with certain dietary habits?

Breaking the data into subsets can reveal important facts, such as whether men and women respond to the treatment differently. However, Peto felt that the editors were asking him to divide his sample into too many subgroups. He therefore objected to the request, arguing that it would result in purely coincidental correlations. Writing about this story in the *Washington Post*, journalist Rick Weiss said, "When the editors insisted, Peto capitulated, but among other things he divided his patients by zodiac birth signs and demanded that his findings be included in the published paper. Today, like a warning sign to the statistically uninitiated, the wacky numbers are there for all to see: Aspirin is useless for Gemini and Libra heart-attack victims but is a lifesaver for people born under any other sign."

The moral of this story is that a "fishing expedition" for correlations can often produce them. That doesn't make the correlations meaningful, even though they may appear significant by standard statistical measures.

Correlation Does *Not* Imply Causality

Perhaps the most important caution about interpreting correlations is one we've already mentioned: ***Correlation does not necessarily imply causality.*** In general, correlations can appear for any of the following three reasons.

Possible Explanations for a Correlation

1. The correlation may be a *coincidence*.

2. Both correlation variables might be directly influenced by some *common underlying cause*.

3. One of the correlated variables may actually be a *cause* of the other. But note that, even in this case, it may be just one of several causes.

For example, the correlation between infant mortality and life expectancy in Figure 7.4 is a case of common underlying cause: Both variables respond to the underlying variable *quality of health care*. The correlation between smoking and lung cancer reflects the fact that smoking causes lung cancer. Coincidental correlations are also quite common; Example 2 below discusses one such case.

Caution about causality is particularly important in light of the fact that many statistical studies are designed to look for causes. Because these studies generally begin with the search for correlations, it's tempting to think that the work is over as soon as a correlation is found.

EXAMPLE ② How to Get Rich in the Stock Market (Maybe)

Every financial advisor has a strategy for predicting the direction of the stock market. Most focus on fundamental economic data, such as interest rates and corporate profits. But an alternative strategy might rely on a famous correlation between the Super Bowl winner in January and the direction of the stock market for the rest of the year: The stock market tends to rise when a team from the old, pre-1970 NFL wins the Super Bowl and tends to fall when the winner is not from the old NFL. This correlation successfully matched 28 of the first 32 Super Bowls to the stock market, which made the "Super Bowl Indicator" a far more reliable predictor of the stock market than any professional stock broker during the same period. In fact, detailed calculations show that the probability of such success by pure chance is less than 1 in 100,000. Should you therefore make a decision about whether to invest in the stock market based on the NFL origins of the most recent Super Bowl winner?

SOLUTION   The extremely strong correlation might make it seem like a good idea to base your investments on the Super Bowl Indicator, but sometimes you need to apply a bit of common sense. No matter how strong the correlation might be, it seems inconceivable to imagine that the origin of the winning team actually *causes* the stock market to move in a particular direction. The correlation is undoubtedly a coincidence, and the fact that its probability of occurring by pure chance was less than 1 in 100,000 is just another illustration of the fact that you can turn up surprising correlations if you go fishing for them. This fact was borne out in more recent Super Bowls: Following Super Bowl 32, the indicator successfully predicted the stock market direction in only 5 of the next 10 years—exactly the fraction that would be expected by pure chance.   ··●

⟨ASE STUDY Oat Bran and Heart Disease

If you buy a product that contains oat bran, there's a good chance that the label will tout the healthful effects of eating oats. Indeed, several studies have found correlations in which people who eat more oat bran tend to have lower rates of heart disease. But does this mean that everyone should eat more oats?

Not necessarily. Just because oat bran consumption is correlated with reduced risk of heart disease does not mean that it *causes* reduced risk of heart disease. In fact, the question of causality is quite controversial in this case. Other studies suggest that people who eat a lot of oat bran tend to have generally healthful diets. Thus, the correlation between oat bran consumption and reduced risk of heart disease may be a case of a common underlying cause: Having a healthy diet leads people both to consume more oat bran and to have a lower risk of heart disease. In that case, for some people, adding oat bran to their diets might be a *bad* idea because it could cause them to gain weight, and weight gain is associated with *increased* risk of heart disease.

This example shows the importance of using caution when considering issues of correlation and causality. It may be a long time before medical researchers know for sure whether adding oat bran to your diet actually causes a reduced risk of heart disease.

Useful Interpretations of Correlation

In discussing uses of correlation that might lead to wrong interpretations, we have described the effects of outliers, inappropriate groupings, fishing for correlations, and incorrectly concluding that correlation implies causality. But there are many correct and useful interpretations of correlation, some of which we have already studied. So while you should be cautious in interpreting correlations, they remain a valuable tool in any field in which statistical research plays a role.

Section 7.4 Exercises

Statistical Literacy and Critical Thinking

1. **Correlation and Causality.** In clinical trials of the drug Lisinopril, it is found that increased dosages of the drug correlated with lower blood pressure levels. Based on the correlation, can we conclude that Lisinopril treatments cause lower blood pressure? Why or why not?

2. **SIDS.** An article in the *New York Times* on infant deaths included a statement that, based on the study results, putting infants to sleep in the supine position decreased deaths due to SIDS (sudden infant death syndrome). What is wrong with that statement?

3. **Outliers.** When studying salaries paid to CEOs of large companies, it is found that almost all of them range from a few hundred thousand dollars to several million dollars, but one CEO is paid a salary of $1. Is that salary of $1 an outlier? In general, how might outliers affect conclusions about correlation?

4. **Scatterplot.** Does a scatterplot reveal anything about a cause and effect relationship between two variables?

Does It Make Sense? For Exercises 5–8, decide whether the statement makes sense (or is clearly true) or does not make sense (or is clearly false). Explain clearly; not all of these statements have definitive answers, so your explanation is more important than your chosen answer.

5. **Scatterplot.** A set of paired sample data results in a correlation coefficient of $r = 0$, so the scatterplot will show that there is no pattern of the plotted points.

6. **Causation.** If we have 20 pairs of sample data with a correlation coefficient of 1, then we know that one of the two variables is definitely the cause of the other.

7. **Causation.** If we conduct a study showing that there is a strong negative correlation between resting pulse rate and amounts of time spent in rigorous exercise, we can conclude decreases in resting pulse rates are somehow associated with increases in exercise.

8. **Causation.** If we have two variables with one being the direct cause of the other, then there may or may not be a correlation between those two variables.

Concepts and Applications

Correlation and Causality. Exercises 9–16 make statements about a correlation. In each case, state the correlation clearly. (For example, we might state that "there is a positive correlation between variable A and variable B.") Then state whether the correlation is most likely due to coincidence, a common underlying cause, or a direct cause. Explain your answer.

9. **Guns and Crime Rate.** In one state, the number of unregistered handguns steadily increased over the past several years, and the crime rate increased as well.

10. **Running and Weight.** It has been found that people who exercise regularly by running tend to weigh less than those who do not run, and those who run longer distances tend to weigh less than those who run shorter distances.

11. **Study Time.** Statistics students find that as they spend more time studying, their test scores are higher.

12. **Vehicles and Waiting Time.** It has been found that as the number of registered vehicles increases, the time drivers spend sitting in traffic also increases.

13. **Traffic Lights and Car Crashes.** It has been found that as the number of traffic lights increases, the number of car crashes also increases.

14. **Galaxies.** Astronomers have discovered that, with the exception of a few nearby galaxies, all galaxies in the universe are moving away from us. Moreover, the farther the galaxy, the faster it is moving away. That is, the more distant a galaxy, the greater the speed at which it is moving away from us.

15. **Gas and Driving.** It has been found that as gas prices increase, the distances vehicles are driven tend to get shorter.

16. **Melanoma and Latitude.** Some studies have shown that, for certain ethnic groups, the incidence of melanoma (the most dangerous form of skin cancer) increases as latitude decreases.

17. **Outlier Effects.** Consider the scatterplot in Figure 7.15.

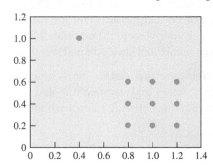

Figure 7.15

   a. Which point is an outlier? Ignoring the outlier, estimate or compute the correlation coefficient for the remaining points.

   b. Now include the outlier. How does the outlier affect the correlation coefficient? Estimate or compute the correlation coefficient for the complete data set.

18. Outlier Effects. Consider the scatterplot in Figure 7.16.

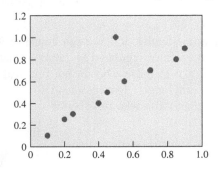

Figure 7.16

a. Which point is an outlier? Ignoring the outlier, estimate or compute the correlation coefficient for the remaining points.

b. Now include the outlier. How does the outlier affect the correlation coefficient? Estimate or compute the correlation coefficient for the complete data set.

19. Grouped Shoe Data. The following table gives measurements of weight and shoe size for 10 people (including both men and women).

a. Construct a scatterplot for the data. Estimate or compute the correlation coefficient. Based on this correlation coefficient, would you conclude that shoe size and weight are correlated? Explain.

Weight (pounds)	Shoe size
105	6
112	4.5
115	6
123	5
135	6
155	10
165	11
170	9
180	10
190	12

b. You later learn that the first five data values in the table are for women and the next five are for men. How does this change your view of the correlation? Is it still reasonable to conclude that shoe size and weight are correlated?

20. Grouped Temperature Data. The following table shows the average January high temperature and the average July high temperature for 10 major cities around the world.

City	January high	July high
Berlin	35	74
Geneva	39	77
Kabul	36	92
Montreal	21	78
Prague	34	74
Auckland	73	56
Buenos Aires	85	57
Sydney	78	60
Santiago	85	59
Melbourne	78	56

a. Construct a scatterplot for the data. Estimate or compute the correlation coefficient. Based on this correlation coefficient, would you conclude that January and July temperatures are correlated for these cities? Explain.

b. Notice that the first five cities in the table are in the Northern Hemisphere and the next five are in the Southern Hemisphere. How does this change your view of the correlation? Would you now conclude that January and July temperatures are correlated for these cities? Explain.

21. Birth and Death Rates. Figure 7.17 shows the birth and death rates for different countries, measured in births and deaths per 1,000 population.

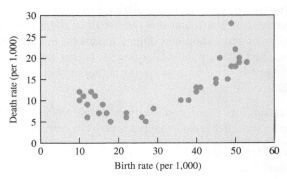

Figure 7.17 Birth and death rates for different countries.
Source: United Nations.

a. Estimate the correlation coefficient and discuss whether there is a strong correlation between the variables.

b. Notice that there appear to be two groups of data points within the full data set. Make a reasonable guess as to the makeup of these groups. In which group might you find a relatively wealthy country like Sweden? In which group might you find a relatively poor country like Uganda?

c. Assuming that your guess about groups in part b is correct, do there appear to be correlations within the groups? Explain. How could you confirm your guess about the groups?

22. Reading and Test Scores. The following (hypothetical) data set gives the number of hours 10 sixth-graders read per week and their performance on a standardized verbal test (maximum of 100).

Reading time per week	Verbal test score
1	50
1	65
2	56
3	62
3	65
4	60
5	75
6	50
10	88
12	38

a. Construct a scatterplot for these data. Estimate or compute the correlation coefficient. Based on this correlation coefficient, would you conclude that reading time and test scores are correlated? Explain.

b. Suppose you learn that five of the children read only comic books while the other five read regular books. Make a guess as to which data points fall in which group. How could you confirm your guess about the groups?

c. Assuming that your guess in part b is correct, how does it change your view of the correlation between reading time and test scores? Explain.

PROJECTS FOR THE INTERNET & BEYOND

23. Football-Stock Update. Find data for recent years concerning the Super Bowl winner and the end-of-year change in the stock market (positive or negative). Do recent results still agree with the correlation described in Example 2? Explain.

24. Real Correlations.

a. Describe a real situation in which there is a positive correlation that is the result of coincidence.

b. Describe a real situation in which there is a positive correlation that is the result of a common underlying cause.

c. Describe a real situation in which there is a positive correlation that is the result of a direct cause.

d. Describe a real situation in which there is a negative correlation that is the result of coincidence.

e. Describe a real situation in which there is a negative correlation that is the result of a common underlying cause.

f. Describe a real situation in which there is a negative correlation that is the result of a direct cause.

IN THE NEWS

25. Misinterpreted Correlations. Find a recent news report in which you believe that a correlation may have been misinterpreted. Describe the correlation, the reported interpretation, and the problems you see in the interpretation.

26. Well-Interpreted Correlations. Find a recent news report in which you believe that a correlation has been presented with a reasonable interpretation. Describe the correlation and the reported interpretation, and explain why you think the interpretation is valid.

Modeling

8.1   SOLVING EQUATIONS

To solve an equation means to find the number or constant that, when substituted for the variable, makes the equation a true statement. This solution is found by changing the equation to an equivalent equation of the following form:

$$x = \boxed{}$$

    ↑   ↑

The variable is isolated   The number or constant is
(alone on one side   isolated on the other side.
with coefficient 1).

Using the Addition Property to Solve Linear Equations

One of the properties that we use in solving equations involves adding. Consider the equation $\frac{6}{3} = 2$. Adding 4 to each side of the equation gives us $\frac{6}{3} + 4 = 2 + 4$. Using mental arithmetic, we see that $\frac{6}{3} + 4 = 2 + 4$ is also a true statement. In general, adding the same number to each side of a true equation results in another true equation. So adding -3 to both sides of the equation $x + 3 = 7$ gives us the equivalent equation $x + 3 + (-3) = 7 + (-3)$, or $x = 4$. This example suggests the following property.

> **Addition Property of Equality**
>
> For any real numbers a, b, and c, $a = b$ and $a + c = b + c$ are equivalent.

This property states that when adding any real number to each side of an equation, the result is an equivalent equation. Now, let's apply this property to solving equations.

EXAMPLE 1

Solve and check: $x - 5 = -11$

SOLUTION   To solve this equation, we isolate the variable by adding 5, which is the additive inverse of -5, to each side of the equation.

$$x - 5 = -11$$
$$x - 5 + 5 = -11 + 5 \qquad \text{Add 5 to each side of the equation, getting an equivalent equation.}$$
$$x + 0 = -6$$
$$x = -6 \qquad \text{Recall that } x + 0 = x.$$

CHECK $x - 5 = -11$
$$-6 - 5 \stackrel{?}{=} -11 \qquad \text{Substitute } -6 \text{ for } x \text{ in the original equation.}$$
$$-11 = -11 \qquad \text{True}$$

So the solution is -6.   · · ●

Can you explain why checking a solution is important?

> **PRACTICE 1**
>
> Solve and check: $y - 12 = -7$

EXAMPLE 2

Solve and check: $-9 = a + 6$

SOLUTION

$$-9 = a + 6$$
$$-9 + (-6) = a + 6 + (-6) \qquad \text{Add } -6 \text{ to each side of the equation.}$$
$$-15 = a + 0$$
$$-15 = a$$
$$\text{or} \qquad a = -15$$

CHECK $-9 = a + 6$
$$-9 \overset{?}{=} (-15) + 6 \qquad \text{Substitute } -15 \text{ for } a.$$
$$-9 = -9 \qquad \text{True}$$

So the solution is -15.

PRACTICE 2

Solve and check: $-2 = n + 15$

Are the solutions to the equations $-9 = a + 6$ and $a + 6 = -9$ the same? Explain.

Because subtracting a number is the same as adding its opposite, the addition property allows us to subtract the same value from each side of an equation. For instance, suppose $a = b$. Subtracting c from each side gives us $a - c = b - c$. So an alternative approach to solving Example 2 is to subtract the same number, namely 6, from each side of the equation, as follows:

$$-9 = a + 6$$
$$-9 - 6 = a + 6 - 6$$
$$-15 = a, \text{ or } a = -15$$

Note that this approach gives us the same solution, namely -15, that we got using the approach in Example 2.

EXAMPLE 3

Solve and check: $r + \dfrac{1}{5} = -\dfrac{3}{5}$

SOLUTION

$$r + \frac{1}{5} = -\frac{3}{5}$$
$$r + \frac{1}{5} - \frac{1}{5} = -\frac{3}{5} - \frac{1}{5} \qquad \text{Subtract } \frac{1}{5} \text{ from each side of the equation.}$$
$$r + 0 = -\frac{4}{5}$$
$$r = -\frac{4}{5}$$

CHECK $r + \dfrac{1}{5} = -\dfrac{3}{5}$

$$-\frac{4}{5} + \frac{1}{5} \overset{?}{=} -\frac{3}{5} \qquad \text{Substitute } -\frac{4}{5} \text{ for } r.$$
$$-\frac{3}{5} = -\frac{3}{5} \qquad \text{True}$$

PRACTICE 3

Solve and check: $-\dfrac{3}{8} = s + \dfrac{1}{8}$

PRACTICE 4

Solve and check:
$5 = 4.9 - (-x)$

EXAMPLE 4

Solve and check: $m - (-26.1) = 32$

SOLUTION

$$m - (-26.1) = 32$$
$$m + 26.1 = 32$$
$$m + 26.1 - 26.1 = 32 - 26.1 \qquad \text{Subtract 26.1 from each side of the equation.}$$
$$m = 5.9$$

CHECK
$$m - (-26.1) = 32$$
$$5.9 - (-26.1) \overset{?}{=} 32 \qquad \text{Substitute 5.9 for } m.$$
$$5.9 + 26.1 \overset{?}{=} 32$$
$$32 = 32 \qquad \text{True}$$

So the solution is 5.9.

Equations are often useful *mathematical models* that represent real-world situations. Although there is no magic formula for solving applied problems in algebra, it is a good idea to keep the following problem-solving steps in mind.

> **To Solve an Applied Problem Using an Equation**
> • Read the problem carefully.
> • Translate the problem to an equation.
> • Solve the equation.
> • Check the solution in the original equation.
> • State the conclusion.

We have discussed how to translate word phrases to algebraic expressions. Now, let's look at some examples of translating word sentences to equations, namely those involving addition or subtraction.

Word sentence: A number increased by 1.1 equals 8.6.

Equation: $n \quad + \quad 1.1 \quad = \quad 8.6$

Word sentence: A number minus one-half equals five.

Equation: $y \quad - \quad \dfrac{1}{2} \quad = \quad 5$

Note that in both examples we used a variable to represent the unknown number.

In solving applied problems, first we translate the given word sentences to equations, and then we solve the equations.

EXAMPLE 5

The mean distance between the planet Venus and the Sun is 31.2 million mi more than the mean distance between the planet Mercury and the Sun. (*Source: The New York Times Almanac 2010*)

a. Using the following diagram, write an equation to find Mercury's mean distance from the Sun.

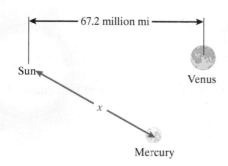

PRACTICE 5

As a result of a chemical reaction, the temperature of a substance rose. The original temperature had been 23.7°C, and the final temperature was 36.0°C. Find the change in temperature.

b. Solve this equation.

SOLUTION

a. Let x represent Mercury's mean (or average) distance from the Sun. From the diagram, we see that the mean distance between Venus and the Sun is 67.2 million mi. This distance is 31.2 million mi more than Mercury's mean distance to the Sun. So we translate this sentence to an equation:

$$\text{Word sentence:} \quad 67.2 \quad \text{is} \quad 31.2 \quad \text{plus} \quad x$$

$$\text{Equation:} \quad 67.2 \quad = \quad 31.2 \quad + \quad x$$

b. Solve the equation:

$$67.2 = x + 31.2$$
$$67.2 - 31.2 = x + 31.2 - 31.2 \quad \text{Subtract 31.2 from each side of the equation.}$$
$$36.0 = x$$

CHECK
$$67.2 = x + 31.2$$
$$67.2 = 36.0 + 31.2 \quad \text{Substitute 36.0 for } x.$$
$$67.2 = 67.2 \quad \text{True}$$

So we conclude that Mercury's mean distance from the Sun is 36.0 million mi. $\cdot \cdot \bullet$

Solving Linear Equations: The Multiplication Property

In the previous section, we used the addition property of equality to solve equations. Another property that is useful in solving equations involves multiplication. Consider the equation $\frac{6}{3} = 2$. If we were to multiply each side of this equation by 9, we would get $\frac{6}{3} \cdot 9 = 2 \cdot 9$. Note that each side of the equation equals 18. In general, multiplying each side of a true equation by the same number results in another true equation. So multiplying both sides of the equation $\frac{x}{2} = 5$ by 2 gives us the equivalent equation $2 \cdot \frac{x}{2} = 2 \cdot 5$, or $x = 10$. This example suggests the following property:

> **Multiplication Property of Equality**
> For any real numbers a, b, and c, $c \neq 0$, $a = b$ and $a \cdot c = b \cdot c$ are equivalent.

This property states that when multiplying each side of an equation by any nonzero real number, the result is an equivalent equation. Let's apply the multiplication property to solving equations.

PRACTICE 6

Solve and check: $\dfrac{y}{3} = 21$

EXAMPLE 6

Solve and check: $\dfrac{x}{4} = 11$

SOLUTION   In this equation, note that $\dfrac{x}{4}$ is the same as $\dfrac{1}{4} \cdot x$. To solve this equation, we isolate the variable by multiplying each side of the equation by 4, the reciprocal of $\dfrac{1}{4}$.

$$\frac{x}{4} = 11$$

$$4 \cdot \frac{x}{4} = 4 \cdot 11 \qquad \text{Mutiply each side of the equation by 4,}$$
$$\text{getting an equivalent equation.}$$

$$1x = 44 \qquad 4 \cdot \frac{x}{4} = 4 \cdot \frac{1}{4}x = 1x$$

$$x = 44 \qquad 1x = x$$

CHECK $\dfrac{x}{4} = 11$

$$\frac{44}{4} \overset{?}{=} 11 \qquad \text{Substitute 44 for } x.$$

$$11 = 11 \qquad \text{True}$$

So the solution is 44. $\cdots \bullet$

PRACTICE 7

Solve and check: $7y = 63$

EXAMPLE 7

Solve and check: $9x = -72$

SOLUTION
$$9x = -72$$

$$\left(\frac{1}{9}\right)9x = \left(\frac{1}{9}\right)(-72) \qquad \text{Multiply each side of the equation by } \frac{1}{9}.$$

$$1x = -8 \qquad \frac{1}{9} \cdot 9 = 1$$

$$x = -8$$

CHECK $9x = -72$

$$9(-8) \overset{?}{=} -72 \qquad \text{Substitute } -8 \text{ for } x.$$

$$-72 = -72 \qquad \text{True}$$

So the solution is -8. $\cdots \bullet$

Because dividing by a number is the same as multiplying by its reciprocal, the multiplication property allows us to divide each side of an equation by a non-zero number. For instance, suppose $a = b$. Multiplying each side by $\dfrac{1}{c}$ gives us $a \cdot \dfrac{1}{c} = b \cdot \dfrac{1}{c}$, for $c \neq 0$. This equation is equivalent to $\dfrac{a}{c} = \dfrac{b}{c}$. So an alternative approach to solving Example 2 is to divide each side of the equation by the same number, namely 9, as shown:

$$9x = -72$$

$$\frac{9x}{9} = \frac{-72}{9}$$

$$x = -8$$

Note that this approach gives us the same solution, -8, that we got using the approach in Example 7.

EXAMPLE 8

Solve and check: $-y = -15$

SOLUTION

$$-y = -15$$

$$-1y = -15 \qquad \text{The coefficient of } -y \text{ is } -1.$$

$$\frac{-1y}{-1} = \frac{-15}{-1} \qquad \text{Divide each side of the equation by } -1.$$

$$y = 15$$

CHECK

$$-y = -15$$

$$-1(15) \overset{?}{=} -15 \qquad \text{Substitute 15 for } y.$$

$$-15 = -15 \qquad \text{True}$$

So the solution is 15.

PRACTICE 8

Solve and check: $-x = 10$

EXAMPLE 9

Solve and check: $46 = -4.6n$

SOLUTION

$$46 = -4.6n$$

$$\frac{46}{-4.6} = \frac{-4.6n}{-4.6} \qquad \text{Divide each side of the equation by } -4.6.$$

$$-10 = n \quad \text{or}$$

$$n = -10$$

CHECK

$$46 = -4.6n$$

$$46 \overset{?}{=} -4.6(-10) \qquad \text{Substitute } -10 \text{ for } n.$$

$$46 = 46 \quad \text{True}$$

So the solution is -10.

PRACTICE 9

Solve and check:
$-11.7 = -0.9z$

EXAMPLE 10

Solve and check: $\dfrac{2w}{3} = 8$

SOLUTION

$$\frac{2w}{3} = 8$$

$$\frac{2}{3}w = 8$$

$$\frac{3}{2} \cdot \frac{2}{3}w = \frac{3}{2} \cdot 8 \qquad \text{Multiply each side of the equation by } \frac{3}{2}.$$

$$w = 12 \qquad \frac{3}{2} \cdot \frac{2}{3} = 1 \text{ and } 1w = w.$$

PRACTICE 10

Solve and check: $\dfrac{6y}{7} = -12$

CHECK

$$\frac{2}{3}w = 8$$

$$\frac{2}{3}(12) \stackrel{?}{=} 8 \qquad \text{Substitute 12 for } w.$$

$$2 \cdot 4 \stackrel{?}{=} 8 \qquad \text{Simplify.}$$

$$8 = 8 \qquad \text{True}$$

So the solution is 12. $\cdots \bullet$

Can you show another way to solve Example 10? Explain.

Let's now consider applied problems involving the multiplication property. To solve these problems, we translate word sentences to equations involving multiplication or division as follows:

Word sentence: Three times a number x equals -12.

$$\downarrow \quad \downarrow \quad \quad \downarrow \quad \quad \downarrow \quad \quad \downarrow$$
$$3 \quad \cdot \quad \quad x \quad \quad = \quad -12$$

Equation: $\qquad\qquad\qquad 3x \quad = \quad -12$

Word sentence: A number d divided by -2 equals 8.

$$\downarrow \quad\quad\quad \downarrow \quad\quad \downarrow \quad \downarrow \quad \downarrow$$

Equation: $\quad d \qquad \div \qquad -2 \quad = \quad 8$

$$\frac{d}{-2} = 8$$

PRACTICE 11

A mechanic billed a customer $189.50 for labor to repair his car. If one-fourth of the bill was for labor, how much was the total bill?

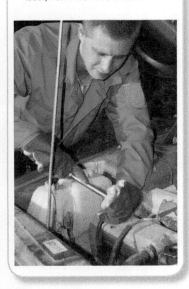

EXAMPLE

A student applies for a job that pays an hourly overtime wage of $15.90. The overtime wage is 1.5 times the regular hourly wage. What is the regular hourly wage for the job?

SOLUTION   Letting w represent the regular hourly wage, we write the word sentence, and then translate it to an equation.

Word sentence:
The overtime wage $15.90 is 1.5 times the regular hourly wage.

$$\downarrow \quad \downarrow \quad \downarrow \quad \downarrow \qquad\qquad\qquad \downarrow$$

Equation: $\quad 15.90 = 1.5 \quad \cdot \qquad\qquad\qquad w$

$$15.90 = 1.5w$$

Next, we solve the equation for w.

$$15.9 = 1.5w$$

$$\frac{15.9}{1.5} = \frac{1.5}{1.5}w$$

$$10.6 = w, \text{ or } w = 10.6$$

CHECK

$$15.90 = 1.5w$$

$$15.90 \stackrel{?}{=} 1.5(\mathbf{10.6}) \qquad \text{Substitute 10.6 for } w.$$

$$15.90 = 15.90 \qquad \text{True}$$

So the regular wage is $10.60. $\cdots \bullet$

Let's now turn to a particular kind of applied problem—a problem involving *motion*. To solve such problems, we need to use the equation $d = rt$, where d is distance, r is the average rate or speed, and t is time.

EXAMPLE 12

One of the fastest pitchers in the history of Japanese baseball was Yoshinori Sato, whose pitches were clocked at about 147 ft/sec. If the distance from the pitcher's mound to home plate is 60.5 ft, approximate the time it took Sato's pitches to reach home plate, to the nearest hundredth of a second. (*Source:* japantoday.com)

PRACTICE 12

A driver makes a trip from Washington, D.C., the U.S. capital, to Philadelphia, Pennsylvania, the home of Independence Hall. If she averages 60 mph, how long, to the nearest tenth of an hour, will it take her to get to Philadelphia? (*Source:* mapquest.com)

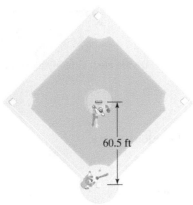

60.5 ft

130 mi Philadelphia
Washington, D.C.

SOLUTION   The distance between the pitcher's mound and home plate is 60.5 ft and the rate of the ball thrown is 147 ft/sec. Using the equation $d = rt$, we can find the time.

$$d = rt$$
$$60.5 = 147t \qquad \text{Substitute 60.5 for } d \text{ and 147 for } r.$$
$$\frac{60.5}{147} = \frac{147t}{147}$$
$$0.41 \approx t, \quad \text{or}$$
$$t \approx 0.41$$

CHECK   Since the solution of the original equation is a rounded value, the check will not result in an exact equality. To verify the solution, check that the expressions on each side of the equation are approximately equal to one another.

$$60.5 = 147t$$
$$60.5 \stackrel{?}{\approx} 147 \cdot 0.41 \qquad \text{Substitute 0.41 for } t.$$
$$60.5 \approx 60.3 \qquad \text{True}$$

So Sato's pitches took approximately 0.41 sec to reach home plate. $\cdots \bullet$

Solving Linear Equations by Combining Properties

In the previous sections, we solved simple equations involving either the addition property or the multiplication property. We now turn our attention to solving equations that involve both properties.

Solving Equations Using Both the Addition and Multiplication Properties

We need to use both the addition property and the multiplication property to solve equations such as:

$$3x + 4 = 7 \quad \text{and} \quad \frac{r}{2} - 5 = 9$$

To solve these equations, we first use the addition property to get the variable term alone on one side. Then, we use the multiplication property to isolate the variable.

PRACTICE 13

Solve and check: $2y + 1 = 9$

EXAMPLE ⓭

Solve and check: $3x + 4 = 7$

SOLUTION

$$3x + 4 = 7$$
$$3x + 4 - 4 = 7 - 4 \qquad \text{Subtract 4 from each side of the equation.}$$
$$3x = 3$$
$$\frac{3x}{3} = \frac{3}{3} \qquad \text{Divide each side of the equation by 3.}$$
$$x = 1$$

CHECK $3x + 4 = 7$
$$3(1) + 4 \stackrel{?}{=} 7 \qquad \text{Substitute 1 for } x.$$
$$3 + 4 \stackrel{?}{=} 7$$
$$7 = 7 \qquad \text{True}$$

So the solution is 1. $\cdots \bullet$

In solving Example 13, would we get the same solution if we divided before subtracting? Explain.

PRACTICE 14

Solve and check: $\dfrac{c}{5} - 1 = 8$

EXAMPLE ⓮

Solve and check: $\dfrac{r}{2} - 5 = 9$

SOLUTION

$$\frac{r}{2} - 5 = 9$$
$$\frac{r}{2} - 5 + 5 = 9 + 5 \qquad \text{Add 5 to each side of the equation.}$$
$$\frac{r}{2} = 14$$
$$2 \cdot \frac{r}{2} = 2 \cdot 14 \qquad \text{Multiply each side of the equation by 2.}$$
$$r = 28$$

CHECK $\dfrac{r}{2} - 5 = 9$
$$\frac{28}{2} - 5 \stackrel{?}{=} 9 \qquad \text{Substitute 28 for } r.$$
$$14 - 5 \stackrel{?}{=} 9$$
$$9 = 9 \qquad \text{True}$$

So the solution is 28. $\cdots \bullet$

PRACTICE 15

Solve: $-6b - 5 = 13$

EXAMPLE ⓯

Solve: $-4s + 7 = 3$

SOLUTION

$$-4s + 7 = 3$$

$$-4s + 7 - 7 = 3 - 7 \qquad \text{Subtract 7 from each side of the equation.}$$

$$-4s = -4$$

$$\frac{-4s}{-4} = \frac{-4}{-4} \qquad \text{Divide each side by } -4.$$

$$s = 1$$

So the solution is 1.   · · ●

Solving Equations by Combining Like Terms

Now, let's consider an equation that has like terms on the same side of the equation. In order to solve this kind of equation, we combine all like terms before using the addition and multiplication properties.

EXAMPLE 16

Solve and check: $2x - 5x = 12$

SOLUTION

$$\underbrace{2x - 5x}_{} = 12$$

$$-3x = 12 \qquad \text{Combine like terms.}$$

$$\frac{-3x}{-3} = \frac{12}{-3} \qquad \text{Divide each side of the equation by } -3.$$

$$x = -4$$

CHECK

$$2x - 5x = 12$$

$$2(-4) - 5(-4) \stackrel{?}{=} 12 \qquad \text{Substitute } -4 \text{ for } x.$$

$$-8 + 20 \stackrel{?}{=} 12$$

$$12 = 12 \qquad \text{True}$$

So the solution is −4.   · · ●

> **PRACTICE 16**
>
> Solve and check:
>
> $8n + 10n = 24$

EXAMPLE 17

Solve and check: $7x - 3x - 6 = 6$

SOLUTION

$$\underbrace{7x - 3x}_{} - 6 = 6$$

$$4x - 6 = 6 \qquad \text{Combine like terms.}$$

$$4x - 6 + 6 = 6 + 6 \qquad \text{Add 6 to each side of the equation.}$$

$$4x = 12$$

$$\frac{4x}{4} = \frac{12}{4} \qquad \text{Divide each side of the equation by 4.}$$

$$x = 3$$

CHECK

$$7x - 3x - 6 = 6$$

$$7(3) - 3(3) - 6 \stackrel{?}{=} 6 \qquad \text{Substitute 3 for } x.$$

$$21 - 9 - 6 \stackrel{?}{=} 6$$

$$6 = 6 \qquad \text{True}$$

So the solution is 3.   · · ●

> **PRACTICE 17**
>
> Solve and check: $5 - t - t = -1$

Suppose an equation has like terms that are on opposite sides of the equation. To solve, we use the addition property to get the like terms together on the same side so that they can be combined.

PRACTICE 18

Solve: $3f - 12 = -f - 15$

EXAMPLE 18

Solve: $13z + 5 = -z + 12$

SOLUTION

$$13z + 5 = -z + 12$$

$$z + 13z + 5 = z + (-z) + 12 \qquad \text{Add } z \text{ to each side of the equation.}$$

$$14z + 5 = 12 \qquad \text{Combine like terms.}$$

$$14z + 5 - 5 = 12 - 5 \qquad \text{Subtract 5 from each side of the equation.}$$

$$14z = 7$$

$$\frac{14z}{14} = \frac{7}{14} \qquad \text{Divide each side of the equation by 14.}$$

$$z = \frac{1}{2}$$

So the solution is $\frac{1}{2}$. ••●

Some equations have fractional terms. The key to solving a fractional equation is to *clear the equation of the fractional terms.* We do this by first determining their *least common denominator* (LCD), and then by multiplying both sides of the equation by the LCD.

PRACTICE 19

Solve and check: $\frac{1}{3}w - \frac{1}{6}w = \frac{2}{3}$

EXAMPLE 19

Solve and check: $\frac{1}{2}x + \frac{1}{5}x = \frac{7}{10}$

SOLUTION

The fractional terms in this equation are $\frac{1}{2}x, \frac{1}{5}x$ and $\frac{7}{10}$.

The denominators of these terms are 2, 5, and 10, so the LCD is 10. To clear the equation of the fractional terms, we multiply each side of the equation by 10.

$$\frac{1}{2}x + \frac{1}{5}x = \frac{7}{10}$$

$$10 \cdot \left(\frac{1}{2}x + \frac{1}{5}x\right) = 10 \cdot \frac{7}{10} \qquad \text{Multiply each side of the equation by the LCD.}$$

$$10 \cdot \frac{1}{2}x + 10 \cdot \frac{1}{5}x = 10 \cdot \frac{7}{10} \qquad \text{Use the distributive property.}$$

$$5x + 2x = 7 \qquad \text{Simplify.}$$

$$7x = 7 \qquad \text{Combine like terms.}$$

CHECK $\qquad \frac{1}{2}x + \frac{1}{5}x = \frac{7}{10}$

$$\frac{1}{2}(1) + \frac{1}{5}(1) \overset{?}{=} \frac{7}{10} \qquad \text{Substitute 1 for } x.$$

$$\frac{1}{2} + \frac{1}{5} \stackrel{?}{=} \frac{7}{10}$$

$$\frac{5}{10} + \frac{2}{10} \stackrel{?}{=} \frac{7}{10}$$

$$\frac{7}{10} = \frac{7}{10} \quad \text{True}$$

So the solution is 1.

$\cdots \bullet$

Solving Equations Containing Parentheses

Some equations contain parentheses. To solve these equations, we first remove the parentheses using the distributive property. Then, we proceed as in previous examples.

EXAMPLE 20

Solve and check: $2c = -3(c - 5)$

SOLUTION

$$2c = -3(c - 5)$$
$$2c = -3c + 15 \qquad \text{Use the distributive property.}$$
$$3c + 2c = 3c - 3c + 15 \qquad \text{Add } 3c \text{ to each side of the equation.}$$
$$5c = 15 \qquad \text{Combine like terms.}$$
$$\frac{5c}{5} = \frac{15}{5} \qquad \text{Divide each side of the equation by 5.}$$
$$c = 3$$

CHECK

$$2c = -3(c - 5)$$
$$2(3) \stackrel{?}{=} -3(3 - 5) \qquad \text{Substitute 3 for } c.$$
$$6 \stackrel{?}{=} -3(-2)$$
$$6 = 6 \qquad \text{True}$$

So the solution is 3.

$\cdots \bullet$

As Example 20 suggests, we use the following procedure to solve linear equations:

PRACTICE 20

Solve and check: $-5(z + 6) = z$

To Solve a Linear Equation
- Use the distributive property to clear the equation of parentheses, if necessary.
- Combine like terms where appropriate.
- Use the addition property to isolate the variable term.
- Use the multiplication property to isolate the variable.
- Check by substituting the solution in the original equation.

A. *Indicate what must be done to each side of the equation in order to isolate the variable.*

1. $\dfrac{x}{3} = -4$ **2.** $\dfrac{a}{-6} = 1$

3. $-5x = 20$ **4.** $-4x = 30$

5. $-2.2n = 4$ **6.** $1.5x = -6$

7. $\dfrac{3}{4}x = 12$ **8.** $\dfrac{2}{3}x = -6$

9. $-\dfrac{5y}{2} = 15$ **10.** $-\dfrac{8n}{5} = 4$

Solve and check.

11. $6x = -30$ **12.** $-8y = 8$

13. $\dfrac{n}{2} = 9$ **14.** $\dfrac{w}{10} = -21$

15. $\dfrac{a}{4} = 1.2$ **16.** $\dfrac{n}{7} = -1.3$

17. $-5x = 2.5$ **18.** $-2y = 0.08$

19. $42 = -6c$ **20.** $50 = -2x$

21. $11 = -\dfrac{r}{2}$ **22.** $4 = \dfrac{-m}{3}$

23. $\dfrac{5}{6}x = 10$ **24.** $\dfrac{3}{4}d = -3$

25. $-\dfrac{2}{5}y = 1$ **26.** $\dfrac{2}{3}r = -8$

27. $\dfrac{3n}{4} = 6$ **28.** $\dfrac{5a}{6} = 5$

29. $\dfrac{4c}{3} = -4$ **30.** $-\dfrac{2z}{7} = 8$

31. $-\dfrac{x}{2.4} = -1.2$ **32.** $-\dfrac{n}{0.5} = -1.3$

33. $-2.5a = 5$ **34.** $-2.25 = -1.5t$

35. $\dfrac{2}{3}y = \dfrac{4}{9}$ **36.** $\dfrac{5}{6}c = \dfrac{2}{3}$

Solve. Round to the nearest hundredth.

37. $\dfrac{x}{-1.515} = 1.515$ **38.** $\dfrac{n}{-2.968} = -3.85$

39. $-3.14x = 21.4148$ **40.** $2.54z = 6.4516$

Translate each sentence to an equation. Then, solve and check.

41. The product of -4 and a number is 56.

42. The product of -8 and a number is 72.

43. A number divided by 0.2 is 1.1.

44. A number divided by 0.6 is 1.8.

45. The quotient of a number and 3.5 is 30.

46. The quotient of a number and 2.5 is 40.

47. $\dfrac{1}{6}$ of a number is $2\frac{4}{5}$.

48. $\dfrac{5}{8}$ of a number is 20.

Choose the equation that best describes the situation.

49. A shopper used half his money to buy a backpack. If the backpack cost $20, how much money did he have prior to this purchase?

   a. $20 = 2m$ **b.** $20m = \dfrac{1}{2}$

   c. $20 = \dfrac{m}{2}$ **d.** $\dfrac{m}{20} = \dfrac{1}{2}$

50. A child's infant brother weighs 12 lb. If this is $\dfrac{1}{4}$ of her weight, how much does she weigh?

   a. $4w = 12$ **b.** $\dfrac{w}{4} = 12$

   c. $12w = \dfrac{1}{4}$ **d.** $\dfrac{w}{12} = \dfrac{1}{4}$

51. A student plans to buy a DVD player 6 weeks from now. If the DVD player costs $150, how much money must she save per week in order to buy it?

   a. $6p = 150$ **b.** $150p = 6$

   c. $\dfrac{p}{6} = 150$ **d.** $\dfrac{p}{150} = 6$

52. The student government at a college sold tickets to a play. From ticket sales, it collected $800, which was twice the cost of the play. How much did the play cost?

   a. $\dfrac{c}{800} = 2$ **b.** $800c = 2$

   c. $\dfrac{c}{2} = 800$ **d.** $2c = 800$

Mixed Practice

Solve and check.

53. $5x = -20$

54. $\dfrac{2n}{7} = 4$

55. $8 = -\dfrac{a}{3}$

56. $-\dfrac{y}{3.8} = -0.3$

Translate each sentence to an equation. Then, solve and check.

57. The quotient of a number and 5 is equal to 2.

58. $\dfrac{3}{8}$ of a number is 12.

Indicate what must be done to each side of the equation in order to isolate the variable.

59. $-5.2m = 4$.

60. $\dfrac{b}{7} = 3$.

Applications

B. *Write an equation that best describes the situation. Then, solve and check.*

61. According to a geologist, sediment at the bottom of a local lake accumulated at the rate of 0.02 centimeter per year. How long did it take to create a layer of sediment 10.5 cm thick?

62. Because of evaporation, the water level in an aquarium drops at a rate of $\dfrac{1}{10}$ inch per hour. In how many hours will the level drop 2 in.?

63. The bus trip from Miami to San Francisco takes 70 hr. What is the average speed of the bus rounded to the nearest mile per hour? (*Source*: Greyhound)

64. The coat in the ad shown is selling at $\dfrac{1}{4}$ the regular price. What was the regular price?

65. A customer has only $20 to spend at a local print shop that charges $0.05 per copy. At this rate, how many copies can she afford to make?

66. Consider the two parcels of land shown—one a rectangle and the other a square. For which value of x do the two parcels have the same area?

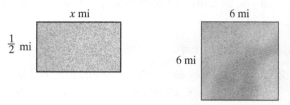

67. A city offers to pay a disposal company $40 per ton to bury 20,000 tons of toxic waste. If this deal represents $\dfrac{2}{3}$ of the disposal company's projected income, what is that income?

68. The diameter of a tree trunk increases as the tree ages and adds rings. Suppose a trunk's diameter increases by 0.2 inch per year. How many years will it take the tree to increase in diameter from 4 in. to 12 in.?

69. The maximum depth of the Caspian Sea is approximately 1000 m. If this depth is about $\dfrac{1}{5}$ the maximum depth of the Mediterranean Sea, what is the maximum depth of the Mediterranean Sea? (*Source:* wikipedia.org)

70. A top-secret plane flew 3000 mi in $1\frac{1}{2}$ hr. What was the average speed of this plane?

71. A student takes a job in the college's student center so that she can buy books that cost $187.50. How many hours must she work to make this amount if she earns $7.50/hr?

72. A double-trailer truck is driven at an average speed of 54 mph from Atlanta to Cincinnati, a driving distance of 457 mi. To the nearest tenth of an hour, how long did the trip take? (Source: mapquest.com)

73. Last year, a young couple paid a total of $10,020 in rent for their apartment. How much money did they pay per month in rent?

74. An equilateral triangle is a triangle that has three sides equal in length. If the perimeter of an equilateral triangle is $10\frac{1}{2}$ ft, how long is each side?`

MINDSTRETCHERS

Mathematical Reasoning

1. In the course of solving a linear equation, you reach the step, $5x = 3x$
   If you then divide both sides by x, you get $5 = 3$, which is impossible. Did you make an error? Explain.

Critical Thinking

2. If you multiply each side of the equation $0.24r = -12.48$ by 100, the result is an equivalent equation. Explain why it is helpful to carry out this multiplication in solving the equation.

Writing

3. Write two different word problems that are applications of each equation.

   a. $6x = 18$ **b.** $\dfrac{x}{3} = 10$

C. *Solve and check.*

75. $3x - 1 = 8$

76. $7r - 8 = 13$

77. $9t + 17 = -1$

78. $2y + 1 = 9$

79. $20 - 5m = 45$

80. $25 - 3c = 34$

81. $\dfrac{n}{2} - 1 = 5$

82. $\dfrac{s}{3} - 2 = -4$

83. $\dfrac{x}{5} + 15 = 0$

84. $\dfrac{y}{3} + 3 = 42$

85. $3 - t = 1$

86. $2 - x = 2$

87. $-8 - b = 11$

88. $5 - y = 8$

89. $\dfrac{2}{3}x - 9 = 17$

90. $\dfrac{4}{5}d - 3 = 13$

91. $\dfrac{4}{5}r + 20 = -20$

92. $\dfrac{3y}{8} + 14 = -10$

93. $3y + y = -8$

94. $4a + 3a = -21$

95. $7z - 2z = -30$

96. $4x - x = 18$

97. $28 - a + 4a = 7$

98. $5 - 8x - 2x = -25$

99. $1 = 1 - 6t - 4t$

100. $-1 = 5 - z - z$

101. $3y + 2 = -y - 2$

102. $3n + 6 = -n - 6$

103. $5r - 4 = 2r + 6$

104. $7 - m = 5 + 3m$

D. *Solve and check.*

105. $4(x + 7) = 7 + x$

106. $3t - 2 = 4(t - 2)$

107. $5(y - 1) = 2y + 1$

108. $5a - 4 = 7(a + 2)$

109. $3a - 2(a - 9) = 4 + 2a$

110. $5 - 2(3x - 4) = 3 - x$

111. $5(2 - t) - (1 - 3t) = 6$

112. $\dfrac{3}{5}(15y + 10) - 3(4y + 3) = 0$

113. $2y - 3(y + 1) = -(5y + 3) + y$

114. $9n + 5(n + 3) = -(n + 13) - 2$

115. $2[3z - 5(2z - 3)] = 3z - 4$

116. $5[2 - (2n - 4)] = 2(5 - 3n)$

117. $-8m - [2(11 - 2m) + 4] = 9m$

118. $7 - [4 + 2(a - 3)] = 11(a + 2)$

Solve. Round to the nearest hundredth.

119. $\dfrac{y}{0.87} + 2.51 = 4.03$

120. $7.02x - 3.64 = 8.29$

121. $7.37n + 4.06 = -1.98n + 6.55$

122. $10.13p = 3.14(p - 7.82)$

Choose the equation that best describes the situation.

123. A car leaves Seattle traveling at a rate of 45 mph. One hour later, a second car leaves from the same place, along the same road, at 54 mph. If the first car travels for t hr, in how many hours will the second car overtake the first car?

   a. $54(t - 1) = 45t$

   b. $45(t + 1) = 54t$

   c. $54(t + 1) = 45t$

   d. $45(t - 1) = 54t$

124. A company budgets $600,000 for an advertising campaign. It must pay $4000 for each television commercial and $1000 per radio commercial. If the company plans to air 50 fewer radio commercials than television commercials, find the number of television commercials t that will be in the advertising campaign.

   a. $4000t + 1000(t + 50) = 600,000$

   b. $4000t + 1000(t - 50) = 600,000$

   c. $4000t + 1000t - 50 = 600,000$

   d. $1000t + 4000(t - 50) = 600,000$

125. A taxi fare is $3.00 for the first mile and $1.25 for each additional mile. If a passenger's total cost was $5.50, how far did she travel in the taxi?

   a. $3.00x + 1.25 = 5.50$

   b. $3.00 + 1.25x = 5.50$

   c. $3.00 + 1.25(x + 1) = 5.50$

   d. $3.00 + 1.25(x - 1) = 5.50$

126. A family's budget allows $\frac{1}{3}$ of the family's monthly income for housing and $\frac{1}{4}$ of its monthly income for food. If a total of $1050 a month is budgeted for housing and food, what is the family's monthly income?

   a. $\frac{1}{3}x = 1050 + \frac{1}{4}x$

   b. $\frac{1}{3}x - \frac{1}{4}x = 1050$

   c. $\frac{1}{3}x + \frac{1}{4}x = 1050$

   d. $\frac{1}{4}x - \frac{1}{3}x = 1050$

Mixed Practice

Solve and check.

127. $5 - 5x + x = 21$

128. $16 - 3t = 31$

129. $4z + 3(5 - z) = -(z - 3) + 8$

130. $\frac{r}{7} + 3 = 11$

131. $-2.31y + 0.14 = -9.23$
   (Round to the nearest hundredth.)

132. $7y - 6 = 3(y - 6)$

Applications

E. *Write an equation and solve.*

133. A part-time student at a college pays a student fee of $45 plus $135 per credit. How many credits is a part-time student carrying who pays $1260 in all?

134. A health club charges members $10 per month plus $5 per hour to use the facilities. If a member was charged $55 this month, how many hours did she use the facilities?

135. In a local election, a newspaper reported that one candidate received twice as many votes as the other. Altogether, they received a total of 3690 votes. How many votes did each candidate receive?

136. Calcium carbonate (chalk) consists of 10 parts of calcium for each 3 parts of carbon and 12 parts of oxygen by weight. Find the amount of calcium in 75 lb of chalk.

137. A parking garage charges $3 for the first hour and $2 for each additional hour or fraction thereof. If $9 was paid for parking, how many hours was the car parked in the garage?

138. A machinist earns $11.50 an hour for the first 35 hr and $15.30 for each hour over 35 per week. How many hours did he work this week if he earned $555.50?

139. The office manager of an election campaign office needs to print 5000 postcards. It costs 2 cents to print a large postcard and 1 cent to print a small postcard. If $85 is allocated for printing postcards, how many of each type of postcard can be printed?

140. The owner of a small factory has 8 employees. Some of the employees make $10 per hour, whereas the others make $15 per hour. If the total payroll is $105 per hour, how many employees make the higher rate of pay?

141. Twenty minutes after a father left for work on the bus, he noticed that he had left his briefcase at home. His son left home, driving at 36 mph, to catch the bus that was traveling at 24 mph. How long did it take the son to catch the bus?

142. In the rush hour, a commuter drives to work at 30 mph. Returning home off-peak, she takes $\frac{1}{4}$ hr less time driving at 40 mph. What is the distance between the commuter's work and her home?

143. The two snails shown below crawl toward each other at rates that differ by 2 cm/min. If it takes the snails 27 min to meet, how fast is each snail crawling?

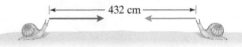

432 cm

144. A signal is sent from a station on the ground to a satellite. The signal bounces off the satellite and then is received at a second ground station. If the signal traveled 2400 mi in all, at what speed was it traveling?

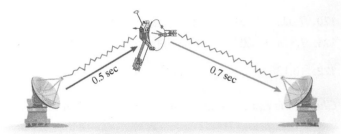

0.5 sec   0.7 sec

145. Two trucks leave a depot at the same time, traveling in opposite directions. One truck goes 4 mph faster than the other. After 2 hr, the trucks are 212 mi apart. What is the speed of the slower truck?

146. If a student drives from college to home at 40 mph, then he is 15 min late. However, if he makes the same trip at 50 mph, he is 12 min early. What is the distance between his college and his home?

MINDSTRETCHERS

Mathematical Reasoning

1. Give an example of an equation that involves combining like terms and that has:

a. no solution.   **b.** an infinite number of solutions.

Patterns

2. Tables can be useful in solving equations.

a. Complete the following table. After examining your results, identify the solution to the following equation:

$3(x - 2) = 2(x + 1)$.

x	0	2	4	6	8	10	12
3 (x − 2)							
3 (x + 1)							

b. Try a similar approach to solving the equation $7x = 5x + 11$. What conclusion can you draw about the solution?

x	0	2	4	6	8	10	12
7x							
5x + 11							

Groupwork

3. Working with a partner, choose a month on a calendar.

a. Ask your partner to select four days of the month that form a 2 × 2 square, but only to tell you the sum of the four days. Determine the four days.

b. Reverse roles with your partner and repeat part (a).

c. Compare how you and your partner responded to part (a).

8.2 INTRODUCTION TO GRAPHING LINES··

The Graph of a Linear Equation in Two Variables

The graph of an equation, more precisely the graph of the *solutions* of that equation, is a kind of picture of the equation.

> **Definition**
>
> The **graph** of a linear equation in two variables consists of all points whose coordinates make the equation true.

Given a linear equation, how do we find its graph? A general strategy is to first isolate one of the variables, unless it is already done. Then, we identify several solutions of the equation, keeping track of the x- and y-values in a table. We plot the points and then sketch the line passing through them. That line is the graph of the given equation, as the following example illustrates.

Let's graph the equation $y = 3x + 1$. The variable y is already isolated, so we find y-values by substituting arbitrary values of x. For instance, let x equal 0. To find y, we substitute 0 for x.

$$y = 3x + 1 = 3 \cdot 0 + 1 = 0 + 1 = 1$$

So $x = 0$ and $y = 1$ is a solution of this equation. We say that the ordered pair $(0, 1)$ is a solution of $y = 3x + 1$.

Let's choose three other values of x, say -1, 1, and 2. Substituting -1 for x in the equation, we get:

$$y = 3x + 1 = 3(-1) + 1 = -2$$

Substituting 1 for x, we get:

$$y = 3x + 1 = 3 \cdot 1 + 1 = 4$$

Substituting 2 for x gives us:

$$y = 3x + 1 = 3 \cdot 2 + 1 = 7$$

Next, we enter these results in a table.

x	−1	0	1	2
y	−2	1	4	7

Then, we plot on a coordinate plane the four points $A(-1, -2)$, $B(0, 1)$, $C(1, 4)$, and $D(2, 7)$. If we have not made a mistake, the points will all lie on the same line. We know that the line segments $\overline{AB}$, $\overline{BC}$, and $\overline{CD}$ are part of the same line because they all have equal slopes. The graph of the equation $y = 3x + 1$ is the line passing through these points. So any point on this line satisfies the equation $y = 3x + 1$.

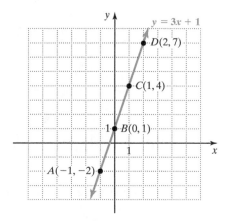

Do you think that if we had chosen three other x-values we would have gotten the same graph? Check to see that this is the case.

This example suggests the following procedure for graphing a linear equation:

To Graph a Linear Equation in Two Variables

- Isolate one of the variables—usually y—if it is not already done.
- Choose three x-values, entering them in a table.
- Complete the table by calculating the corresponding y-values.
- Plot the three points—two to draw the line and the third to serve as a *checkpoint*.
- Check that the points seem to lie on the same line.
- Draw the line passing through the points.

A couple of observations about the preceding example are worth making:

- The slope of the line graphed is 3. We can see this by taking any pair of points on the line, for example $(0, 1)$ and $(1, 4)$, and computing the slope of the line between them.

$$m = \frac{y_2 - y_1}{x_2 - x_1} = \frac{1 - 4}{0 - 1} = \frac{-3}{-1} = 3$$

- This slope is identical to the coefficient of x in the equation $y = 3x + 1$.

We also see that the point where the graph crosses the y-axis is $(0, 1)$. This point is called the *y-intercept*. Note that the constant term in the equation $y = 3x + 1$ is also 1.

These relationships are more than a coincidence, and we will say more about them.

PRACTICE 1

Graph the equation $y = -\frac{2}{5}x$.

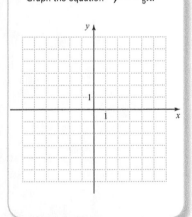

EXAMPLE 1

Graph the equation $y = -\frac{3}{2}x$ by choosing three points whose coordinates satisfy the equation.

SOLUTION   We begin by choosing x-values. In this case, we choose multiples of 2 for the x-values. Then, we find the corresponding y-values.

x	$y = -\frac{3}{2}x$	(x, y)
y	$y = -\frac{3}{2}(0) = 0$	$(0, 0)$
2	$y = -\frac{3}{2}(2) = -3$	$(2, -3)$
4	$y = -\frac{3}{2}(4) = -6$	$(4, -6)$

We plot the points, and then draw a line passing through them to get the desired line.

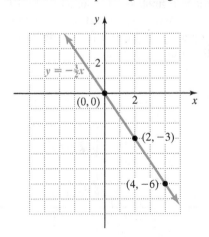

Note that in Example 1, we chose multiples of 2 for the x-values. Can you explain why?

EXAMPLE 2

Consider the equation $2x + y = 3$.

a. Graph the equation.

b. Find the slope of the line.

SOLUTION

a. We begin by solving the equation for y.

$$2x + y = 3$$
$$y = -2x + 3 \qquad \text{Subtract } 2x \text{ from each side.}$$

Next, we choose three values for x, for instance, -1, 0, and 2. Then, we enter them into a table and find their corresponding y-values as follows:

x	$y = -2x + 3$	(x, y)
-1	$y = -2(-1) + 3 = 2 + 3 = 5$	$(-1, 5)$
0	$y = -2(0) + 3 = 0 + 3 = 3$	$(0, 3)$
2	$y = -2(2) + 3 = -4 + 3 = -1$	$(2, -1)$

Now, we plot the points on the coordinate plane. Since the points seem to lie on the same line, we draw a line passing through the points.

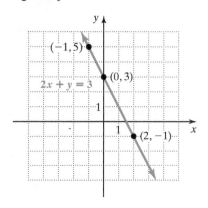

b. To find the slope of the line, we can consider the points $(0, 3)$ and $(2, -1)$.

$$m = \frac{3 - (-1)}{0 - 2} = \frac{4}{-2} = -2$$

Note that the slope is the coefficient of x in the equation $y = -2x + 3$. $\cdots \bullet$

We have graphed equations in general form by first isolating y and then computing y-values for arbitrary x-values. Now, we graph equations in general form with a different approach using x- and y-intercepts. Note that intercepts stand out on a graph and are easy to plot. Since an x-intercept lies on the x-axis, its y-value must be 0. Similarly, since a y-intercept lies on the y-axis, the x-value of a y-intercept must be 0.

> **Definition**
>
> The **x-intercept** of a line is the point where the graph crosses the x-axis. The **y-intercept** is the point where the graph crosses the y-axis.

The following graph shows a line passing through two points, $(0, 4)$ and $(3, 0)$, which are both intercepts.

PRACTICE 2

Consider the equation
$-2x + y = -5$.

a. Graph the equation.

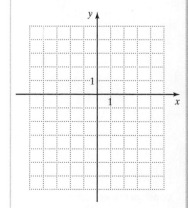

b. Find the slope of the line.

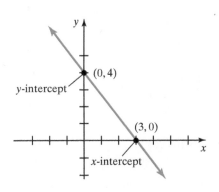

Using the *x*- and *y*-intercepts to graph equations can save work, especially when the coefficients of the two variables are factors of the constant term, as shown in the next example.

EXAMPLE 3

Consider the equation $2x + 3y = 6$.   Find the x- and y-intercepts. Then, graph.

SOLUTION   Since the y-intercept has x-value 0, we let $x = 0$ and then solve for y.
For $x = 0$:

$$2x + 3y = 6$$
$$2 \cdot 0 + 3y = 6 \qquad \text{Substitute 0 for } x.$$
$$3y = 6$$
$$\frac{3y}{3} = \frac{6}{3}$$
$$y = 2$$

So the *y*-intercept is $(0, 2)$.
Similarly, the *x*-intercept has *y*-value 0. So we let $y = 0$ and then solve for *x*.
For $y = 0$:

$$2x + 3y = 6$$
$$2x + 3 \cdot 0 = 6 \qquad \text{Substitute 0 for } y.$$
$$2x = 6$$
$$\frac{2x}{2} = \frac{6}{2}$$
$$x = 3$$

So the *x*-intercept is $(3, 0)$.
   Before graphing, we choose a third point to be used as a checkpoint.

For $2x + 3y = 6$,   let $x = 6$:

$$2x + 3y = 6$$
$$2 \cdot 6 + 3y = 6 \qquad \text{Substitute 6 for } x.$$
$$12 + 3y = 6$$
$$3y = -6$$
$$y = -2$$

So the checkpoint is $(6, -2)$.
   Plotting the points $(0, 2)$, $(3, 0)$, and $(6, -2)$ on a coordinate plane, we confirm that they seem to lie on the same line. Finally, we draw a line through the points, getting the desired graph.

PRACTICE 3

Consider the equation
$x - 2y = 4$. Find the *x*- and
y-intercepts. Then, graph.

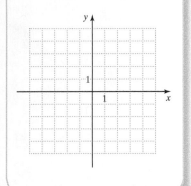

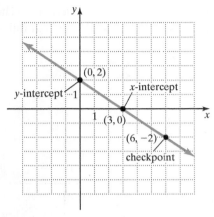

Example 3 suggests the following procedure:

> **To Graph a Linear Equation in Two Variables Using the x- and y-intercepts**
> - Let $x = 0$, and find the y-intercept.
> - Let $y = 0$, and find the x-intercept.
> - Find a checkpoint.
> - Plot the three points.
> - Check that the points seem to lie on the same line.
> - Draw the line passing through the points.

We know that the general form of a linear equation in two variables is $Ax + By = C$. Sometimes in a linear equation one of the two variables is missing, that is, the coefficient of one of the two variables is zero. Consider the following equations:

$$y = 9 \quad \rightarrow \quad 0x + y = 9$$
$$x = -5.8 \quad \rightarrow \quad x + 0y = -5.8$$

Let's look at the graphs of these equations.

EXAMPLE 4

Graph:

a. $y = 9$ **b.** $x = -5.8$

SOLUTION

a. For the line $y = 9$, the coefficient of the x-term is 0. The x-value can be any real number and the y-value is always 9. So the graph is as follows:

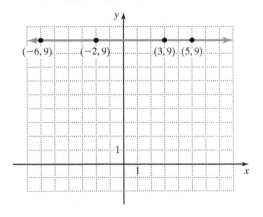

The graph of this equation is a horizontal line. Recall that the slope of a horizontal line is 0.

PRACTICE 4

On the given coordinate plane, graph:

a. $y = -1$ **b.** $x = 2.5$

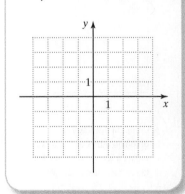

b. For the line $x = -5.8$, the coefficient of the y-term is 0. The y-value can be any real number and the x-value is always -5.8. So the graph is as follows:

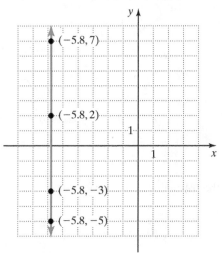

The graph of this equation is a vertical line. The slope of this line is undefined. ·· ●

In general, the graph of the equation $x = a$ is a vertical line passing through the point $(a, 0)$, and the graph of the equation $y = b$ is a horizontal line passing through the point $(0, b)$. What are the equations of the x- and y-axes?

Now, let's use our knowledge of graphing linear equations to solve applied problems.

EXAMPLE 5

For cable television, a homeowner pays $30 per month plus $5 for each pay-per-view movie ordered.

a. Express as an equation the relationship between the monthly bill B and the number n of pay-per-view movies.

b. Draw the graph of this equation in Quadrant I of a coordinate plane.

c. Compute the slope of this graph. In terms of the cable TV bill, explain the significance of the slope.

d. In terms of the cable TV bill, explain the significance of the B-intercept of the graph.

e. From the graph in part (b), estimate what the cable bill would be if the homeowner had ordered 15 pay-per-view movies that month.

SOLUTION

a. The monthly bill (in dollars) amounts to the sum of 30 and 5 times the number of pay-per-view movies which the homeowner ordered, so

$$B = 5n + 30.$$

b. To draw the graph of this equation in Quadrant I, we enter several nonnegative n-values, say 0, 10, and 20, in a table and then compute the corresponding B-values.

n	$B = 5n + 30$	(n, B)
0	$B = 5(0) + 30 = 30$	$(0, 30)$
10	$B = 5(10) + 30 = 80$	$(10, 80)$
20	$B = 5(20) + 30 = 130$	$(20, 130)$

PRACTICE 5

A stockbroker charges as her commission on stock transactions $40 plus 3% of the value of the sale.

a. Write as an equation the commission C in terms of the sales s.

b. Draw a graph showing this relationship on sales up to $1000. Be sure to choose an appropriate scale for each axis.

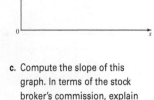

c. Compute the slope of this graph. In terms of the stock broker's commission, explain the significance of the slope.

d. If the value of a sale is $500, estimate from the graph in part (b) the broker's commission.

Since the monthly bill B depends on the number n of pay-per-view movies ordered each month, we label the horizontal axis with the independent variable n and the vertical axis with the dependent variable B. Now, we choose an appropriate scale for each axis and plot $(0, 30)$, $(10, 80)$, and $(20, 130)$. Then, we draw the line passing through these points.

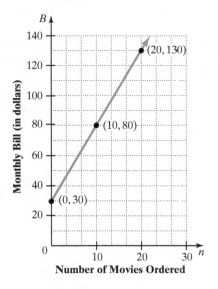

We restricted the graph to Quadrant I because the number of movies ordered n and the corresponding bill B are always nonnegative.

c. Substituting n and B for x and y, respectively, in the slope formula, we get the following slope:

$$m = \frac{B_2 - B_1}{n_2 - n_1} = \frac{80 - (30)}{10 - (0)} = \frac{50}{10} = 5.$$

Note that we could have predicted this answer since we know that the bill increases by \$5 for every additional pay-per-view movie ordered.

d. Since the B-intercept is the point $(0, 30)$, \$30 would be the amount of the bill if the homeowner had watched no pay-per-view movies at all during the month.

e. From the graph, it appears that if $n = 15$, then $B = 105$, that is, the cable bill would be \$105.   • • ●

EXAMPLE 6

A dietician uses milk and cottage cheese as sources of calcium in her diet. One serving of milk contains 300 mg of calcium, and one serving of cottage cheese contains 100 mg of calcium. The recommended daily amount (RDA) of calcium is 1000 mg.

a. If m represents the number of servings of milk and c the number of servings of cottage cheese in a diet that contains the RDA of calcium, write an equation that relates m and c.

b. Graph this equation.

c. Explain the significance of the two intercepts in terms of the number of servings.

d. Explain how we could have predicted that the slope of this graph would be negative.

SOLUTION

a. The amount of calcium in the milk is $300m$, and the amount of calcium in the cottage cheese is $100c$. Since the RDA of calcium is 1000 mg, the following equation holds:

$$300m + 100c = 1000, \text{ or } 3m + c = 10$$

PRACTICE 6

An athlete has just signed a contract with a total value of \$10 million. According to the terms of the contract, she earns \$2 million in some years and \$1 million in other years.

a. Let x stand for the number of years in which she earns \$2 million and y the number of \$1 million years. Write an equation that relates x and y.

b. Choose an appropriate scale for each axis on the coordinate plane. Graph the equation found in part (a).

c. Describe in terms of the contract the significance of the slope of the graph.

d. Describe in terms of the contract the significance of the x- and y-intercepts of the graph.

b. To graph, we identify the *m*- and *c*-intercepts, as well as a third point, say with $m = 1$.

m	0	$3\frac{1}{3}$	1
c	10	0	7

Next, we choose an appropriate scale for each axis and plot the three points, checking that the points all lie on the same line. Then, we draw the line passing through them.

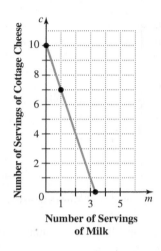

Number of Servings of Milk

c. The *m*-intercept represents the number of servings she would need to meet the daily minimum requirement if she uses only milk as her source of calcium. The *c*-intercept represents the number of servings she would need to meet the RDA if she uses only cottage cheese as her source of calcium.

d. Even without drawing this line, we know that its slope has to be negative for the following reason: The RDA of calcium is a fixed amount (1000 mg). So larger values of *m* must correspond to smaller values of *c*. The line will therefore have to be decreasing, falling to the right and with a negative slope.

$\cdots\bullet$

Slope-Intercept Form

One approach to graphing an equation written in general form is to isolate *y*.

$$-5x + y = 2 \qquad \text{An equation in general form}$$
$$y = 5x + 2 \qquad \text{Solve for y.}$$

The linear equation $y = 5x + 2$ is said to be in slope-intercept form. The graph of this equation has slope 5, which is equal to the coefficient of *x*, and *y*-intercept $(0, 2)$, where 2 is the constant term of the equation.

> **Definition**
>
> A linear equation is in **slope-intercept form** if it is written as
>
> $$y = mx + b,$$
>
> where *m* and *b* are constants. In this form, *m* is the slope and $(0, b)$ is the *y*-intercept of the graph of the equation.

This form is used for identifying the slope and *y*-intercept of the graph of a linear equation without drawing the graph of the equation. The coefficient of *x* is the slope *m*, and the constant term *b* is the *y*-coordinate of the *y*-intercept $(0, b)$.

The following table gives additional examples of equations written in slope-intercept form:

Equation	Slope m	y-intercept $(0, b)$
$y = \frac{1}{2}x + 1$	$\frac{1}{2}$	$(0, 1)$
$y = 2x - 1$	2	$(0, -1)$
$y = -7x \rightarrow y = -7x + 0$	-7	$(0, 0)$
$y = 5 \rightarrow y = 0x + 5$	0	$(0, 5)$

EXAMPLE 7

Find the slope and y-intercept of the equation $y = 3x - 5$.

SOLUTION   The equation $y = 3x - 5$ or $y = 3x + (-5)$ is already in slope-intercept form, $y = mx + b$. The slope m is 3, and the y-intercept is $(0, -5)$ since the equation has constant term -5.   • • ●

PRACTICE 7

Find the slope and y-intercept of the equation $y = -2x + 3$.

EXAMPLE 8

For the graph of $y = 3x$, find the slope and y-intercept.

SOLUTION   We can rewrite $y = 3x$ as $y = 3x + 0$. Now, the equation $y = 3x + 0$ is in slope-intercept form, with slope $m = 3$ and $b = 0$. Since $b = 0$, the y-intercept is $(0, 0)$. That is, the graph passes through the origin.   • • ●

PRACTICE 8

Find the slope and y-intercept of the graph of $y = -x$.

EXAMPLE 9

Express $3x + 5y = 6$ in slope-intercept form.

SOLUTION   Since the slope-intercept form of an equation is $y = mx + b$, we need to solve the given equation for y.

$$3x + 5y = 6$$
$$5y = -3x + 6$$
$$\frac{5y}{5} = \frac{-3}{5}x + \frac{6}{5}$$
$$y = -\frac{3}{5}x + \frac{6}{5}$$

So $y = -\frac{3}{5}x + \frac{6}{5}$ is the equation written in slope-intercept form,

where m is $-\frac{3}{5}$ and b is $\frac{6}{5}$.   • • ●

PRACTICE 9

Express $3x - 2y = 4$ in slope-intercept form.

EXAMPLE 10

Write $y - 1 = 5(x - 1)$ in slope-intercept form.

SOLUTION   To get the equation in the form $y = mx + b$. we must solve for y.
$$y - 1 = 5(x - 1)$$
$$y - 1 = 5x - 5$$
$$y = 5x - 5 + 1$$
$$y = 5x - 4$$

So $y = 5x - 4$ is the equation written in slope-intercept form, where m is 5 and b is -4.

PRACTICE 10

Change the equation $y - 2 = 4(x + 1)$ to slope-intercept form.

We can use the slope-intercept form to write the equation of a line when given its slope and y-intercept.

$\cdots\bullet$

EXAMPLE 11

Write the equation of the line with slope $-\dfrac{4}{5}$ and y-intercept $(0, -3)$.

SOLUTION   We are given that the slope is $-\dfrac{4}{5}$ and the y-intercept is $(0, -3)$. So $m = -\dfrac{4}{5}$ and $b = -3.$ We substitute these values in the slope-intercept form:

$$y = mx + b$$

$$y = -\frac{4}{5}x + (-3), \quad \text{or } y = -\frac{4}{5}x - 3$$

The next two examples deal with the equations of lines that are parallel or perpendicular.

$\cdots\bullet$

EXAMPLE 12

Find an equation of the line that is parallel to the graph of $y = 4x + 1$ and has y-intercept $(0, 3)$.

SOLUTION   The line $y = 4x + 1$ is in slope-intercept form. The slope of this line is 4. Since parallel lines have the same slope, the line we want will also have slope $m = 4$. Since its y-intercept is $(0, 3)$, $b = 3$. Therefore, the desired equation is $y = 4x + 3$. $\cdots\bullet$

EXAMPLE 13

What is the equation of the line that is perpendicular to the graph of $y = 3x - 1$ and has y-intercept $(0, 1)$?

SOLUTION   The line $y = 3x - 1$ is written in slope-intercept form. So its slope must be 3. We know that the slopes of two perpendicular lines are negative reciprocals of each other.

Therefore, the slope of the line we want has slope $m = -\dfrac{1}{3}$. Since its y-intercept is $(0, 1)$, $b = 1$.

So the desired equation is $y = -\dfrac{1}{3}x + 1$. $\cdots\bullet$

EXAMPLE 14

At her college, a student pays $75 per credit-hour plus a flat student fee of $100. Find an equation in slope-intercept form that relates the amount A that she pays to the number h of credit-hours in her program.

SOLUTION   The amount A in dollars that the student pays is the sum of 75 times the number h of credit-hours in her program and 100. So we have:

$$A = 75h + 100$$

This equation is written in slope-intercept form. $\cdots\bullet$

We have already graphed equations of the form $y = mx + b$ by finding three points whose coordinates satisfy the equation. Now, let's focus on graphing such equations using the slope and the y-intercept.

Consider the equation $y = 3x - 1$, which has slope 3 and y-intercept $(0, -1)$. Since 3 is $\frac{3}{1}$, we know from the definition of slope that the *rise* is 3 and the *run* is 1. Starting at $(0, -1)$, we move up 3 units and then 1 unit to the right to find a second point $(1, 2)$ on the line. Then, we draw the line through the two points $(0, -1)$ and $(1, 2)$.

This example leads us to the following rule:

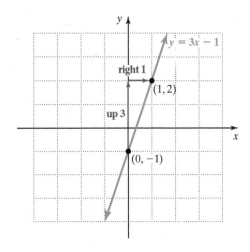

> **To Graph a Linear Equation in Two Variables Using the Slope and the y-intercept**
> - First, locate the y-intercept.
> - Then, use the slope to find a second point on the line.
> - Finally, draw the line through the two points.

EXAMPLE 15

Graph $y = -\dfrac{3}{2}x + 2$ using the slope and y-intercept.

SOLUTION Since $y = -\dfrac{3}{2}x + 2$ is in slope-intercept form, the slope is $-\dfrac{3}{2}$ and the y- intercept is $(0, 2)$. First, we locate the y-intercept $(0, 2)$ Since the slope $-\dfrac{3}{2}$ equals $\dfrac{-3}{2}$, from the point $(0, 2)$ we move *down* 3 units and then 2 units to the *right* to find the second point $(2, -1)$. Then, we draw the line through the points $(0, 2)$ and $(2, -1)$ as shown in the graph.

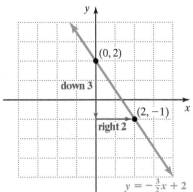

Note that since $\frac{-3}{2} = \frac{3}{-2}$, from the point $(0, 2)$ we could have moved *up* 3 units, and then 2 units to the *left* to find the second point $(-2, 5)$. Then we could have drawn the line through $(0, 2)$ and $(-2, 5)$ to obtain the same graph of the equation, as shown on the coordinate plane to the right.

PRACTICE 15

Use the slope and y-intercept to graph $y = -\dfrac{1}{3}x - 4$.

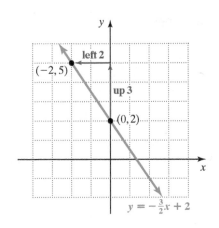

$$y = -\frac{3}{2}x + 2$$

We graphed $2x + 3y = 6$ using the intercepts. We can also graph this equation using the slope and y-intercept. Which method do you prefer? Explain why.

Section 8.2 Exercises

FOR EXTRA HELP   MyMathLab   Math XL   PRACTICE   WATCH   READ   REVIEW

Mathematically Speaking

Fill in each blank with the most appropriate term or phrase from the given list.

three *x*-values	vertical	*x*-intercept
graph	solution	horizontal
y-intercept	three points	

1. A(n) _____ of an equation in two variables is an ordered pair of numbers that when substituted for the variables makes the equation true.

2. The _____ of a linear equation in two variables consists of all points whose coordinates satisfy the equation.

3. One way of graphing a linear equation in two variables is to plot _____.

4. The _____ of a line is the point where the graph crosses the *x*-axis.

5. One way to graph a linear equation using intercepts is to first let $x = 0$ and then find the _____.

6. The graph of the equation $y = c$ is a(n) _____ line passing through the point $(0, c)$.

A. *Complete each table so that the ordered pairs are solutions of the given equation.*

7. $y = 3x - 8$

x	4	7	1
y			0

8. $y = 2x - 5$

x	0		
y		15	17

9. $y = -5x$

x	3.5	6		
y			$\frac{1}{2}$	-8

10. $y = -10x$

x	$\frac{1}{5}$	2.9		
y			-6	-1

11. $3x + 4y = 12$

x	0	-4		
y			-3	0

12. $4x + y = 8$

x	5	0		
y			0	16

13. $y = \frac{1}{3}x - 1$

x	3	6	-3	
y				-1

14. $y = -\dfrac{3}{2}x + 2$

x	$\frac{4}{3}$	6	-2	
y				2

B. *Graph each equation by finding three points whose coordinates satisfy the equation.*

15. $y = x$

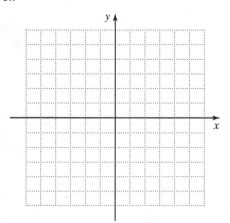

16. $y = 3x$

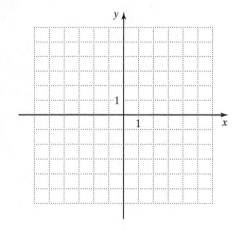

17. $y = \dfrac{1}{2}x$

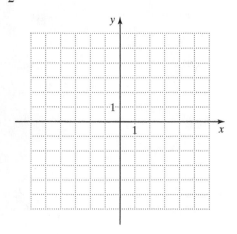

18. $y = \dfrac{1}{4}x$

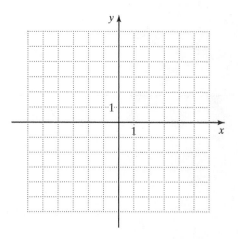

19. $y = -\dfrac{5}{4}x$

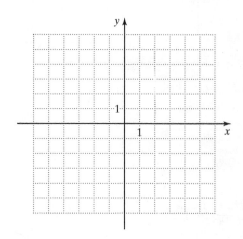

20. $y = -\dfrac{3}{2}x$

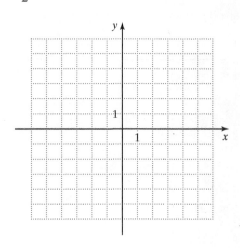

21. $y = 2x + 1$

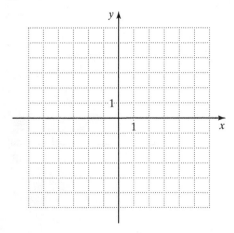

22. $y = 3x + 1$

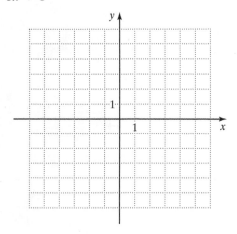

23. $y = -\dfrac{1}{3}x + 1$

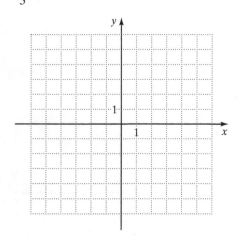

24. $y = -\dfrac{3}{4}x + 2$

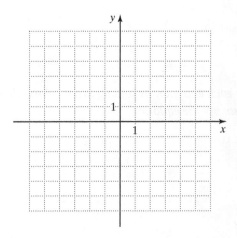

25. $y - 2x = -3$

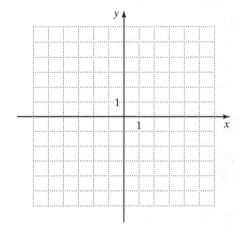

26. $y - 3x = 2$

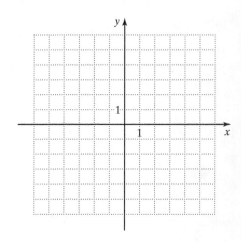

27. $x + y = 6$

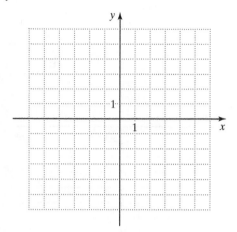

30. $x - 3y = 15$

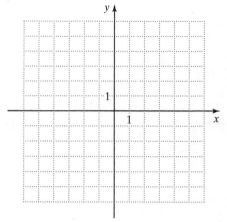

28. $3x + y = 4$

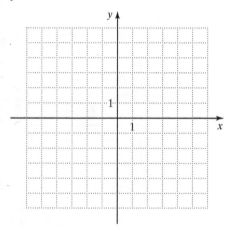

For each equation, find the x- and y-intercepts. Then, use the intercepts to graph the equation.

31. $5x + 3y = 15$

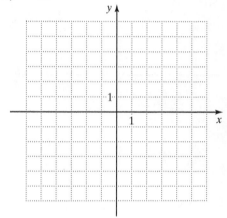

29. $x - 2y = 4$

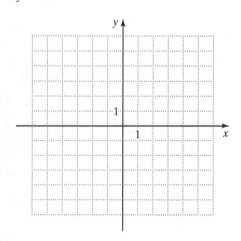

32. $4x + 5y = 20$

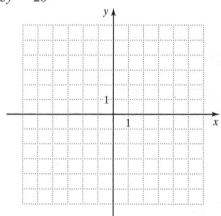

33. $3x - 6y = 18$

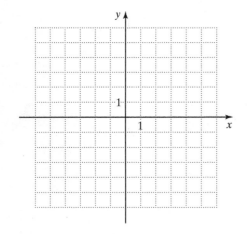

36. $4y - 5x = 10$

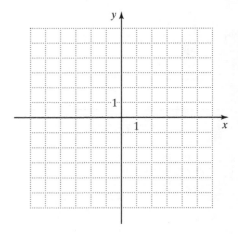

34. $7x - 2y = -7$

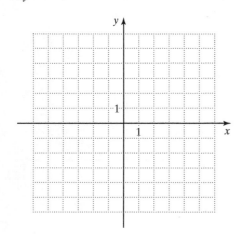

37. $9y + 6x = -9$

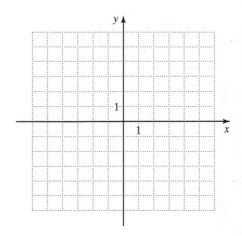

35. $3y - 2x = -6$

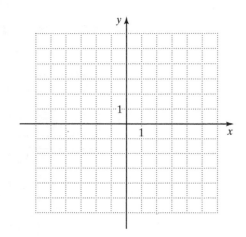

38. $4y + 8x = -4$

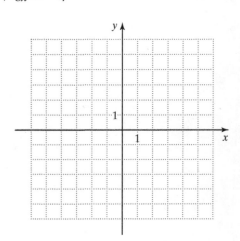

39. $y = \dfrac{1}{2}x + 2$

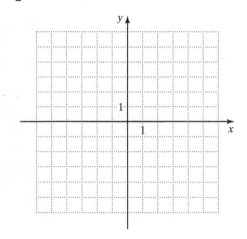

40. $y = \dfrac{5}{4}x - 5$

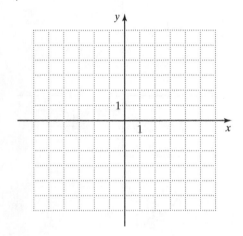

Graph.

41. $y = -2$

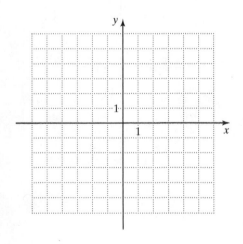

42. $y = 0$

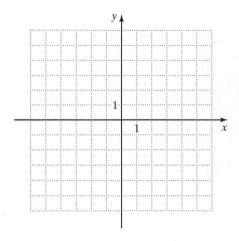

43. $x = 3$

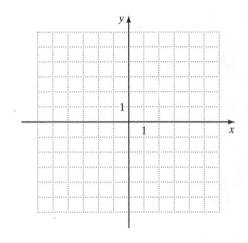

44. $x = 0$

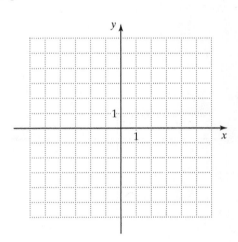

45. $x = -5.5$

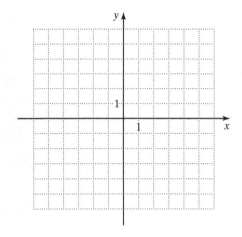

46. $y = -0.5$

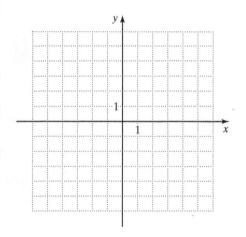

47. $y = \dfrac{1}{2}x + 3$

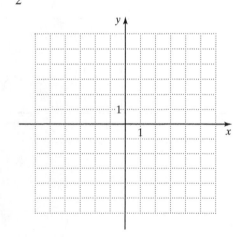

48. $y = \dfrac{1}{2}x + 6$

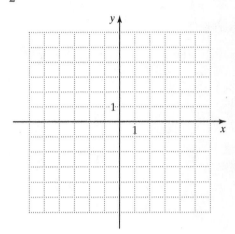

49. $3x + 5y = -15$

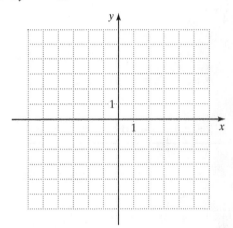

50. $3y - 5x = 15$

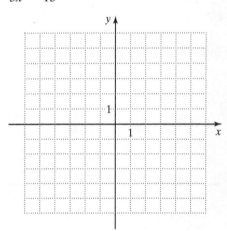

51. $y = -\dfrac{3}{5}x + \dfrac{2}{5}$

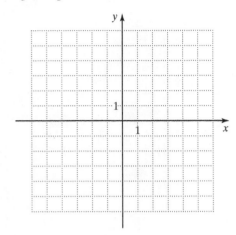

52. $y = -\dfrac{1}{4}x + \dfrac{3}{4}$

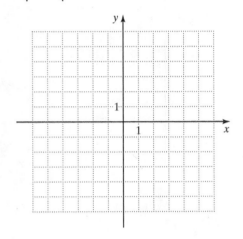

Mixed Practice

Complete each table so that the ordered pairs are solutions of the given equation.

53. $y = -2x + 6$

x	−3	$\dfrac{5}{2}$		
y			−10	4

54. $3x - 4y = 6$

x	0		−6	
y		0		3

For each equation, find the x- and y-intercepts, and another point whose coordinates satisfy the equation. Then, use these points to graph the equation.

55. $y = -\dfrac{1}{2}x + 2$

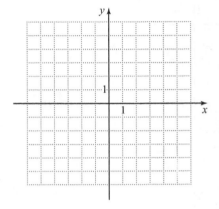

56. $2x - y = 4$

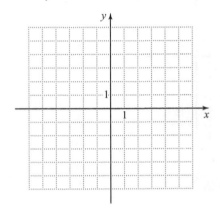

57. $6x - 2y = -12$

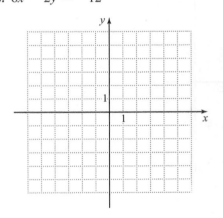

58. $y = \dfrac{3}{2}x - 3$

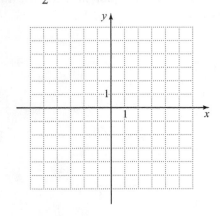

59. $y = -4x$

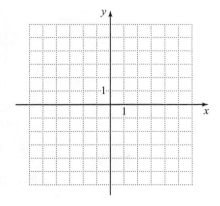

60. $y = \dfrac{3}{4}x$

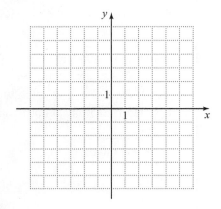

61. $3y + 6x = -3$

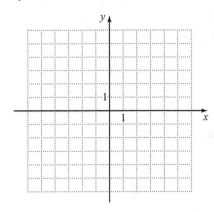

Graph.

62. $x = -3\dfrac{1}{2}$

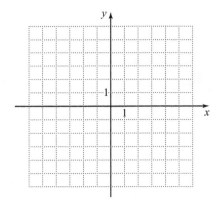

63. $y = -0.5x + 3$

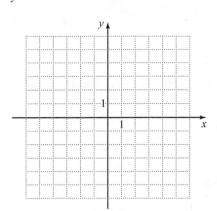

64. $2y - 4x = 8$

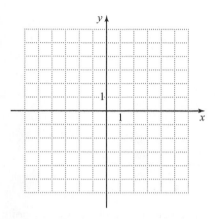

Applications

C. *Solve.*

65. In a physics lab, students study the mathematics of motion. They learn that if an object is tossed straight upward with an initial velocity of 10 ft/sec, then after t sec the object will be traveling at a velocity of v ft/sec, where

$$v = 10 - 32t.$$

a. Complete the table at the right.

t	0		1	1.5	2
v		−6			

Explain what a positive value of v means. What does a negative value of v mean?

b. Choose an appropriate scale for each axis, and then graph this equation.

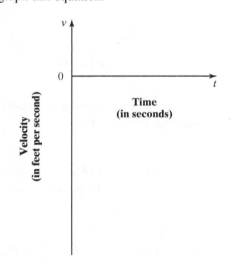

c. In terms of the object's motion, explain the significance of the v-intercept.

d. In terms of the object's motion, explain the significance of the t-intercept.

66. Each day, a local grocer varies the price p of an item in dollars, and then keeps track of the number s of items sold. According to his records, the following equation describes the relationship between s and p:

$$s = -2p + 12$$

a. Complete the table shown at the right.

p	1	3	5	
s				0

b. Choose appropriate scales for the axes, and then graph the equation.

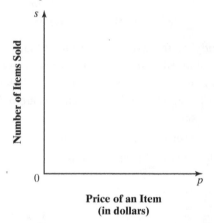

Price of an Item
(in dollars)

c. Explain why it makes sense to consider the graph only in Quadrant I.

d. From the graph, estimate the price required to sell 4 items.

67. A young couple buys furniture for $2000, agreeing to pay $500 down and $100 at the end of each month until the entire debt is paid off.

a. Express the amount P paid off in terms of the number m of monthly payments.

b. Complete the table shown at the right.

m	1	2	3
P			

c. Choose an appropriate scale for the axes, and then graph this equation.

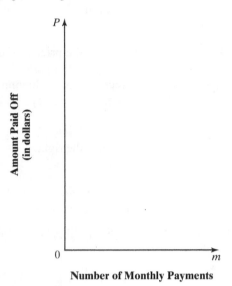

Number of Monthly Payments

68. Students studying forensic science know that when the femur bone of an adult female is unearthed, a good estimate of her height h is 29 more than double the length l of the femur bone, where all measurements are in inches. (*Source:* nsbri.org)

a. Express this relationship as a formula.

b. Complete the table shown at the right.

l	20	25	30
h			

c. Choose an appropriate scale for the axes, and then graph this relationship.

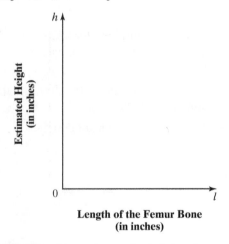

Length of the Femur Bone (in inches)

d. Use the graph to estimate the height of a woman whose femur bone was 14 in. in length.

69. The coins in a cash register, with a total value of $2, consist of n nickels and d dimes.

a. Represent this relationship as an equation.

b. Graph the equation found in part (a).

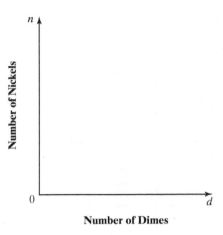

Number of Dimes

c. Explain in a sentence or two why not every point on this graph in Quadrant I is a reasonable solution to the problem.

70. On the first leg of a trip, a truck driver drove for x hr at a constant speed of 50 mph. On the second leg of the trip, he drove for y hr consistently at 40 mph. In all, he drove 1000 mi.

a. Translate this information into an equation.

b. Choose appropriate scales for the axes, and then graph the equation found in part (a).

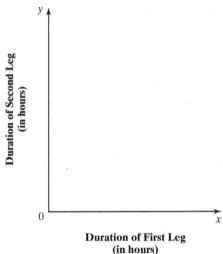

Duration of First Leg (in hours)

c. What are the x- and y-intercepts of this graph? Explain their significance in terms of the trip.

d. Find the slope of the line. Explain whether you would have expected the slope to be positive or negative, and why.

71. At a computer rental company, the fee F for renting a laptop is $40 plus $5 for each of the d days that the laptop is rented.

a. Express this relationship as an equation.

b. Choose appropriate scales for the axes, and then graph the equation expressed in part (a).

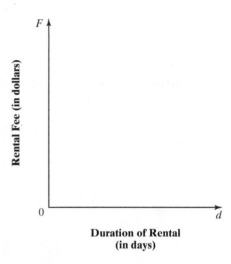

**Duration of Rental
(in days)**

c. Explain the significance of the *F*-intercept in this context.

72. At a local community center, the annual cost *c* to use the swimming pool includes an annual membership fee of $75 plus $5 per hour for *h* hr of pool time.

a. Write an equation for the annual cost of swimming at the community center in terms of the number of hours of pool time.

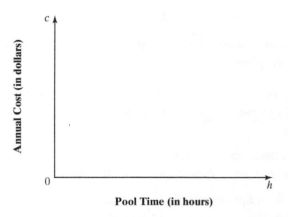

Pool Time (in hours)

b. Choose appropriate scales for the axes, and then graph the equation for up to and including 150 hr.

c. Use the graph to estimate the annual cost of using the pool for 25 hr.

d. Suppose the annual cost for swimming was $500. Estimate the number of hours of pool time.

MINDSTRETCHERS

Groupwork

1. Not all graphs are linear. For example, the graph of the equation $y = x^2 - 4$ is nonlinear, as the graph at the right illustrates:

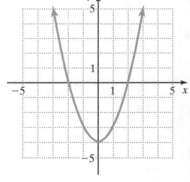

a. Identify the *x*- and *y*-intercepts for the graph shown.

b. Show that the *x*- and *y*-intercepts found in part (a) satisfy the equation $y = x^2 - 4$.

Writing

2. Give some advantages and disadvantages of graphing a linear equation by finding three arbitrary points versus using the intercepts.

Mathematical Reasoning

3. Recall that for a linear equation to be in general form, it must be written as $Ax + By = C$, where A, B, and C are real numbers and A and B are not both 0. What would the graph of this equation look like if A and B were both 0?

Mathematically Speaking

Fill in each blank with the most appropriate term or phrase from the given list.

standard	point-slope	slope
x-intercept	y-intercept	slope-intercept

73. A linear equation is in _____ form if it is written as $y = mx + b$, where m and b are constants.

74. For an equation of a line written in slope-intercept form, m is the _____ of the line.

75. For an equation of a line written in slope-intercept form, $(0, b)$ is the _____ of the line.

76. The _____ form of a linear equation is written as $y - y_1 = m(x - x_1)$, where x_1, y_1, and m are constants.

D. *Complete each table.*

77.

Equation	Slope m	y-intercept (0, b)	Which Graph Type Best Describes the Line? ╱ ╲ — |	x-intercept
$y = 3x - 5$				
$y = -2x$				
$y = 0.7x + 3.5$				
$y = \frac{3}{4}x - \frac{1}{2}$				
$6x + 3y = 12$				
$y = -5$				
$x = -2$				

78.

Equation	Slope m	y-intercept (0, b)	Which Graph Type Best Describes the Line? ╱ ╲ — |	x-intercept
$y = -3x + 5$				
$y = 2x$				
$y = 1.5x + 6$				
$y = \frac{2}{3}x + \frac{1}{2}$				
$4x + 6y = 24$				
$y = 0.3$				
$x = 2$				

Find the slope and y-intercept of each equation.

79. $y = -x + 2$

80. $y = -\frac{1}{2}x + 3$

81. $y = 3x - 4$

82. $y = 4x - 2$

E. *Write the following equations in slope-intercept form.*

83. $x - y = 10$

84. $3x - y = 15$

85. $x + 10y = 10$

86. $x + y = 7$

87. $6x + 4y = 1$

88. $3x + 5y = 15$

89. $2x - 5y = 10$

90. $4x - 8y = 12$

91. $y + 1 = 3(x + 5)$

92. $y - 1 = 3(x - 5)$

F. *Match the equation to its graph.*

93. $4x - 2y = 6$

94. $-2x + 4y = 8$

95. $2y - x = 8$

96. $6x + 3y = -9$

a.

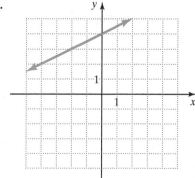

b.

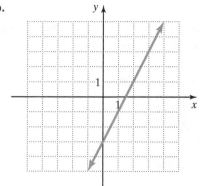

c.

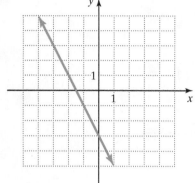

d.

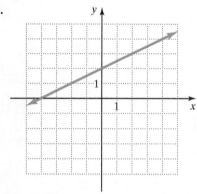

Graph the following equations using the slope and y-intercept.

97. $y = 2x + 1$

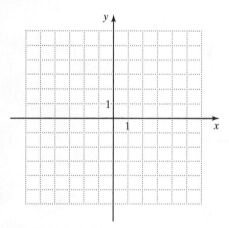

98. $y = 3x + 1$

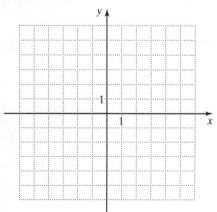

99. $y = -\dfrac{2}{3}x + 6$

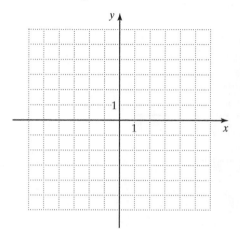

100. $y = -\dfrac{3}{2}x - 6$

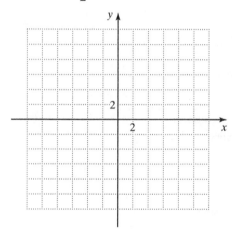

101. $x + y = 1$

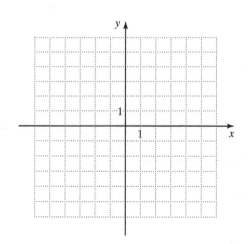

102. $x + y = -4$

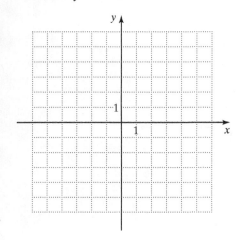

103. $y = -\dfrac{3}{4}x$

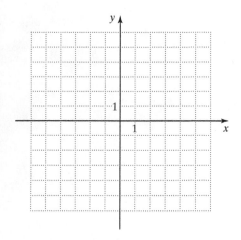

104. $y = -\dfrac{1}{2}x$

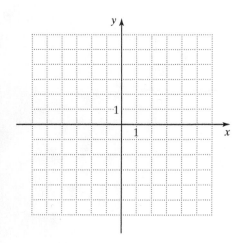

105. $x + 2y = 4$

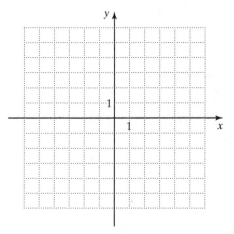

106. $2x + 3y = 12$

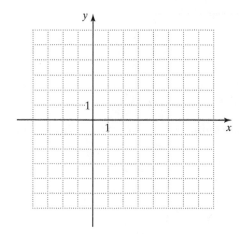

107. $y = 3.735x + 1.056$

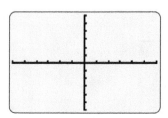

108. $y = -0.875x + 2.035$

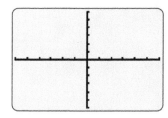

G. *Solve.*

109. Find the equation of the line with slope 3 that passes through the point $(0, 7)$.

110. What is the equation of the line that has slope -1 with y-intercept $(0, -2)$?

111. Find the equation of the line that is parallel to the graph of $y = 5x - 1$ and has y-intercept $(0, -20)$.

112. What is the equation of the line that is parallel to the graph

$y = \frac{1}{3}x - 1$ and has y-intercept $(0, 4)$?

113. What is the equation of the line that is perpendicular to the graph of $y = 2x$ and that passes through $(-2, 5)$?

114. Find the equation of the line that is perpendicular to the graph $y = -x$ and that passes through the point $(1, -3)$.

115. What is the equation of the line passing through the points $(2, 1)$ and $(1, 2)$?

116. The points $(5, 1)$ and $(2, -3)$ lie on a line. Find its equation.

117. Find the equation of the line passing through points $(-1, -5)$ and $(-7, -6)$.

118. What is the equation of the line passing through the origin and the point $(3, 5)$?

119. Write the equation of the vertical line that passes through the point $(-3, 5)$.

120. What is the equation of the vertical line passing through the point $(1, -8)$?

121. What is the equation of the horizontal line passing through the point $(2, -6)$?

122. What is the equation of the horizontal line passing through the point $(-4, 7)$?

Find the equation of each graph.

123.

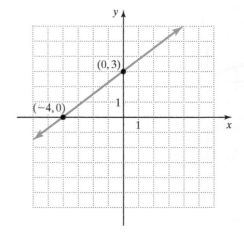

124.

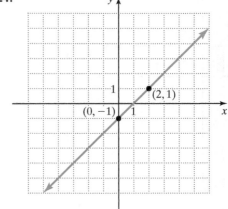

125.

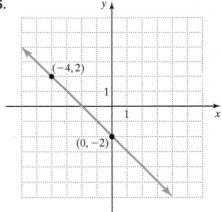

126.

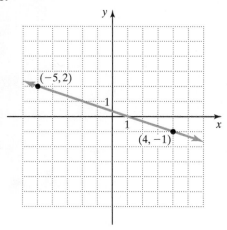

127.

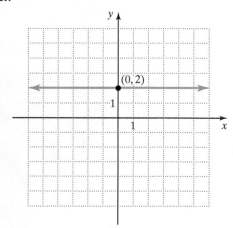

128.

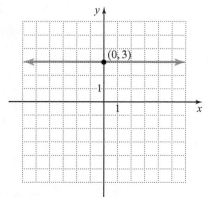

129.

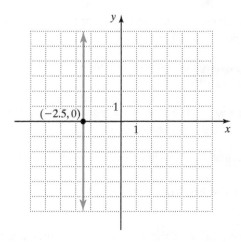

130.

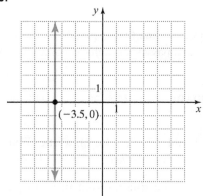

Mixed Practice

131. Complete the table.

Equation	Slope m	y-intercept $(0, b)$	Which Graph Type Best Describes the Line? $\diagdown$ — $\mid$	x-intercept
$y = -7x + 2$				
$y = 4x$				
$y = 2.5x + 10$				
$y = \dfrac{2}{3}x - \dfrac{1}{4}$				
$5x + 4y = 20$				
$x = 9$				
$y = -3.2$				

132. Find the slope and y-intercept of $y = -\dfrac{2}{5}x + 3$.

Write the following equations in slope-intercept form.

133. $4x - y = 5$

134. $3x - 6y = 8$

135. Which equation describes the graph?
   a. $-4x + y = 5$
   b. $4x + y = -5$
   c. $-5x + y = -4$
   d. $5x + y = -4$

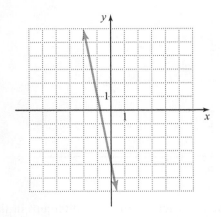

136. What is the equation of the line that is parallel to the graph $y = \dfrac{1}{2}x + 2$ and has x-intercept $(3, 0)$?

137. What is the equation of the line that is perpendicular to the graph of $y = -2x + 1$ that passes through the point $(4, 1)$?

138. What is the equation of the line that passes through the points $(2, -2)$ and $(-2, 1)$?

139. $y = \dfrac{3}{5}x - 2$

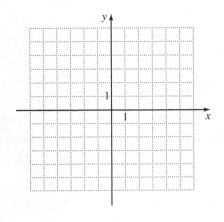

140. $3x + 2y = 4$

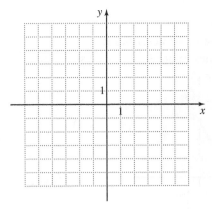

Find the equation of each graph.

141.

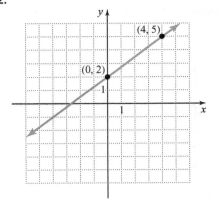

142.

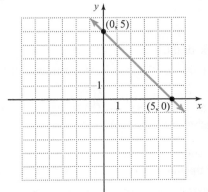

Applications

H. *Solve.*

143. The following graph describes the relationship between Fahrenheit temperature F and Celsius temperature C.

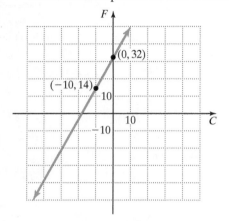

a. Find the slope of the line.

b. Find the equation of the line in slope-intercept form.

c. Water boils at 212°F. Use part (b) to find the Celsius temperature at which water boils.

144. The owner of a shop buys a piece of machinery for $1500. The value V of the machinery declines by $150 per year.

a. Write an equation for V after t years in slope-intercept form.

b. Graph the equation found in part (a).

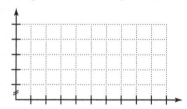

c. Explain the significance of the two intercepts in this context.

145. Each month, a utility company charges its residential customers a flat fee for electricity plus 6 cents per kilowatt-hour (kWh) consumed. Last month, a customer used 500 kWh of electricity, and his bill amounted to $45.

a. Express as an equation in point-slope form the relationship between the customer's monthly bill y in cents and the number x of kilowatt-hours of electricity consumed.

b. Express the equation found in part (a) in slope-intercept form.

c. What does the y-intercept represent in this situation?

146. A condo unit has been appreciating in value at $5000 per year. Three years after it was purchased, it was worth $65,000.

a. Find an equation that expresses the value y of the condo in terms of the number x of years since it was purchased.

b. Graph the equation found in part (a).

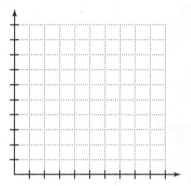

c. What is the significance of the y-intercept in this situation?

147. A salesperson earns a salary of $1500 per month plus a commission of 3% of the total monthly sales.

a. Write a linear equation giving the salesperson's total monthly income I in terms of sales S.

b. Graph the equation found in part (a).

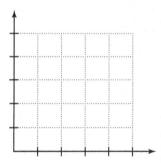

c. Find the salesperson's income on monthly sales of $6200.

148. When the brakes on a train are applied, the speed of the train decreases by the same amount every second. Two seconds after applying the brakes, the train's speed is 88 mph. After 4 sec, its speed is 60 mph.

    a. Write an equation expressing the speed s of the train in terms of the time t seconds after applying the brakes.

    b. Graph the equation found in part (a).

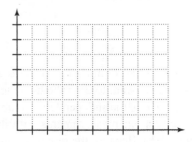

    c. What was the speed of the train when the brakes were first applied?

149. Pressure under water increases with greater depth. The pressure P on an object and the depth d below sea level are related by a linear equation. The pressure at sea level is 1 atmosphere (atm), whereas 33 ft below sea level the pressure is 2 atm. Find the equation expressing P in terms of d.

150. The length of a heated object and the temperature of the object are related by a linear equation. A rod at 0° Celsius is 10 m long, and at 25° Celsius it is 10.1 m long. Write an equation for length in terms of temperature.

151. When a force is applied to a spring, its length changes. The length L and the force F are related by a linear equation. The spring shown here was initially 10 in. long when no force was applied. What is the equation that expresses length in terms of force?

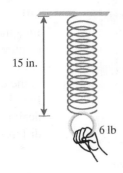

15 in.

6 lb

152. A company purchased a computer workstation for $8000. After 3 yr, the estimated value of the workstation was $4400. If the value V in dollars and the age a of the workstation are related by a linear equation, find an equation that expresses V in terms of a.

MINDSTRETCHERS

Technology

1. Consider $2x - 7 = 0$, which is a linear equation in x.

    a. Solve the equation.

    b. On a graphing calculator or computer with graphing software, graph $y = 2x - 7$. Then, find the x-intercept of the line. Explain in a sentence or two how you can use this approach to solve the equation $2x - 7 = 0$.

Critical Thinking

2. Consider the equation $y = mx + b$. Explain under what circumstances its graph lies completely in Quadrants I and II.

Mathematical Reasoning

3. What kind of line corresponds to an equation that can be written in *general form* but in neither slope-intercept form nor point-slope form?

8.3

LINEAR MODELING

We represented functions with tables and graphs. We now turn our attention to a more common and versatile way of representing functions: with equations. Although equations are more abstract than pictures, they are easier to manipulate mathematically and give us greater power when creating and analyzing mathematical models. We can understand the basic principles of mathematical modeling by focusing on the simplest models: *linear models*, which can be represented by *linear functions*, meaning functions that have straight-line graphs.

Linear Functions

Imagine that we measure the depth of rain accumulating in a rain gauge as a steady rain falls (Figure 8.1(a)). The rain stops after 6 hours, and we want to describe how the rain depth varied with time during the storm. In this situation, *time* is the independent variable and *rain depth* is the dependent variable. Suppose that, based on our measurements with the rain gauge, we find the rain depth function shown in Figure 8.1(b). Because the graph is a straight line, we are dealing with a **linear function**. If we use this linear function as a model to predict rain depth at different times, then we are using it as a **linear model**.

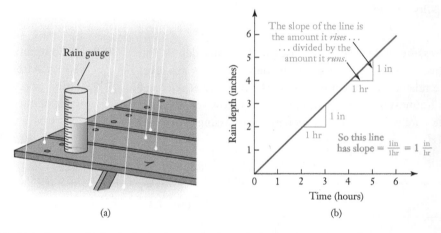

(a)   (b)

Figure 8.1   (a) A rain gauge. (b) Graph of a function showing how rain depth varies with time during a storm.

Rate of Change

The graph shows that, during the storm, the rain depth increased by 1 inch each hour. We say that the **rate of change** of the rain depth with respect to time was 1 inch per hour, or 1 in/hr. This rate of change was constant throughout the storm: No matter which hour we choose to study, the rain depth increased by 1 inch. This illustrates a key fact about linear functions: *A linear function has a constant rate of change and a straight-line graph.*

Figure 8.2 shows graphs for three other steady rainstorms. The constant rate of change is 0.5 in/hr in Figure 8.2(a), 1.5 in/hr in Figure 8.2(b), and 2 in/hr in Figure 8.2(c). Comparing the three graphs in Figure 8.2 leads to another crucial observation: *The greater the rate of change, the steeper the graph.*

The small triangles on the graphs show the **slope** of each line, defined as the amount that the graph *rises* vertically for a given distance that it *runs* horizontally. That is, *the slope is the rise over the run*. More importantly, Figure 8.1 also shows that the slope is equal to the rate of change.

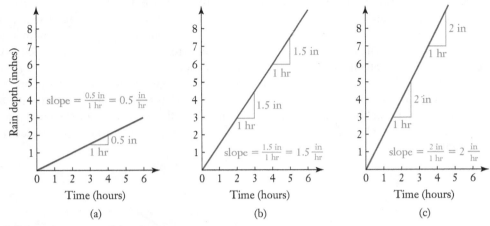

Figure 8.2 Three more rain depth functions, with slopes increasing from (a) to (c).

Linear Functions

A linear function has a constant rate of change and a straight-line graph. For all linear functions,

- The rate of change is equal to the slope of the graph.
- The greater the rate of change, the steeper the slope.
- We can calculate the rate of change by finding the slope between any two points on the graph (Figure 8.3):

$$\text{rate of change} = \text{slope} = \frac{\text{change in } \textit{dependent variable}}{\text{change in } \textit{independent variable}}$$

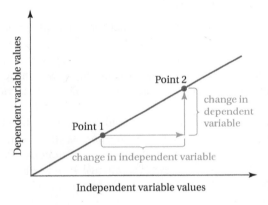

Figure 8.3 To find the slope of a straight line, we can look at any two points and divide the change in the dependent variable by the change in the independent variable.

EXAMPLE 1   Drawing a Linear Model

You hike a 3-mile trail, starting at an elevation of 8000 feet. Along the way, the trail gains elevation at a rate of 650 feet per mile. The elevation along the trail (in feet) can be viewed as a function of distance walked (in miles). What is the domain of the elevation function? From the given data, draw a graph of a linear function that gives your elevation as you hike along the trail. Does this model seem realistic?

SOLUTION   Because your elevation depends on the distance you've walked, *distance* is the independent variable and *elevation* is the dependent variable. The domain is 0 to 3 miles, which represents the length of the trail. We are given one data point: (0 mi, 8000 ft) represents the 8000-foot elevation at the start of the trail. We are also given that the rate of change of elevation with respect to distance is 650 feet per mile. Therefore, a second point on the graph is (1 mi, 8650 ft). We draw the graph by connecting these two points with a straight line and extending the line over the domain from 0 to 3 miles (Figure 8.4). As we expect, the rate of change is the slope of the graph.

This model assumes that elevation increases at a constant rate along the entire 3-mile trail. While an elevation change of 650 feet per mile seems reasonable as an average, the actual rate of change probably varies from point to point along the trail. The model's predictions are likely to be reasonable *estimates*, rather than exact values, of your elevation at different points along the trail. $\cdot \cdot \bullet$

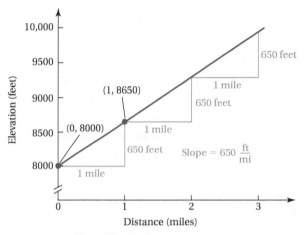

Figure 8.4 Linear function for Example 1.

EXAMPLE 2 A Price-Demand Function

A small store sells fresh pineapples. Based on data for pineapple prices between $2 and $5, the storeowners created a model in which a linear function is used to describe how the demand (number of pineapples sold per day) varies with the price (Figure 8.5). For example, the point ($2, 80 pineapples) means that, at a price of $2 per pineapple, 80 pineapples can be sold on an average day. What is the rate of change for this function? Discuss the validity of this model.

SOLUTION The rate of change of the demand function is the slope of its graph. We identify *price* as the independent variable and *demand* as the dependent variable. We can calculate the slope using any two points on the graph. Let's choose Point 1 as ($2, 80 pineapples) and Point 2 as ($5, 50 pineapples). The change in *price* between the two points is $5 − $2 = $3. The change in *demand* between the two points is

50 pineapples − 80 pineapples = −30 pineapples

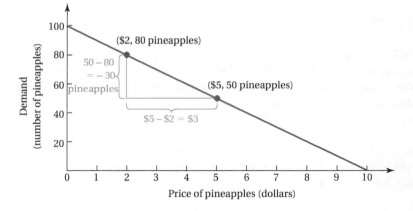

Figure 8.5 Linear functions for Example 2.

The change in demand is negative because demand *decreases* from Point 1 to Point 2. The rate of change is

$$\text{rate of change} = \frac{\text{change in demand}}{\text{change in price}} = \frac{-30 \text{ pineapples}}{\$3} = \frac{-10 \text{ pineapples}}{\$1}$$

The rate of change of the demand function is -10 pineapples per dollar: For every dollar that the price *increases,* the number of pineapples sold *decreases* by 10.

This model seems reasonable within the domain for which the storeowners gathered data: between prices of $2 and $5. Outside this domain, the model's predictions probably are not valid. For example, the model predicts that the store could sell one pineapple per day at a price of $9.90, but could *never* sell a pineapple at a price of $10. On the other extreme, the model predicts that the store could "sell" only 100 pineapples if they were free! As with many models, this price-demand model is useful only in a limited domain. • • ●

The Change in the Dependent Variable

Consider again the rain depth function in Figure 8.1 Suppose we want to know how much the rain depth changes in a 4-hour period. Because the rate of change for this function is 1 in/hr, the total change after 4 hours is

$$\text{change in rain depth} = 1 \underbrace{\frac{\text{in}}{\text{hr}}}_{\text{rate of change}} \times \underbrace{4 \text{ hr}}_{\text{elapsed time}} = 4 \text{ in}$$

Notice how the units work out. Note also that the *elapsed time* is the change in the independent variable and the change in rain depth is the change in the dependent variable. We can generalize this idea to other functions.

> *She knew only that if she did or said thus-and-so, men would unerringly respond with the complimentary thus-and-so. It was like a mathematical formula and no more difficult, for mathematics was the one subject that had come easy to Scarlett in her schooldays.*
>
> —Margaret Mitchell,
> Gone with the Wind

> **The Rate Of Change Rule**
>
> The rate of change rule allows us to calculate the change in the dependent variable from the change in the independent variable:
>
> $$\text{Change in dependent variable} = \left(\begin{array}{c}\text{rate of}\\\text{change}\end{array}\right) \times \left(\begin{array}{c}\text{change in}\\\text{independent variable}\end{array}\right)$$

EXAMPLE ③ Change in Demand

Using the linear demand function in Figure 8.5, predict the change in demand for pineapples if the price increases by $3.

SOLUTION The independent variable is the *price* of the pineapples, and the dependent variable is the *demand* for pineapples. In Example 2, we found that the rate of change of demand with respect to price is -10 pineapples per dollar. The change in demand for a price increase of $3 is

$$\text{change in } demand = \text{rate of change} \times \text{change in } price$$

$$= -10 \frac{\text{pineapples}}{\$} \times \$3$$

$$= -30 \text{ pineapples}$$

This model predicts that a $3 price increase will lead to 30 *fewer* pineapples being sold per day. • • ●

General Equation for a Linear Function

Suppose your job is to oversee an automated assembly line that manufactures computer chips. You arrive at work one day to find a stock of 25 chips that were produced during the night. If chips are produced at a constant rate of 4 chips per hour, how large is the stock of chips at any particular time during your shift?

Answering this question requires finding a function that describes how the number of chips depends on the time of day. We identify *time*, which we'll denote by t, as the independent variable. *Number of chips*, which we'll denote by N, is the dependent variable. At the start of your shift, $t = 0$ and your initial stock is $N = 25$ chips. Because the stock grows by 4 chips every hour, the *rate of change* of this function is 4 chips per hour. We construct a graph by starting at the initial point (0 hr, 25 chips) and drawing a straight line with a slope of 4 chips per hour (Figure 8.6).

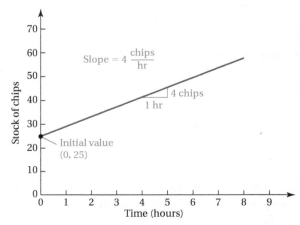

Figure 8.6   Linear function with initial value of 25 chips and slope of 4 chips/hr.

The goal is to write an equation for the function. First, let's describe the stock of chips at any particular time with a word equation:

$$\text{number of chips} = \text{initial number of chips} + \text{change in number of chips}$$

For the change in the number of chips, we have

$$\underbrace{\text{change in } \textit{number of chips}}_{\text{change in dependent variable}} = \underbrace{4\ \frac{\text{chips}}{\text{hr}}}_{\text{rate of change}} \times \underbrace{\textit{elapsed time}}_{\substack{\text{change in independent}\\\text{variable}}}$$

Using this result and 25 for the initial number of chips, we get the following equation for the number of chips:

$$\textit{number of chips} = 25 \text{ chips} + \left(4\ \frac{\text{chips}}{\text{hr}} \times \textit{elapsed time}\right)$$

Simplifying the notation, we replace *elapsed time* by t and *number of chips* by N to produce the following compact equation:

$$N = 25 + 4t$$

Note that, because we no longer show the units explicitly, we must remember 25 represents a number of chips and 4 represents a rate of change in units of chips/hr. We can use this equation to find the number of chips at any time. For example, after $t = 3.5$ hours, the number of chips is

$$N = 25 + (4 \times 3.5) = 39$$

To generalize from this example to any linear function, note that

- The number of chips, N, is the **dependent variable**.
- The time, t, is the **independent variable**.
- The initial stock of 25 chips represents the **initial value** of the dependent variable when $t = 0$.
- The term 4 chips/hr is the **rate of change** of N with respect to t, so chips/hr $\times t$ is the *change* in N.

General Formula for a Linear Function

dependent variable = initial value + (rate of change × independent variable)

USING TECHNOLOGY

GRAPHING FUNCTIONS

A graphing calculator makes it easy to graph almost any function, but there are other ways to accomplish the same task. A search on "graphing calculator" will turn up numerous websites offering applets that mimic graphing calculators. You can graph functions in Excel by making a table of (x, y) data points for the function. Create the table with x values in one column and corresponding y values in a second column; then you can use Excel's chart type "scatter" to make the graph.

The Equation of a Line

If you have taken a course in algebra, you may be familiar with the equation for a linear function in a slightly different form. In algebra, x is commonly used for the independent variable and y for the dependent variable. For a straight line, the slope is usually denoted by m and the initial value, or y **intercept**, is denoted by b. With these symbols, the equation for a linear function becomes

$$y = mx + b$$

which has the same form as the general equation of a linear function given above. For example, the equation $y = 4x - 4$ represents a straight line with a slope of 4 and a y-intercept of -4. As shown in Figure 8.7(a), the y-intercept tells us where the line crosses the y-axis.

Figure 8.7(b) shows the effects of keeping the same y-intercept but changing the slope. A positive slope $(m > 0)$ means the line rises to the right. A negative slope $(m < 0)$ means the line falls to the right. A zero slope $(m = 0)$ means a horizontal line.

Figure 8.7(c) shows the effects of changing the y-intercept for a set of lines that have the same slope. All the lines rise at the same rate but cross the y-axis at different points.

TECHNICAL NOTE

The equation of a line can be written in other forms. For example, any equation of the form $Ax + By + C = 0$ (where A, B, and C are constants) describes a straight line. We can see why by solving the equation for y (assuming $B \neq 0$), which gives $y = -(A/B)x - (C/B)$. In this form, we identify the slope as $-(A/B)$ and the y-intercept as $-(C/B)$.

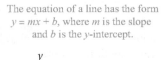
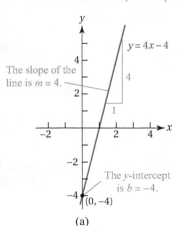
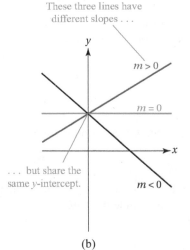
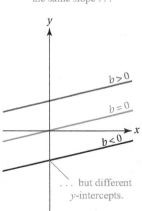

(a)   (b)   (c)

Figure 8.7 (a) Graph of $y = 4x - 4$. (b) Lines with same y-intercept but different slope. (c) Lines with the same slope but different y-intercepts.

EXAMPLE ④ Rain Depth Equation

Using the function shown in Figure 8.1, write an equation that describes the rain depth at any time after the storm began. Use the equation to find the rain depth 3 hours after the storm began.

SOLUTION   For the rain depth function in Figure 8.1, the rate of change is 1 in/hr and the initial value of the rain depth when the storm begins is 0 inches. The general equation for this function is

$$\underbrace{rain\ depth}_{\text{dependent variable}} = \underbrace{0\ in}_{\text{initial value}} + \underbrace{1\frac{in}{hr}}_{\text{rate of change}} \times \underbrace{time}_{\text{independent variable}}$$

We can write this equation more compactly by letting r represent *rain depth* (in inches) and t represent *time* (in hours):

$$r = 0 + (1 \times t), \quad \text{or} \quad r = t$$

Substituting $t = 3$ hours in this equation, we find that the rain depth 3 hours after the storm began is $r = 3$ inches.   ⋅⋅●

EXAMPLE ⑤ Alcohol Metabolism

The purpose of models is not to fit the data but to sharpen the questions.

—Samuel Karlin, mathematician

Alcohol is metabolized by the body (through enzymes in the liver) in such a way that the blood alcohol content decreases linearly. A study by the National Institute on Alcohol Abuse and Alcoholism showed that, for a group of fasting males who consumed four drinks rapidly, the blood alcohol content rose to a maximum of 0.08 g/100 mL about an hour after the drinks were consumed. Three hours later, the blood alcohol content had decreased to 0.04 g/100 mL. Find a linear model that describes the elimination of alcohol after the peak blood alcohol content is reached. According to the model, what is the blood alcohol content five hours after the peak is reached?

SOLUTION   We seek a linear function that relates the independent variable *time* to the dependent variable *blood alcohol content* (BAC, for short). To avoid confusion, we'll write the BAC values without the units. If we let $t = 0$ represent the time at which the BAC reached a peak, the study gives us two points: $(0\ hr, 0.08)$ and $(3\ hr, 0.04)$. We can use these two points to find the rate of change, or slope, of the function:

$$\text{slope} = \frac{\text{change in BAC}}{\text{change in } time} = \frac{(0.04 - 0.08)}{(3 - 0)\ hr} = \frac{-0.04}{3\ hr} \approx \frac{-0.0133}{hr}$$

That is, for each hour, the BAC *decreases* by about 0.0133. The initial value for the BAC is 0.08. Therefore, the general linear equation for this function becomes

$$\underbrace{\text{BAC}}_{\text{dependent variable}} = \underbrace{0.08}_{\text{initial value}} + \left(\underbrace{-0.0133\frac{1}{hr}}_{\text{rate of change}} \times \underbrace{time}_{\text{independent variable}}\right)$$

We can write the equation more compactly as

$$\text{BAC} = 0.08 - (0.0133 \times t)$$

Figure 8.8 shows the graph of this function. The slope is -0.0133, and the vertical intercept is 0.08. To determine the BAC five hours after the peak BAC is reached, we set $t = 5$ and evaluate BAC:

$$\text{BAC} = 0.08 - (0.0133 \times 5) = 0.0135$$

Five hours after the peak BAC is reached (six hours after the drinks were consumed), the BAC is still significant. In fact, it's roughly 15% of the legal limit in most states.

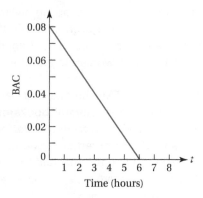

Figure 8.8 Linear function for Example 5.

· · ●

EXAMPLE ⑥ Price from Demand

Write an equation for the linear demand function in Figure 8.5. Then determine the price that should result in a demand of 80 pineapples per day.

SOLUTION   Earlier, we found that the rate of change, or slope, for this function is -10 pineapples per dollar. The initial value, or y-intercept, is 100 pineapples, because that is the demand predicted for a price of \$0. Let's use p for the independent variable *price* and d for the dependent variable *demand*. With the slope of -10 and y-intercept of 100, the equation for this function is

$$d = 100 - 10p$$

Because we are asked to find the price for a given demand, we must solve this equation for the price, p. We do so by first subtracting 100 from both sides, then dividing both sides by -10 and finally interchanging the left and right sides. You should confirm that this gives the following result:

$$p = \frac{d - 100}{-10}$$

Substituting a demand of $d = 80$ pineapples, we find

$$p = \frac{80 - 100}{-10} = \frac{-20}{-10} = 2$$

Based on this model, the price should be set at \$2 if the storeowners want to sell 80 pineapples each day. Note that we must find the units (dollars) for the answer by looking back to the original data.

· · ●

Linear Functions from Two Data Points

Suppose we have two data points and want to find a linear function that fits them. We can find the equation for this linear function by using the two data points to determine the rate of change (slope) and the initial value for the function. The following three steps summarize the process, which is described for variables (x, y); of course, you can use any symbols you wish.

IN YOUR WORLD Algebra's Baghdad Connection

After the fall of ancient Rome in the 5th century, European civilization entered the period known as the Dark Ages. However, it was not a dark time in the Middle East, where a new center of intellectual achievement arose in the city of Baghdad (in modern-day Iraq). Jews, Christians, and Muslims in Baghdad worked together in scholarly pursuits during this period.

One of the greatest scholars was a Muslim named Muhammad ibn Musa al-Khwarizmi (780–850 C.E.). Al-Khwarizmi wrote several books on astronomy and mathematics, including one entitled *Hisab al-jabr wal-muqabala*, which translates roughly as "the science of equations." This book preserved and extended the work of the Greek mathematician Diophantus (210–290 C.E.) and thereby laid the foundations of algebra. In fact, the word *algebra* comes directly from the Arabic words *al-jabr* in the book's title. The introduction to the book states its purpose to teach

what is easiest and most useful in arithmetic, such as men constantly require in cases of inheritance, legacies, partition, lawsuits, and trade, and in all their dealings with one another, or where the measuring of lands, the digging of canals, geometrical computations, and other objects of various sorts and kinds are concerned.

Notice the practical intent of this first algebra book, which stands in stark contrast to the abstract nature of many algebra books today.

In another of his works, al-Khwarizmi described the numeral system developed by Hindu mathematicians, thereby popularizing the decimal system and the use of the numeral zero. Although he did not claim credit for the Hindu work, later writers often attributed it to him. That is why modern numerals are known as *Hindu-Arabic* rather than solely Hindu. Some later authors even attributed the numerals to al-Khwarizmi personally. In a sloppy writing of his name, the use of Hindu numerals became known as *algorismi*, which later became the English words *algorism* (arithmetic) and *algorithm*. Historians consider al-Khwarizmi one of the most important mathematicians of all time, and his work lies at the foundation of modern mathematics.

Creating a Linear Function from Two Data Points

Step 1. Let x be the independent variable and y be the dependent variable. Find the change in each variable between the two given points, and use these changes to calculate the slope, or rate of change:

$$\text{slope} = \frac{\text{change in } y}{\text{change in } x}$$

Step 2. Substitute this slope and the *numerical values* of y and x from either data point into the equation $y = mx + b$. You can then solve for the y-intercept, b, because it will be the only unknown in the equation.

Step 3. Now use the slope and y-intercept to write the equation of the linear function in the form $y = mx + b$.

EXAMPLE 7 Crude Oil Use Since 1850

Until about 1850, humans used so little crude oil that we can call the amount zero—at least in comparison to the amount used since that time. By 1960, humans had used a total (cumulative) of 600 billion cubic meters of oil. Create a linear model that describes world oil use since 1850. Discuss the validity of the model.

SOLUTION We seek a function that describes how *total oil used* varies with *time*. We identify *time* as the independent variable, which we'll denote by t and measure in years C.E. *Total oil used* is the dependent variable, so we'll call it y and measure it in billions of cubic meters.

We are given two data points. The first is (1850, 0), indicating that no oil had been used by 1850. The second is (1960, 600), which represents the 600 billion cubic meters used by 1960. We now use the three-step procedure to find an equation for a linear function fitting the two points.

Step 1. Note that we've used t rather than x for the independent variable, because it helps us remember that we are dealing with time. That is, we let t play the role of x in finding the slope:

$$m = \text{slope} = \frac{\text{change in } y}{\text{change in } t} = \frac{600 - 0}{1960 - 1850} = \frac{600}{110} = 5.45 \,(\text{billion m}^3 \text{ per year})$$

Step 2. We are looking for an equation of the form $y = mt + b$. We already have the slope, $m = 5.45$. If we use the numerical values from the first data point, $t = 1850$ and $y = 0$, this equation becomes

$$0 = 5.45 \times 1850 + b$$

We solve for b by subtracting the product 5.45×1850 from both sides and then interchanging the left and right sides. We find

$$b = -5.45 \times 1850 = -10{,}083 \,(\text{billion cubic meters})$$

Step 3. We now have both the slope, $m = 5.45$, and the y-intercept, $b = -10{,}083$. The equation for the linear function is

$$y = mt + b = 5.45t - 10{,}083$$

Figure 8.9 shows the graph of this function.

Now that we have the function, we can ask about its validity as a model for oil consumption. First, note that we draw the graph only for years after 1850. Years prior to 1850, in which we assumed oil consumption to be zero, are not in the domain of the function. The more significant issue is whether the rise in oil consumption has been linear. The rate of oil consumption tends to increase with population. In fact, it has increased more rapidly than population because the average person uses more oil now than in the past. We know that population has risen exponentially since the mid-19th century, so a better model for oil consumption would be exponential instead of linear. The blue curve in Figure 8.9 shows an exponential fit to the two data points; we will discuss the creation of exponential models in the next unit.

BY THE WAY

Annual world oil consumption in 2009 was more than triple annual oil consumption in 1960.

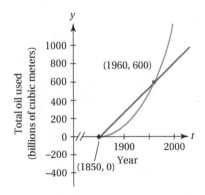

Figure 8.9 The red line shows a linear model for the two data points. The blue curve fits the data with an exponential function.

Quick Quiz

Choose the best answer to each of the following questions. Explain your reasoning with one or more complete sentences.

1. A *linear function* is characterized by

   a. an increasing slope.

   b. a decreasing slope.

   c. a constant slope.

2. You have a graph of a linear function. To determine the function's rate of change, you should

   a. identify the domain.

   b. measure the slope.

   c. compare the function to another, closely related linear function.

3. The graph of a linear function is sloping downward (from left to right). This tells us that

   a. its domain is decreasing.

   b. its range is decreasing.

   c. it has a negative rate of change.

4. Suppose that Figure 9.11 is an accurate representation of elevation changes for the first 3 miles of a much longer trail. If you have no data other than those shown, what should you predict for the elevation at mile 5 of the trail?

   a. The elevation is $(8000 + 5 \times 650)$ feet.

   b. You should not make a prediction, because the elevation at 5 miles must be higher than the 10,000-foot maximum shown on the graph.

   c. You should not make a prediction, because mile 5 of the trail is not within the domain of the function shown.

5. Which town would have the steepest slope on a graph showing its population as a function of time?

   a. a town growing at a constant rate of 50 people per year

   b. a town growing at a constant rate of 75 people per year

   c. a town growing at a constant rate of 100 people per year

6. Consider the function $price = \$100 - (\$3/yr) \times time$. The initial value of this function is

   a. $100.   b. $3.   c. $0.

7. Consider the demand function given in Example 6, which is $d = 100 - 10p$. A graph of this function would

   a. slope upward, starting from a price of $100.

   b. slope upward, starting from a price of $0.

   c. slope downward, starting from a price of $100.

8. A line intersects the *y*-axis at a value of $y = 7$ and has a slope of -2. The equation of this line is

   a. $y = -2x + 7$.

   b. $y = 7x - 2$.

   c. $y = 2x - 7$.

9. Consider a line with equation $y = 12x - 3$. Which of the following lines has the same slope but a different *y*-intercept?

   a. $y = \dfrac{12}{3}x - \dfrac{3}{3}$ b. $y = 12x + 3$

   c. $y = -12x - 3$

10. Charlie picks apples in the orchard at a constant rate. By 9:00 a.m. he has picked 150 apples, and by 11:00 a.m. he has picked 550 apples. If we use *A* for the number of apples and *t* for time measured in hours since 9:00 a.m., which of the following functions describes his harvesting?

    a. $A = 150t + 2$

    b. $A = 550t + 150$

    c. $A = 200t + 150$

Exercises

Review Questions

1. What does it mean to say that a function is linear?

2. Define *rate of change*, and describe how a rate of change is stated in words (that is, using "with respect to").

3. How is the rate of change of a linear function related to the slope of its graph?

4. How do you find the change in the dependent variable, given a change in the independent variable? Give an example.

5. Describe the general equation for a linear function. How is it related to the standard algebraic form $y = mx + b$?

6. Describe the process of creating an equation for a linear function from two data points. How are such models useful?

Does it Make Sense? Decide whether each of the following statements makes sense (or is clearly true) or does not make sense (or is clearly false). Explain your reasoning.

7. When I graphed the linear function, it turned out to be a wavy curve.

8. I graphed two linear functions, and the one with the greater rate of change had the greater slope.

9. My freeway speed is the rate of change in my distance with respect to time.

10. It's possible to make a linear model from any two data points, but there's no guarantee that the model will fit other data points.

Basic Skills & Concepts

11–16: Linear Functions. Consider the following graphs.

  a. In words, describe the function shown on the graph.

  b. Find the slope of the graph and express it as a rate of change (be sure to include units).

  c. Briefly discuss the conditions under which a linear function is a realistic model for the given situation.

11.

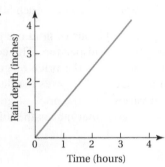

12.

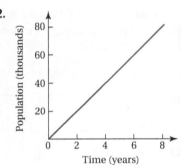

13.

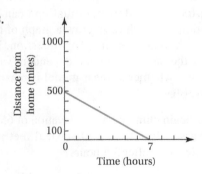

14.

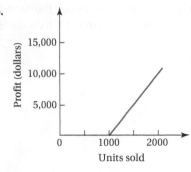

15.

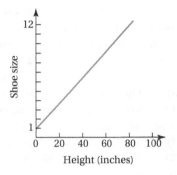

16.

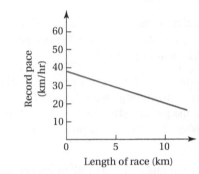

17–22: Rate of Change Rule. The following situations involve a rate of change that is constant. Write a statement that describes how one variable varies with respect to the other, give the rate of change numerically (with units), and use the rate of change rule to answer any questions.

Example: Every week your fingernails grow 5 millimeters. How much will your fingernails grow in 2.5 weeks?

Solution: The length of your fingernails varies with respect to time, with a rate of change of 5 mm/wk. In 2.5 weeks, your fingernails will grow 5 mm / wk × 2.5 wk = 12.5 millimeters.

17. The water depth in a lake decreases at a rate of 2 inches per day because of evaporation. How much does the water depth change in 8 days? in 15 days?

18. You run along a path at a constant speed of 5.5 miles per hour. How far do you travel in 1.5 hours? in 3.8 hours?

19. A 1-degree change (increase or decrease) on the Celsius temperature scale is equivalent to a 9/5-degree change on the Fahrenheit temperature scale. How much does the Fahrenheit temperature increase if the Celsius temperature increases 5 degrees? How much does the Fahrenheit temperature decrease if the Celsius temperature decreases 25 degrees?

20. A gas station owner finds that for every penny increase in the price of gasoline, she sells 80 fewer gallons of gas per week. How much more or less gas will she sell if she raises the price by 8 cents per gallon? if she decreases the price by 6 cents per gallon?

21. Snow accumulates during a storm at a constant rate of 3.5 inches per hour. How much snow accumulates in the first 6.3 hours? in the first 9.8 hours?

22. According to one formula, your maximum heart rate (in beats per minute) is 220 minus your age (in years). How much does your maximum heart rate change from age 25 to age 40? What is your maximum heart rate at age 70?

23–28: Linear Equations. The following situations can be modeled by linear functions. In each case, write an equation for the linear function and use it to answer the given question. Be sure you clearly identify the independent and dependent variables. Then briefly discuss whether a linear model is reasonable for the situation described.

23. The price of a particular model car is $18,000 today and rises with time at a constant rate of $900 per year. How much will a new car cost in 3.5 years?

24. In 2012, Dana Vollmer set the women's world record in the 100-meter butterfly (swimming) with a time of 55.98 seconds. Assume that the record falls at a constant rate of 0.05 second per year. What does the model predict for the record in 2020?

25. A snowplow has a maximum speed of 40 miles per hour on a dry highway. Its maximum speed decreases by 1.1 miles per hour for every inch of snow on the highway. According to this model, at what snow depth will the plow be unable to move?

26. The cost of leasing a car is $1000 for a down payment and processing fee plus $360 per month. For how many months can you lease a car with $3680?

27. You can rent time on computers at the local copy center for a $10 setup charge and an additional $2 for every 5 minutes. How much time can you rent for $25?

28. In 2000, the population of Boom Town began increasing at a rate of 300 people per year. The 2000 population was 1500 people. What is your projection for the population in the year 2020?

29–34: Equations from Two Data Points. Create the required linear function, and use it to answer the following questions.

29. Suppose your pet dog weighed 2.5 pounds at birth and weighed 15 pounds one year later. Based on these two data points, find a linear function that describes how weight varies with age. Use this function to predict your dog's weight at 5 and 10 years of age. Comment on the validity of the model.

30. You can purchase a motorcycle for $6500 or lease it for a down payment of $200 and $150 per month. Find a function that describes how the cost of the lease depends on time. How long can you lease the motorcycle before you've paid more than its purchase price?

31. A Campus Republicans fundraiser offers raffle tickets for $10 each. The prize for the raffle is a $350 television set, which must be purchased with proceeds from the ticket sales. Find a function that gives the profit/loss for the raffle as it varies with the number of tickets sold. How many tickets must be sold for the raffle sales to equal the cost of the prize?

32. The Campus Democrats plan to pay a visitor $100 to speak at a fundraiser. Tickets will be sold for $4 apiece. Find a function that gives the profit/loss for the event as it varies with the number of tickets sold. How many people must attend the event for the club to break even?

33. A $1200 washing machine in a laundromat is depreciated for tax purposes at a rate of $75 per year. Find a function for the depreciated value of the washing machine as it varies with time. When does the depreciated value reach $0?

34. A mining company can extract 2000 tons of gold ore per day with a purity of 3 ounces of gold per ton. The cost of extraction is $1000 per ton. If p is the price of gold in dollars per ounce, find a function that gives the daily profit/loss of the mine as it varies with the price of gold. What is the minimum price of gold that makes the mine profitable?

Further Applications

35–42: Algebraic Linear Equations. For the following functions, find the slope of the graph and the intercept. Then sketch the graph for values of x between -10 and 10.

35. $y = 2x + 6$

36. $y = -3x + 3$

37. $y = -5x - 5$

38. $y = 4x + 1$

39. $y = 3x - 6$

40. $y = -2x + 5$

41. $y = -x + 4$

42. $y = 2x + 4$

43–48: Linear Graphs. The following situations can be modeled by linear functions. In each case, draw a graph of the function and use the graph to answer the given question. Be sure you clearly identify the independent and dependent variables. Then briefly discuss whether a linear model is reasonable for the situation described.

43. A group of climbers begin climbing at an elevation of 6500 feet and ascend at a steady rate of 600 vertical feet per hour. What is their elevation after 3.5 hours?

44. The diameter of a tree increases by 0.2 inch with each passing year. When you started observing the tree, its diameter was 4 inches. Estimate the time at which the tree started growing.

45. The cost of publishing a poster is $2000 for setting up the printing equipment, plus $3 per poster printed. What is the total cost to produce 2000 posters?

46. The amount of sugar in a fermenting batch of beer decreases with time at a rate of 0.1 gram per day, starting from an initial amount of 5 grams. When is the sugar gone?

47. The cost of a particular private school begins with a one-time initiation fee of $2000, plus annual tuition of $10,000. How much will it cost to attend this school for six years?

48. The maximum speed of a semitrailer truck up a steep hill varies with the weight of its cargo. With no cargo, it can maintain a maximum speed of 50 miles per hour. With 20 tons of cargo, its maximum speed drops to 40 miles per hour. At what load does a linear model predict a maximum speed of 0 miles per hour?

49. Wildlife Management. A common technique for estimating populations of birds or fish is to tag and release individual animals in two different outings. This procedure is called *catch and release*. If the wildlife remain in the sampling area and are randomly caught, a fraction of the animals tagged during the first outing are likely to be caught again during the second outing. Based on the number tagged and the fraction caught twice, the total number of animals in the area can be estimated.

  a. Consider a case in which 200 fish are tagged and released during the first outing. During a second outing in the same area, 200 fish are again caught and released, of which one-half are already tagged. Estimate N, the *total* number of fish in the entire sampling area. Explain your reasoning.

  b. Consider a case in which 200 fish are tagged and released during the first outing. During a second outing in the same area, 200 fish are again caught and released, of which one-fourth are already tagged. Estimate N the *total* number of fish in the entire sampling area. Explain your reasoning.

  c. eneralize your results from parts (a) and (b) by letting p be the fraction of tagged fish that are caught during the second outing. Find a formula for the function

$N = f(p)$ that relates the total number of fish, N, to the fraction tagged during the second outing, p.

  d. Graph the function obtained in part (c). What is the domain? Explain.

  e. Suppose that 15% of the fish in the second sample are tagged. Use the formula from part (c) to estimate the total number of fish in the sampling area. Confirm your result on your graph.

  f. Locate a real study in which catch and release methods were used. Report on the specific details of the study and how closely it followed the theory outlined in this problem.

In Your World

50. Linear Models. Describe at least two situations from the news or your own life in which predictions must be made and a linear model seems appropriate. Briefly discuss why the linear model works well.

51. Nonlinear Models. Describe at least one situation from the news or your own life in which predictions must be made but a linear function is *not* a good model. Briefly discuss the shape (on a graph) that you would expect the function to take.

52. Alcohol Metabolism. Most drugs are eliminated from the blood through an exponential decay process with a constant half-life. Alcohol is an exception in that it is metabolized through a linear decay process. Find data showing how the blood alcohol content (BAC) decreases over time, and use the data to develop a linear model. Discuss the validity of the model. What assumptions (for example, gender, weight, number of drinks) were used in creating the model?

53. Property Depreciation. Go to the IRS website, and examine the rules for depreciation of some type of property, such as a rental property or a piece of business equipment. Make a linear model that describes the depreciation function.

8.4

BEST-FIT LINES AND PREDICTION

Suppose you are lucky enough to win a 1.5-carat diamond in a contest. Based on the correlation between weight and price, it should be possible to predict the approximate value of the diamond. We need only study the graph carefully and decide where a point corresponding to 1.5 carats is most likely to fall. To do this, it is helpful to draw a **best-fit line** (also called a *regression line*) through the data, as shown in Figure 8.10. This line is a "best fit" in the sense that, according to a standard statistical measure (which we discuss shortly), the data points lie closer to this line than to any other straight line that we could draw through the data.

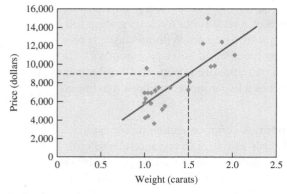

Figure 8.10   Best-fit line for the data from.

> ### Definition
> The **best-fit line** (or *regression line*) on a scatterplot is a line that lies closer to the data points than any other possible line (according to a standard statistical measure of closeness).

Of all the possible straight lines that can be drawn on a diagram, how do you know which one is the best-fit line? In many cases, you can make a good estimate of the best-fit line simply by looking at the data and drawing the line that visually appears to pass closest to all the data points. This method involves drawing the best-fit line "by eye." As you might guess, there are methods for calculating the precise equation of a best-fit line (see the optional topic at the end of this section), and many computer programs and calculators can do these calculations automatically. For our purposes in this text, a fit by eye will generally be sufficient.

It is a capital mistake to theorize before one has data.

—Arthur Conan Doyle

Predictions with Best-Fit Lines

We can use the best-fit line in Figure 8.10 to predict the price of a 1.5-carat diamond. As indicated by the dashed lines in the figure, the best-fit line predicts that the diamond will cost about $9,000. Notice, however, that two actual data points in the figure correspond to 1.5-carat diamonds, and both of these diamonds cost less than $9,000. That is, although the predicted price of $9,000 sounds reasonable, it is certainly not guaranteed. In fact, the degree of scatter among the data points in this case tells us that we should *not* trust the best-fit line to predict accurately the price for any individual diamond. Instead, the prediction is meaningful only in a statistical sense: It tells us that if we examined many 1.5-carat diamonds, their mean price would be about $9,000.

This is only the first of several important cautions about interpreting predictions with best-fit lines. A second caution is to beware of using best-fit lines to make predictions that go beyond the bounds of the available data. Figure 8.11 shows a best-fit line for the correlation between infant mortality and longevity. According to this line, a country with a life expectancy of more than about 80 years would have a *negative* infant mortality rate, which is impossible.

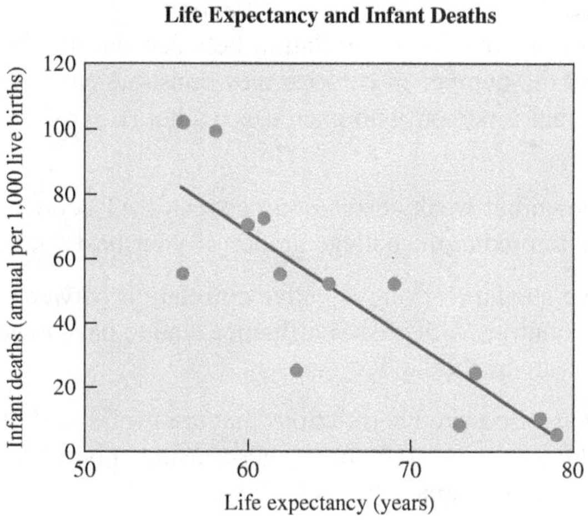

Life Expectancy and Infant Deaths

Figure 8.11 A best-fit line for the correlation between infant mortality and longevity.
Source: United Nations.

A third caution is to avoid using best-fit lines from old data sets to make predictions about current or future results. For example, economists studying historical data found a strong negative correlation between unemployment and the rate of inflation. According to this correlation, inflation should have risen dramatically in the mid-2000s when the unemployment rate fell below 6%. But inflation remained low, showing that the correlation from old data did not continue to hold.

Fourth, a correlation discovered with a sample drawn from a particular population cannot generally be used to make predictions about other populations. For example, we can't expect that the correlation between aspirin consumption and heart attacks in an experiment involving only men will also apply to women.

Fifth, remember that we can draw a best-fit line through any data set, but that line is meaningless when the correlation is not significant or when the relationship is nonlinear. For example, there is no correlation between shoe size and IQ, so we could not use shoe size to predict IQ.

It's tough to make predictions, especially about the future.

—attributed to Niels Bohr,
Yogi Berra, and others

Cautions in Making Predictions from Best-Fit Lines

1. Don't expect a best-fit line to give a good prediction unless the correlation is strong and there are many data points. If the sample points lie very close to the best-fit line, the correlation is very strong and the prediction is more likely to be accurate. If the sample points lie away from the best-fit line by substantial amounts, the correlation is weak and predictions tend to be much less accurate.

2. Don't use a best-fit line to make predictions beyond the bounds of the data points to which the line was fit.

3. A best-fit line based on past data is not necessarily valid now and might not result in valid predictions of the future.

4. Don't make predictions about a population that is different from the population from which the sample data were drawn.

5. Remember that a best-fit line is meaningless when there is no significant correlation or when the relationship is nonlinear.

EXAMPLE 1 Valid Predictions?

State whether the prediction (or implied prediction) should be trusted in each of the following cases, and explain why or why not.

a. You've found a best-fit line for a correlation between the number of hours per day that people exercise and the number of calories they consume each day. You've used this correlation to predict that a person who exercises 18 hours per day would consume 15,000 calories per day.

b. There is a well-known but weak correlation between SAT scores and college grades. You use this correlation to predict the college grades of your best friend from her SAT scores.

c. Historical data have shown a strong negative correlation between national birth rates and affluence. That is, countries with greater affluence tend to have lower birth rates. These data predict a high birth rate in Russia.

d. A study in China has discovered correlations that are useful in designing museum exhibits that Chinese children enjoy. A curator suggests using this information to design a new museum exhibit for Atlanta-area school children.

e. Scientific studies have shown a very strong correlation between children's ingesting of lead and mental retardation. Based on this correlation, paints containing lead were banned.

f. Based on a large data set, you've made a scatterplot for salsa consumption (per person) versus years of education. The diagram shows no significant correlation, but you've drawn a best-fit line anyway. The line predicts that someone who consumes a pint of salsa per week has at least 13 years of education.

SOLUTION

a. No one exercises 18 hours per day on an ongoing basis, so this much exercise must be beyond the bounds of any data collected. Therefore, a prediction about someone who exercises 18 hours per day should not be trusted.

b. The fact that the correlation between SAT scores and college grades is weak means there is much scatter in the data. As a result, we should not expect great accuracy if we use this weak correlation to make a prediction about a single individual.

c. We cannot automatically assume that the historical data still apply today. In fact, Russia currently has a very low birth rate, despite also having a low level of affluence.

d. The suggestion to use information from the Chinese study for an Atlanta exhibit assumes that predictions made from correlations in China also apply to Atlanta. However, given the cultural differences between China and Atlanta, the curator's suggestion should not be considered without more information to back it up.

e. Given the strength of the correlation and the severity of the consequences, this prediction and the ban that followed seem quite reasonable. In fact, later studies established lead as an actual *cause* of mental retardation, making the rationale behind the ban even stronger.

f. Because there is no significant correlation, the best-fit line and any predictions made from it are meaningless.   ⋯●

EXAMPLE 2 Will Women Be Faster Than Men?

Figure 8.12 shows data and best-fit lines for both men's and women's world record times in the 1-mile race. Based on these data, predict when the women's world record will be faster than the men's world record. Comment on the prediction.

BY THE WAY

In the United States, lead was banned from house paint in 1978 and from food cans in 1991, and a 25-year phaseout of lead in gasoline was completed in 1995. Nevertheless, many young children—especially children living in poor areas—still have enough lead in their blood to damage their health. Major sources of ongoing lead hazards include paint in older housing and soil near major roads, which has high lead content from past use of leaded gasoline.

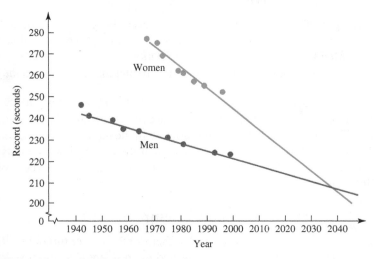

Figure 8.12 World record times in the mile (men and women).

SOLUTION   If we accept the best-fit lines as drawn, the women's world record will equal the men's world record by about 2040. However, this is *not* a valid prediction because it is based on extending the best-fit lines beyond the range of the actual data. In fact, notice that the most recent world records (as of 2011) date all the way back to 1999 for men and 1996 for women, while the best-fit lines predict that the records should have fallen by several more seconds since those dates.   ·· ●

The Correlation Coefficient and Best-Fit Lines

Earlier, we discussed the correlation coefficient as one way of measuring the strength of a correlation. We can also use the correlation coefficient to say something about the validity of predictions with best-fit lines.

For mathematical reasons (not discussed in this text), the *square* of the correlation coefficient, or r^2, is the proportion of the variation in a variable that is accounted for by the best-fit line (or, more technically, by the linear relationship that the best-fit line expresses). For example, the correlation coefficient for the diamond weight and price data (see Figure 8.10) turns out to be $r = 0.777$. If we square this value, we get $r^2 = 0.604$ which we can interpret as follows: About 0.6, or 60%, of the variation in the diamond prices is accounted for by the best-fit line relating weight and price. That leaves 40% of the variation in price that must be due to other factors, presumably such things as depth, table, color, and clarity—which is why predictions made with the best-fit line in Figure 8.10 are not very precise.

A best-fit line can give precise predictions only in the case of a perfect correlation ($r = 1$ or $r = -1$); we then find $r^2 = 1$, which means that 100% of the variation in a variable can be accounted for by the best-fit line. In this special case of $r^2 = 1$, predictions should be exactly correct, except for the fact that the sample data might not be a true representation of the population data.

Best-Fit Lines and r^2

The *square* of the correlation coefficient, or r^2, is the proportion of the variation in a variable that is accounted for by the best-fit line.

TECHNICAL NOTE

Statisticians call r^2 the coefficient of determination.

EXAMPLE ③ Retail Hiring

You are the manager of a large department store. Over the years, you've found a strong correlation between your September sales and the number of employees you'll need to hire for peak efficiency during the holiday season; the correlation coefficient is 0.950. This year your September sales are fairly strong. Should you start advertising for help based on the best-fit line?

SOLUTION   In this case, we find that $r^2 = 0.950^2 = 0.903$, which means that 90% of the variation in the number of peak employees can be accounted for by a linear relationship with September sales. That leaves only 10% of the variation in the number of peak employees unaccounted for. Because 90% is so high, we conclude that the best-fit line accounts for the data quite well, so it seems reasonable to use it to predict the number of employees you'll need for this year's holiday season.   ⋯●

EXAMPLE ④ Voter Turnout and Unemployment

Political scientists are interested in knowing what factors affect voter turnout in elections. One such factor is the unemployment rate. Data collected in presidential election years since 1964 show a very weak negative correlation between voter turnout and the unemployment rate, with a correlation coefficient of about $r = -0.1$ (Figure 8.13). Based on this correlation, should we use the unemployment rate to predict voter turnout in the next presidential election?

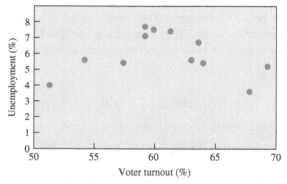

Figure 8.13 Data on voter turnout and unemployment, 1964–2008.
Source: U.S. Bureau of Labor Statistics.

SOLUTION   The square of the correlation coefficient is $r^2 = (-0.1)^2 = 0.01$, which means that only about 1% of the variation in the data is accounted for by the best-fit line. Nearly all of the variation in the data must therefore be explained by other factors. We conclude that unemployment is *not* a reliable predictor of voter turnout.   ⋯●

Multiple Regression

All who drink his remedy recover in a short time, except those whom it does not help, who all die. Therefore, it is obvious that it fails only in incurable cases.

—Galen, Roman "doctor"

If you've ever purchased a diamond, you might have been surprised that we found such a weak correlation between color and price. Surely a diamond cannot be very valuable if it has poor color quality. Perhaps color helps to explain why the correlation between weight and price is not perfect. For example, maybe differences in color explain why two diamonds with the same weight can have different prices. To check this idea, it would be nice to look for a correlation between the price and some combination of *weight and color together*.

> **TIME ⏱ UT TO THINK**
>
> Check this idea in Table 7.1. Notice, for example, that Diamonds 4 and 5 have nearly identical weights, but Diamond 4 costs only $4,299 while Diamond 5 costs $9,589. Can differences in their color explain the different prices? Study other examples in Table 7.1 in which two diamonds have similar weights but different prices. Overall, do you think that the correlation with price would be stronger if we used weight and color together instead of either one alone? Explain.

There is a method for investigating a correlation between one variable (such as price) and a *combination* of two or more other variables (such as weight and color). The technique is called **multiple regression**, and it essentially allows us to find a *best-fit equation* that relates three or more variables (instead of just two). Because it involves more than two variables, we cannot make simple diagrams to show best-fit equations for multiple regression. However, it is still possible to calculate a measure of how well the data fit a linear equation. The most common measure in multiple regression is the *coefficient of determination*, denoted R^2. It tells us how much of the scatter in the data is accounted for by the best-fit equation. If R^2 is close to 1, the best-fit equation should be very useful for making predictions within the range of the data values. If R^2 is close to zero, then predictions with the best-fit equation are essentially useless.

> **Definition**
>
> The use of **multiple regression** allows the calculation of a best-fit equation that represents the best fit between one variable (such as price) and a *combination* of two or more other variables (such as weight and color). The coefficient of determination, R^2, tells us the proportion of the scatter in the data accounted for by the best-fit equation.

In this text, we will not describe methods for finding best-fit equations by multiple regression. However, you can use the value of R^2 to interpret results from multiple regression. For example, the correlation between price and *weight and color together* results in a value of $R^2 = 0.79$. This is somewhat higher than the $r^2 = 0.61$ that we found for the correlation between price and weight alone. Statisticians who study diamond pricing know that they can get stronger correlations by including additional variables in the multiple regression (such as depth, table, and clarity). Given the billions of dollars spent annually on diamonds, you can be sure that statisticians play prominent roles in helping diamond dealers realize the largest possible profits.

EXAMPLE 5 Alumni Contributions

You've been hired by your college's alumni association to research how past contributions were associated with alumni income and years that have passed since graduation. It is found that $R^2 = 0.36$. What does that result tell us?

SOLUTION   With $R^2 = 0.36$, we conclude that 36% of the variation in past contributions can be explained by the variation in alumni income and years since graduation. It follows that 64% of the variation in past contributions can be explained by factors other than alumni income level and years since graduation. Because such a large proportion of the variation can be explained by other factors, it would make sense to try to identify any other factors that might have a strong effect on past contributions.   · · ●

Finding Equations for Best-Fit Lines (Optional Section)

The mathematical technique for finding the equation of a best-fit line is based on the following basic ideas. If we draw *any* line on a scatterplot, we can measure the *vertical* distance between each data point and that line. One measure of how well the line fits the data is the *sum of the squares* of these vertical distances. A large sum means that the vertical distances of data points from the line are fairly large and hence the line is not a very good fit. A small sum means the data points lie close to the line and the fit is good. Of all possible lines, the best-fit line is the line that minimizes the sum of the squares of the vertical distances. Because of this property, the best-fit line is sometimes called the *least squares line*.

You may recall that the equation of any straight line can be written in the general form

$$y = mx + b$$

BY THE WAY

One study of alumni donations found that, in developing a multiple regression equation, one should include these variables: income, age, marital status, whether the donor belonged to a fraternity or sorority, whether the donor is active in alumni affairs, the donor's distance from the college, and the nation's unemployment rate, used as a measure of the economy (Bruggink and Siddiqui, "An Econometric Model of Alumni Giving: A Case Study for a Liberal Arts College," *The American Economist*, Vol. 39, No. 2).

where *m* is the *slope* of the line and *b* is the *y-intercept* of the line. The formulas for the slope and y-intercept of the best-fit line are as follows:

$$\text{slope} = m = r \times \frac{s_y}{s_x}$$

$$y - \text{intercept} = b = \bar{y} - (m \times \bar{x})$$

In the above expressions, *r* is the correlation coefficient, s_x denotes the standard deviation of the *x* values (or the values of the first variable), s_y denotes the standard deviation of the *y* values, $\bar{x}$ represents the mean of the values of the variable *x*, and $\bar{y}$ represents the mean of the values of the variable *y*. Because these formulas are tedious with manual calculations, we usually use a calculator or computer to find the slope and y-intercept of best-fit lines. Statistical software packages and some calculators, such as the TI-83/84 Plus family of calculators, are designed to automatically generate the equation of a best-fit line.

When software or a calculator is used to find the slope and intercept of the best-fit line, results are commonly expressed in the format $y = b_0 + b_1 x$, where b_0 is the intercept and b_1 is the slope, so be careful to correctly identify those two values.

Section 8.4 Exercises

Statistical Literacy and Critical Thinking

1. **Best-Fit Line.** What is a best-fit line (also called a regression line)? How is a best-fit line useful?

2. **r^2.** For a study involving paired sample data, it is found that $r = -0.4$. What is the value of r^2? In general, what is r^2 called, what does it measure, and how can it be interpreted? That is, what does its value tell us about the variables?

3. **Regression.** An investigator has data consisting of heights of daughters and the heights of the corresponding mothers and fathers. She wants to analyze the data to see the effect that the height of the mother and the height of the father has on the height of the daughter. Should she use a (linear) regression or multiple regression? What is the basic difference between (linear) regression and multiple regression?

4. **R^2.** Using data described in Exercise 3, it is found that $R^2 = 0.68$. Interpret that value. That is, what does that value tell us about the data?

Does It Make Sense? For Exercises 5–8, decide whether the statement makes sense (or is clearly true) or does not make sense (or is clearly false). Explain clearly; not all of these statements have definitive answers, so your explanation is more important than your chosen answer.

5. **r^2 Value.** A value of $r^2 = 1$ is obtained from a sample of paired data with one variable representing the amount of gas (gallons) purchased and the total cost of the gas.

6. **r^2 Value.** A value of $r^2 = -0.040$ is obtained from a sample of men, with each pair of data consisting of the height in inches and the SAT score for one man.

7. **Height and Weight.** Using data from the National Health Survey, the equation of the best-fit line for women's heights and weights is obtained, and it shows that a woman 120 inches tall is predicted to weigh 430 pounds.

8. **Old Faithful.** Using paired sample data consisting of the duration time (in seconds) of eruptions of Old Faithful geyser and the time interval (in minutes) after the eruption, a value of $r^2 = 0.926$ is calculated, indicating that about 93% of the variation in the interval after eruption can be explained by the relationship between those two variables as described by the best-fit line.

PROJECTS FOR THE INTERNET & BEYOND

9. **Lead Poisoning.** Research lead poisoning, its sources, and its effects. Discuss the correlations that have helped researchers understand lead poisoning. Discuss efforts to prevent it.

10. **Asbestos.** Research asbestos, its sources, and its effects. Discuss the correlations that have helped researchers understand adverse health effects from asbestos exposure. Discuss efforts to prevent those adverse health effects.

11. **Worldwide Population Indicators.** The following table gives five population indicators for eleven selected countries. Study these data and try to identify possible correlations. Doing additional research if necessary, discuss the possible correlations you have found, speculate on

the reasons for the correlations, and discuss whether they suggest a causal relationship. Birth and death rates are per 1,000 population; fertility rate is per woman.

Country	Birth rate	Death rate	Life expectancy	Percent urban	Fertility rate
Afghanistan	50	22	43	20	6.9
Argentina	21	8	72	88	2.6
Australia	15	7	78	85	1.9
Canada	14	7	78	77	1.6
Egypt	29	8	64	45	3.4
El Salvador	30	6	68	45	3.1
France	13	9	78	73	1.6
Israel	21	7	77	91	2.8
Japan	10	7	79	78	1.5
Laos	45	15	51	22	6.7
United States	16	9	76	76	2.0

Source: The New York Times Almanac.

IN THE NEWS

16. Predictions in the News. Find a recent news report in which a correlation is used to make a prediction. Evaluate the validity of the prediction, considering all of the cautions described in this section. Overall, do you think the prediction is valid? Why or why not?

17. Best-Fit Line in the News. Although scatterplots are rare in the news, they are not unheard of. Find a scatterplot of any kind in a news article (recent or not). Draw a best-fit line by eye. Discuss what predictions, if any, can be made from your best-fit line.

18. Your Own Multiple Regression. Come up with an example from your own life or work in which a multiple regression analysis might reveal important trends. Without actually doing any analysis, describe in words what you would look for through the multiple regression and how the answers might be useful.

8.5 GROWTH: LINEAR VERSUS EXPONENTIAL

Imagine two communities, Straightown and Powertown, each with an initial population of 10,000 people (Figure 8.14). Straightown grows at a constant rate of 500 people per year, so its population reaches 10,500 after 1 year, 11,000 after 2 years, 11,500 after 3 years, and so on. Powertown grows at a constant rate of 5 *percent* per year. Because 5% of 10,000 is 500, Powertown's population also reaches 10,500 after 1 year. In the second year, however, Powertown's population increases by 5% of 10,500, which is 525, to 11,025. In the third year, Powertown's population increases by 5% of 11,025, or by 551 people. Figure 8.14 contrasts the populations of the two towns over a 45-year period. Note that Powertown's population rises ever more steeply and quickly outpaces Straightown's.

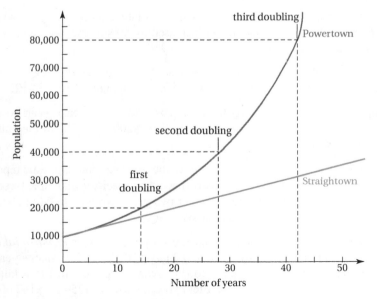

Figure 8.14 Straightown grows linearly, while Powertown grows exponentially.

Straightown and Powertown illustrate two fundamentally different types of growth. Straightown grows by the same *absolute* amount—500 people—each year, which is characteristic of **linear growth.** In contrast, Powertown grows by the same *relative* amount—5%—each year, which is characteristic of **exponential growth.**

> **Two Basic Growth Patterns**
>
> **Linear growth** occurs when a quantity grows by the same *absolute* amount in each unit of time.
>
> **Exponential growth** occurs when a quantity grows by the same *relative* amount—that is, by the same *percentage*—in each unit of time.

The terms *linear* and *exponential* can also be applied to quantities that decrease with time. For example, *exponential decay* occurs when a quantity decreases by the same relative amount in each unit of time. In the rest of this unit, we will explore the surprising properties of exponential growth.

EXAMPLE 1 Linear or Exponential?

In each of the following situations, state whether the growth (or decay) is linear or exponential, and answer the associated questions.

a. The number of students at Wilson High School has increased by 50 in each of the past four years. If the student population was 750 four years ago, what is it today?

b. The price of milk has been rising 3% per year. If the price of a gallon of milk was $4 a year ago, what is it now?

c. Tax law allows you to depreciate the value of your equipment by $200 per year. If you purchased the equipment three years ago for $1000, what is its depreciated value today?

d. The memory capacity of state-of-the-art computer storage devices is doubling approximately every two years. If a company's top-of-the-line drive holds 16 terabytes today, what will it hold in six years?

e. The price of high-definition TV sets has been falling by about 25% per year. If the price is $1000 today, what can you expect it to be in two years?

SOLUTION

a. The number of students increased by the same absolute amount each year, so this is *linear growth*. Because the student population increased by 50 students per year, in four years it grew by $4 \times 50 = 200$ students, from 750 to 950.

b. The price rises by the same percent each year, so this is *exponential growth*. If the price was $4 a year ago, it increased by $0.03 \times \$4 = \$0.12$, making the price $4.12.

c. The equipment value decreases by the same absolute amount each year, so this is *linear decay*. In three years, the value decreases by $3 \times \$200 = \$600$, so the value decreases from $1000 to $400.

d. A doubling is the same as a 100% increase, so the two-year doubling time represents *exponential growth*. With a doubling every two years, the capacity will double three times in six years: from 16 terabytes to 32 terabytes after two years, from 32 to 64 terabytes after four years, and from 64 to 128 terabytes after six years.

e. The price decreases by the same percentage each year, so this is *exponential decay*. From $1000 today, the price will fall by 25%, or $0.25 \times \$1000 = \$250$, in one year. Therefore, next year's price will be $750. The following year, the price will again fall by 25%, or $0.25 \times \$750 = \$187.50$, so the price after two years will be $750 − \$187.50 = \$562.50$

• • ●

The Impact of Doublings

Look again at the graph of Powertown's population in Figure 8.14. After about 14 years, the original population has doubled to 20,000. In the next 14 years, it doubles again to 40,000. It then doubles again, to 80,000, 14 years after that. This type of repeated *doubling*, in which each doubling occurs in the same amount of time, is a hallmark of exponential growth.

The time it takes for each doubling depends on the rate of the exponential growth. The doubling time depends on the percentage growth rate. Here we'll explore three parables that show how doublings make exponential growth so very different from linear growth.

Parable 1: From Hero to Headless in 64 Easy Steps

Legend has it that, when chess was invented in ancient times, a king was so enchanted that he said to the inventor, "Name your reward."

"If you please, king, put one grain of wheat on the first square of my chessboard," said the inventor. "Then place two grains on the second square, four grains on the third square, eight grains on the fourth square, and so on." The king gladly agreed, thinking the man a fool for asking for a few grains of wheat when he could have had gold or jewels. But let's see how it adds up for the 64 squares on a chessboard.

Table 8.1 shows the calculations. Each square gets twice as many grains as the previous square, so the number of grains on any square is a power of 2. The third column shows the total number of grains up to each point, and the last column gives a simple formula for the total number of grains.

TABLE 8.1

Square	Grains on This Square	Total Grains Thus Far	Formula for Total Grains
1	$1 = 2^0$	1	$2^1 - 1$
2	$2 = 2^1$	$1 + 2 = 3$	$2^2 - 1$
3	$4 = 2^2$	$3 + 4 = 7$	$2^3 - 1$
4	$8 = 2^3$	$7 + 8 = 15$	$2^4 - 1$
5	$16 = 2^4$	$15 + 16 = 31$	$2^5 - 1$
⋮	⋮	⋮	⋮
64	2^{63}		$2^{64} - 1$

From the pattern in the last column, we see that the grand total for all 64 squares is $2^{64} - 1$ grains. How much wheat is this? With a calculator, you can confirm that $2^{64} = 1.8 \times 10^{19}$, or about 18 *billion billion*. Not only would it be difficult to fit so many grains on a chessboard, but this number is larger than the total number of grains of wheat harvested in all human history. The king never finished paying the inventor and, according to legend, instead had him beheaded.

Parable 2: The Magic Penny

One lucky day, you meet a leprechaun who promises to give you fantastic wealth, but hands you only a penny before disappearing. You head home and place the penny under your pillow. The next morning, to your surprise, you find two pennies under your pillow. The following morning, you find four pennies, and the fourth morning, eight pennies. Apparently, the leprechaun gave you a *magic* penny: While you sleep, each magic penny turns into *two* magic pennies. Table 8.2 shows your growing wealth. Note that "day 0" is the day you met the leprechaun. Generalizing from the first four rows of the table, the amount under your pillow after t days is

$$\$0.01 \times 2^t$$

We can use this formula to figure out how long it will be until you have fantastic wealth. After $t = 9$ days, you'll have $\$0.01 \times 2^9 = \$5.12$, which is barely enough to buy lunch. But by the end of a month, or $t = 30$ days, you'll have $\$0.01 \times 2^{30} = \$10,737,418.24$. That is, you'll be a millionaire within a month, and you'll need a much larger pillow! In fact, if your magic pennies keep doubling, by the end of just 51 days you'll have $\$0.01 \times 2^{51} \approx \$22.5$ trillion, which is more than enough to pay off the national debt of the United States.

TABLE 8.2	
Day	Amount Under Pillow
0	$\$0.01 \times 2^0 = \$0.01$
1	$\$0.01 \times 2^1 = \$0.02$
2	$\$0.01 \times 2^2 = \$0.04$
3	$\$0.01 \times 2^3 = \$0.08$
4	$\$0.01 \times 2^4 = \$0.16$
$\vdots$	$\vdots$
t	$\$0.01 \times 2^t$

Parable 3: Bacteria in a Bottle

For our third parable, we return to the topic explored in the chapter-opening question. Suppose you place a single bacterium in a bottle at 11:00 a.m. It grows and at 11:01 divides into two bacteria. These two bacteria each grow and at 11:02 divide into four bacteria, which grow and at 11:03 divide into eight bacteria, and so on.

Now, suppose the bacteria continue to double every minute, and the bottle is full at 12:00. You may already realize that the number of bacteria at this point must be (because they doubled every minute for 60 minutes), but the important fact is that we have a bacterial disaster on our hands: Because the bacteria have filled the bottle, the entire bacterial colony is doomed. Let's examine this disaster in greater detail by asking a few questions about the demise of the colony.

- *Question 1:* The disaster occurred because the bottle was completely full at 12:00. When was the bottle *half*-full?

  Answer: Because it took one hour to fill the bottle, many people guess that it was half-full after a half-hour, or at 11:30. However, because the bacteria *double* in number every minute, they must also have doubled during the last minute, which means the bottle went from being half-full to full during the final minute. That is, the bottle was half-full at 11:59, just 1 minute before the disaster.

- *Question 2:* Imagine that *you* are a mathematically sophisticated bacterium, and at 11:56 you recognize the impending disaster. You immediately jump on your soapbox and warn that unless your fellow bacteria slow their growth dramatically, the end is just 4 minutes away. Will anyone believe you?

  Answer: Note that the question is *not* whether you are correct, because you are; the bottle will indeed be full in just 4 minutes. Rather, the question is whether others who have not done the calculations will believe you. As we've already seen, the bottle would be half-full at 11:59. Continuing to work backward through the doublings each minute, we find that it would be $\frac{1}{4}$ full at 11:58, $\frac{1}{8}$ full at 11:57, and $\frac{1}{16}$ full at 11:56. Therefore, if your fellow bacteria look around the bottle at 11:56, they'll see that only $\frac{1}{16}$ of the bottle's space has been used. In other words, 15/16 of the bottle's space is unused, which means the amount of unused space is *15 times* the amount of used space. You are asking your fellow bacteria to believe that, in just the next 4 minutes, they'll fill 15 times as much space as they did in their entire 56-minute history. Unless they do the mathematics for themselves, they are unlikely to take your warnings seriously. Figure 8.15 shows the situation graphically. Note that the bottle remains nearly empty for most of the 60 minutes, but the continued doublings fill it rapidly in the final 4 minutes.

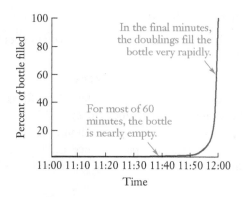

Figure 8.15 The population of the bacteria in the bottle.

- *Question 3:* It's 11:59 and, with the bottle half-full, your fellow bacteria are finally taking your warnings seriously. They quickly start a space program, sending little bacterial spaceships out into the lab in search of new bottles. Thankfully, they discover three more bottles (making a total of four, including the one already occupied). Working quickly, they initiate a mass migration by packing bacteria onto spaceships and sending them to the new bottles. They successfully distribute the population evenly among the four bottles, just in time to avert the disaster. Given that they now have four bottles rather than just one, how much time have they gained for their civilization?

  Answer: Because it took one hour to fill one bottle, you might guess that it would take four hours to fill four bottles. But remember that the bacterial population continues to *double* each minute. If there are enough bacteria to fill one bottle at 12:00, there will be enough to fill two bottles by 12:01 and four bottles by 12:02. The discovery of three new bottles gives them only 2 additional minutes.

- *Question 4:* Suppose the bacteria continue their space program, constantly looking for more bottles. Is there any hope that further discoveries will allow the colony to continue its exponential growth?

  Answer: Let's do some calculations. After n minutes, the bacterial population is 2^n. For example, it is $2^0 = 1$ when the first bacterium starts the colony at 11:00, $2^1 = 2$ at 11:01, $2^2 = 4$ at 11:02, and so on. There are 2^{60} bacteria when the first bottle fills at 12:00, and 2^{62} bacteria when four bottles are full at 12:02. Suppose that, somehow, the bacteria managed to keep doubling every minute until 1:00. By that time, the number of bacteria would be 2^{120} because it has been 120 minutes since the colony began. Now, we must figure out how much space they'd require for this population.

  The smallest bacteria measure approximately 10^{-7}m (0.1 micrometer) across. If we assume that the bacteria are roughly cube-shaped, the volume of a single bacterium is

$$(10^{-7}\,\text{m})^3 = 10^{-21}\,\text{m}^3$$

  Therefore, the colony of 2^{120} bacteria would occupy a total volume of

$$2^{120} \times 10^{-21}\,\text{m}^3 \approx 1.3 \times 10^{15}\,\text{m}^3$$

With this volume, the bacteria would cover the entire surface of the Earth in a layer more than 2 meters deep! (See Exercise 80 to calculate this result for yourself.)

In fact, if the doublings continued for just $5\frac{1}{2}$ hours, the volume of bacteria would exceed the volume of the entire universe. Needless to say, this cannot happen. The exponential growth of the colony cannot possibly continue for long, no matter what technological advances might be imagined.

Facts do not cease to exist because they are ignored.

—Aldous Huxley

EXAMPLE 2 Number of Bottles

How many bottles would the bacteria fill at the end of the second hour?

SOLUTION

For this calculation, we start with the fact that the bacteria have filled 1 bottle at the end of the first hour (12:00). As they continue to double, they fill $2^1 = 2$ bottles at 12:01, $2^2 = 4$ bottles at 12:02, and so on. In other words, during the second hour, the number of bottles filled is 2^m, where m is the number of minutes that have passed since 12:00. Because there are 60 minutes in the second hour, the number of bottles at the end of the second hour is 2^{60}. With a calculator, you will find that

$$2^{60} \approx 1.15 \times 10^{18}$$

At the end of the second hour, the bacteria would fill approximately 10^{18} bottles. Using the rules for working with powers of 10, we can write $10^{18} = 10^6 \times 10^{12}$. We recognize that $10^6 = 1$ million and $10^{12} = 1$ trillion. Therefore, 10^{18} is a *million trillion*.　　···●

TIME OUT TO THINK

Some people have suggested that we could find room for an exponentially growing human population by colonizing other planets in our solar system. Is this possible?

Doubling Lessons

The three parables reveal at least two key lessons about the repeated doublings that arise with exponential growth. First, if you look back at Table 8.1, you'll notice that the number of grains on each square is nearly equal to the total number of grains on all previous squares combined. For example, the 16 grains on the fifth square are 1 more than the total of 15 grains on the first four squares combined.

Second, all three parables show quantities growing to impossible proportions. We cannot possibly fit all the wheat harvested in world history on a chessboard, we cannot fit $22 trillion worth of pennies under your pillow, and a colony of bacteria could not keep growing until it filled the universe. The following box summarizes the two lessons.

Key Facts about Exponential Growth

- Exponential growth leads to repeated doublings. With each doubling, the amount of increase is approximately equal to the *sum* of all preceding doublings.

- Exponential growth cannot continue indefinitely. After only a relatively small number of doublings, exponentially growing quantities reach impossible proportions.

Quick Quiz

Choose the best answer to each of the following questions. Explain your reasoning with one or more complete sentences.

1. A town's population increases in one year from 100,000 to 110,000. If the population is growing *linearly,* at a steady rate, then at the end of a second year it will be

   a. 110,000.   b. 120,000.   c. 121,000.

2. A town's population increases in one year from 100,000 to 110,000. If the population is growing *exponentially* at a steady rate, then at the end of a second year it will be

   a. 110,000.   b. 120,000.   c. 121,000.

3. The balance owed on your credit card doubles from $1000 to $2000 in 6 months. If your balance is growing *exponentially,* how much longer will it be until it reaches $4000?

   a. 6 months   b. 12 months   c. 18 months

4. The number of songs in your iPod has increased from 200 to 400 in 3 months. If the number of songs is increasing *linearly,* how much longer will it be until you have 800 songs?

   a. 3 months   b. 6 months   c. $1\frac{1}{2}$ months

5. Which of the following is an example of *exponential decay?*

   a. The population of a rural community decreases by 100 people per year.

   b. The price of gasoline decreases by $0.02 per week.

   c. Government support for education decreases 1% per year.

6. On a chessboard with 64 squares, you place 1 penny on the first square, 2 pennies on the second square, 4 pennies on the third square, and so on. If you could follow this pattern to fill the entire board, about how much money would you need in total?

   a. about $1.28

   b. about $500,000

   c. about 10,000 times as much as the current U.S. federal debt

7. At 11:00 you place a single bacterium in a bottle, and at 11:01 it divides into 2 bacteria, which at 11:02 divide into 4 bacteria, and so on. How many bacteria will be in the bottle at 11:30?

   a. 2×30 b. 2^{30} c. 2×10^{30}

8. Consider the bacterial population described in Exercise 7. How many more bacteria are in the bottle at 11:31 than at 11:30?

   a. 30   b. 2^{30} c. 2×10^{30}

9. Consider the bacterial population described in Exercise 7. If the bacteria occupy a volume of 1 cubic meter at 12:02 and continue their exponential growth, when will they occupy a volume of 2 cubic meters?

   a. 12:03   b. 12:04
   c. 1:02

10. Which of the following is *not* true of any exponentially growing population?

    a. With every doubling, the population increase is nearly equal to the total increase from all previous doublings.

    b. The steady growth makes it easy to see any impending crisis long before the crisis becomes severe.

    c. The exponential growth must eventually stop.

Exercises

Review Questions

1. Describe the basic differences between linear growth and exponential growth.

2. Briefly explain how repeated doublings characterize exponential growth. Describe the impact of doublings, using the chessboard or magic penny parable.

3. Briefly summarize the story of the bacteria in the bottle. Be sure to explain the answers to the four questions asked in the text, and describe why the answers are surprising.

4. Explain the meaning of the two key facts about exponential growth given at the end of this unit. Then create your own example of exponential growth and describe the influence and impact of repeated doubling.

Does It Make Sense? Decide whether each of the following statements makes sense (or is clearly true) or does not make sense (or is clearly false). Explain your reasoning.

5. Money in a bank account earning compound interest at an annual percentage rate of 3% is an example of exponential growth.

6. Suppose you had a magic bank account in which your balance doubled each day. If you started with just $1, you'd be a millionaire in less than a month.

7. A small town that grows exponentially can become a large city in just a few decades.

8. Human population has been growing exponentially for a few centuries, and we can expect this trend to continue forever in the future.

Basic Skills & Concepts

9–16: Linear or Exponential? State whether the growth (or decay) is linear or exponential, and answer the associated question.

9. The population of MeadowView is increasing at a rate of 300 people per year. If the population is 2500 today, what will it be in four years?

10. The population of Winesburg is increasing at a rate of 3% per year. If the population is 100,000 today, what will it be in three years?

11. During an episode of hyperinflation that occurred in Brazil in 1999, the price of food increased at a rate of 30% per month. If your food bill was R$100 one month during this period, what was it four months later? (R$ is the symbol for the real, Brazil's unit of currency.)

12. The price of a gallon of gasoline is increasing by 4¢ per week. If the price is $3.10 per gallon today, what will it be in ten weeks?

13. The price of computer memory is decreasing at a rate of 14% per year. If a memory chip costs $50 today, what will it cost in three years?

14. The value of your car is decreasing by 10% per year. If the car is worth $12,000 today, what will it be worth in two years?

15. The value of your house is increasing by $2000 per year. If it is worth $100,000 today, what will it be worth in five years?

16. The value of your house is increasing by 4% per year. If it is worth $250,000 today, what will it be worth in three years?

17–20: Chessboard Parable. Use the chessboard parable presented in the text. Assume that each grain of wheat weighs 1/7000 pound.

17. How many grains of wheat should be placed on square 16 of the chessboard? Find the total number of grains and their total weight (in pounds) at this point.

18. How many grains of wheat should be placed on square 32 of the chessboard? Find the total number of grains and their total weight (in pounds) at this point.

19. What is the total weight of all the wheat when the chessboard is full?

20. The total world harvest of all grains (wheat, rice, and corn) in 2010 was about 2.2 billion tons. How does this total compare to the weight of the wheat on the chessboard? (1 ton = 2000 pounds.)

21–24: Magic Penny Parable. Use the magic penny parable presented in the text.

21. How much money would you have after 22 days?

22. Suppose that you stacked the pennies after 22 days. How high would the stack rise, in kilometers? (*Hint:* Find a few pennies and a ruler.)

23. How many days would elapse before you had a total of more than $1 billion? (*Hint:* Proceed by trial and error.)

24. Suppose that you could keep making a single stack of the pennies. After how many days would the stack be long enough to reach the nearest star (beyond the Sun), which is about 4.3 light-years (4.0×10^{13} km) away? (*Hint:* Proceed by trial and error.)

25–28: Bacteria in a Bottle Parable. Use the bacteria parable presented in the text.

25. How many bacteria are in the bottle at 11:50? What fraction of the bottle is full at that time?

26. How many bacteria are in the bottle at 11:15? What fraction of the bottle is full at that time?

27. **Knee-Deep in Bacteria.** The total surface area of Earth is about 5.1×10^{14} m^2. Assume that the bacteria continued their doublings for a total of two hours (as discussed in the text), at which point they were distributed uniformly over Earth's surface. How deep would the bacterial layer be? Would it be knee-deep, more than knee-deep, or less than knee-deep? (*Hint:* You can find the approximate depth by dividing the bacteria volume by Earth's surface area.)

28. **Bacterial Universe.** Suppose the bacteria in the parable continued to double their population every minute. How long would it take until their volume exceeded the total volume of the observable universe, which is about 10^{79} m^3? (*Hint:* Proceed by trial and error.)

Further Applications

29. **Human Doubling.** Human population in the year 2000 was about 6 billion and was increasing with a doubling time of 50 years. Suppose population continued this growth pattern from the year 2000 into the future.

a. Extend the following table, showing the population at 50-year intervals under this scenario, until you reach the year 3000. Use scientific notation, as shown.

Year	Population
2000	6×10^9
2050	$12 \times 10^9 = 1.2 \times 10^{10}$
2100	$24 \times 10^9 = 2.4 \times 10^{10}$
⋮	⋮

b. The total surface area of Earth is about 5.1×10^{14} m^2. Assuming that people could occupy all this area (in reality, most of it is ocean), approximately when would people be so crowded that every person would have only 1 m^2 of space?

c. Suppose that, when we take into account the area needed to grow food and to find other resources, each person actually requires about 10^4 m^2 of area to survive. About when would we reach this limit?

d. Suppose that we learn to colonize other planets and moons in our solar system. The total surface area of the worlds in our solar system that could potentially be colonized (not counting gas planets such as Jupiter) is roughly five times the surface area of Earth. Under the assumptions of part (c), could humanity fit in our solar system in the year 3000? Explain.

30. Doubling Time versus Initial Amount.

a. Would you rather start with one penny ($0.01) and double your wealth every day or start with one dime ($0.10) and double your wealth every five days (assuming you want to get rich)? Explain.

b. Would you rather start with one penny ($0.01) and double your wealth every day or start with $1000 and double your wealth every two days (assuming you want to get rich in the long run)? Explain.

c. Which is more important in determining how fast exponential growth occurs: the doubling time or the initial amount? Explain.

31. Facebook Users. The table shows the number of monthly active users of Facebook (the number of people who use Facebook at least once a month) over a three-year period.

Month	March 2009	March 2010	March 2011	March 2012
Monthly active users (millions)	197	431	680	901
Absolute change over previous year	—			
Percent change over previous year	—			

a. Fill in the third row of the table showing the absolute change in the number of active monthly users.

b. Fill in the fourth row of the table showing the percent change in the number of active monthly users.

c. Is the increase in Facebook users linear or exponential? Justify your answer.

In Your World

32. **Linear Growth.** Identify at least two news stories that describe a quantity undergoing *linear* growth or decay. Describe the growth or decay process in each.

33. **Exponential Growth.** Identify at least two news stories that describe a quantity undergoing *exponential* growth or decay. Describe the growth or decay process in each.

34. **Computing Power.** Choose an aspect of computing power (such as processor speed or memory chip capacity) and investigate its growth. Has the growth been exponential? How much longer is the exponential growth likely to continue? Explain.

35. **Web Growth.** Investigate the growth of the Web itself, in terms of both number of users and number of Web pages. Has the growth been linear or exponential? How do you think the growth will change in the future? Explain.

Focus on

EDUCATION

What Helps Children Learn to Read?

Everyone has an idea about how best to teach reading to children. Some advocate a phonetic approach, teaching students to "sound out" words. Some advocate a "whole language" approach, teaching students to recognize words from their context. Others advocate a combination of these approaches, or something else entirely. These differing ideas would be unimportant if they were merely opinions. But in a nation that spends more than a *trillion dollars* per year on education, differing approaches to teaching reading involve major political confrontations among groups with different special interests.

The huge stakes involved in teaching reading demand statistics to measure the effectiveness of various approaches. Some of the most important educational statistics are those that come from the National Assessment of Educational Progress (NAEP), often known more simply as "the Nation's Report Card." The NAEP is an ongoing survey of student achievement conducted by a government agency, the National Center for Education Statistics, with authorization and funding from the U.S. Congress.

The NAEP uses stratified random sampling (see Chapter 1) to choose representative samples of fourth-, eighth-, and 12th-grade students of varying ethnicity, family income, type of school attended, and so on. Students chosen for the samples are given tests designed to measure their academic achievement in a particular subject area, such as reading, mathematics, or history. Samples are chosen on both state and national levels. Overall, a few thousand students are chosen for each test. Results from NAEP tests inevitably make the news, with articles touting improvements or decrying drops in test scores.

But what really causes improvement in reading performance? Researchers begin by searching for correlations between reading performance and other factors. Sometimes the correlations are clear, but offer no direction for improving reading. For example, parental education is clearly correlated with reading achievement—children with more highly educated parents tend to read more proficiently than those with uneducated parents—but this correlation doesn't offer much guidance for the schools because children do not choose their parents. Other times the correlations may suggest ways to improve reading. For example, students who report reading more pages daily in school and for homework tend to score higher than students who read fewer pages. This suggests that schools should assign more reading.

Of course, the high stakes involved in education make education statistics particularly prone to misinterpretation or misuse. Consider just a few of the problems that make the NAEP reading tests difficult to interpret:

- They are standardized tests that are mostly multiple choice. Some people believe that such tests are inevitably biased and cannot truly measure reading ability.
- Because the tests generally don't affect students' grades, some students may not take the tests seriously, in which case test results may not reflect actual reading ability.
- State-by-state comparisons may not be valid if the makeup of the student population (particularly in its fraction of students for whom English is a second language) varies significantly among states.
- There is some evidence of cheating on the part of the *adults* involved in the NAEP tests by, for example, choosing samples that are not truly representative but instead skewed toward students who read better.

You can probably think of a dozen other problems that make it difficult to interpret NAEP results. So what can you do, as an individual, to help a child to read? Fortunately, the NAEP studies also reveal a few correlations that are uncontroversial and agree with common sense. For example, higher reading performance correlates with each of the following factors:

- more total reading, both for school and for pleasure
- more choice in reading—that is, allowing children to pick their own books to read
- more writing, particularly of extended pieces such as essays or long letters
- more discussion of reading material with friends and family
- less television watching

These correlations give at least some guidance on how to help a child learn to read and should be good starting points for discussions of how to increase literacy.

QUESTIONS FOR DISCUSSION

1. One result of the NAEP reading tests is that students in private schools tend to score significantly higher than students in public schools. Does this imply that private schools are "better" than public schools? Defend your opinion.

2. Do you think that standardized tests like those of the NAEP are valid ways to measure academic achievement? Why or why not?

3. Currently, the NAEP tests are given to only a few thousand of the millions of school children in the United States. Some people advocate giving similar tests to all students, on either a voluntary or a mandatory basis. Do you think such "standardized national testing" is a good idea? Why or why not?

4. Have you ever helped a child learn to read? Compare your experiences with those of other classmates who have worked with young children.

5. Read the latest edition of the *NAEP Reading Report Card* (available online). What are some of the latest results with regard to the teaching of reading in the United States?

• • • • • • • • • • • • • • • •

F OCUS ON
ENVIRONMENT

What Is Causing Global Warming?

Global warming is one of the most important issues of our time, yet surveys and media reports suggest that many people doubt that it is real or that humans are responsible for it. In this Focus, we will investigate the evidence that has led the vast majority of climate scientists to conclude that human activity is the cause of global warming.

As we discussed in the Focus on Environment for Chapter 3 (page 137), measurements clearly show that the atmospheric carbon dioxide concentration is rising rapidly and is now significantly higher than it has been at any time during at least the past 800,000 years (see Figure 3.47). Chemical analysis shows the added carbon dioxide is coming primarily from human activity, especially the burning of fossil fuels. Moreover, data from ice cores show that the carbon dioxide concentration is strongly *correlated* with the global average temperature. The key question, then, is whether this correlation implies causality. To answer it, we must understand how a gas like carbon dioxide can affect the temperature and then investigate whether the recent increase in the concentration is having the expected effects.

The fact that some atmospheric gases—called **greenhouse gases**—can trap heat has been well-known for more than 150 years, ever since Irish physicist John Tyndall measured the heat-absorbing effects of carbon dioxide and water vapor in his laboratory in 1859. Other scientists, most notably Swedish scientist Svante Arrhenius (1859–1927), later pointed out that the burning of fossil fuels releases carbon dioxide, and that this might therefore cause global warming. Today, the mechanism by which carbon dioxide and other greenhouse gases (the most important others being water vapor and methane) warm a planet is called the **greenhouse effect**. It is well understood and summarized in Figure 8.16.

Scientists can further test this understanding of the greenhouse effect by checking to see whether it successfully accounts for the temperatures of various planets. In the absence of greenhouse gases, a world's average temperature would be determined by only two major factors: its distance from the Sun and the fraction of the incoming sunlight that its surface absorbs (the rest is reflected back into space). There is a simple equation that allows the calculation of the temperature in this case, and it successfully predicts the temperatures of worlds with no atmosphere, such as the Moon and the planet Mercury. For planets with atmospheres, however, scientists can successfully predict their temperatures only by taking the greenhouse effect into account, and the results clearly show

that more greenhouse gases mean more excess heating. Our planetary neighbors vividly demonstrate this fact. Mars has a very thin carbon dioxide atmosphere that gives it a fairly weak greenhouse effect, making the planet about 11°F warmer than it would be otherwise. Venus, which has an extremely dense atmosphere containing nearly 200,000 times as much carbon dioxide as Earth's atmosphere, has a correspondingly extreme greenhouse effect that makes its surface about 850°F hotter than it would be otherwise—giving it a surface hot enough to melt lead.

Earth is the lucky intermediate case. Without the greenhouse effect, Earth's average temperature would be well below freezing, at about –16°C (3°F). But thanks to the carbondioxide, methane, and water vapor in our atmosphere, the actual

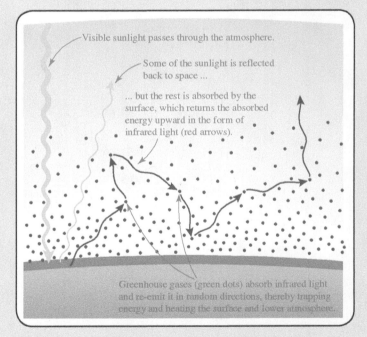

Figure 8.16 This diagram shows the basic mechanism of the greenhouse effect. The greater the abundance of greenhouse gases, the more the escape of infrared light is slowed and the warmer the planet becomes.

temperature is close to 15°C (60°F). From that standpoint, the greenhouse effect is a very good thing, because our lives would not be possible without it. Just keep in mind that the case of Venus offers proof that it's possible to have too much of this good thing.

The evidence from laboratory measurements and studies of other planets leave no reasonable doubt that carbon dioxide and other greenhouse gases cause a planet's temperature to be hotter than it would be otherwise. Nevertheless, because carbon dioxide is not the only thing that affects our planet's temperature, we might wonder whether any effects due to the recent rise in carbon dioxide might be offset by, say, reductions in the amount of other greenhouse gases or an increase in how much sunlight our planet reflects. Scientists can test this idea in two basic ways. First, they look at data showing changes in Earth's average temperature. As you'll see in Figure 8.17, Earth's average temperature has indeed been rising, and the data give at least some hint that the rise has been accelerating in recent decades.

The second way to test the idea that human burning of fossil fuels is causing global warming is to conduct experiments. We obviously cannot perform controlled experiments with our entire planet, so scientists instead build *computer models* designed to simulate the way Earth's climate works. Earth's climate is incredibly complex, so the models cannot be perfect. Nevertheless, today's models match real climate data quite well, giving scientists confidence that the models have predictive value. Figure 8.18 compares real data to models with and without the human contribution to the greenhouse gas concentration. We see a good match only for models that include the human contribution.

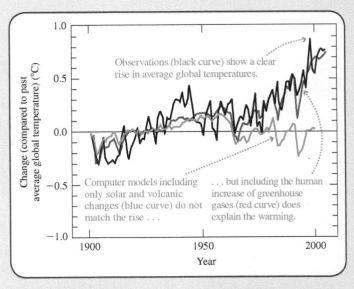

Figure 8.18 This graph compares observed temperature changes (black curve) with the predictions of climate models that include only natural factors such as changes in the brightness of the Sun and effects of volcanoes (blue curve), and models that also include the human-made increase in the greenhouse gas (red curve). Only the red curve matches the observations well. (The red and blue model curves are each averages of many scientists' independent models of global warming, which generally agree with each other to within 0.1°C − 0.2°C.)

The conclusion is clear: Laboratory measurements of the greenhouse effect, studies of other planets, data for Earth's rising carbon dioxide concentration and temperature, and computer models of the climate all provide evidence in favor of the claim that human activity is causing global warming. It is the fact that so many lines of evidence are all in agreement that makes scientists so confident that the causality is real.

QUESTIONS FOR DISCUSSION

1. Look back at the six guidelines for establishing causality. Discuss whether or how each guideline is met by current data and understanding of global warming.

2. Look back at the legal levels of confidence in causality. Would you say that the case for human activity as the cause of global warming is now at the level of possible cause, probable cause, or cause beyond reasonable doubt? Defend your opinion.

3. Investigate some of the likely consequences of global warming. If current trends continue, what changes can you expect in the world by the year 2050? 2100?

4. Based on what you've learned about the cause of global warming and its potential consequences, what do *you* think we should be doing about it, if anything?

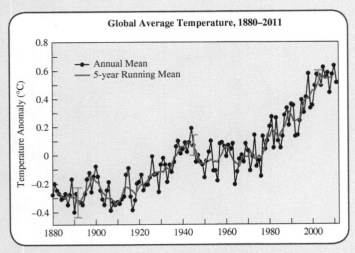

Figure 8.17 Clear evidence of a warming Earth: The black curve shows the mean global average temperature during each year; the red curve shows a running mean computed over 5-year periods. The vertical scale ("temperature anomaly") shows the difference between each year's actual average temperature and the average during the period 1951–1980. The blue bars represent the uncertainty ranges in the data at three different times; the uncertainty is lower for recent times because measurements have become more precise.

EPILOGUE: A PERSPECTIVE ON STATISTICS

A single introductory statistics course cannot transform you into an expert statistician. After studying statistics in this book, you may feel that you have not yet mastered the material to the extent necessary to use statistics confidently in real applications. Nevertheless, by now you should understand enough about statistics to interpret critically the reports of statistical research that you see in the news and to converse with experts in statistics when you need more information. And, if you go on to take further course work in statistics, you should be well prepared to understand important topics that are beyond the scope of this introductory book.

Most importantly, while this book is not designed to make you an expert statistician, it is designed to make you a better-educated person with improved job marketability. You should know and understand the basic concepts of probability and chance. You should know that in attempting to gain insight into a data set, it's important to investigate measures of center (such as mean and median), measures of variation (such as range and standard deviation), the nature of the distribution (via a frequency table or graph), and the presence of outliers. You should know and understand the importance of estimating population parameters (such as a population mean or proportion), as well as testing hypotheses about population parameters. You should understand that a correlation between two variables does not necessarily imply that there is also some cause-and-effect relationship. You should know the importance of good sampling. You should recognize that many surveys and polls obtain very good results, even though the sample sizes might seem to be relatively small. Although many people refuse to believe it, a nationwide survey of only 1,700 voters can provide good results if the sampling is carefully planned and executed.

There once was a time when a person was considered educated if he or she could read, but we are in a new millennium that is much more demanding. Today, an educated person must be able to read, write, understand the significance of the Renaissance, operate a computer, and apply statistical reasoning. The study of statistics helps us see truths that are sometimes distorted by a failure to approach a problem carefully or concealed by data that are disorganized. Understanding statistics is now essential for both employers and employees—for all citizens. H. G. Wells once said, "Statistical thinking will one day be as necessary for efficient citizenship as the ability to read and write." That day is now.

APPENDIX A: Z-SCORE TABLES

Table A-1 is a more detailed version of Table 5.1; note that the areas under the curve shown here correspond to *percentiles*. To read this table, find the first two digits of the z-score in the left column, then read across the rows for third digit. Negative z-scores are on the left page and positive z-scores are on the right page.

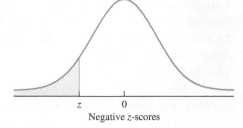

z   0
Negative z-scores

TABLE A-1	Standard Normal (z) Distribution: Cumulative Area from the LEFT									
z	.00	.01	.02	.03	.04	.05	.06	.07	.08	.09
−3.50 and lower	.0001									
−3.4	.0003	.0003	.0003	.0003	.0003	.0003	.0003	.0003	.0003	.0002
−3.3	.0005	.0005	.0005	.0004	.0004	.0004	.0004	.0004	.0004	.0003
−3.2	.0007	.0007	.0006	.0006	.0006	.0006	.0006	.0005	.0005	.0005
−3.1	.0010	.0009	.0009	.0009	.0008	.0008	.0008	.0008	.0007	.0007
−3.0	.0013	.0013	.0013	.0012	.0012	.0011	.0011	.0011	.0010	.0010
−2.9	.0019	.0018	.0018	.0017	.0016	.0016	.0015	.0015	.0014	.0014
−2.8	.0026	.0025	.0024	.0023	.0023	.0022	.0021	.0021	.0020	.0019
−2.7	.0035	.0034	.0033	.0032	.0031	.0030	.0029	.0028	.0027	.0026
−2.6	.0047	.0045	.0044	.0043	.0041	.0040	.0039	.0038	.0037	.0036
−2.5	.0062	.0060	.0059	.0057	.0055	.0054	.0052	.0051	.0049*	.0048
−2.4	.0082	.0080	.0078	.0075	.0073	.0071	.0069	.0068	.0066	.0064
−2.3	.0107	.0104	.0102	.0099	.0096	.0094	.0091	.0089	.0087	.0084
−2.2	.0139	.0136	.0132	.0129	.0125	.0122	.0119	.0116	.0113	.0110
−2.1	.0179	.0174	.0170	.0166	.0162	.0158	.0154	.0150	.0146	.0143
−2.0	.0228	.0222	.0217	.0212	.0207	.0202	.0197	.0192	.0188	.0183
−1.9	.0287	.0281	.0274	.0268	.0262	.0256	.0250	.0244	.0239	.0233
−1.8	.0359	.0351	.0344	.0336	.0329	.0322	.0314	.0307	.0301	.0294
−1.7	.0446	.0436	.0427	.0418	.0409	.0401	.0392	.0384	.0375	.0367
−1.6	.0548	.0537	.0526	.0516	.0505*	.0495	.0485	.0475	.0465	.0455
−1.5	.0668	.0655	.0643	.0630	.0618	.0606	.0594	.0582	.0571	.0559
−1.4	.0808	.0793	.0778	.0764	.0749	.0735	.0721	.0708	.0694	.0681
−1.3	.0968	.0951	.0934	.0918	.0901	.0885	.0869	.0853	.0838	.0823
−1.2	.1151	.1131	.1112	.1093	.1075	.1056	.1038	.1020	.1003	.0985
−1.1	.1357	.1335	.1314	.1292	.1271	.1251	.1230	.1210	.1190	.1170
−1.0	.1587	.1562	.1539	.1515	.1492	.1469	.1446	.1423	.1401	.1379
−0.9	.1841	.1814	.1788	.1762	.1736	.1711	.1685	.1660	.1635	.1611
−0.8	.2119	.2090	.2061	.2033	.2005	.1977	.1949	.1922	.1894	.1867
−0.7	.2420	.2389	.2358	.2327	.2296	.2266	.2236	.2206	.2177	.2148
−0.6	.2743	.2709	.2676	.2643	.2611	.2578	.2546	.2514	.2483	.2451
−0.5	.3085	.3050	.3015	.2981	.2946	.2912	.2877	.2843	.2810	.2776
−0.4	.3446	.3409	.3372	.3336	.3300	.3264	.3228	.3192	.3156	.3121
−0.3	.3821	.3783	.3745	.3707	.3669	.3632	.3594	.3557	.3520	.3483
−0.2	.4207	.4168	.4129	.4090	.4052	.4013	.3974	.3936	.3897	.3859
−0.1	.4602	.4562	.4522	.4483	.4443	.4404	.4364	.4325	.4286	.4247
−0.0	.5000	.4960	.4920	.4880	.4840	.4801	.4761	.4721	.4681	.4641

Note: For values of z below −3.49, use 0.0001 for the area.

*Use these common values that result from interpolation:

z-score	Area
−1.645	0.0500
−2.575	0.0050

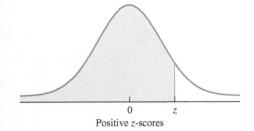

Positive z-scores

TABLE A-1	(*continued*) Cumulative Area from the LEFT								
z	.00	.01	.02	.03	.04	.05	.06	.07	.08	.09
0.0	.5000	.5040	.5080	.5120	.5160	.5199	.5239	.5279	.5319	.5359
0.1	.5398	.5438	.5478	.5517	.5557	.5596	.5636	.5675	.5714	.5753
0.2	.5793	.5832	.5871	.5910	.5948	.5987	.6026	.6064	.6103	.6141
0.3	.6179	.6217	.6255	.6293	.6331	.6368	.6406	.6443	.6480	.6517
0.4	.6554	.6591	.6628	.6664	.6700	.6736	.6772	.6808	.6844	.6879
0.5	.6915	.6950	.6985	.7019	.7054	.7088	.7123	.7157	.7190	.7224
0.6	.7257	.7291	.7324	.7357	.7389	.7422	.7454	.7486	.7517	.7549
0.7	.7580	.7611	.7642	.7673	.7704	.7734	.7764	.7794	.7823	.7852
0.8	.7881	.7910	.7939	.7967	.7995	.8023	.8051	.8078	.8106	.8133
0.9	.8159	.8186	.8212	.8238	.8264	.8289	.8315	.8340	.8365	.8389
1.0	.8413	.8438	.8461	.8485	.8508	.8531	.8554	.8577	.8599	.8621
1.1	.8643	.8665	.8686	.8708	.8729	.8749	.8770	.8790	.8810	.8830
1.2	.8849	.8869	.8888	.8907	.8925	.8944	.8962	.8980	.8997	.9015
1.3	.9032	.9049	.9066	.9082	.9099	.9115	.9131	.9147	.9162	.9177
1.4	.9192	.9207	.9222	.9236	.9251	.9265	.9279	.9292	.9306	.9319
1.5	.9332	.9345	.9357	.9370	.9382	.9394	.9406	.9418	.9429	.9441
1.6	.9452	.9463	.9474	.9484	.9495 *	.9505	.9515	.9525	.9535	.9545
1.7	.9554	.9564	.9573	.9582	.9591	.9599	.9608	.9616	.9625	.9633
1.8	.9641	.9649	.9656	.9664	.9671	.9678	.9686	.9693	.9699	.9706
1.9	.9713	.9719	.9726	.9732	.9738	.9744	.9750	.9756	.9761	.9767
2.0	.9772	.9778	.9783	.9788	.9793	.9798	.9803	.9808	.9812	.9817
2.1	.9821	.9826	.9830	.9834	.9838	.9842	.9846	.9850	.9854	.9857
2.2	.9861	.9864	.9868	.9871	.9875	.9878	.9881	.9884	.9887	.9890
2.3	.9893	.9896	.9898	.9901	.9904	.9906	.9909	.9911	.9913	.9916
2.4	.9918	.9920	.9922	.9925	.9927	.9929	.9931	.9932	.9934	.9936
2.5	.9938	.9940	.9941	.9943	.9945	.9946	.9948	.9949	.9951 *	.9952
2.6	.9953	.9955	.9956	.9957	.9959	.9960	.9961	.9962	.9963	.9964
2.7	.9965	.9966	.9967	.9968	.9969	.9970	.9971	.9972	.9973	.9974
2.8	.9974	.9975	.9976	.9977	.9977	.9978	.9979	.9979	.9980	.9981
2.9	.9981	.9982	.9982	.9983	.9984	.9984	.9985	.9985	.9986	.9986
3.0	.9987	.9987	.9987	.9988	.9988	.9989	.9989	.9989	.9990	.9990
3.1	.9990	.9991	.9991	.9991	.9992	.9992	.9992	.9992	.9993	.9993
3.2	.9993	.9993	.9994	.9994	.9994	.9994	.9994	.9995	.9995	.9995
3.3	.9995	.9995	.9995	.9996	.9996	.9996	.9996	.9996	.9996	.9997
3.4	.9997	.9997	.9997	.9997	.9997	.9997	.9997	.9997	.9997	.9998
3.50 and up	.9999									

Note: For values of z above 3.49, use 0.9999 for the area.

*Use these common values that result from interpolation:

z-score	Area
1.645	0.9500
2.575	0.9950

TABLE A-2	Select Critical Values of *z*		
	Left-tailed test	**Right-tailed test**	**Two-tailed test**
0.05 significance level	− 1.645	1.645	− 1.96 and 1.96
0.01 significance level	− 2.33	2.33	− 2.576 and 2.576

APPENDIX B: TABLE OF RANDOM NUMBERS

For many statistical applications it is useful to generate a set of randomly chosen numbers. You can generate such numbers with most calculators and computers, but sometimes it is easier to use a table such as the one given below. This table was generated by randomly selecting one of the digits 0, 1, 2, 3, 4, 5, 6, 7, 8, or 9 for each position in the table; that is, each of these digits is equally likely to appear in any position. Thus, you can generate a sequence of random digits simply by starting at any point in the table and taking the digits in the order in which they appear. A larger set of random numbers is available on the text Web site (www.aw.com/bbt).

Example 1: Generate a random list of yes/no responses.
Solution: Start at an arbitrary point in the table. If the digit is 0, 1, 2, 3, or 4, call it a *yes* response. If the digit is 5, 6, 7, 8, or 9, call it a *no* response. Continue through the table from your starting point, using each digit shown to determine either a *yes* or a *no* response for your list.

Example 2: Generate a random list of letter grades A, B, C, D, or F.
Solution: Let 0 or 1 be an A, 2 or 3 be a B, 4 or 5 be a C, 6 or 7 be a D, and 8 or 9 be an F. Start at an arbitrary point in the table and use each digit shown to determine a grade for your list.

```
9 9 3 2 7    5 6 0 8 1    6 0 2 3 2    8 3 3 1 2    4 7 6 3 4
9 7 1 8 1    6 6 7 6 6    5 4 4 7 7    6 8 1 7 1    0 8 4 9 9
8 1 7 5 0    7 8 5 2 0    9 4 3 9 0    7 6 1 9 1    0 8 7 3 4
0 5 1 0 2    8 7 4 0 3    9 2 6 2 5    8 4 2 2 5    1 9 8 3 4
2 7 8 0 8    1 8 5 6 6    4 4 5 5 4    9 3 5 2 8    6 5 5 4 3

4 8 8 3 3    8 4 6 9 1    8 2 5 7 6    9 7 1 2 3    6 5 1 8 2
5 4 5 8 7    3 8 4 5 7    4 5 2 2 2    7 7 0 2 3    0 2 4 8 6
4 1 9 4 3    0 7 1 9 0    7 3 1 4 0    8 3 2 8 0    5 0 1 0 1
2 8 7 4 6    5 7 7 6 0    0 8 9 5 5    4 0 7 3 9    1 6 3 3 2
5 8 6 8 6    9 6 7 7 5    1 3 5 2 9    7 6 6 3 5    9 4 6 0 5

8 0 9 4 8    5 0 5 6 9    1 0 6 9 5    9 0 7 8 9    9 4 8 3 7
6 1 0 4 1    7 4 0 0 3    5 6 4 2 1    5 1 1 9 0    0 2 5 0 7
3 4 0 9 1    9 3 9 5 1    0 7 4 8 1    1 9 7 0 7    1 4 5 2 6
9 9 6 5 0    7 8 6 1 0    4 9 8 7 7    4 4 7 4 0    7 8 6 4 9
1 5 0 7 8    1 6 3 6 9    5 4 9 5 4    2 4 6 0 4    3 2 6 8 4

5 7 2 8 5    8 3 1 6 4    4 2 2 3 7    0 6 6 3 2    3 5 0 4 6
1 2 3 5 7    1 9 7 7 6    5 5 3 1 9    6 0 5 1 6    3 8 0 3 4
3 4 9 3 5    0 3 7 4 6    2 1 8 5 1    4 1 7 0 2    1 4 9 4 9
2 4 2 6 6    9 9 7 2 1    7 7 3 2 0    6 7 0 7 3    9 3 3 7 5
9 9 1 5 2    8 3 9 9 4    8 9 6 0 6    7 4 6 3 1    3 6 9 8 3

2 6 3 3 9    3 4 1 9 3    0 6 9 1 2    4 1 9 9 8    7 3 2 6 9
1 3 7 8 0    1 0 6 1 6    5 4 9 3 0    7 0 7 2 3    1 7 8 9 2
8 8 4 8 4    0 2 8 5 5    7 3 7 1 2    1 8 3 5 2    0 1 5 3 2
4 2 9 2 8    8 8 9 1 2    4 6 7 1 7    5 1 5 1 9    3 2 2 8 0
1 3 7 2 1    0 6 4 7 6    1 0 8 4 8    9 7 6 3 5    5 1 2 2 9
```

Against the Gods: The Remarkable Story of Risk, P. Bernstein, Wiley, 1996.

The Arithmetic of Life, G. Shaffner, Ballantine Books, 1999.

The Arithmetic of Life and Death, G. Shaffner, Ballantine Books, 2001.

The Bell Curve Debate, R. Jacoby and N. Glauberman (eds.), Times Books, 1995.

Beyond Numeracy: Ruminations of a Number Man, J. A. Paulos, Vintage, 1992.

Billions and Billions, C. Sagan, Random House, 1997.

The Broken Dice and Other Mathematical Tales of Chance, I. Ekeland, University of Chicago Press, 1993.

Can You Win?, M. Orkin, Freeman, 1991.

The Complete How to Figure It, D. Huff, Norton, 1996.

Damned Lies and Statistics, J. Best, University of California Press, 2001.

Ecological Numeracy: Quantitative Analysis of Environmental Issues, R. Herendeen, Wiley, 1998.

Elementary Statistics, 12th ed., M. Triola, Pearson, 2014.

Emblems of Mind: The Inner Life of Music and Mathematics, E. Rothstein, Random House, 1995.

Envisioning Information, E. Tufte, Connecticut Graphics Press, Cheshire, 1983.

Games, Gods, and Gambling, F. N. David, Dover, 1998.

Go Figure! The Numbers You Need for Everyday Life, N. Hopkins and J. Mayne, Visible Ink Press, 1992.

The Honest Truth About Lying with Statistics, C. Holmes, Charles C Thomas, 1990.

How Many People Can the Earth Support, J. E. Cohen, Norton, 1995.

How to Lie with Statistics, D. Huff, Norton, 1993.

How to Tell the Liars from the Statisticians, R. Hooke, Dekker, 1983.

How to Use (and Misuse) Statistics, G. Kimble, Prentice-Hall, 1978.

Innumeracy, J. A. Paulos, Hill and Wang, 1988.

The Jungles of Randomness, I. Peterson, Wiley, 1998.

The Lady Tasting Tea: How Statistics Revolutionized Science in the 20th Century, D. Salsburg, Freeman, 2001.

Life by the Numbers, K. Devlin, Wiley, 1998.

Math for Life: Crucial Ideas You Didn't Learn in School, J. Bennett, Roberts & Co Publishers, 2012.

The Mathematical Tourist, I. Peterson, Freeman, 1988.

A Mathematician Reads the Newspaper, J. A. Paulos, Basic Books, 1995.

Mathematics, the Science of Patterns: The Search for Order in Life, Mind, and the Universe, K. Devlin, Scientific American Library, 1994.

The Mismeasure of Man, S. J. Gould, Norton, 1981.

The Mismeasure of Woman, C. Tavris, Touchstone Books, 1993.

Misused Statistics: Straight Talk for Twisted Numbers, A. Jaffe and H. Spirer, Dekker, 1998.

Nature's Numbers, I. Stewart, Basic Books, 1995.

Once Upon a Number, J. A. Paulos, Basic Books, 1998.

Overcoming Math Anxiety, S. Tobias, Houghton Mifflin, 1978. Revised edition, Norton, 1993.

Pi in the Sky: Counting, Thinking, and Being, J. D. Barrow, Little, Brown, 1992.

The Population Explosion, P. R. Ehrlich and A. H. Ehrlich, Simon and Schuster, 1990.

Probabilities in Everyday Life, J. McGervey, Ivy Books, 1989.

The Psychology of Judgment and Decision Making, S. Plous, McGraw-Hill, 1993.

Randomness, D. Bennett, Harvard University Press, 1998.

The Statistical Exorcist: Dispelling Statistics Anxiety, M. Hollander and F. Proschan, Dekker, 1984.

Statistics, 4th ed., D. Freedman, R. Pisani, R. Purves, and A. Adhikari, Norton, 2007.

Statistics: Concepts and Controversies, 7th ed., D. Moore, W. Notz, Freeman, 2009.

Statistics with a Sense of Humor, F. Pyrczak, Fred Pyrczak Publisher, 1989.

Tainted Truth: The Manipulation of Fact in America, C. Crossen, Simon and Schuster, 1994.

The Tipping Point: How Little Things Can Make a Big Difference, M. Gladwell, Little, Brown, 2000.

200% of Nothing, A. K. Dewdney, Wiley, 1993.

The Universe and the Teacup: The Mathematics of Truth and Beauty, K. C. Cole, Harcourt Brace, 1998.

The Visual Display of Quantitative Information, E. Tufte, Connecticut Graphics Press, Cheshire, 1983.

Vital Signs, compiled by the Worldwatch Institute, Norton, 1998 (updated annually).

What Are the Odds? Chance in Everyday Life, L. Krantz, Harper Perennial, 1992.

What Is a P-Value, Anyway?, A. Vickers, Pearson, 2009.

CREDITS

Photo Credits

Chapter 1 p. 1, Bill Pugliano/Getty Images; p. 3, Anthony J. Causi/ Icon SMI 942/Newscom; p. 7, Olivier Asselin/Alamy; p. 11, Golden Pixels LLC/Alamy; p. 13, Jeffrey Bennett; p. 14, Photodisc/Getty Images; p. 22, Corbis; p. 25, Andersen Ross/Digital Vision/Getty Images; p. 27, Photodisc/Getty Images; p. 31, Photodisc/Getty Images; p. 34, Picture Press/Alamy; p. 35, Doug Martin/Photo Researchers, Inc.; p. 47, Gazmandhu/Shutterstock; p. 49, Warren Goldswain/Shutterstock

Chapter 2 p. 51, Monkey Business Images/Shutterstock; p. 71, View Stock/Alamy; p. 72, Arctic Images/Alamy; p. 78, Lynnette Peizer/Alamy; p. 80, Igor Stepovik/Shutterstock

Chapter 3 p. 83, Sergej Khakimullin/Shutterstock; p. 95, Stock Connection Blue/Alamy; p. 105, Warner Bros/Everett Collection; p. 123, Charles & Josette Lenars/Corbis; p. 129, Corbis; p. 131, British Antarctic Survey/Photo Researchers, Inc.

Chapter 4 p. 133, United States Geological Survey; p. 138, Timothy A. Clary/AFP/Newscom; p. 151, Laurent Rebours/AP Images; p. 158, Beth Anderson/Pearson Education, Inc.; p. 164, Toru Hanai/Reuters; p. 170, Prisma Bildagentur AG/Alamy; p. 172, Chuck Wagner/ Shutterstock

Chapter 5 p. 175, Liming/EPA/Newscom; p. 178, Beth Anderson/ Pearson Education, Inc.; p. 187, Craig Wactor/Shutterstock; p. 193, The United States Army; p. 199, VIPDesignUSA/ Shutterstock; p. 201, Auremar/Shutterstock

Chapter 6 p. 203, James "BO" Insogna/Shutterstock; p. 204, Helene C. Stikkel/USA.gov; p. 205, The Royal Society; p. 209, Doris Ulmann/Library of Congress Prints and Photographs Division [LC-USZC4-4940]; p. 213, Francois Etienne du Plessis/Shutterstock; p. 226, Morgan Lane Photography/Shutterstock; p. 227, Corbis Bridge/Alamy; p. 230, Morgan Hill/Alamy; p. 231, Anastasia E Kozlova/Shutterstock; p. 235, Jocelyn William KRT/Newscom; p. 245, Stephen VanHorn/Shutterstock; p. 247, SIU Biomed Comm/ Custom Medical Stock Photo/Newscom

Chapter 7 p. 249, ZUMA Press, Inc./Alamy; p. 260, Beth Anderson/Pearson Education, Inc.; p. 261, Galina Barskaya/ Shutterstock; p. 278, AptTone/Shutterstock; p. 288, Gorilla/ Shutterstock

Chapter 8 p. 297, Stephen Coburn/Shutterstock; p. 304, Tselichtchev/Shutterstock; p. 351, Samuel Karlin, The Eleventh R. A. Fisher Memorial Lecture: Kin Selection and Altruism, *Proc R. Soc. Lond. B.*, October 22, 1983, Royal Society of London; p. 354, J. Marshall/Tribaleye Images/Alamy; p. 355, Angelo Giampiccolo/Fotolia; p. 360, Stock Connection Distribution/Alamy; p. 365, Dmitriy Shironosov/Shutterstock; p. 370, Courtesy of Al Bartlett; p. 376, Wave Break Media, Ltd./Shutterstock; p. 378, Jan Martin Will/Shutterstock

Technology Credits

Section 1.1

1. A population is the complete set of people or things being studied, while a sample is a subset of the population. The difference is that the sample is only a part of the complete population.

3. A sample statistic is a numerical measure of a characteristic of a *sample* found by consolidating or summarizing raw data. A population parameter is a numerical measure of a characteristic of a *population*. Because it is usually impractical to directly measure population parameters for large populations, we usually infer likely values of the population parameters from the measured sample statistics.

5. Does not make sense. Population parameters are typically inferred from sample statistics. When population parameters are known, sample statistics are not needed and the concept of "margin of error" does not apply.

7. Does not make sense; in fact, the statement is clearly false. The confidence interval in this case runs from $54\% - 3\% = 51\%$ to $54\% + 3\% = 57\%$. Assuming the margin of error is defined as it is in most cases, this interval is a 95% confidence interval, meaning that we can be 95% confident that Johnson received between 51% and 57% of the vote. While this makes it quite likely that Johnson really did receive a majority of the vote (assuming the poll was conducted well), it is not a certainty, as there is still a 5% chance that her true percentage of the vote was above 57% or below 51% — and it is possible that it could be enough below so that she did not win a majority of the votes.

9. Does not make sense. The sample should be drawn from the population of all people who have suffered through a family tragedy, which is not the same as the population of patients in support groups for loss of a spouse. There are many types of family tragedies besides loss of a spouse, and not all of those people join support groups.

11. *Sample:* The 1,018 adults selected. *Population:* All adults in the United States. *Sample statistic:* 22%. The value of the population parameter is not known, but it is the percentage of all adults in the United States who smoked cigarettes in the past week.

13. *Sample:* The 47 subjects treated with Garlicin. *Population:* The complete set of all adults. *Sample statistic:* 3.2. The value of the population parameter is not known, but it is the average (mean) change in LDL cholesterol.

15. 57% to 63%

17. 93% to 99%

19. Yes. Although there is no guarantee, the results suggest that the majority of adults believe that immediate government action is required, because the percentage is most likely between 53% and 57%.

21. Yes. Based on the survey, the actual percentage of voters is expected to be between 67% and 73%, which does not include the 61% value based on actual voter results. If the survey was conducted well, then it is unlikely that it would be so different from the actual results, implying either that respondents intentionally lied to appear favorable to the pollsters or that their memories may have been inaccurate.

23. a. *Goal:* Determine the percentage of all adults in favor of the death penalty for people convicted of murder. *Population:* The complete set of all adults. *Population parameter:* The percentage of all adults who are in favor of the death penalty for people convicted of murder. **b.** *Sample:* The 511 selected subjects. *Raw data:* Individual responses to the question. *Sample statistic:* 64%. **c.** 60% to 68%

25. a. *Goal:* Determine the percentage of households with a TV tuned to the Super Bowl. *Population:* The complete set of all U.S. households. *Population parameter:* The percentage of all U.S. households tuned to the Super Bowl. **b.** *Sample:* The sample of 9,000 households selected for the survey. *Raw data:* Individual indications of whether the household has a TV tuned to the Super Bowl. *Sample statistic:* 45%. **c.** 44% to 46%

27. *Step 1.* Goal: Identify the percentage of all drivers who use cell phones while they are driving. *Step 2.* Choose a sample of drivers. *Step 3.* Collect data from the sample of drivers to determine the percentage of them who use a cell phone while driving. *Step 4.* Use the techniques of the science of statistics to make an inference about the percentage of all people who use cell phones while they are driving. *Step 5.* Based on the likely value of the population parameter, form a conclusion about the percentage of people who use cell phones while they are driving.

Section 1.2

1. A census is the collection of data from every member of the population, but a sample is a collection of data from only part of the population.

3. With cluster sampling, we select all members of randomly selected subgroups (or clusters), but with stratified sampling, we select samples from each of the different subgroups (or strata).

5. Does not make sense because it is not possible or practical to survey every student, as would be required for a census.

7. Makes sense. Because it is obvious that the percentage of Americans more than 6 feet tall is well under 75%, the study must have somehow used a biased sample.

9. A census is practical because the population consists of the small number of players on the LA Lakers team, and it is easy to obtain their heights.

11. A census is not practical. The number of statistics instructors is large, and it would be extremely difficult to get them all to take an IQ test.

13. The sample is the service times of the 4 selected senators. The population consists of the service times of all 100 senators. This is an example of random sampling (or simple random sampling).

However, because the sample is so small, it is not likely to be representative of the population.

15. The sample is the 1,059 selected adults, and the population is the complete set of all adults. This is an example of simple random sampling. Because the sample is fairly large and it was obtained by a reputable firm, the sample is likely to be representative of the population.

17. Most representative: Sample 3, because the list is likely to represent the most people, and there is no reason to think that people with the first 1,000 numbers would differ in any particular way from other people. Sample 1 is biased because it involves owners of expensive vehicles. Sample 2 is biased because it involves people from only one geographic region. Sample 4 is biased because it involves a self-selected sample consisting of people who are more likely to have strong feelings about the issue of credit card debt.

19. Yes. Because the film critic indirectly works for Disney, he or she may be more inclined to submit a more favorable review.

21. Yes. The university scientists receive the funding from Monsanto, so they might be inclined to please the company in the hopes of getting further funding in the future. Thus, there may be an inclination to provide favorable results. To determine whether this bias is a problem, you would need to explore the methods and conclusions very carefully.

23. The sample is a simple random sample that is likely to be representative because there is no bias in the selection process.

25. The sample is a cluster sample. It is likely to be representative, although the exact method of selecting the polling stations could affect whether the sample is biased.

27. The sample is a convenience sample. It is likely to be biased, because the sample consists of family members likely to have the same socio-economic backgrounds and interests.

29. The sample is a stratified sample. It is likely to be biased because people from those age groups are not evenly distributed throughout the population. However, the results could be weighted to reflect the age distribution of the population.

31. The sample is a systematic sample. The sample is likely to be representative, because there is nothing about the alphabetical ordering that is likely to result in a biased sample.

33. The sample is a stratified sample. It is likely to be biased because the population does not have equal numbers of people in each of the three categories. However, the results could be weighted to reflect the actual distribution of the population.

35. The sample is a convenience sample. It is likely to be biased because it is a self-selected sample and consists of those with strong feelings about the issue.

37. The sampling plan results in a simple random sample, so it is likely to be representative.

39. Simple random sampling of the student body. Be sure you use a large enough sample size to get meaningful results.

41. Cluster sampling of death records should give good data for this case.

Section 1.3

1. A placebo is physically similar to a treatment, but it lacks any active ingredients, so it should not by itself produce any effects. A placebo is important so that results from subjects given a real treatment can be compared with the results from subjects given a placebo.

3. Confounding is the mixing of effects from different factors so that we cannot determine the effects from the specific factors being studied. If males are given the treatment and females are given placebos, we would not know whether effects are due to the treatment or the sex of the participant.

5. It makes sense to use a double-blind experiment, but the experimental design is tricky because the subjects can clearly see the clothing that they are wearing, and the evaluators can also see those colors. Blinding might be used by not telling the subjects about the experiment, so their knowledge of their clothes colors does not affect their results. Because it is difficult to use blinding for the evaluators, it is important to obtain results based on objective measures not subject to the judgments of the evaluators.

7. The experimenter effect occurs when a researcher or experimenter somehow influences subjects through such factors as facial expression, tone of voice, or attitude. The experimenter effect can be avoided by using blinding so that those who evaluate the results do not know which subjects are given an actual treatment and which subjects are given no treatment or a placebo.

9. Observational because the batteries are measured, but they are not treated.

11. Experiment. The treatment group consists of the subjects given the magnetic bracelets, and the control group consists of the subjects given the bracelets that have no magnetism. It is probably not possible to use blinding with this study, because the passengers could easily test their bracelets to see if they are magnetic (by holding them near metal).

13. This is an observational, retrospective study examining how a characteristic determined before birth (identical or fraternal twins) affected mental skills later.

15. Experiment because the subjects are given a treatment. The treatment group consists of the 152 couples given the YSORT treatment. The control group consists of others not given any treatment.

17. This is an experiment. The treatment group consists of the genetically modified corn, and the control group consists of corn not genetically modified.

19. This is an experiment. The treatment group consists of those treated with magnets. The control group consists of those given the non-magnetic devices.

21. Confounding is likely to occur. If there are differences in effects from the two groups, there is no way to know if those differences are attributable to the treatment (fertilizer or irrigation) or the type of region (moist or dry). This confounding can be avoided by using blocks of fertilized trees in both the moist region and dry region and using blocks of irrigated trees in both the moist region and dry region.

23. Confounding is likely. If there are differences in the amounts of gasoline consumed, there would be no way to know whether those differences are due to the octane rating of the gasoline or the type of vehicle. Confounding can be avoided by using 87 octane gasoline in half of the vans and half of the sport utility vehicles and by using 91 octane gasoline in the other vehicles. Even better, conduct an experiment in which identical vehicles are driven under the same conditions (speed, distance, etc.) with the different octane gasolines.

25. Subjects clearly know whether they are treated with running, so confounding is possible from a placebo effect. Moreover, there is no objective way to measure back pain, so different subjects may report changes in back pain differently. Also, there could be an experimenter effect that can be avoided with blinding of those who evaluate results.

27. In this case, the tennis balls play the role of placebos. Confounding can occur because of a placebo effect and/or an experimenter effect, because it will be obvious to both subjects and experimenters whether they are lifting heavy weights. It would be better to use the heavy weights and the tennis balls with the same subjects at different times, to see if the different regimens affect blood pressure.

29. The control group consists of those who do not listen to Beethoven and the treatment group consists of those who do listen to Beethoven. By using subjects who are coded, blinding could be used so that those who measure intelligence are not influenced by their knowledge about the participants.

31. The control group consists of cars using gasoline without the ethanol additive, and the treatment group consists of cars using gasoline with the ethanol additive. Blinding is not necessary for the cars, and it is probably unnecessary for the researchers because the mileage will likely be measured with objective tools.

Section 1.4

1. Peer review is a process in which experts in a field evaluate a research report before the report is published. It is useful for lending credibility to the research because it implies that other experts agree that it was carried out properly.

3. When participants select themselves for a survey, those with strong opinions about the topic being surveyed are more likely to participate, and this group is typically not representative of the general population.

5. Does not make sense. A survey involving a large sample could be very poor if it involves a poor sampling method (such as a self-selected sample), while a smaller sample could produce much better results if it involves a sound sampling method (such as a simple random sample).

7. Does not make sense. We often don't even know if confounding variables are present, so we cannot be certain they've all been taken into account.

9. The survey was funded by a source that can benefit through increased sales fostered by the survey results, so there is a potential for bias in the survey. Guideline 2 is most relevant.

11. "Good" is not well defined and is difficult to measure. Guideline 4 is most relevant.

13. The sample is self-selected, so participation bias is a serious issue. Guideline 3 is most relevant.

15. The wording of the question is biased and tends to elicit negative responses. Guideline 6 is most relevant.

17. Because much of the funding was provided by Mars and the Chocolate Manufacturers Association, the researchers may have been more inclined to provide favorable results. The bias could have been avoided if the researchers were not paid by the chocolate manufacturers. If that was the only way the research could be done, then the researchers should institute procedures to ensure that they publish all results, including negative ones.

19. The wording of the question was biased to strengthen opposition against a particular candidate, and is likely to be a "push poll" financed by supporters of another candidate, rather than a legitimate poll. A better sampling method would involve questions devoid of such bias.

21. The word "wrong" in the first question could be misleading. Some people might believe that abortion is wrong, but still favor choice. The second question could also be confusing, as some people might think that "advice of her doctor" means that the woman's life is in danger, which could alter their opinion about abortion in this situation. Groups opposed to abortion would be likely to cite the results of the first question, while groups favoring abortion would be more likely to cite the results of the second question.

23. The first question requires a study of Internet dates. The second question involves a study of married people to determine whether their first date was an Internet date. The two questions are likely to yield very different types of information. For example, the second question would tell you what percentage of current marriages began with Internet dates, but the first would only tell you how often Internet dating leads to marriage, which might not be any different from how often other forms of dating lead to marriage. The goals of the study need to be better defined and the questions framed to meet the goals.

25. The first question involves a study of college students in general, and the second question involves a study of those who do binge drinking. The first question might be addressed by surveying college students. The second question would be addressed by surveying binge drinkers, and it would be much more difficult to survey this group.

27. The headline refers to drugs whereas the story refers to "drug use, drinking, or smoking." Because "drugs" is generally considered to consist of drugs other than cigarettes or alcohol, the headline is very misleading.

29. No information is given about the meaning of "confidence." The sample size and margin of error are not provided.

31. No information is given to justify the statement that "more" companies try to bet on weather forecasting. If only the four cited companies are new, the increase is relatively insignificant.

Section 1.5

1. Qualitative data consist of values that can be placed into different nonnumerical categories, whereas quantitative data consist of values representing counts or measurements.

3. Yes. Data consist of either qualities or quantities (numbers), so all data are either qualitative or quantitative.

5. Blood groups are qualitative because they don't measure or count anything.

7. Braking reaction times are quantitative because they consist of measurements.

9. The answers to multiple choice test questions are qualitative because they don't measure or count anything.

11. The television shows are qualitative because they don't measure or count anything.

13. Head circumferences are quantitative because they consist of measurements.

15. The grade point averages are quantitative because they are measures of course grades.

17. The numbers are discrete because only the counting numbers are used, and no values between counting numbers are possible.

19. The numbers are discrete because they are counts. Only the counting numbers are used, and no values between counting numbers are possible.

21. The times are continuous data because they can be any value within some range of values.

23. The numerical test scores are discrete data because they can be counting numbers only.

25. The speeds are continuous data because they can be any value within some range of values.

27. The numbers are discrete data because they can be counting numbers only.

29. Ratio

31. Nominal

33. Ordinal

35. Ordinal

37. Nominal

39. Ratio

41. The ratio level does not apply. The ratio is not meaningful because the stars don't measure or count anything. Differences between star values are not meaningful.

43. The ratio level does not apply. IQ tests do not measure intelligence on the type of scale required for the ratio level. Someone with an IQ score of 140 is not necessarily twice as intelligent as someone with an IQ score of 70.

45. The ratio level applies. The age of 1,000 years is twice as long as the age of 500 years.

47. The ratio level applies. The $150,000 salary amount is twice the salary of $75,000, so the ratio of "twice" is meaningful.

49. The data are quantitative and are at the ratio level. The data are continuous. The times have a natural zero starting point and the times can be any values within a particular range.

51. The data are qualitative and are at the nominal level of measurement. The numbers are different ways to express the names, and they don't measure or count anything.

53. The data are quantitative and are at the interval level of measurement. The data are discrete because they consist of whole numbers only. The years are measured from an arbitrary reference (the year 0), not a natural zero starting point. Differences between the years are meaningful values, but ratios are not meaningful.

55. The data are qualitative at the ordinal level of measurement. The ratings consist of an ordering, but they do not represent counts or measurements.

Chapter 1 Review Exercises

1. a. 12% to 16%   **b.** All adults in the United States **c.** It is an observational study because the subjects were not treated or modified in any way. The variable of interest is whether the subject has a tattoo. For this survey, that variable has two values: yes or no.   **d.** The value is a sample statistic because it is based on the sample of 2,320 adults, not the population of all adults.   **e.** No, because it would be a self-selected sample with a likely participation bias.   **f.** Use a computer to randomly generate Social Security numbers, identify the people with those Social Security numbers, then select those people.   **g.** Select a sample of subjects in each state.   **h.** Select all of the adults in several randomly selected streets.   **i.** Select every 10th adult, by address, on each street in a city.   **j.** Select your classmates.

3. a. No, because there is no information about the occurrence of headaches among people who do not use Bystolic. Based on the given information, it is possible that 7% of the population experiences headaches whether or not Bystolic is used.   **b.** It appears that Bystolic users have about the same rate of headaches as those given a placebo, so headaches do not appear to be an adverse reaction to Bystolic use.   **c.** This is an experiment because subjects are given a treatment.   **d.** With blinding, the trial participants do not know whether they are getting Bystolic or a placebo, and those who evaluate the results also do not know.   **e.** An experimenter effect occurs if the experimenter somehow influences subjects through such factors as facial expression, tone of voice, or attitude. It can be avoided through the use of blinding.

Chapter 1 Quiz

1. c   **3.** a   **5.** c   **7.** c   **9.** b

11. b   **13.** b   **15.** b

Section 2.1

1. $\frac{4}{5}$ **3.** $\frac{2}{5}$ **5.** $\frac{3}{10}$ **7.** $\frac{7}{22}$ **9.** 160 million

Exercises

1. $\frac{19}{5}$ **3.** $5\frac{3}{4}$ **5.** $\frac{1}{2}$ **7.** $5\frac{1}{2}$ **9.** $\frac{5}{9}$ **11.** $\frac{1}{4}$ **13.** $\frac{34}{35}$ **15.** $\frac{1}{4}$

17. $6\frac{1}{2}$ **19.** $10\frac{3}{5}$ **21.** $3\frac{1}{3}$ **23.** $1\frac{4}{5}$ **25.** $6\frac{1}{2}$ **27.** $2\frac{7}{8}$

29. $\frac{2}{15}$ **31.** 14   **33.** $\frac{91}{6}$, or $15\frac{1}{6}$ **35.** $\frac{17}{3}$, or $5\frac{2}{3}$ **37.** $\frac{1}{9}$

39. $\frac{24}{7}$, or $3\frac{3}{7}$ **41.** $\frac{1}{2}$

Section 2.2

1. a. $\frac{1}{2}$ **b.** $2\frac{73}{1000}$ **3.** 748.08 **5.** 1.179 **7.** 327,000 **9.** 0.00086

Exercises

1. $\frac{7}{8}$ **3.** Hundredths **5.** Seventy-two hundredths

7. Three and nine thousandths **9.** 7.3 **11.** 4.39 **13.** 18.11

15. 1.873 **17.** 2.912 **19.** 2710 **21.** 0.0015 **23.** 5

25. 7.35 **27.** 14.5

Section 2.3

1. $\frac{7}{100}$ **3.** 2.5% **5.** 0.40, or 0.4

Exercises

1. $\frac{3}{4}$ **3.** $1\frac{3}{50}$ **5.** 0.06 **7.** 1.5 **9.** 31% **11.** 1.45%

13. 10% **15.** 80%

Section 2.4

1. 2^5 **3.** $10^9 6$ **5.** 0.0000000043 **7.** 7.1×10^{-11}

Exercises

1. 6^5 **3.** $2^2 \cdot 10^3$ **5.** 25,000 **7.** 3 **9.** 14 **11.** 4

Section 2.5

1. a. $414 million **b.** 8.4% **c.** 2.8% decrease
d. $5066.35 million

3. The statement that the margin of error is 3% incorrectly implies that the error can be up to 3% of 25%, which is 0.75%, but the actual error can be up to 3 percentage points away from 25% (from 22% to 28%).

5. Does not make sense. The number of people with cell phones may have increased by 1.2 million, but 1.2 million people is not a percentage, so the statement is not sensible.

7. Makes sense. The 100% increase indicates that the loan rate doubled. For example, if the loan rate doubled from 5% to 10%, it increased the loan rate by 100%.

9. a. 75/100 or 3/4, 0.75, 75% **b.** 3/8, 0.375, 37.5% **c.** 4/10 or 2/5, 0.4, 40% **d.** 80/100 or 4/5, 0.8, 80%

11. a. 71% **b.** 33% **c.** 41% **d.** 81%

13. −38% (38% decrease from 1990)

15. 18% (18% increase from January 1996)

17. 14%. The *Wall Street Journal* has 14% more circulation than *USA Today*.

19. −25%. O'Hare handled 25% fewer passengers than Atlanta's Hartsfield Airport.

21. 66

23. 834

25. 140%. The truck weighs 100% of the car's weight plus another 40%.

27. 80%. The population of Montana is the population of New Hampshire minus 20%.

29. Yes. Three percentage points corresponds to a range from 86% to 92%, which was intended. A margin of error of 3% corresponds to 3% of 89%, which is $0.03 \times 0.89 = 0.0267$, but this is not what was meant.

31. −15.5 percentage points; −22.7%

33. 22 percentage points; 56.4%

Chapter 2 Posttest

1. 512 **3.** 1, 2, 4, 5, 10, 20 **5.** $\frac{5}{18}$ **7.** $12\frac{1}{24}$ **9.** $3\frac{19}{20}$

11. 2 **13.** Two and three hundred ninety-six thousandths **15.** 6.99

17. 2070 **19.** 0.125; 12.5% **21.** 6 times **23.** 625.3 m^2

25. 15 times

Section 3.1

1. A frequency table has two columns, one for categories and one for frequencies. Categories are the different values that a variable may have (for example, different eye colors or different ranges of income). Frequencies are the counts of the numbers of data values in each category.

3. 4, 16, 32, 38, 40

5. The statement does not make sense, because a column in the frequency table must consist of frequency counts, but neither of the columns of *State* and *Median Income* consist of frequency counts.

7. The statement does not make sense, because each individual frequency is a whole number, and any sum of frequencies must also be a whole number, so 25.5 is not a possible value of a cumulative frequency.

9.

Grade	Frequency	Relative frequency	Cumulative frequency
A	3	10.0%	3
B	10	33.3%	13
C	11	36.7%	24
D	2	6.7%	26
F	4	13.3%	30
Total	30	100%	30

11.

Weight (pounds)	Frequency	Relative frequency	Cumulative frequency
0.7900–0.7949	1	1/36	1
0.7950–0.7999	0	0	1
0.8000–0.8049	1	1/36	2
0.8050–0.8099	3	3/36	5
0.8100–0.8149	4	4/36	9
0.8150–0.8199	17	17/36	26
0.8200–0.8249	6	6/36	32
0.8250–0.8299	4	4/36	36
Total	36	100%	36

13. The age category of 40 to 49 includes the most actors.

Age	Number of Actors
20—29	1
30—39	27
40—49	35
50—59	14
60—69	6
70—79	1

15.

Category	Frequency	Relative frequency
A	12	24%
B	9	18%
C	12	24%
D	11	22%
F	6	12%
Total	**50**	**100%**

17. a. 200   **b.** 142   **c.** 16%   **d.** 0.135, 0.155, 0.210, 0.200, 0.140, 0.160   **e.** 27, 58, 100, 140, 168, 200

19. a.

Rating	Frequency	Relative frequency
0–2	20	38.5%
3–5	14	26.9%
6–8	15	28.8%
9–11	2	3.8%
12–14	1	1.9%
Total	**52**	**100%**

b.

Rating	Frequency	Relative frequency
0–2	33	63.5%
3–5	19	36.5%
6–8	0	0%
9–11	0	0%
12–14	0	0%
Total	**52**	**100%**

c. The Dvorak keyboard appears more efficient because it has more lower ratings and fewer high ones.

Section 3.2

1. A false positive occurs when the test indicates use of banned substances for someone who does not actually use them. A false negative occurs when the test indicates that banned substances are not used by someone who actually does use them. A true positive occurs when the player tests positive and he actually does use banned substances. A true negative occurs when the player tests negative and he does not use banned substances.

3. True negative

5. Makes sense.

7. Does not make sense.

9. Josh; Josh; Jude

11. a. New Jersey; Nebraska

13. a. Whites: 0.18%; nonwhites: 0.54%; total 0.19%.   **b.** Whites: 0.16%; nonwhites: 0.34%; total 0.23%.   **c.** The rate for both whites and nonwhites was higher in New York than in Richmond,

yet the overall rate was higher in Richmond than in New York. The percentage of nonwhites was significantly lower in New York than in Richmond.

15. a. Spelman has a better record for home games (34.5% vs. 32.1%) and away games (75.0% vs. 73.3%), individually.   **b.** Morehouse has a better overall average.   **c.** Morehouse has a better team, as teams are generally rated on overall records.

17. a. 57 appeared to be lying. 15 of them were telling the truth, and 42 were actually lying. 26% of those who appear to be lying were not actually lying.   **b.** 41 appeared to be telling the truth. 32 of them were actually telling the truth, and 9 were lying. 78% of those who appeared to be telling the truth were actually truthful.

19. A higher percentage of women than men were hired in both the white-collar and blue-collar positions, suggesting a hiring preference for women. Overall, 20% of the 200 females (40) who applied for white-collar positions were hired, and 85% of the 100 females (85) who applied for blue-collar positions were hired. Thus $40 + 85 = 125$ of the $200 + 100 = 300$ females who applied were hired, a percentage of 41.7. Overall, 15% of the 200 males (30) who applied for white-collar positions were hired, and 75% of the 400 males (300) who applied for blue-collar positions were hired. Thus $30 + 300 = 330$ of the $200 + 400 = 600$ males who applied were hired, a percentage of 55.0.

21. a. In the general population, $57 + 3 = 60$ of the 20,000 in the sample are infected. This is an incidence rate of $60/20000 = 0.003$ or 0.3%. In the "at-risk" population, $475 + 25 = 500$ of the 5,000 in the sample are infected. This is an incidence rate of $500/5000 = 10.0\%$.   **b.** In the "at-risk" category, 475 out 500 infected with HIV test positive, or 95%. Of those who test positive, 475 out of $475 + 225 = 700$ have HIV, a percentage of $475/700 = 0.679$ or 67.9%. These two figures are different because they measure different things. The 700 who test positive include 225 who were false positives. While the test correctly identifies 95% of those who have HIV, it also incorrectly identifies some who do not have HIV. Thus only 67.9 % of those who test positive actually have HIV.   **c.** In the "at-risk" population, a patient who tests positive for the disease has about a 68% chance of actually having the disease. This is nearly 7 times as great as the incidence rate (10%) of the disease in the at-risk category. Thus the test is very valuable in identifying those with HIV.   **d.** In the general population, patients with HIV test positive 57 times out of 60, or 95% of the time. Of those who test positive, 57 out of $57 + 997 = 1054$ actually have HIV, a percentage of $57/1054 = 0.054$ or 5.4%. These two figures are different because they measure different things. The 1054 who test positive include 997 who were false positives. While the test correctly identifies 95% of those who have HIV, it also incorrectly identifies some who do not have HIV. Thus only 5.4 % of those who test positive actually have HIV.   **e.** In the general population, a patient who tests positive for the disease has about a 5.4% chance of actually having the disease. This is 18 times as great as the incidence rate (0.3%) of the disease in the general population. Thus the test is very valuable in identifying those with HIV.

Section 3.3

1. The distribution of data is the way data values are spread over all possible values.

3. By arranging bars from highest to lowest, the Pareto chart draws attention to the most important categories. The pie chart does not do that.

5. Does not make sense. Histograms require quantitative data, and names of political parties are qualitative.

7. Makes sense.

9. A histogram would work well to show the frequencies of the different categories of incomes.

11. A time series graph would be effective in showing any trend in the number of movie theaters.

13. a.

Reading Category	Relative Frequency
Popular fiction	50.4%
Cooking/Crafts	10.2%
General nonfiction	8.9%
Religious	8.6%
Psychology/Recovery	6.3%
Technical/Science/Education	5.6%
Art/Literature/Poetry	3.7%
Reference	2.6%
All other categories	2.5%
Travel/Regional	1.3%

b.

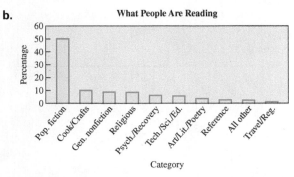

c. The Pareto chart makes it easier to see which categories are more popular.

15.

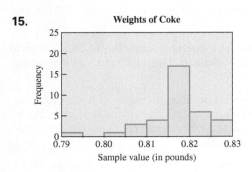

17.

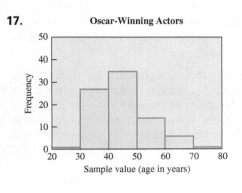

19.

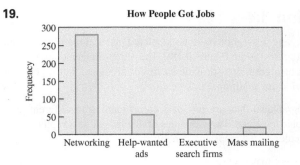

21.

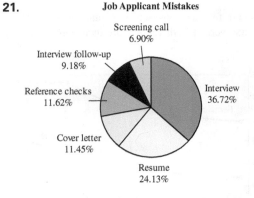

23.

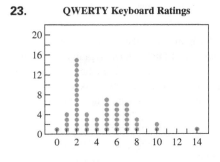

25.

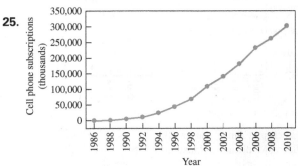

The graph does not appear to show linear growth.

27.

Stem	Leaves
6	7
7	25
8	5899
9	09
10	0

The lengths of the rows are similar to the height of bars in a histogram, so that longer rows of data correspond to higher frequencies.

Section 3.4

1. Yes, any histogram can be depicted as a three-dimensional histogram (as in Figure 3.18). The three-dimensional version of a histogram does provide more visual appeal, but it does not provide any additional information.

3. Geographical data are raw data corresponding to different geographic locations. Two examples of displays of geographical data are color-coded maps and contour maps.

5. Does not make sense.

7. Makes sense.

9. a. The numbers of females consistently outnumber the numbers of males. The numbers of both genders are increasing gradually over time.

b.

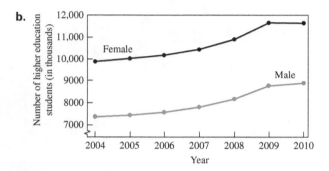

11. a. Males consistently have much higher median salaries than females, and both males and females have steadily increasing salaries over time.   **b.** The line graph makes it easier to examine the trend over time. Also, the line graph is less cluttered, so that the information is easier to understand and interpret.

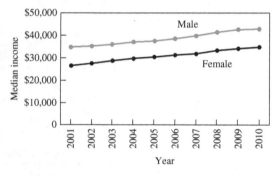

13. The stack plot shows that entitlement spending (Social Security, Medicare, Medicaid, and insurance subsidies) is projected to grow dramatically in coming decades. The graph shows that, without an increase in tax revenues, this entitlement spending would consume all government revenue by mid-century, which would leave no room for any other government programs, including the military. The clear message is that without changes, entitlement spending is on a track that would cause severe budgetary problems.

15. There appears to be a general trend of higher melanoma mortality in southern states and western states. This might be the result of people in these states spending more time outdoors, exposed to sunlight. As a researcher, you might be particularly interested in regions that deviate from general trends. For example, a county in eastern Washington state stands out with a very

high melanoma mortality. You might first want to verify that the data point is accurate, and not an error of some type. If it is accurate, you may want to find out why this one county has a higher melanoma mortality than surrounding counties.

17.

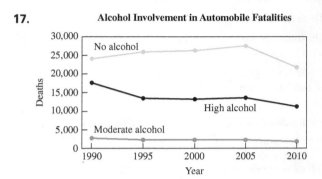

19.

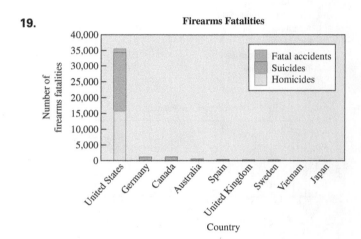

Section 3.5

1. The difference of 1 foot is not meaningful. By drawing a bar graph with a vertical scale starting at a value such as 130 feet, the difference will be greatly exaggerated.

3. The scale is called an exponential scale. The advantage of such a scale is that it allows us to include values that vary over a very large range.

5. By starting the vertical scale at 30 instead of 0, the difference between the two amounts of fuel consumption is greatly exaggerated. The graph would not be misleading if it is changed so that the vertical scale begins at 0.

7. The amount of oil used by each country appears to be related to the volume of the barrels in the pictograph, when it is really related to the height of the barrels. The U.S. consumption is about four times that of Japan, not 64 times as suggested by the volumes of the barrels.

9. a, b. Because of the three-dimensional appearance of the pie charts, the sizes of the wedges on the page do not match the percentages. Instead they show how the wedges would look if the entire pie was tilted at an angle. This distortion makes it difficult to see the true relationships among the categories.

c.

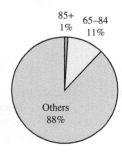 1990 Age Distribution

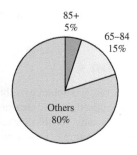 2050 Age Distribution

d. In 2050, there will be relatively more older people and fewer younger people in the U.S. population than in 1990. Note, however, that because of population growth, all age groups are expected to be larger in number in 2050 than in 1990.

11. The percent change in the CPI is greatest in 1990. In 2009, the percent change in CPI is negative, so prices decreased from those in 2008. Prices have increased in every year (except for 2009), but the increases near the end of the time period are lower than those near the beginning.

13. The actual minimum wage in unadjusted dollars has either remained constant or has risen steadily since 1955. The purchasing power increased from 1955 to 1968, then decreased from 1968 to 1989, and it has been relatively stable in recent years. The purchasing power in 2011 is just slightly higher than it was in 1955.

Chapter 3 Review Exercises

1. a. The frequencies are 5, 12, 12, 5, 0, 2. **b.** The frequencies are 5, 5, 16, 8, 2. **c.** The weights of regular Pepsi are consistently larger than those of Diet Pepsi. The weights of regular Pepsi are larger because of the sugar content that is not included in the cans of Diet Pepsi.

3. a.

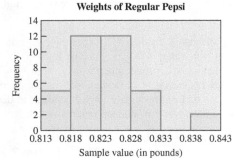
Weights of Regular Pepsi

b.

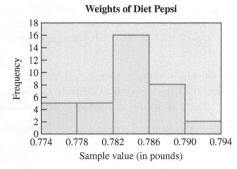
Weights of Diet Pepsi

c. The shapes of the histograms are not dramatically different, indicating that the distributions of the weights are similar. However, the range of values is very different, indicating that the weights of regular Pepsi are considerably higher than those of Diet Pepsi.

5. By drawing attention to the most frustrating sounds, the Pareto chart is more effective. By using a meaningful scale, the Pareto chart also does a better job of showing the relative importance of the different frustrating sounds.

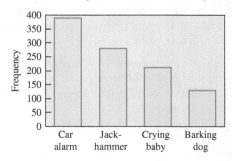

Chapter 3 Quiz

1. Histogram

3. 61 min, 62 min, 62 min, 62 min, 62 min, 67 min, 69 min

5. 25% of the values are between 20 and 29 inclusive.

7. Using a vertical scale that does not start at zero causes the difference between the two frequencies to be exaggerated.

9. 0, 1, 1, 10, 11, 12, 49, 49

Section 4.1

1. $F = \frac{9}{5}C + 32$ **3. a.** $K = C + 273$ **b.** K is 267.

Section 4.2

1. No. The mean refers specifically to the sum of all data values divided by the number of data values. The term "average" could refer to any one of several different statistics, including the mean, median, or mode.

3. Yes. The executive secretary's income is much higher than the incomes of the other 23 students, so it is an outlier. In general, the definition of an outlier is somewhat vague, so an outlier cannot be clearly and objectively identified. (However, statisticians have created rules that can be applied to identify outliers in some cases.)

5. Does not make sense.

7. Makes sense.

9. Mean. For the population of basketball players, there are only a few heights that are extreme, and they are not extreme by very large amounts. In this case, the mean would be better because it takes every height into account.

11. Median. The exact values of "over" ages are not known, so the mean cannot be computed.

13. Mean: 53.3; median: 52.0; mode: none

15. Mean: 58.3 sec; median: 55.5 sec; mode: 49 sec

17. Mean: 0.188; median: 0.165; mode: 0.16

19. Mean: 0.9194 g; median: 0.9200 g; there is no mode

21. a. Mean: 157,586; median: 104,100   **b.** Alaska is an outlier on the high end. Without Alaska the mean is 81,317 and the median is 78,650.   **c.** Connecticut is an outlier on the low end. Without Connecticut (but with Alaska) the mean is 182,933 and the median is 109,050.

23. a. 85.0   **b.** 100   **c.** No; a mean of 90 for five quizzes requires a total of 450 points, which you cannot reach even with 100 on the fifth quiz.

25. Mean score of your students: 74.7; median score: 70.0. So it depends on the meaning of "average." If it is mean, then your students are above average in their scores. If it is median, then your students are below average.

27. 0.39 pound

29. Each student is taking three classes with enrollments of 20 each and one class with an enrollment of 100, so the mean class size for each student is $(20 + 20 + 20 + 100)/4 = 40$. There are three classes with 100 students each and 45 classes with 20 students each, so the 48 courses have a mean class size of $(300 + 900)/48 = 25$. The two means are very different.

31. 0.417; it is the average number of hits per at-bat.

33. Probably not. The overall rate of defects would be 3% only if both sites produce the same number of batteries.

35. The outcome is no, by 600 votes to 400 votes.

37. Mean: 1.9; median: 2; mode: 1. The mode of 1 correctly indicates that the smooth yellow peas occur more than any other phenotype, but the mean and median don't make sense with these data at the nominal level of measurement.

Section 4.3

1. The distribution is not symmetric.

3. Because the professors have successfully completed a rigorous program of education, their IQ scores are likely to all be higher than average and closer together, so they probably have less variation than IQ scores of randomly selected adults. The lower variation of IQ scores of the professors results in a graph that is narrower with less spread than the graph of IQ scores from the randomly selected adults.

5. Does not make sense.

7. Makes sense.

9. Two modes, left-skewed, wide variation.

11. Single-peaked, nearly symmetric, moderate variation.

13. a. The distribution is right-skewed. It is not symmetric.
b. 409 (half of 817)

15. a. One mode of $0   **b.** Right-skewed, because there will be many students making little or nothing.

17. a. One mode   **b.** Symmetric

19. a. One mode   **b.** Symmetric

21. a. One mode   **b.** Left-skewed

23. a. One mode   **b.** Right-skewed

25. a. One mode   **b.** Right-skewed

Section 4.4

1. The range is found by subtracting the lowest sample value from the highest. It is a measure of variation. A major disadvantage of the range is that its value depends on only the lowest and highest sample values and it does not take every value into account.

3. The statement is incorrect because it defines the standard deviation as a value that depends on the minimum and maximum values, but the standard deviation uses every data value.

5. Does not make sense.

7. Makes sense.

9. Range: 45.0 words; standard deviation: 15.7 words

11. Range: 26.0 sec; standard deviation: 9.5 sec

13. Range: 0.170; standard deviation: 0.057

15. Range: 0.1160 g; standard deviation: 0.0336 g

17. *Cat on a Hot Tin Roof:* range $= 10.0$ and standard deviation $= 2.6$. *The Cat in the Hat:* range $= 3.0$ and standard deviation $= 0.9$. There is much less variation among the word lengths in *The Cat in the Hat*.

19. One day: range $= 11.0$ degrees and standard deviation $= 2.6$. degrees. Five day: range $= 15.0$ degrees and standard deviation $= 4.5$ degrees. As expected, there appears to be greater variation in errors from the five-day forecast.

21. a. 5th percentile   **b.** 69th percentile   **c.** 48th percentile

23. Answers for data set (1) only: **a.** Histogram has frequency of 7 for data value of 9; no other values.   **b.** low value $= 9$; lower quartile $= 9$;   median $= 9$;   upper quartile $= 9$;   high value $= 9$ **c.** 0

25. a. Faculty: mean $= 2$, median $= 2$, range $= 4$; student: mean $= 6.2$, median $= 6$, range $= 9$.   **b.** Faculty: low $= 0$, lower quartile $= 1$, median $= 2$, upper quartile $= 3$, high $= 4$; student: low $= 1$, lower quartile $= 4$, median $= 6$, upper quartile $= 9$, high $= 10$.   **c.** Faculty: st. dev. $= 1.2$; student: st. dev. $= 3.0$. **d.** Faculty: range/4 $= 1.0$; student: range/4 $= 2.3$.

27. a. First 7: mean $= 58.3$, median $= 57$, range $= 4$; Last 7: mean $= 56.1$, median $= 54$, range $= 23$.   **b.** First 7: low $= 57$, lower quartile $= 57$, median $= 57$, upper quartile $= 61$, high $= 61$; Last 7: low $= 46$, lower quartile $= 47$, median $= 54$, upper quartile $= 64$, high $= 69$.   **c.** First 7: st. dev. $= 1.9$; Last 7: st. dev. $= 8.7$.   **d.** First 7: range/4 $= 1$; Last 7: range/4 $= 5.75$.

29. The second site has better quality. Although the second site has a mean that is a little farther from the target of 12 volts, the standard deviation is much less, so the voltages will be more consistent.

31. Having more stocks in the portfolio reduces the variation in the returns, because some stocks are likely to go up and others go down. The reduced variation means reduced risk, though also a lower likelihood of large gains.

Chapter 4 Review Exercises

1. a. Non-filtered: Mean is 1.28 mg and median is 1.15 mg. Filtered: Mean is 0.93 mg and median is 1.00 mg.   **b.** Non-filtered: Range is 0.70 mg and standard deviation is 0.26 mg. Filtered: Range is 0.80 mg and standard deviation is 0.24 mg.

c.

d. Non-filtered: Standard deviation is estimated to be 0.18 mg and it is actually 0.26 mg. Filtered: Standard deviation is estimated to be 0.20 and it is actually 0.24 mg. Both estimates are in the general ballpark of the actual vales.   **e.** There does appear to be a difference. The nicotine in filtered cigarettes appears to be generally lower, so the filters appear to be at least somewhat effective.

3. a. 0   **b.** Although both batteries have the same mean lifetime, the batteries with the smaller standard deviation are better because their lifetimes will be closer to the mean, and fewer of them will strand drivers by failing sooner than expected.   **c.** The outlier pulls the mean either up or down depending on whether it is above or below the mean, respectively.   **d.** The outlier has no effect on the median.   **e.** The outlier increases the range.   **f.** The outlier increases the standard deviation.

Chapter 4 Quiz

1. Mean   **3.** 27.0

5. The mean and median are equal.

7. 1.50 sec and 2.50 sec   **9.** Zero

Section 5.1

1. The word *normal* has a special meaning in statistics. It refers to a specific category of distributions, all of them being bell-shaped.

3. No. The ten different possible digits are all equally likely, so the graph of the distribution will tend to be flat, not bell-shaped.

5. Makes sense.

7. Does not make sense.

9. Distribution b is not normal. Distribution c has the larger standard deviation.

11. Normal. It is common for a manufactured product, such as quarters, to have a distribution that is normal. The weights typically vary above and below the mean weight by about the same amounts, so the distribution has one peak and is symmetric.

13. Not normal. The outcomes of the numbers between 1 and 49 are all equally likely, so the distribution tends to be uniform, not normal. A graph of the distribution will tend to be very flat, not bell-shaped.

15. Normal. Such physical measurements generally tend to be normally distributed. A small number of females will have extremely low counts, a small number will have extremely high counts, and the distribution will tend to peak around the value of the mean.

17. Not normal. The waiting times will tend to be uniformly distributed.

19. Not normal. Movie lengths have a minimum length (zero) and no maximum length.

21. Nearly normal. The deviations from the mean are evenly distributed around the mean.

23. a. 1   **b.** 0.20   **c.** 0.80   **d.** 0.35   **e.** 0.45

25. a. 115   **b.** 15%   **c.** 45%   **d.** 15%

Section 5.2

1. 0

3. No. The rule applies to normal distributions, but the outcomes from a die roll have a uniform distribution, not a normal distribution.

5. Does not make sense.   **7.** Does not make sense.

9. a. 50%   **b.** 84%   **c.** 2.5%   **d.** 84%   **e.** 81.5%

11. a. 68%   **b.** 95%   **c.** 99.7%   **d.** 47.5%

13. 50%   **15.** 2.28%

17. 97.72%   **19.** 93.32%

21. 68.26%   **23.** 84.00%

25. 50.00%   **27.** 84.13%

29. 99.38%   **31.** 0.13%

33. 68.26%   **35.** 89.25%

37. In all cases, 5% of coins are rejected. Cents: 2.44 gm to 2.56 gm; Nickels: 4.88 gm to 5.12 gm; Dimes: 2.208 gm to 2.328 gm; Quarters: 5.530 gm to 5.810 gm; Half dollars: 11.060 gm to 11.620 gm.

39. a. 6.68%   **b.** 48.01%   **c.** 36.54%

41. a. 0.47%   **b.** Approximately 4%   **c.** 30.055 to 30.745 inches   **d.** The best estimate would be the mean of the readings, or 30.4 inches.

43. Approximately 96.33%

Chapter 5 Review Exercises

1. a. Because the 38 outcomes are all equally likely, the distribution is uniform, not normal.   **b.** Weights of members in a homogeneous population, such as twelve-year old girls, typically have a normal distribution.   **c.** Approximately normal. Such test scores tend to be normally distributed.

3. a. 90 percentile   **b.** 1.29   **c.** No, the data value lies less than 2 standard deviations from the mean.   **d.** 0.0065   **e.** The temperature is unusual; it lies more than 2 standard deviations above the mean.   **f.** 99.22   **g.** 97.18   **h.** Fewer than 0.01%; yes, this temperature seems appropriate for claiming that a patient has a fever.   **i.** The sample mean is 6.6 standard deviations below the mean; the chance of selecting such a sample is extremely small. The assumed mean (98.60) may be incorrect.

Chapter 5 Quiz

1. b, c, and d are correct.   **3.** 95.44%

5. 4.9   **7.** 84%   **9.** 81.85%

Section 6.1

Quick Quiz

1. b **3.** a **5.** a **7.** a **9.** a

Exercises

7. Does not make sense **9.** Does not make sense

11. Does not make sense **13.** Natural

15. Rational **17.** Rational

19. Real **21.** Rational

23. Real **25.** Rational

27. Real

29. {January, February, March,...November, December}

31. {New Mexico, Oklahoma, Arkansas, Louisiana}

33. {9, 16, 25} **35.** {3, 9, 15, 21, 27}

37. 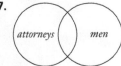 **39.**

41. 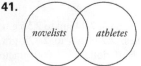 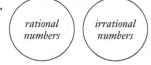 **43.**

45. b. *Subject:* widows. *Predicate:* women.

c.   **d.** No

47. a. All U.S. presidents are people over 30 years old.

b. *Subject:* U.S. presidents. *Predicate:* people over 30.

c.   **d.** Yes

49. a. No monkeys are gambling animals.

b. *Subject:* monkeys. *Predicate:* gambling animals.

c.  **d.** No

51. a. All winners are people who smile.

b. *Subject:* winners. *Predicate:* people who smile.

c. 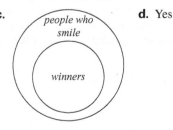 **d.** Yes

53.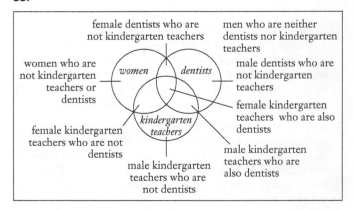

55.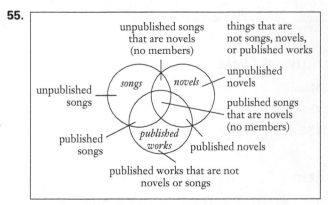

57.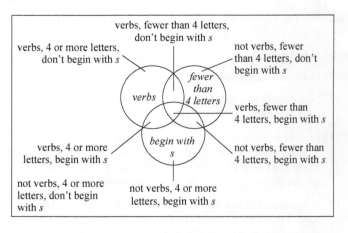

59. a. 16 **b.** 22 **c.** 44 **d.** 81

61.

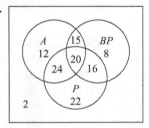

63. a. 20   **b.** 22   **c.** 8   **d.** 34

65. a.

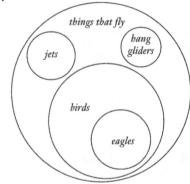

b. 95   **c.** 23   **d.** 82   **e.** 15   **f.** 117

67. a.

	Favorable	Non-favorable
Comedy	8	15
Non-comedy	10	12

b.

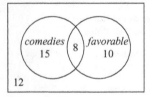

c. 15   **d.** 10

69. a.

	Hip-hop	Rock
NY	30	10
LA	20	40

b.

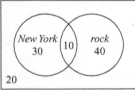

c. 10

71.

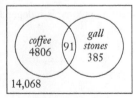

73.

	Vegetarian	Meat/fish	Total
Wine	20	40	60
No wine	45	15	60
Total	65	55	120

75.

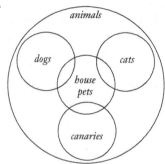

77.

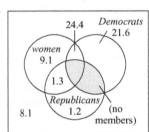

79. a.

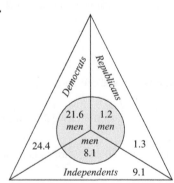

b.

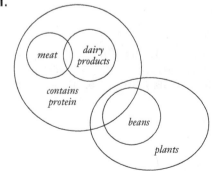

81.

There could not be beans that are dairy products. Meat that is a dairy product is not excluded by premises. No dairy products are plants. There could be plants with protein.

83. a.

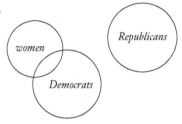

b. Yes. **c.** Yes.

85. a. 16 options

b.

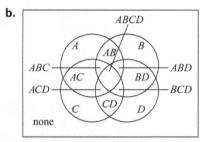

c. There are no regions for A and D only and for B and C only.

d. 32 options   **e.** 2^N options

Section 6.3

1. $P(A)$ represents the probability that you answer the question correctly, $P(\text{not } A)$ is the probability that you do not answer the question correctly, and $P(\overline{A})$ also represents the probability that you do not answer the question correctly. Each of the three values is 0.5.

3. There is one chance out of 524,288 that all 20 babies are of the same gender. Such an event is unusual because its probability is so small.

5. Makes sense.   **7.** Makes sense.

9. Does not make sense.

11. 2/3, assuming that the die is fair and the outcomes are equally likely.

13. 18/38 or 9/19, assuming that the 38 slots all have the same chance of being selected.

15. 1/365, assuming that births on the 365 days are equally likely.

17. 1/2 or 0.5

19. 0   **21.** 6/7

23. 0.45   **25.** 0.720

27. 0.22; 0.33; 0.44; 0.56

29. a. 1/8 = 0.125 (GGG)   **b.** 3/8 = 0.375 (BBG, BGB, GBB)   **c.** 1/8 = 0.125 (GBB)   **d.** 7/8 = 0.875 (GGG, BGG, GBG, GGB, BBG, BGB, GBB)   **e.** 4/8 = 0.5 (BBG, BGB, GBB, BBB)

31. 0.60   **33.** $P(\text{success}) = 0.86$

35. The probability that a person you meet at random is over 65 will be 34.7/281 = 0.123 in 2000 and will be 78.9/394 = 0.200 in 2050. Thus your chances will be greater in 2050.

37. a.

Outcomes for Rolling Four Fair Coins					
Coin 1	Coin 2	Coin 3	Coin 4	Outcome	Probability
H	H	H	H	HHHH	1/16
H	H	H	T	HHHT	1/16
H	H	T	H	HHTH	1/16
H	H	T	T	HHTT	1/16
H	T	H	H	HTHH	1/16
H	T	H	T	HTHT	1/16
H	T	T	H	HTTH	1/16
H	T	T	T	HTTT	1/16
T	H	H	H	THHH	1/16
T	H	H	T	THHT	1/16
T	H	T	H	THTH	1/16
T	H	T	T	THTT	1/16
T	T	H	H	TTHH	1/16
T	T	H	T	TTHT	1/16
T	T	T	H	TTTH	1/16
T	T	T	T	TTTT	1/16

b.

Probability Distribution for the Number of Heads in Rolling Four Fair Coins	
Result	Probability
4 Heads (0 Tails)	1/16
3 Heads (1 Tail)	4/16
2 Heads (2 Tails)	6/16
1 Head (3 Tails)	4/16
0 Heads (4 Tails)	1/16
Total	1

c. 6/16 = 0.375   **d.** 15/16 = 0.9375   **e.** 2 heads (Probability is 0.375)

Section 6.4

1. The occurrence of event A does not affect the probability of event B, so the two events are independent.

3. Sampling with replacement. The second outcome is independent of the first.

5. Does not make sense.

7. Makes sense.

9. 1/2 or 0.5   **11.** 1/260,000

13. a. 0.0039   **b.** 0.00098   **c.** 0.125   **d.** 0.0625   **e.** 1/60 = 0.0167. There are 60 equally likely songs available for each selection. No matter which song is played first, the probability that the next one is the same is 1/60 = 0.0167.

15. $P(\text{guilty plea or sent to prison}) = 1014/1028 = 0.986$

17. 0.865   **19.** 0.381   **21.** 0.410

23. 0.920   **25.** 0.0195

27. a. 0.733   **b.** 1   **c.** 0.643   **d.** 0.22

29. a. 0.5625   **b.** 0.375   **c.** 0.0625

d.

Event	Probability
AA	0.5625
Aa	0.1875
aA	0.1875
aa	0.0625

e. 0.9375

31. a. 0.518   **b.** 0.491

Chapter 6 Review Exercises

1. $576/3562 = 0.162$

3. $3466/3562 = 0.973$

5. $2330/3562 = 0.654$

7. $480/576 = 0.833$

9. a. 0.73   **b.** 0.073   **c.** 1.35   **d.** 0.0014; you should doubt the stated yield.

Chapter 6 Quiz

1. 0.30

3. Answer varies, but an answer such as 0.01 or lower is reasonable.

5. 0.6   **7.** $572/586 = 0.976$ **9.** $10/586 = 0.0171$

Section 7.1

1.

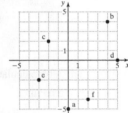

3.

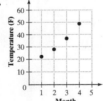

5. From A to B and B to C, the line segments slant up to the right, indicating that the runner's heartbeats per minute increase over this period of time. From C to D, the line segment slants downward, to the right, indicating that the runner's heartbeats per minute decrease. Possible scenario: The runner starts out warming up by jogging slowly for a certain length of time (A to B), then the runner jogs more quickly for some time (B to C), and finally, the runner jogs more slowly (C to D), resting at D.

Exercises

1. origin   **3.** ordered pair   **5.** below

7.

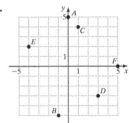

9.

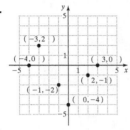

11. III   **13.** II   **15.** IV   **17.** I

19.

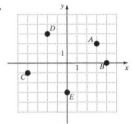

21. II   **23.** I

25. a. $A(20, 40), B(52, 90), C(76, 80)$, and $D(90, 28)$

b. Students A, B, and C scored higher in English than in mathematics.

27.

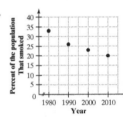

29. a.

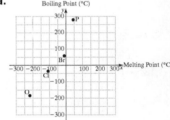

b. The y-coordinate is larger. The pattern shows that for each substance its boiling point is higher than its melting point.

31. The number of senators from a state (2) is the same regardless of the size of the state's population.

33. The graph in (a) could describe this motion. As the child moves away from the wall, the distance from the wall increases (line segment slants upward to the right). When the child stands still, the distance from the wall does not change (horizontal line segment). Finally, as the child moves toward the wall, the child's distance from the wall decreases (line segment slants downward to the right).

Section 7.2

1. $m = \frac{1}{3}$

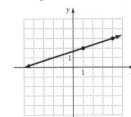

3.

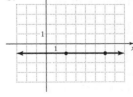

5. Slope of $\overleftrightarrow{PQ}: -\frac{2}{3}$; slope of $\overleftrightarrow{RS}: -\frac{1}{2}$

7.

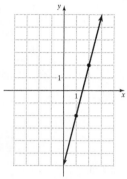

Exercises

1. rate of change   **3.** negative   **5.** horizontal   **7.** parallel

9. $\frac{3}{4}$ **11.** undefined

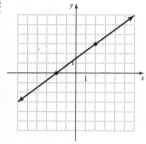   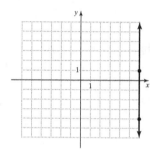

13. $-\frac{2}{5}$ **15.** 0

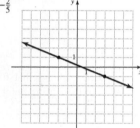   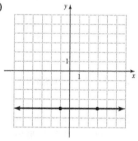

17. -7

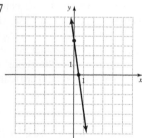

19. The slope of $\overleftrightarrow{AB}$ is -1. The slope of $\overleftrightarrow{CD}$ is 2.   **21.** Positive slope; neither   **23.** Negative slope; neither   **25.** Undefined slope; vertical   **27.** Zero slope; horizontal

29.

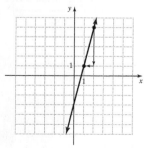

31.

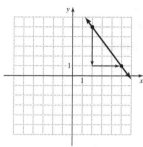

33.

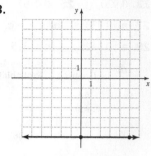

35.

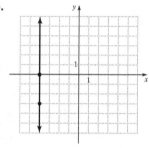

37. a. $\overleftrightarrow{PQ}: m = 4$; $\overleftrightarrow{RS}: m = 4$; the lines are parallel.

b. $\overleftrightarrow{PQ}: m = -\frac{3}{2}$; $\overleftrightarrow{RS}: m = \frac{2}{3}$; the lines are perpendicular.

39. Zero slope; horizontal

41.

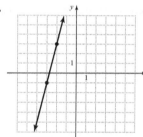

43. a. $\overleftrightarrow{AB}: m = -\frac{1}{2}$; $\overleftrightarrow{CD}: m = 2$; the lines are perpendicular.

b. $\overleftrightarrow{AB}: m = -\frac{4}{3}$; $\overleftrightarrow{CD}: m = -\frac{4}{3}$; the lines are parallel.

45. Undef.

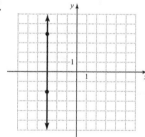

47. a. The slope is positive. **b.** A positive slope indicates that as the temperature of the gas increases, the pressure in the tube increases.

49. a. Motorcycle A   **b.** Motorcycle B **c.** The slope is the change in distance over time, or the average speed of the motorcycles.

51. The slope of each line is 1. Since the slopes of the lines are equal, the garbage deposits at the landfills are growing at the same rate.

53. a.

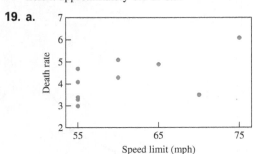

b. The slopes are 12 and 7. Since the slopes are not equal, the rate of increase did change over time.

55. The product of the slopes of the two lines is $-5 \cdot \frac{1}{3}$, which is not equal to -1, so $\overleftrightarrow{AD}$ is not the shortest route.

57. a. Graph II; As the car travels, its distance increases with time. This implies a positive slope. **b.** Graph I; The car is set for a constant speed. The speed of the car does not change over time. This implies a 0 slope.

Section 7.3

1. r is called the (linear) correlation coefficient, and it measures how well the paired sample data fit the pattern of a straight line.

3. No. It is possible that there is some correlation that corresponds to a scatterplot with a pattern that is not a straight-line pattern.

5. Does not make sense.   **7.** Does not make sense.

9. Positive correlation. As the weight goes up, the cost will also go up.

11. Negative correlation. Airliners that weigh more tend to use more fuel, so as weight increases, the fuel consumption in miles per gallon will decrease.

13. The variables are not correlated.

15. The variables are not correlated.

17. There is a strong positive correlation, with the correlation coefficient approximately 0.8 or 0.9.

19. a.

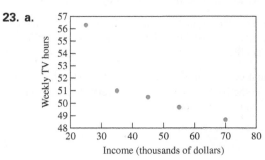

b. There is a moderate positive correlation; $r = 0.59$ exactly.
c. With the exception of Britain, the higher speed limits are generally associated with higher death rates. Death rates are also influenced by other factors beside speed limits.

21. a.

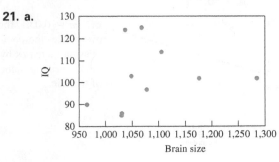

b. Because the points are scattered with no obvious pattern, there does not appear to be a correlation between brain size and IQ. The value of the correlation coefficient is approximately 0.2.   **c.** The data suggest that there is not a correlation between brain size and IQ.

23. a.

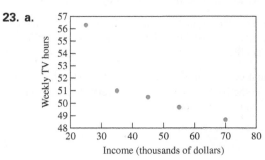

b. There is a strong negative correlation between income and the number of TV hours per week ($r = -0.86$ exactly).   **c.** Families with more income have more opportunities to do other things. No.

25. a.

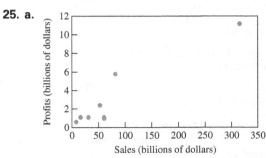

b. There is a strong correlation between sales and earnings ($r = 0.92$ exactly). The strong correlation in this case is highly affected by the Wal-Mart data.   **c.** Higher sales do not necessarily translate into higher earnings. Some companies have larger expenses, driving earnings down.

27. The variables x and y appear symmetrically in the formula (interchanging x and y does not change the formula).

Section 7.4

1. The correlation is consistent with the possibility that Lisinopril lowers blood pressure, but without further study we cannot be sure this is the case, since the correlation could be due to other factors or coincidence.

3. Outliers are values that are very far away from almost all of the other values in a data set, so the salary of $1 is an outlier. Outliers can have a significant effect on the correlation coefficient and the conclusions we form. Outliers might make it appear that there is a significant correlation that is not real, or they might mask a real correlation.

5. Does not make sense.

7. Makes sense.

9. There is a positive correlation that is probably due to a common underlying cause. Many crimes are committed with handguns that are not registered.

11. There is a positive correlation that is due to a direct cause. As students study more, they gain a better understanding of the subject and their test scores are likely to be higher.

13. There is a positive correlation that is probably due to a common cause, such as the general increase in the number of cars and traffic.

15. There is a negative correlation that is probably due to a direct cause. As gas prices increase by large amounts, people can't afford to drive as much, so they cut costs by driving less.

17. a. The outlier is the upper left point (0.4, 1.0). Without the outlier, the correlation coefficient is 0.0.   **b.** With the outlier, the correlation coefficient is -0.58.

19. a. The actual correlation coefficient is $r = 0.92$, which is significant at the 0.01 level, so there is a very strong correlation between weight and shoe size.

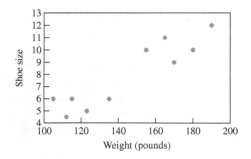

b. Within each of the two groups the correlation is less strong than the overall correlation.

21. a. The actual correlation coefficient is $r = 0.77$. This is significant at the 0.01 level, indicating a strong correlation.

b. The 16 points to the right correspond to relatively poor countries, such as Uganda. The remaining points on the left correspond to relative affluent countries, such as Sweden.   **c.** There appears to be a negative correlation between the variables for the poorer countries and a positive correlation for the wealthier countries.

c. Wealthier countries have a negative correlation; higher birth rates go with lower death rates. Poorer countries have a positive correlation; higher birth rates go with higher death rates.

Section 8.1

1. $y = 5$ **3.** $s = -\frac{1}{2}$ **5.** An increase of 12.3°C   **7.** $y = 9$

9. $z = 13$ **11.** The total bill was $758.   **13.** $y = 4$

15. $b = -3$ **17.** $t = 3$ **19.** $w = 4$

Exercises

1. Multiply by 3.   **3.** Divide by -5.   **5.** Divide by -2.2.

7. Multiply by $\frac{4}{3}$.   **9.** Multiply by $-\frac{2}{5}$.   **11.** $x = -5$

13. $n = 18$ **15.** $a = 4.8$ **17.** $x = -0.5$ **19.** $c = -7$

21. $r = -22$ **23.** $x = 12$ **25.** $y = -\frac{5}{2}$ **27.** $n = 8$

29. $c = -3$ **31.** $x = 2.88$ **33.** $a = -2$ **35.** $y = \frac{2}{3}$

37. $x = -2.30$ **39.** $x = -6.82$ **41.** $-4x = 56; x = -14$

43. $\frac{n}{0.2} = 1.1; n = 0.22$ **45.** $\frac{x}{3.5} = 30; x = 105$

47. $\frac{1}{6}x = 2\frac{4}{5}; x = \frac{84}{5}$ **49.** c   **51.** a   **53.** $x = -4$

55. $a = -24$ **57.** $\frac{x}{5} = 2; x = 10$ **59.** Divide by -5.2.

61. $0.02x = 10.5; x = 525$ yr   **63.** $70r = 3348; r \approx 48$ mph

65. $0.05c = 20; c = 400$ copies

67. $\frac{2}{3}x = 800{,}000; x = \$1{,}200{,}000$ **69.** $\frac{1}{5}d = 1000; d = 5000$ m

71. $7.50t = 187.50; t = 25$ hr

73. $12x = 10{,}020; x = \$835$ per month   **75.** $x = 3$

77. $t = -2$ **79.** $m = -5$ **81.** $n = 12$ **83.** $x = -75$

85. $t = 2$ **87.** $b = -19$ **89.** $x = 39$ **91.** $r = -50$

93. $y = -2$ **95.** $z = -6$ **97.** $a = -7$ **99.** $t = 0$

101. $y = -1$ **103.** $r = \frac{10}{3}$ **105.** $x = -7$ **107.** $y = 2$

109. $a = 14$ **111.** $t = \frac{3}{2}$ **113.** $y = 0$ **115.** $z = 2$

117. $m = -2$ **119.** $y = 1.32$ **121.** $n = 0.27$ **123.** a   **125.** d

127. $x = -4$ **129.** $z = -2$ **131.** $y = 4.06$

133. $45 + 135x = 1260; x = 9$. The student is carrying 9 credits.

135. $x + 2x = 3690; x = 1230$. One candidate received 1230 votes; the other candidate received 2460 votes.

137. $3 + 2(t - 1) = 9; t = 4$. The car was parked in the garage for 4 hr.

139. $0.02x + 0.01(5000 - x) = 85; x = 3500$. 3500 large postcards and 1500 small postcards can be printed.

141. $24(t + \frac{1}{3}) = 36t; t = \frac{2}{3}$. It took $\frac{2}{3}$ hr, or 40 min, to catch the bus.

143. $27r + 27(r + 2) = 432; r = 7$. One snail is crawling at a rate of 7 cm/min, the other is crawling at a rate of 9 cm/min.

145. $2r + 2(r + 4) = 212; r = 51$. The speed of the slower truck is 51 mph.

Section 8.2

1.

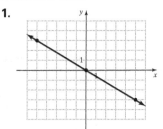

3. x-intercept: $(4, 0)$;
y-intercept: $(0, -2)$;

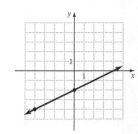

5. a. $C = 0.03s + 40$

b.

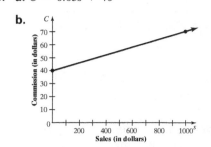

c. $m = 0.03$; for every sale, the commission increases by 0.03 times the value of the sale.

d. $55

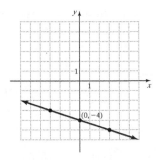

7. Slope is -2; y-intercept is $(0, 3)$.   **9.** $y = \frac{3}{2}x - 2$

11. $y = 1x + 2$, or $y = x + 2$ **13.** $y = -\frac{1}{2}x - 2$

15.

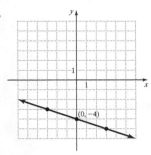

Exercises

1. solution   **3.** three points   **5.** y-intercept

7.

x	4	7	$\frac{8}{3}$
y	4	13	0

9.

x	3.5	6	$-\frac{1}{10}$	$\frac{8}{5}$
y	-17.5	-30	$\frac{1}{2}$	-8

11.

x	0	-4	8	4
y	3	6	-3	0

13.

x	3	6	-3	0
y	0	1	-2	-1

15.

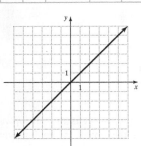

17.

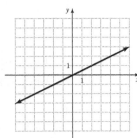

19.

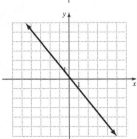

21.

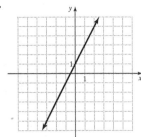

23.

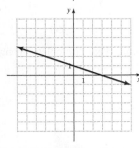

25.

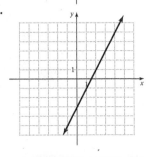

27.

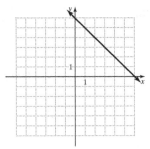

29.

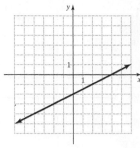

31.

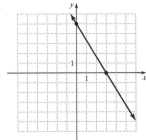

x-intercept: $(3, 0)$
y-intercept: $(0, 5)$

33.

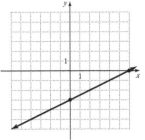

x-intercept: $(6, 0)$
y-intercept: $(0, -3)$

35.

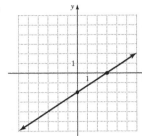

x-intercept: $(3, 0)$
y-intercept: $(0, -2)$

37.

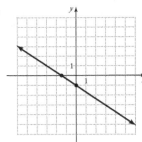

x-intercept: $\left(-\frac{3}{2}, 0\right)$
y-intercept: $(0, -1)$

39.

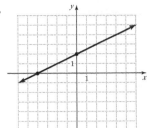

x-intercept: $(-4, 0)$
y-intercept: $(0, 2)$

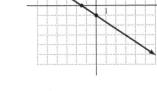

41.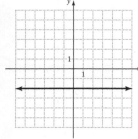

43.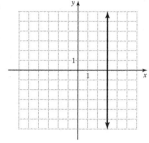

45.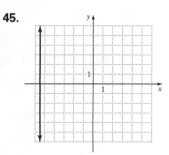

47.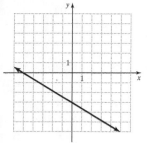

49.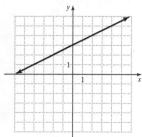

51.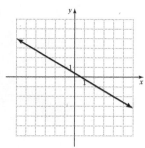

53.

x	−3	$\frac{5}{2}$	8	1
y	12	1	−10	4

55.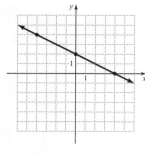

x-intercept: $(4, 0)$
y-intercept: $(0, 2)$
possible third point: $(-4, 4)$

57.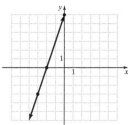

x-intercept: $(-2, 0)$
y-intercept: $(0, 6)$
possible third point: $(-3, -3)$

59.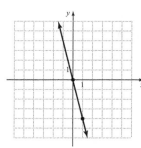

x-intercept: $(0, 0)$
y-intercept: $(0, 0)$
possible third point: $(1, -4)$

61.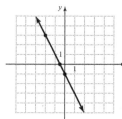

x-intercept: $\left(-\frac{1}{2}, 0\right)$
y-intercept: $(0, -1)$
possible third point: $(-2, 3)$

63.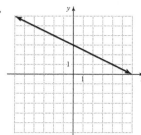

65. a.

t	0	0.5	1	1.5	2
v	10	−6	−22	−38	−54

A positive value of v means that the object is moving upward. A negative value of v means that the object is moving downward. **b.**

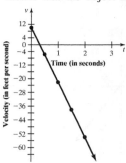

c. The v-intercept is the initial velocity of the object.

d. The t-intercept represents the time when the object changes from an upward motion to a downward motion.

67. a. $P = 100m + 500$ **b.**

m	1	2	3
p	600	700	800

c.

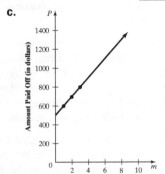

Number of Monthly Payments

69. a. $0.05n + 0.1d = 2$ **b.**

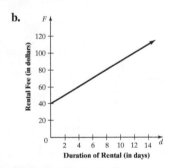

Number of Dimes

c. Only nonnegative integer values make sense, since you cannot have fractions of a nickel or a dime.

71. a. $F = 5d + 40$

b.

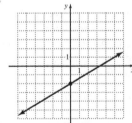

Duration of Rental (in days)

73. Slope-intercept   **75.** y-intercept

77. For $y = 3x - 5$: 3, $(0, -5)$, ⟋, $(\frac{5}{3}, 0)$;
for $y = -2x$: -2, $(0, 0)$, ⟍, $(0, 0)$; for $y = 0.7x + 3.5$: 0.7,
$(0, 3.5)$, ⟋, $(-5, 0)$; for $y = \frac{3}{4}x - \frac{1}{2}$: $\frac{3}{4}$, $(0, -\frac{1}{2})$ ⟋, $(\frac{2}{3}, 0)$;
for $6x + 3y = 12$: -2, $(0, 4)$; ⟍, $(2, 0)$;
for $y = -5$: 0, $(0, -5)$, —, no x-intercept; for $x = -2$:
undefined, no y-intercept, |, $(-2, 0)$

79. Slope: -1; y-intercept: $(0, 2)$ **81.** Slope: 3; y-intercept: $(0, -4)$

83. $y = x - 10$ **85.** $y = -\frac{1}{10}x + 1$ **87.** $y = -\frac{3}{2}x + \frac{1}{4}$

89. $y = \frac{2}{5}x - 2$ **91.** $y = 3x + 14$ **93.** b   **95.** a

97.

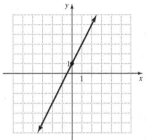

99.

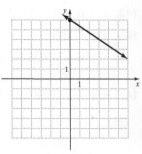

101.

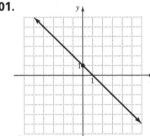

103.

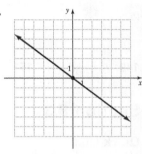

105.

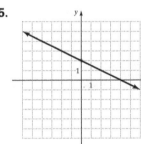

107.

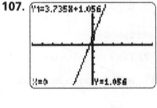

109. $y = 3x + 7$ **111.** $y = 5x - 20$ **113.** $y = -\frac{1}{2}x + 4$

115. $y = -x + 3$ **117.** $y = \frac{1}{6}x - \frac{29}{6}$ **119.** $x = -3$

121. $y = -6$ **123.** $y = \frac{3}{4}x + 3$ **125.** $y = -x - 2$

127. $y = 2$ **129.** $x = -2.5$ **131.** For $y = -7x + 2$: -7, $(0, 2)$, ⟍,
$(\frac{2}{7}, 0)$; for $y = 4x$: 4, $(0, 0)$, ⟋, $(0, 0)$; for $y = 2.5x + 10$:
2.5, $(0, 10)$, ⟋, $(-4, 0)$; for $y = \frac{2}{3}x - \frac{1}{4}$: $\frac{2}{3}$, $(0, -\frac{1}{4})$, ⟋,
$(\frac{3}{8}, 0)$; for $5x + 4y = 20$: $-\frac{5}{4}$, $(0, 5)$, ⟍, $(4, 0)$; for $x = 9$:
undefined, no y-intercept, |, $(9, 0)$; for
$y = -3.2$: 0, $(0, -3.2)$, —, no x-intercept

133. $y = 4x - 5$ **135.** d   **137.** $y = \frac{1}{2}x - 1$

139.

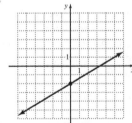

141. $y = -x + 5$

143. a. $\frac{9}{5}$ **b.** $F = \frac{9}{5}C + 32$ **c.** Water boils at 100°C.

145. a. $y - 4500 = 6(x - 500)$ **b.** $y = 6x + 1500$

 c. The y-intercept represents the monthly flat fee the utility company charges its residential customers.

147. a. $I = 0.03S + 1500$ **b.** 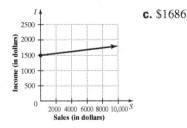 **c.** $1686

149. $P = \frac{1}{33}d + 1$ **151.** $L = \frac{5}{6}F + 10$

Section 8.3

Quick Quiz

1. c **3.** c **5.** c **7.** c **9.** b

Exercises

7. Does not make sense   **9.** Makes sense

11. a. Rain depth increases linearly with time.

 b. $\frac{4}{3}$ inch per hour

 c. Good model if rainfall rate is constant for 4 hours

13. a. On a long trip, distance from home decreases linearly with time.

 b. -71.4 miles per hour

 c. Good model if speed is constant for 7 hours

15. a. Shoe size increases linearly with the height of the individual.

 b. 0.1375 size per inch

 c. The model is a rough approximation at best.

17. The water depth decreases with respect to time at a rate of 2 inches per day. The rate of change is $-2\,\text{in}/\text{day}$. In 8 days, the water depth decreases by 16 inches. In 15 days, the water depth decreases by 30 inches.

19. The Fahrenheit temperature changes with respect to the Celsius temperature at a rate of 9/5 degrees F per degree C. The rate of change is 9/5 degrees F/degree C. An increase of 5 degrees C results in an increase of 9 degrees F. A decrease of 25 degrees C results in a decrease of 45 degrees F.

21. The snow depth increases by 3.5 inches per hour. The rate of change is 3.5 inches per hour. In 6.3 hours, the snow depth will increase by 22.05 inches. In 9.8 hours, the snow depth will increase by 34.3 inches.

23. The independent variable is time (or t) measured in years. We will let $t = 0$ represent today. The dependent variable is price (or p). The equation of the price function is $p = 18,000 + 900t$. The price of the car in 3.5 years will be $21,150. This function doesn't give a good model of car prices.

25. The variables in this problem are (snow depth, maximum speed), or (d, s), where snow depth is measured in inches and maximum speed is measured in mph. The equation for the function is $s = 40 - 1.1d$. The plow has zero maximum speed when the snow depth reaches 36 inches, or 3 feet. The plowing rate most likely is not a constant, so this model is an approximation.

27. The variables in this problem are (time, rental cost), or (t, r), where t is measured in minutes. The cost per minute is $2/5\,\text{minutes} = $0.40\,\text{per minute}$. The equation for the function is $r = 10 + 0.40t$. The number of minutes you can rent for $25 is almost 37.5 minutes. This function gives a good model of rental costs, if you are allowed to rent for any amount of time at the rate of $0.40/minute. However, many rentals require that you pay the full $2 for each 5-minute period, even if you do not use the full 5 minutes.

29. $w = 2.5 + 12.5t$; 65 lb; 127.5 lb. Model is accurate for small ages only.

31. $P = -350 + 10n$; 35 tickets

33. $V = 1200 - 75t$; 16 years

35. The equation $y = 2x + 6$ describes a straight line with y-intercept of $(0, 6)$ and slope 2.

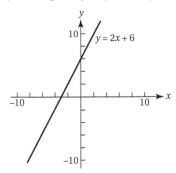

37. The equation $y = -5x - 5$ describes a straight line with y-intercept of $(0, -5)$ and slope -5.

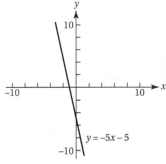

39. The equation $y = 3x - 6$ describes a straight line with y-intercept of $(0, -6)$ and slope 3.

41. The equation $y = -x + 4$ describes a straight line with y-intercept of $(0, 4)$ and slope -1.

43. The variables are (time, elevation).

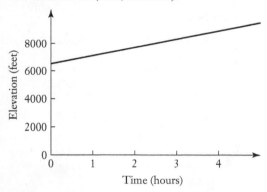

After 3.5 hours, the elevation is 8600 feet. Provided the rate of ascent is really a constant, this linear equation gives a good model of the climb.

45. The variables are (number of posters, cost).

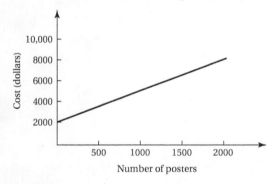

The cost of printing 2000 posters is $8000. This function probably gives a fairly realistic estimate of printing costs.

47. The variables in this problem are (time, cost).

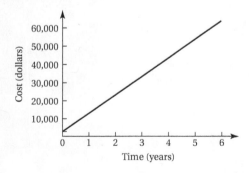

The cost of six years of school is $62,000. Provided costs do not change during the six-year period, this function is an accurate model of the cost.

49. a. $N = 400$ **b.** $N \approx 800$ **c.** $N \approx 200/\mathrm{p}$ **d.** $N \approx 1333$

Section 8.4

1. A best fit line (or regression line) is a line on a scatter diagram that lies closer to the data points than any other possible line (according to the standard statistical measure of closeness). A best fit line is useful for predicting the value of a variable given some value of the other variable.

3. The investigator should use multiple regression. Multiple regression involves determination of the best-fit equation that represents the best fit between one variable and a combination of two or more other variables and, in this case, she wants the best fit between the variable representing the heights of daughters and the two variables representing heights of mothers and heights of fathers.

5. Makes sense.   **7.** Does not make sense.

Section 8.5

Quick Quiz

1. b **3.** a **5.** c **7.** b **9.** a

Exercises

5. Makes sense   **7.** Makes sense

9. Linear; 3700   **11.** Exponential; R$285.61

13. Exponential; $31.80   **15.** Linear; $110,000

17. 32,768 grains; 65,535 grains; about 9.36 pounds

19. 1.3×10^{12} tons   **21.** $41,943.04

23. About 37 days   **25.** 2^{50} bacteria; 1/1024 full

27. 2.5 meters; more than knee-deep

29. a. (Only 100-year intervals are shown here.)

Year	Population
2000	6.0×10^9
2100	2.4×10^{10}
2200	9.6×10^{10}
2300	3.8×10^{11}
2400	1.5×10^{12}
2500	6.1×10^{12}
2600	2.5×10^{13}
2700	9.8×10^{13}
2800	3.9×10^{14}
2900	1.6×10^{15}
3000	6.3×10^{15}

b. Between 2800 and 2850 **c.** About 2150 **d.** No

31. a. b.

Month	March 2009	March 2010	March 2011	March 2012
Monthly active users (millions)	197	431	680	901
Absolute change over previous year	–	234	249	221
Percent change over previous year	–	118.8%	57.8%	32.5%

c. The absolute change is roughly constant; the percent change is decreasing. So the growth is closer to linear.

INDEX